Teaching Children Science:
An Inquiry Approach

Second Edition

Teaching Children Science:
An Inquiry Approach

Second Edition

Louis I. Kuslan

A. Harris Stone

Southern Connecticut State College

Wadsworth Publishing Company, Inc.
Belmont, California

ISBN: 0-534-00131-9

L. C. Cat. Card No.: 70-184482

Printed in the United States of America

1 2 3 4 5 6 7 8 9 10 – 76 75 74 73 72

Acknowledgments

American Association for the Advancement of Science: for excerpts from *Science — A Process Approach — Description of the Program*, Part D. Reprinted by permission.

Elementary Science Study of Education Development Center, Inc.: for excerpts from *Introduction to the Elementary Science Study* (Boston: Houghton Mifflin Co., 1965); and for excerpts from *Teacher's Guide for Behavior of Mealworms* (St. Louis: Webster Division, McGraw-Hill Book Co.). Reprinted by permission.

Far West Laboratory for Educational Research and Development: for excerpts from *Elementary Science Study ESS Program Report*, 1970. Reprinted by permission.

Stanley Helgeson: for excerpts from An Investigation Into the Relationships Between Concepts of Force Attained and Maturity as Indicated by Grade Levels, unpublished Ph.D. dissertation, University of Wisconsin, 1967, pp. 167, 168, 170, 196. Reprinted by permission.

Nuffield Foundation: for excerpts from *Nuffield Junior Science, Teacher's Guide I* (London: William Collins Sons, 1967) pp. 190-191. Reprinted by permission.

Melba Partin: for excerpts from An Investigation of the Effectiveness of the AAAS Process Method Upon the Achievement and Interest in Science for Selected Fourth Grade Students, unpublished Ed.D. dissertation, University of Mississippi, 1967, pp. 102-8. Reprinted by permission.

Rand McNally & Co.: for excerpts from Teacher's Guide for Interaction and Systems, pp. 30-37, 39-42. Reprinted by permission.

Science and Children: for excerpts from "Messing About in Science" by David Hawkins in *Science and Children*, 3: 6, February 1965. Reprinted by permission.

Eldon Scriven: for excerpts from An Analyses of the Types of Concepts Used by Fourth Through Ninth Graders to Explain Meaning, doctoral dissertation, 1968, pp. 132-33. Reprinted by permission of Dr. Eldon G. Scriven.

Alvin Weinberg: for excerpts from "In Defense of Science," *Science*, 167: 142, January 9, 1970. Reprinted by permission of the author.

Preface

Teaching Children Science introduces preservice and inservice teachers to the joys and satisfactions as well as the quandaries and difficulties of teaching science in the elementary school. Science instruction in the seventies is much different from the traditional book-centered science once imposed on children. Instead of "learning" science from books alone, children will learn even more from direct experience with scientific phenomena. This approach to learning–teaching is closely related to scientific investigation and has been referred to as process-centered, inquiry, or discovery learning. From the educational, psychological, and scientific points of view, we believe that this strategy for teaching and learning science is uniquely valuable.

When teachers realize that functional science teaching requires more of them than a knowledge of teaching methodology and scientific principles, elementary science teaching will at last make its long promised contribution in preparing children for a complex, scientifically and technologically centered society. In recent years educators have learned a great deal about the different learning styles of children and about the factors that affect this learning. They have discovered more effective ways of directing this learning so that it is both voluntary and productive. For these reasons chapter one of this book describes the tactics and strategy of science in a somewhat different perspective from that of the traditional college science course. This chapter presents a process-centered model of how science operates and pays special attention to the controlling moral and ethical values of the sciences.

Chapter two, which is more comprehensive than the corresponding chapter of other methods textbooks, interprets recent, pertinent research in educational psychology. By providing a strong psychological foundation for teaching science, this chapter, divided into five sections for ease of reading, will help teachers to understand and thereby to eliminate many conditions that hinder learning.

From this base chapter three considers the relevance of the historical development of elementary science teaching for the modern goals of elementary science. Chapters four and five present a rationale, methodology, and interpretation of process-centered science teaching and analyzes three nationally accepted elementary science curricula. The remaining chapters deal in detail with science experiments, demonstrations, field trips, motion pictures, trade books, and evaluative activities — experiences that will serve the classroom teacher as science teaching tools.

Most of the firsthand experiences in chapter eleven are intended for a college level course in elementary science teaching rather than for use in the elementary school. The chapter introduces the beginning teacher to the process of scientific investigation so that she will better understand her pupils' problems and thought patterns as the children explore firsthand science.

Chapter twelve, in keeping with the philosophical orientation of *Teaching Children Science,* is designed to help the teacher plan more effectively for frequent process-oriented science teaching, whether she is in a self-contained classroom, in an "open-air" school, in a departmentalized middle school, or in an "informal" school. The chapter emphasizes flexibility and informally organized experiences from which the teacher should deviate whenever necessary to meet the needs and interests of the children.

Following each chapter is a summary of important ideas, a set of questions to stimulate critical thinking, and a detailed section of notes and references.

We wish to thank the many colleagues, researchers, and students who have assisted us with this book. We are grateful to the elementary science methods instructors who took precious time to give us the benefit of their experience with the first edition of *Teaching Children Science.* We are particularly indebted to Paul DeHart Hurd for his insightful and practical suggestions, which have shaped this new edition. We also wish to thank Dorothy Beisiegel, Dick Greenberg, and Sandra Mangurian for their contributions.

Louis Kuslan

A. Harris Stone

Contents

Teaching Children Science: An Inquiry Approach

Second Edition

The Nature of Science

Science teaching in elementary school is based on two major philosophical understandings: the nature of children and how they learn and the nature of science and scientific thought. This chapter deals with what science is, why it is important for children *and* adults, and how scientists do the tasks that are collectively labeled science. To teach science effectively to children, the teacher must understand the philosophy and structure of science, not merely unrelated scientific facts. The views offered in this chapter are intended to provide a basis on which the would-be teacher can build this understanding.

School View of Science

Many people believe that science is a collection of thousands of important facts and comprehensive theories. This understanding of science is a result of education, which derives from textbooks crammed with scientific facts and theories and from the rituals of traditional science teaching. These textbooks do represent one aspect of science: they are the organized products of science, boiled down compilations of generations of scientific toil. Textbooks are tools that may be used to enrich science teaching to make it more than a ritualistic repetition of narrow, limited facts. Instruction in the sciences ought to be many-faceted. The skilled, innovative teacher who organizes the facts of science into a meaningful body of knowledge will help students to understand the nature of science and its place in modern society.

Instruction in science has usually emphasized information and the classification of information. As a result, students often think of "the scientific endeavor" as their personal struggle to memorize the facts and principles of the sciences. They emerge from their exposure to chemistry, physics, or biology with a painfully acquired store of knowledge, but they seldom learn what impels men to give their lives to science or how the facts and principles they studied were wrenched from a stubborn and resisting nature. Of course, factual information is important—science is built on facts and must always seek new facts. Instruction in science for the nonscientist, however, must also strive to reach goals broader than the acquisition and recall of facts and principles.

Defining Science

Facts are important

Science is difficult to define clearly, and for this reason it has been defined in many different ways. Whatever science is, to identify it as "organized knowledge" is to illustrate only one of its elements. The telephone directory is a well-organized collection of facts, but no one pretends that this useful volume is a scientific treatise. Organized knowledge is often referred to as the *product* of science. This product has a dynamic counterpart: the *process* of science. Science is simultaneously a kind of knowledge—product—and a way of gaining and using that knowledge—process. Process refers to ways of thinking about nature, to the kinds of questions scientists ask, and to the methods by which scientists seek to find answers to these questions. Textbook science tends to be product; real science is both product *and* process, inseparably joined.

Science is a way of thinking

This fusion of product and process is what James B. Conant, the eminent scientist and educator, had in mind when he defined science as "an interconnected series of concepts and conceptual schemes that have developed as a result of experimentation and observation, and are fruitful of further experimentation and observation."[1] Painstaking observation and skilled experimentation lead to verifiable facts. These facts suggest concepts and generalizations, which in turn lead to new observations and experiments by which the validity of these concepts and generalizations is eventually tested.

The larger view

If, as a first approximation, a concept is identified as an abstract idea that results from experiment or observation, then Conant's "conceptual scheme" may be thought of as "a working hypothesis on a grand scale."[2] The statement "We live in an ocean of air" is an example of a conceptual scheme or comprehensive theoretical idea of this kind.[3] In a few words this scheme summarizes the accumulated experience of three centuries of scientific research on air pressure, vacuum, wind currents, gas density, and temperature. For example, it is an observed and experimentally determined fact that under the proper conditions a column of mercury will stand some thirty inches high in a tube. This, together with related facts, leads to the concept (an abstract statement derived from experience) that the atmosphere exerts pressure. The terms *air* and *pressure* are concepts in their own right, and from these and related concepts, scientists built the conceptual scheme "We live in an ocean of air."

New ideas

Unless it leads to new ideas and new knowledge, the conceptual scheme will be of little value to scientists. If further investigation is not stimulated, the scheme is barren and worthless. The conceptual scheme "We live in an ocean of air" was of great value to science because it led to exploration of that ocean, to charting its current, and to investigating its phenomena in much the same way that the great water oceans have been studied.

Science and Power

Power for change

Man has shown convincingly that he has mastered many aspects of nature, but this mastery, admittedly imperfect, did not come from the magical incantations of primitive medicine men. It was the product of man's rational attempt to understand nature and to superimpose on it some kind of organization. Science is relevant to contemporary society in new and crucial ways because man has gained the power to reshape his world in proportion to the depth of his insight into that world. The social, political, and economic problems associated with nuclear energy, automation, pollution, and birth control have dramatized the impact of scientific power on everyday existence. It seems almost inconceivable that only a few decades ago science was regarded by practical men as of little consequence. Conant once described their attitude by an amusing anecdote:

> At the time of our entry into World War I, a representative of the American Chemical Society called on the Secretary of War, Newton Baker, and offered the service of the chemists in the conflict. He was thanked and asked to come back the next day. On so doing, he was told by the Secretary of War that while he appreciated the offer of the chemists, he found that it was unnecessary as he had looked into the matter and found the War Department already had a chemist.[4]

In 1939, the year in which Otto Hahn and Fritz Strassmann discovered the fission of uranium nuclei, the United States government spent about fifty million dollars for scientific research. Today the government spends billions of dollars each year on research and on the application of that research. Although most of the research is for military purposes, much of it has nonmilitary implications.

Science in Modern Society

Science and its related technology are inextricably woven into the fabric of modern society. This intimacy, this everyday encounter, is responsible for many problems that face citizens, who may have been exposed to science teaching but have not been educated in science. They do not understand what scientists are trying to do and how they do it, and they are not prepared to evaluate the aims and aspirations of scientists. This understanding comes from simple scientific investigations, in the course of which the tactics and strategies of scientists become familiar.

The layman should unquestionably know a great deal about the dynamic force of modern science, which affects his very existence. Yet it is unreasonable to expect him to master physics, chemistry, astronomy, biology, and geology, for no one can keep up with the rapid expansion of scientific knowledge. It has been estimated that the lifetime of a hypothesis in certain phases of nuclear physics is only four years, and the number of scientific publications has doubled every ten years for several decades. Hence the citizen who is literate in science faces frustration if he tries to keep up in an age in which it is impossible for a specialist to be aware of all the implications of the new knowledge in his field.

Knowledge changes

Further, scientists, of course, are competent in their specialized fields, and a handful of men contribute to more than one field of science, but the majority of scientifically trained men are not competent in interpreting to the public the effect of science on their society.

Knowledge is not enough

Scientists agree on many facts relating to nuclear fallout, but they disagree on the interpretations to be drawn from these facts. The controversies that find scientists at sword's points in discussing nuclear bomb testing, missile systems, or even such relatively non-emotional conceptual schemes as electron orbits in atoms are well publicized. To many scientists, it seems self-evident that the powerful insecticide DDT has been proved to be a danger to all life. Many other scientists, however, argue that DDT and other potent chemicals must continue to be used despite some hazards because they cannot be replaced without imperiling food production. There is no simple scientific answer to this environmental dilemma.

If these points are valid, it is inconceivable that the teaching of science should be centered on facts and focused on immediate, practical goals. Science and its derivative, technology, move rapidly. Therefore education in science should not emphasize technology, although technology should not be ignored. The goals of science education should bear witness to values more inclusive than practicality.

There are other justifications for a shift of viewpoint in teaching science

Scientific literacy   to meet the demands of a science and technology oriented society. The focus of science education from kindergarten to college should be on the development of the ability to think critically and imaginatively. Science, as both dynamic process and rapidly changing product, is of value in education because it promotes an understanding of its own structure, values, and processes. There are many paths to such understanding, but it is obvious that traditional approaches to the teaching of science to the layman have failed and that a new content and methodology must now be chosen.

How is it possible for the student to understand the meaning of science and the work of scientists unless he is aware of the difficulties, the doubts, the false starts, and the grueling labor involved in postulating and testing new conceptual schemes that may soon be altered or even forgotten? Students who learn how scientists learn simultaneously learn what science is. Instead of visualizing science as a corpus of unchanging facts and theories (product) to be memorized, students should see the dynamic processes of scientific investigation: Why? How do you know? How should we phrase this question to obtain a valid answer? Students may isolate problems, invent working hypotheses, and derive from data the simplest principles or laws. In short the focus of science ought to be on achieving a functional grasp of the language and structure of science rather than on science as a technological innovator or as a better explanation of the physical world. In the attempt to speak the language of science, the student will gain the essential goals of clear and careful thought.

It is important to know many scientific facts and principles. It is reasonable to expect that the more the individual knows, the greater the probability that he will see the relationships between the principles and concepts of science and thereby facilitate personal integration of science. These are important goals, but they are perhaps not as vital to society as fostering the growth of the

The critical mind   critical mind and preparing each individual to make value judgments about science and its effects on daily life. Science is important in everyone's life —

Individual responsibility   whether he knows it or is directly affected. Although many people live their lives without direct contact with science, few escape the technology that comes from science. Hence to avoid a knowledge of science is to give up the right to make knowledgeable decisions about science and therefore about one's life in a society that is deeply affected by science.

Characteristics of Science

How is science related to the other disciplines of modern knowledge? What does it have in common with art? With literature? Every branch of

*Science is based on
philosophy*

knowledge, including the sciences, is permeated by some philosophical structure—the assumptions and untestable beliefs on which the elaborate superstructure of the discipline is built. The meaning of science elucidated by Conant is philosophical—there is no scientific way to validate his definition. One also looks at literature or art or physics from the vantage of his frame of reference, which is the particular theory of knowledge he consciously or unconsciously holds. Science, like art, prospers to the degree that it incorporates the humanistic values of truth, freedom, and tolerance.

Mathematics, the handmaiden of the sciences, is interwoven into each scientific discipline; the extent of its integration is a measure of the "exactness" of the discipline. Astronomy, physics, and chemistry are "exact" in this sense. Biology, psychology, and the social sciences, in that order, are markedly less so. On the other hand the humanities are demonstrably nonmathematical, although symbolic logic is essential to the study of language and meaning. At first glance the sciences and the arts are poles apart, but their lack of relationship is much less clear-cut on further analysis. Each discipline

*The disciplines affect
one another*

shades gently and imperceptibly into its neighbors: behavioral zoologists study the sociology and psychology of animals; archaeologists derive new insights from the rapid advances in chemical and physical analysis; biology draws on chemistry, physics, and geology. This interrelatedness is to be expected. But science also demands of its practitioners the ability to read and write well, for without communication, science reverts to the mystery of its alchemical ancestry.

New disciplines that cross fields are emerging today. The union of physical science and biology is commonplace in the person of the biochemist and the biophysicist and in the biophysical sciences. Also, scientific research is pursued by the research group, a relatively new organizational structure in which scientists pool their specialized skills and knowledge. In cancer research, for example, groups commonly include physical chemists, biochemists, biophysicists, electrical engineers, physicians, physiologists, microbiologists, and pathologists. In response to the problems that confront society, there are strong demands for concentration on environmental science, a combined effort of natural and social scientists who, with representatives of the public, are seeking to halt the rapid deterioration of the quality of life caused by pollution, overcrowding, poor nutrition, and poverty. This change from the lone researcher to team effort has spurred scientific research.

Despite the unifying forces that blur the traditional boundaries of the individual sciences, it is still possible to ascribe to science a more or less precise meaning. As used in this book, *science* is that enterprise characterized by the operations and qualities described in the following sections. The structure proposed is a much simplified model of the scientific process and is therefore to be taken as a suggestive outline only.

Quantification

The sciences rely on measurement

One of the fundamental characteristics of science is its dependence on quantification, or exact measurement. The scientist gives questions of measurement the highest priority: Whatever this phenomenon is, can it be measured? How rapidly does it change? How fast does it move? If he cannot measure it, the scientist is likely to turn to more fruitful topics. This does not mean that measurement is ignored in nonscientific endeavors. There is, for example, a kind of measurement in judging literature and art. Comparisons must be made, and measurement is based on comparison. But the scientist has an advantage in that his measurements are made with rulers of constant length. Under ordinary conditions, a yardstick will reproduce the same length for a table (within certain limits of error) time after time. Few individuals, however, have the capacity or desire to maintain rigid critical standards in judging paintings. There are no fundamental, commonly accepted units of value, interest, satisfaction, or style. As a result different judgments from generation to generation and from critic to critic are the rule. This does not imply that unchanging (invariant) measuring instruments make science "better" than the humanities. These instruments simply make science more convenient and apparently more objective. Scientists are unwilling to study phenomena which are at best only semiquantitative, because they cannot operate with imprecise measuring tools.

Mathematics leads to new insights

Why is science difficult for many students? Why has so much knowledge been amassed in science with no end in sight? Huge books deal with one phase of the chemistry of a single element, each discussion seemingly so complete that the reader assumes the last word has been said. But the information they contain is often out of date even before publication. That much data of the sciences can mathematically be analyzed is a formidable obstacle to many students. Even in the mathematically less-demanding studies of biology and psychology, statistical formulas are commonplace. Here is an odd paradox: unless the phenomena are well understood and relatively simple, it is impossible to propose mathematical models by which these phenomena can be quantified. Despite excellent studies of the physics and physiology of light and color, art is almost completely nonmathematical. Is this not because art, as a supreme expression of human feeling and intellect, is too complex to be analyzed mathematically? Is not this complexity also the rule in economics, psychology, and sociology—the "social" sciences?

Measurement in the sciences and the mathematics by which these data are analyzed are important because they simplify relationships. A scientific law is more easily learned and applied when it is stated in mathematical symbols than when it is expressed in words. For example, $E = hF$ may be stated in this way: The size of a quantum of energy emitted by an atomic oscillator is equal to a constant h multiplied by the frequency of the oscillator. The simplicity of the mathematical expression greatly multiplies its usefulness. This convenience, however, is unavailable to other, less linear disciplines.

To point out the extraordinary success of the scientist in solving his problems is not an arrogant attempt to crown the chemist or physicist as the victor in a race for "the truth." It is simply a reflection of the massive difficulties that face the student of human society, barriers far more formidable than the low hurdles in the way of the physical scientist. Man knows much more about chemistry than he knows about sociology because there is so *little* chemistry to know. Chemistry seems, in a trivial and superficial sense, more complex than sociology only because chemistry is so simple that it can be readily quantified with rigorous mathematical models. Sociology is a young science, which has not yet succumbed to mathematical analysis because of the seemingly unmanageable and oftentimes undefinable variables of human interaction. Chemistry, on the other hand, is a well-charted discipline whose major theories are comprehensive and productive.

Observation and experimentation

The scientific stereotype

The common image of the scientist, carefully nourished by movies and by television advertising, is of an absentminded professor who, dressed in a long white coat, spends every waking moment at his work. In the public mind the scientist and science are inseparably connected with experiments performed in dark, frightening rooms called laboratories. There is a certain degree of validity in this conception, for experimentation and rigorous observation are keystones of scientific studies. As a result science may be distinguished from other disciplines because in it observation and experimentation are carried on to an extreme. Although rigorous observation is essential in many pursuits, only in the natural sciences does controlled experimentation flourish. For the purposes of this discussion *experiment* is defined as a planned change of the conditions in which a certain phenomenon occurs to reveal what effect the change has on the phenomenon. In other words an experiment is a rather precise way of asking questions of nature.

Asking questions about nature

Experimentation is often frustrating and difficult to pursue because the experimenter is struggling against what has been described as "the cursed perversity of inanimate matter." Unknown variables (factors capable of affecting the results) and assumptions of which the experimenter is unaware may exist. The experimenter's apparatus may not respond to the desired event, or it may actually affect the event in some unexpected way. A classic example of this kind of interference is seen in the appearance of certain "structures" in bacteria that have been chemically stained before they are studied through the microscope. These "structures" are sometimes the product of a reaction between the stain and the protoplasm of the cell, and they have no counterpart in the living bacterium. Early experimenters, unaware of this possibility, were deceived by these structures and they came to erroneous conclusions.

The so-called "scientific method"

The existence of difficulties such as these in the relatively simple natural sciences is a warning that experimentation of the kind scientists use may be impossible in the social sciences or, indeed, in any effort to cope with a complex, changing environment. Rigorous experimental control of social phenomena seems to be beyond reach. For this reason, the so-called scientific method may well be a mockery if it is applied to problems outside the quantitatively simple sciences.

Intensive observation of individuals and small groups is an important technique in both the social and the natural sciences. The approach of the botanist who classifies plants according to their structural characteristics is somewhat similar to that of the clinical psychologist. The extent to which significant generalizations emerge from individual and small-group analysis is quite different, however. As a result statistical analysis based on the concept of probability, which is useful in the life sciences, is absolutely essential in the social sciences.

Experience and experiment

The term *experiment* should refer to a specific kind of experience. Manipulation of scientific apparatus is not necessarily an experiment. In experimentation a genuine problem or question exists and the experimenter attempts to discover or to test possible relationships, causes, and effects. If the purpose of the procedure is to verify that which is already known, as is all too often the case in traditional instruction, it is appropriate to speak of a laboratory *experience* and to reserve *experiment* for more creative action.

Controlled experimentation

In experimentation the scientist generally finds it necessary to rely on controls, which he defines as "similar test specimens . . . subjected to as nearly as possible the same treatment as the objects of the experiment, except for the change in the variable under study."[5] For example, if he desires to test the hypothesis that calcium is required for normal growth in chicks, the experimenter compares the growth rate of chicks divided at random into control and experimental groups. The control group, which is fed a "normal" diet, is compared with the experimental group, which is fed a low-calcium or calcium-free diet. Every condition is the same for the two groups, with the exception of the presence or absence of calcium in the diet. But even with these precautions, the discovered effects may be merely chance variations or the result of an undiscovered error that affects one group more than the other group. As a case in point the chemical removal of calcium from foods may cause the loss of other necessary minerals or vitamins. This extra deficiency may therefore cause a more significant change than the elimination of calcium by itself. The probability of chance variations or experimental error may be estimated statistically and may thus give significant information to the experimenter. Errors in procedure may be discovered by the use of different experimental techniques for removing calcium, which affect nutritional materials differently.

Generalization   In general more than one trial or experimental run is necessary to detect errors and estimate the precision of the measurements. The experimenter must beware of the growth experiment on two or three chicks. "A story is told of an investigation in which chickens were subjected to a certain treatment. It was then reported that $33\frac{1}{3}\%$ of the chickens recovered, $33\frac{1}{3}\%$ of the chickens died, and no conclusions could be drawn from the other $33\frac{1}{3}\%$ because that one ran away."[6] If it is necessary to rely on a few poorly chosen specimens because only these few are available, the experimenter should be duly suspicious of his results and limit his conclusions to those few specimens. Conclusions can be extended to a general population only if the experiment is well controlled and the specimens are random choices from that general population. The typical plant or animal experiment in schools seldom satisfies these conditions, and caution in generalizing is therefore essential. Children are apt to jump to superficial conclusions, and their teachers should be aware of the necessity of fitting generalizations to the data. The theory of experimental procedure is complex, and it is not feasible to discuss laboratory experimentation in detail at this point. The suggestions in Chapter 7 will help to guide school experimentation to reasonably dependable conclusions.

Prediction

A third characteristic of science, the requirement for quantitative prediction, comes from the belief that nature is orderly. Once this order is known, quantitative predictions can be made. Although some scientific theories — evolution, for example — are not in themselves sources of predictions by which they may be tested, scientists accept most theories only if they are "fruitful." If we believe that green plants manufacture food only in the presence of light, we may reasonably expect that changes in either the intensity of light or the kind of light will affect the food production of plants in predictable ways. In repeated tests of this oversimplified hypothesis, food production in plants placed in the dark has stopped, and as a result the hypothesis is strengthened, although it is not proved. Indeed a hypothesis cannot be proved in the sense that a geometrical theorem is proved. The best that can be done is to increase the probability that the hypothesis is valid.

The value of prediction in testing the soundness of a hypothesis is well illustrated by the history of the discovery of the planet Neptune.[7] At the time of this epochal event, astronomers assumed that the planets revolved around the sun in elliptical orbits. If the laws of planetary motion that Johannes Kepler and Isaac Newton proposed in the seventeenth century were correct, then some unknown force must affect a planet whose observed position in the heavens is different from its predicted position. What could this force be? In the early 1840s, Urbain J. J. Leverrier, a French astronomer, and John Couch Adams, a young Englishman, attempted independently to answer this question for the planet Uranus. Many observations by astronomers in the decades following the discovery of Uranus showed that the planet was not where it should have been according to the laws of planetary motion. Leverrier showed conclusively that these laws could not explain this strange behavior of Uranus. He strongly believed that the laws were correct, for several attempts to discredit them had ignominiously failed. Leverrier therefore decided to find out why Uranus behaved so irregularly. He knew that earlier astronomers had proposed the presence of a planet beyond Uranus, which by its gravitational force could pull Uranus from its expected orbit. No one, however, had been able to handle the difficult mathematics required to predict where the new planet would be. In 1845 Leverrier defined his problem thus:

Is it possible that Uranus' inequalities may be due to a planet located in the ecliptic; at a mean distance double that of Uranus? and were this so, where is the planet now? What are the elements of its orbit?[8]

To solve the problem, Leverrier was forced to reverse the classical method of astronomical analysis, in which the known mass and orbital path of a planet are used to compute its pull on another planet. Instead he had to infer from the mass and orbit of the disturbed planet the nature of the disturber. This procedure is much like deducing from a given conclusion the set of premises from which the conclusion was drawn—a much more difficult process than deriving a conclusion from a given set of premises.

Leverrier worked feverishly for a year to find a suitable solution. In 1846 he was so sure of his hypothetical planet that he asked Johann G. Galle, a Berlin astronomer, to search for it. Leverrier boldly announced the position and apparent diameter of the planet as well as its density and mass. Within an hour after receiving Leverrier's letter, Galle discovered a faint unrecorded "star," which changed position in the skies during the next twenty-four hours. This star was within one degree of the predicted position, and its apparent diameter was almost identical with Leverrier's prediction.

Galle wrote a letter to Leverrier confirming the existence of Neptune:

> The planet which you described really exists. The very day on which I received your letter I found a star of the eighth magnitude which was not charted on the excellent . . . map published by the Royal Academy of Berlin. Observation on the following day decided that it was the searched-for planet.[9]

English astronomer George B. Airy accurately described this spectacular accomplishment, the discovery of a new world: "Nothing . . . so legitimately bold [since Copernicus' work] has been enunciated by way of prediction."[10] Ironically Adams, Airy's countryman, had solved the problem before Leverrier, but by a strange quirk of fate he had failed to obtain a hearing for his work before Leverrier's announcement.

Surely this extraordinary achievement is a superb example of the inductive and creative aspects of science, even though we now know that it was somewhat flawed by a number of chance factors and mathematical assumptions (unknown to Leverrier) that made success possible. The magnitude of this success vindicated Leverrier's faith in the classical laws of planetary motion and stilled for years further questioning of these laws.

An instructive comparison can be made between this triumph and the bitter failure Leverrier experienced a few years later. Prior to his master stroke with Neptune, Leverrier had struggled to explain a discrepancy in the orbit of Mercury. He returned to this problem with renewed vigor and soon decided that the orbit of Mercury was changing (precessing) by a small but fixed value each century. The planetary laws failed to account for this difference. Was it possible for Newtonian mechanics, which had so dramatically been confirmed only a few years earlier, to be wrong in this case? Leverrier could have solved his problem by changing the estimated mass of the planet Venus by a factor of one tenth of the accepted value, but hundreds of reliable observations and calculations ruled out the possibility of a 10 percent error. To Leverrier the only reasonable explanation was that there must be another unknown planet that moved in an orbit between Mercury and the sun and disturbed Mercury's orbit as Neptune disturbed Uranus. The new planet was christened Vulcan, and astronomers were exhorted to search for it.

A large number of sightings were reported, although few were made by professional astronomers. One scientist, the discoverer of twenty planetoids, reported that on July 29, 1878 he had observed two intra-Mercurial planets during an eclipse. However, of the hundreds of astronomers who witnessed the same eclipse, no one confirmed this observation. Indeed there has never been a confirmed observation of a planet with the characteristics Leverrier attributed to it.

Why were the Newtonian laws so successful in the case of the extra-Uranian planet and apparently so wrong in what appears to be a completely similar situation? Norwood R. Hanson, eminent philosopher of science, maintained that Leverrier was led astray by his faith in the theoretical structure of astronomy:

> The man holding the stakes in both cases was U. J. J. Leverrier. The triumph was his; he drew from the theory what few suspected it possessed. But the failure was not his—it was the theory's. He pressed it onto the problem of Mercury, just as Neptune had taught him to do. But it could not bring forth results which it did not possess.[11]

The point is made   The oddities of Mercury's orbit were unexplained until Albert Einstein proposed his general theory of relativity in 1916. This theory denies the precise and universal applicability of classical Newtonian laws, which are now considered to be a special case of the general theory. The close agreement between Einstein's prediction of the change in Mercury's orbit and the observed change marked the first major success of non-Newtonian planetary theory. As a result it is unnecessary to assume that an intra-Mercurian planet exists, and thus the planet Vulcan perished ignominiously.

The moral to be drawn from this episode in the history of science is that scientists validate their hypotheses, insofar as they can be validated, by agreement between predicted and observed behavior. If close agreement is not found, the investigator must review his assumptions and procedures carefully. Is the hypothesis faulty? Are the observations correct? Or is the experiment improperly designed to test the hypothesis? Scientists are reluctant to abandon a cherished hypothesis or theory, even though it is contradicted by the facts, and they do so only because there is no other alternative. It is probably a truism that the value of a hypothesis is ascertained only by its consequences. No matter how promising or intriguing, the conceptual scheme must be "fruitful of further experimentation and observation."

Cumulation

Science has been characterized by controlled experimentation, by rigorous observation, by "exact" measurement, and by confirmation of its hypotheses by the test of experience. It is also cumulative and progressive to an extent unattainable in the arts. As George Sarton, the great historian of science, once remarked:

> The making of knowledge, unlike that of beauty, is essentially a cumulative process . . . Nothing that has been done or invented gets lost . . . This cumulative process is so obvious that even very young men may be better informed and more learned than their more illustrious predecessors and so they have a chance to see further.[12]

Science is self-correcting

Cumulation is possible only because science is self-correcting. Despite the vigor of argument and counterargument, a consensus is sooner or later achieved. Charles Darwin's theory of natural selection was fiercely debated for decades following its publication in 1859. Not until after the turn of the century was natural selection internationally accepted by scientists. Literally thousands of controversial proposals have been published; sooner or later enough evidence accumulates to permit acceptance, rejection, or modification, and eventual integration into the body of scientific knowledge. Errors are soon exposed by the natural course of scientific growth, and the appropriate adjustments are made. If a chemist misreads a temperature or a biologist mistakes one structure for another, his peers soon expose this mistake by the merciless court of objective experiment. This evaluative process is successful only because thousands of scientific research publications circulate freely. Such well-known attributes of the scientist as honesty, accuracy, and thoroughness are, in a somewhat trivial sense, forced on him because he realizes that his work, and with it his reputation, is in the public domain. The scientific endeavor builds on past triumphs because past error has been eliminated.

The community of scientists

The rapidity of this corrective process is immeasurably increased by the existence of a well-financed, close-knit, international community of scientists:

> [There is] an organization of individuals in close communication with each other. Because of the existence of this organization new ideas spread rapidly, discoveries breed more discoveries, and erroneous observations or illogical notions are on the whole soon corrected. The deep significance of the existence of this organization is often completely missed by those who talk about

science but have no first hand experience with it. Indeed, a failure to appreciate how scientists pool their information and by so doing start a process of cross fertilization in the realm of ideas has resulted in some strange proposals by politicians even in the United States.[13]

On the other hand literature, art, music — few, if any, nonscientific disciplines are self-correcting in this sense and therefore are not cumulative in the same way. Is it meaningful to speak of an error in a Beethoven composition, a Picasso abstraction, or a Norman Mailer novel? Is it meaningful to compare the "correctness" of Simon and Garfunkel to Beethoven? Styles and critical fashions change, and in a sense their ebb and flow is "error correction." The difference, however, is that science is self-correcting because it is essentially a noncontroversial, objectively analytical, coherent body of knowledge. The arts, on the other hand, are so complex in their subjectivity that the rigorous criteria that define science are irrelevant and undesirable. The very notion of irreversible self-correction in the arts is repugnant. But, more to the point, it is impossible!

Process

Scientific method — sound without substance

"The scientific method" is one of the most overworked and hackneyed phrases in the literature of science and science education. Unfortunately many people believe that the scientific method is the scientist's "philosopher's stone," and that conscientious application of the method is sufficient to remove the difficulties confronting the researcher. It is tempting to say that scientists agree there is no scientific method, that it exists only in the writings of those who have either overlooked the new philosophy and history of science or have never pursued scientific research. The phrase, however, still appears in scientific literature and is obviously not becoming obsolete. In science education the analyses of scientific method by Karl Pearson and John Dewey are the philosophical foundations of most textbook discussions. Few science texts omit a token mention; many describe in some detail the logical steps that scientists presumably follow:

1. Identification and statement of the problem.
2. Formulation of hypotheses.
3. Search for evidence to test hypotheses.
4. Assessment of validity of hypotheses.

5. Revision of hypotheses if necessary.

6. Application of conclusions to similar problems.

How simple and concise! How attractive as a guide to the perplexed! Unfortunately this skeletonized summary of scientific process is misleading. It may have value as a logical analysis of scientific investigation, but it is not an infallible guide to action. It should be contrasted with these often quoted words of Nobel prize winner Percy W. Bridgman: "The scientific method, as far as it is a method, is nothing more than doing one's damndest with one's mind, no holds barred."[14]

Some examples

If the scientific method is really a dependable guide to action, why have scientists been so slow in settling some familiar and vexing problems? Why, for example, did it take more than one hundred years of persistent and frustrating research to synthesize quinine? Benjamin Franklin equated lightning with static electricity in 1752. Why, then, is there still no general agreement on the causes of lightning? Scientific discovery should quickly follow the logical and intelligent application of the scientific method, but this rarely happens. There is *no* simple guide for creative discovery, and these rules for tearing loose the secrets of nature are not binding on nature. In Conant's words:

> The stumbling way in which even the ablest of the scientists in every generation have had to fight through thickets of erroneous observations, misleading generalizations, inadequate formulations and unconscious prejudice is rarely appreciated by those who obtain their scientific knowledge from textbooks.[15]

A classic example of these struggles is the work of Gregor Mendel, the Moravian monk whose years of labor breeding plants laid the foundations of the science of genetics. Mendel published his results in the rather obscure journal of his local scientific society in 1866. No one paid attention to it. Mendel wrote to the leading German biologist, Karl Nägeli, describing his results and asking for help. Nägeli, after a long delay, rejected Mendel's ideas. Not until the turn of the century was Mendel's work recognized for its interpretative power. It is difficult to explain why his contemporaries failed to recognize his brilliant insights. Perhaps it was because biologists were busy asking questions that had little relevance for the problems with which they were confronted and because they scorned amateurs such as Mendel who were not members of the establishment.

In the physical sciences the early history of X rays is even more remarkable. Some years prior to Wilhelm Roentgen's discovery of X rays in 1895,

William Crookes, a world-famous experimental physicist, noticed that unexposed photographic plates in his laboratory were often fogged and useless. Crookes was well qualified to investigate the action of a Crookes' tube, an apparatus he had invented which, unknown to him, gave off X rays. Somehow Crookes failed to see the connection between his apparatus and the fogged film and therefore missed discovering X rays. Lord John Rayleigh, also an eminent physicist, is the source of this anecdote concerning Crookes:

> It was a source of great annoyance to Crookes that he missed the discovery of X-rays. According to an account he gave in my hearing, he had definitely found previously unopened boxes of [photographic] plates in his laboratory to be fogged for no assignable reason, and acting, I suppose, in accordance with the usual human instinct for blaming someone else when things go wrong, he complained to the [makers], who naturally had no satisfactory explanation to offer. I believe it was only after Roentgen's discovery that he connected this with the use of highly exhausted vacuum tubes in the neighborhood.[16]

Still more startling is the fact that two American physicists took the first X-ray photographs in 1890, five years before the discovery of X rays. They saw nothing novel in their results; not until 1896 were their plates reexamined, and the true significance of their inadvertent achievement understood.[17]

> [Roentgen alone] discovered the existence and nature of x-radiation. The discovery was in the air—at the very fingertips of dozens of scientists who might have made the same discovery. "The seeds of great discoveries are constantly floating around us" the famous American physicist Joseph Henry once wrote, "but they only take root in minds well-prepared to receive them."[18]

Discovery and creativity

If Roentgen had missed X rays, it is certain that another physicist would have made the discovery within a few years.

These instances should be sufficient proof that innovation in science is not necessarily attained by simply following the steps of the scientific method. It is probably true that published accounts of scientific research exemplify the scientific method, but invariably they omit the problems of strategy that confronted the researcher—how he recognized and defined the questions to be answered, how he created his hypotheses and decided on the experimental and observational situations that tested them. The scientific method, in other words, is a logical analysis of scientific research, but it is an analysis after the fact. It does not tell us *how* each step is to be attained or how to advance from step to step.

Scientific progress may evolve from exhaustive exploration of all possible alternatives—for example, Charles Goodyear's discovery of the vulcanization of rubber and Paul Ehrlich's synthesis of the antisyphilis drug Salvarsan. But the advances which revolutionize science rarely arise from hard work alone. Breakthroughs are more often the result of acts of scientific creativity, of chance events, or of the availability of new instruments without which advance is impossible. The first-rate scientist often speaks of the role of intuition, hunches, chance thoughts, and lucky accidents in his research. Charles Nicolle, who first recognized how typhus was spread, wrote about this "sudden flash of creative illumination . . . This shock, this sudden illumination, this instantaneous self-certainty of a new fact—I know of it, I have experienced it in my own life."[19]

The workings of chance

This creative illumination is frequently the result of a chance event, as in the discovery of penicillin by Alexander Fleming. In September 1928 Fleming observed that one of his bacteriological cultures had been contaminated by a penicillin mold. Contamination of this kind was not uncommon, and the imperfect culture was customarily discarded without delay. Fleming, however, examined this particular specimen carefully and noticed that the bacteria near the mold had disappeared. For some reason he was struck by this event and decided to find out why.[20] Fleming jumped to the conclusion that the mold was secreting some substance inimical to bacteria, and he designed a systematic experiment to test his hypothesis. Eight months later he published his now famous results in *The British Journal of Experimental Pathology*. He had not been the first to observe the bacteria-destroying activity of a mold; such effects had been reported as early as 1875. But he was the first to propose and test a hypothetical explanation that was "fruitful of further experimentation and observation." The workings of chance are illustrated by the fact that the cultured bacteria were staphylococci, a strain particularly sensitive to penicillin.[21]

This brief sketch of the discovery of penicillin has been much oversimplified. Chance factors, after all, were only *one* aspect of the total picture. Fleming had long been interested in the treatment of bacterial infection; he had previously discovered by a brilliant series of experiments the antibacterial enzyme lysozyme. His was, in Pasteur's well-known phrase, "the well-prepared mind." New chemical techniques of separating and concentrating the penicillin mold secretion were also available to him. Had Fleming failed in his investigation, the end result would sooner or later have been the same.

Someone else would have succeeded. It is reasonable to believe, however, that penicillin was made available to the world many years before a systematic study of possible antibiotics could have revealed its existence.

The atmosphere of scientific endeavor is such that significant discoveries are frequently announced at about the same time by independent investigators. The almost simultaneous discovery by Charles Hall, an American, and Paul Héroult, a Frenchman, of the modern process of extracting aluminum and the discovery of electromagnetic induction by Michael Faraday in England and Joseph Henry in the United States, to cite only two cases, prove that scientific ideas, if the time is right, are "in the air," and are seized on by those men who are "well prepared." This phenomenon of independent investigation is characteristic of science, and therein lies a major dissimilarity between science and the arts. There are no unique creations in science—no masterpieces beyond the ability of other humans. The world without Shakespeare would be a world without *Hamlet;* there would be no *Eroica* without Beethoven; but the general theory of relativity, differently named but essentially the same in structure, was virtually certain of creation had Einstein not existed. Newton's law of gravity, "one of those triumphs that humble ordinary men in the presence of genius," had already been foreshadowed by such men as Robert Hooke and Edmund Halley, and would assuredly have been formulated by some other scientist within a few decades following 1687, the year in which Newton gave his work on planetary motion to the world.[22]

Because there is no sure road to success in science, we should be careful to think of the scientific method as a guide that can point out the road but cannot guarantee safe passage. The task of the creative scientist is to find "likeness in unlikeness," "order in disorder." How reminiscent these phrases are of William Coleridge's famous definition of beauty as "unity in variety" and his dictum that in the creation of beauty lies the task of the poet. In a literal sense, both poet and scientist are creators. Their mission is revealed in Herman Melville's poem, "Art":

The great scientist as creator

> What unlike things must meet and mate:
> A flame to melt—a wind to freeze;
> Sad patience—joyous energies;
> Humility—yet pride and scorn;
> Instinct and study; love and hate;
> Audacity—reverence. They must mate,
> and fuse with Jacob's mystic heart,
> To wrestle with the Angel—Art.

The great scientist cuts through the mass of facts that encompasses him and finds or, perhaps better, invents an "order" that cannot be revealed by observation alone. This order does not exist in nature—it is a free creation of the human mind. Jacob Bronowski, in his magnificent essay on human values in science, reminds us that John Dalton, the great English chemist of the early nineteenth century, was visionary enough to fuse the Greek image of the atom with the chemical facts of the late eighteenth century.[23] Dalton is the "inventor" of the modern atom. His creation required the same leap of sensibility and imagination by which the artist fuses certain selected elements of his universe into a new transcendent synthesis. Dalton's synthesis was a supreme leap of the scientific imagination.

The importance of Dalton's achievement is undiminished by the fact that his conceptual scheme has been so changed that he would not recognize it were he alive today. Change is inherent in science, and Dalton's ideas have long since been assimilated into modern atomic theory. His theories marked one of the turning points in the relatively short history of chemistry.

Imagination, perception, and a feel for a possible unity between seemingly unrelated facts and concepts are qualities that distinguish the creative from the noncreative toiler in the scientific vineyard. In none of the notable achievements previously described is it possible to distinguish the strict application of the scientific method. If we assume a problem has been isolated and clearly defined, a task which is frequently of the greatest difficulty, then the next step in the scientific method is to formulate an explanatory hypothesis. Unfortunately it is just at this time, when creative imagination is most essential, that the method is the least helpful. Once the hypothesis has been devised, most scientists are able to invent ways to test it by exploring pertinent facts and by careful observation and controlled experimentation. But these activities, although not routine, are relatively less challenging.

Values

What makes a scientist? Why does he choose a career that requires such long, arduous training? What keeps him to the grindstone of research year after year despite his expectation of frequent failure? How does he dare confront the public whose image of the scientist has in the past been so unflattering:

> He is a brain; he is so involved in his work that he doesn't know what is going on in the world. He has no other interests and neglects his body for his mind. He can only talk, eat, breathe, and sleep science.

Imagination

An image of the scientist

He neglects his family—pays no attention to his wife, never plays with his children. He has no social life, no other intellectual interest, no hobbies or relaxations. He bores his wife, his children and their friends . . . with incessant talk that no one can understand.[24]

Rather extensive psychological and sociological research describes the scientist (in direct contrast to the engineer and technician) as strongly self-directed; a person who prefers situations that challenge his intellect rather than his emotional or social skills. He is personally dominant, but he avoids controversy. Independent of group pressure, he is characterized by high intelligence, early interest in intellectual performance, and a strong drive to find relationships between the phenomena in which he is interested. There is good reason to believe that scientists are "born," not made, and that their psychological characteristics tend to develop at an early age. Therefore it is possible that the scientist is undeterred by public opinion because, as an outsider, he has learned to ignore "the slings and arrows" of his socially centered peer culture.

The derogatory quotation previously cited is a product of the adolescent mind. But many literate, sensitive adults are also repelled by the world of science. George Gissing, the nineteenth century English novelist, expressed the attitude of many:

Another image

I hate and fear "science" because of my conviction that for long to come if not forever it will be the remorseless enemy of mankind. I see it destroying all simplicity and gentleness of life, all beauty of the world; I see it restoring barbarism under the mask of civilization; I see it hardening men's minds and hardening their hearts.[25]

These stark, disturbing words express an awareness of only the negative aspects of technological advance. C. P. Snow, the contemporary scientist–novelist, has coined the phrase "the two cultures" as an epithet for the division of literate men into science-minded and humanities-minded groups. Humanists are dismayed by science and scientists because they assume that scientific and human values are incompatible. Their rejection of the thesis that science is a part of man's cultural heritage, with an intellectual history and liberating energy of its own, is perhaps a reflection of the narrow, textbook-oriented science of their school years.

Scientists try to avoid value judgments in their work because these judgments cannot be tested in the same way and with the same precision as scientific fact. This does not mean, however, that values play no part in scientific endeavor. Albert Einstein once wrote these provocative words:

Science and religion

> . . . Even though the realms of religion and science in themselves are clearly marked off from each other, nevertheless there exist between the two, strong reciprocal relationships and dependencies. Though religion may be that which determines the goal, it has, nevertheless, learned from science, in the broadest sense, what means will contribute to the attainment of the goals it has set up. But science can only be created by those who are thoroughly imbued with the aspiration towards truth and understanding. This source of feeling, however, springs from the sphere of religion . . . Science without religion is lame, religion without science is blind.[26]

Such values as truth, independence, freedom, and tolerance are implicit in the scientific heritage; they originate in man's subjective needs and hopes, not in the physical realm of the sciences. Truth is essential because scientists must rely on the cumulative activities of their colleagues, past and present. Truth to fact, unbiased and unblemished, must exist because science itself will perish if built on error. The self-correcting aspect of science guards against continuing and pernicious error. Because truth is necessary, scientists prize independence, originality, and freedom of dissent. Scientists must have the courage to disagree with the established order—that is, to be nonconformers.

Dissent

Copernicus and Galileo, at great personal risk, dared challenge the idea of the Aristotelian earth-centered universe, which had lasted for fourteen centuries. Austrian physician Ignaz Philipp Semmelweis (1818–65) was driven from his practice by the obstinate medical practitioners of Vienna for advocating antiseptic precautions in surgery. Darwin forced a revolution in scientific and religious thought through his publication of *The Origin of Species* in 1859, a revolution in which he was to suffer personal abuse and ridicule.

Free, independent thought is possible only in a society that values freedom. Therefore science can flourish only if free inquiry, free thought, free speech, and tolerance are encouraged. The relative freedom accorded scientists in the Soviet Union today, in contrast with the restrictions imposed on the average Russian citizen, is indicative of this profound need.

Means and ends

In science there must be no distinction between ends and means by which they are sought. The perversions of Nazi medicine, in which human life was sacrificed on the altar of research, are unimaginable to men and women steeped in the scientific tradition. There is also a new attention on the part of scientists to the moral consequences of scientific labor. It is perhaps true to a greater extent than scientists care to admit that they have often failed to follow up the effects of their research on society and its environment. Many scientists today on both sides of the Iron Curtain idealistically refuse to carry on research with weapons of destruction because of their awareness of the responsibility invested in them. Indeed the values of science are not mere abstractions, nor are they absolutes which man can never attain. Their existence is fundamental to the demands of the search for truth.

Science today, as in the past, is an international enterprise. There is no French chemistry, no American physics, no Danish astronomy. The distribution of Nobel awards in chemistry, physics, and medicine is irrefutable evidence of a world community in science. In a real sense, science is a society open to all who are prepared for it—prepared by virtue of rigorous training and dedication to its value system.

Human Aspects of Scientists

Humanness   Science is, after all, the product of human beings who love, agonize, and rejoice in the enterprise of living. Research scientists are fortunate, as few men are, because they are able to do what they want in ways of their own choice. Artists and university-based scholars also enjoy this freedom. Paradoxically all of them operate independently, yet they are bound by the stream of events that is the summation of their independent efforts. Like artists, musicians, and other creative people, scientists are strongly inner-directed. They glory in the excitement of their work and in retrospect may not even remember the many days of failure and frustration. Their goal-oriented tenacity, their drive to solve, their desire to be first yet to share their knowledge with their colleagues are characteristics of the professional side of the scientist.

When they are not working, they live as other men and women live. They have children, whom they may spoil or escape from, husbands or wives who may or may not provide personal fulfillment in their lives, psychiatrists, and fishing or golf partners from whom they are inseparable. Sometimes they apply their scientific objectivity to their personal problems—more often they do not. They differ from other human beings in one respect only: in creating new visions in science. This difference does not imply that they are better or more select or more valuable to society. In fact some may be totally incompetent or even dangerously wrong when they work at tasks more important or valuable than science in the total scheme of things.

Social Relevance of Science

We have referred to the distrust — in some cases even hatred — of science and scientists expressed by many literate men and women, but the startlingly rapid growth of science as a beneficent force that affects our lives for a while almost obliterated the protests of those opposed to it. For some years after World War II, there seemed to be a consensus that man had finally arrived at the true Baconian age. Science was "good." It had justified itself because man had learned through science "how to make two blades of grass grow where one grew before." Even those university scientists who, as Newtonians, regarded science as "an intellectual exercise" were supported in their theoretical and experimental work.[27] Legislators supported "big science" because they were convinced that it would pay off handsomely. Academic men supported science because it was pure and worthy.

Science as business

Congress established the National Science Foundation, which channeled many millions of dollars to university scientists. The military establishment funneled even larger sums of money into both pure and applied research so that science and technology were supported on an ever-increasing scale. The rapid expansion of the National Aeronautics and Space Administration illustrates the enormous extension of federal funding. When the Russian satellite "Sputnik" was launched on a fateful October day in 1957, the United States was catapulted into the space age, an unprecedented era of scientific and technological frenzy.

"Big Science"

At the same time, scientists in American industry were applying the fruit of previous research gleaned from the entire world. This fulfillment of Bacon's seventeenth century dream was uncritically accepted by Americans, who always supported good works, at least in principle. For example, the DuPont Company, one of the leading chemical manufacturers in the nation, had long preached "Better living through chemistry," and this slogan reflected almost completely the American assessment of science and technology.

With the advent of the 1960s, however, Americans sensed that something had gone seriously wrong. They began to realize that certain technological and scientific advances were causing unexpected hazards to man. The drop in the death rate caused by the introduction of antibiotics, by better sanitation, and by improved food production was inextricably coupled with a much higher birth rate and a huge population boom, especially in developing countries. Even in the wealthy nations population growth has led to major difficulties. The general rise in per capita income enables many American families to own two automobiles, to move to parts of the country which a few years ago could not support communities. The invention of oral contraceptives,

Ecological consequences

which at first thought confirmed the value of science in controlling population, has introduced new health hazards. DDT, once universally hailed as a life-saving insecticide, now pollutes the biological environment. Even common household detergents increase the phosphate content of the natural waters, upset the chemical balance of lakes and rivers, destroy natural life forms, and create liquid deserts. Pollution in many forms pours into these waters, accelerating their biological death. Fumes from automobile exhausts and factories fill the city air, clouding the skies and befouling our lungs. The quality of human life is changing dramatically for the worst, and the accusing finger of society now points at technology as the main culprit.

This destruction of man's environment, serious though it is, is only one aspect of the problem that confronts civilization. The hallmark of the sciences ever since the scientific revolution of the seventeenth century has been their insistence on rational and orderly study of man's world. Contemporary critics of modern science, whose numbers are rapidly increasing, reject this rationality because they fear that rationality itself is being perverted to control mankind. They point to the military applications of science and the environmental problems that confront us as examples of the evil stemming from science, and they call for a halt to all research, except perhaps of research which seeks to eliminate the problems caused by science. They demand that money allocated to science be diverted to socially relevant programs such as improvement of housing in the cities, elimination of malnutrition and hunger, and improvement of educational opportunities for children of the poor.

A rational world view

For these reasons scientists can no longer be content to live completely in the pure, unsullied realms of the "Search for Truth." They must become aware of the moral and social effects of their research and of the necessity of turning their efforts to alleviate the negative effects. As Alvin Weinberg says:

> Is it not clear that the social responsibility of the technologist and his scientific supporter lies in removing the taints that now mar the modern technologies of abundance? Rather than ending technological development, we must invent new technologies, or improve the old, so as to have both our food and our robins, our cars and our clean air.

Social responsibility

> . . . The job and the purpose of science and technology remain overwhelming: to create a more livable world, to restore man to state of balance with his environment, to resolve the remaining elementary and primitive suffering of man — hunger, disease, poverty, and war. These are not small tasks, nor are they new ones; that in science and technology we have the possibility of dealing with them is an article of faith of all who have committed themselves to the scientific way of life. It is the height of irrationality to turn our backs on all this, as is urged by the more radical of the scientific abolitionists. For rationality and science there is no simple or cheap substitute. Should science die under

the onslaught of the nihilists, it could be only a temporary death. That human rationality and human good sense will prevail in the long run we take for granted. It is up to us, members of the older scientific–technological establishment, to persuade our younger impatient scientific nihilists that ours is the course of reason, and that in our arduously built scientific–technological tradition lies our best chance of ultimate survival.[28]

For better or for worse, we live in a complex, scientific–technological world. Scientists must be given the opportunity to make that world one in which we are all proud to live.

Structure

The language of science

Modern theories of teaching science stress student cognition of the structure of science. The "structure of science" is a currently fashionable figure of speech that is nothing more nor less than Conant's "interconnected series of concepts and conceptual schemes." It is, in other words, the conceptual scaffolding uniting the observable phenomena of our universe. Compare this emphasis with such earlier expressions of purpose as "enhancing student understanding of our environment" or "understanding the role of science in technical innovation," which are still important functions of science education today. To be scientifically literate is to comprehend the language of science, a literacy attained only by understanding on the learner's highest level the conceptual interrelationships of the sciences.

Meaning and control

Consider, for example, the familiar kinetic molecular theory of matter, which makes intelligible such apparently different phenomena as the semipermeable membrane and the lowering of the freezing point of water in an automobile radiator when antifreeze is added. The theory is not directed to these phenomena alone—that is, it is not specific to them—but it does make their prediction possible, and by definition it explains their occurrence. The student who has mastered the concepts and assumptions of kinetic theory is better able to explain other related phenomena. Once a principle is understood, it may be drawn on for new explanations. How is evaluation of understanding possible except by successful application to unfamiliar situations? This behavior is a kind of transfer, but it requires much more than the transfer of simple skills or identical elements described in the classic psychological theories of transfer. The fact that the fundamental ideas of science can be generalized—their structure, in other words—is what gives meaning to and control over nature.

Assuredly specific facts are quickly forgotten. The masses of detail—densities, specific heats, the variety of plant and animal tissues—which overwhelm the student as he studies science are retained only by extraordinary memories. Principles, relationships, concepts—abstractions from experience—are remembered much longer. Few individuals can identify rocks by comparing their characteristics with a mental image or with a memorized list of their physical characteristics. Many individuals, however, simplify identification by recalling the general differences that distinguish the common classes of rocks—a much easier task in psychological terms. The science of chemistry would still be an impenetrable maze (compare alchemy, which was such a maze) were it not for the chemist's understanding of the relationships between the chemical elements and of the structures of their compounds.

The psychological evidence for these statements is well known. Educators have been aware for many years that efficiency in learning requires stressing principles instead of the masses of facts from which the principles are derived. But somehow the actual business of teaching dilutes and negates learning theory so that facts become ends in themselves. Laws, principles, and theories are important elements of science curricula, but they in turn often become facts to be memorized and their significance in clarifying relationships is ignored.

The words _law, theory, fact,_ and _principle_ have been used intuitively in the preceding discussion. What precise meanings can be extended to these terms? How are they related to each other? How are they incorporated into the structure of science?

Figure 1 is a simplified delineation of these relationships:

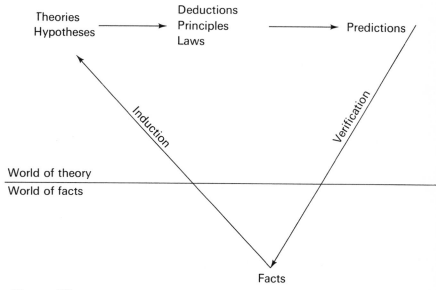

Figure 1[29]

The reader must consider this scheme to be presented for purposes of discussion; it is not a guide to scientific research. Note that its foundation is *fact* — the recognition and observation of "a single event."[30] Hypotheses and theories are abstractions of observable facts. From hypotheses and theories, principles and laws are deduced. Predictions may then be made and tested by comparing them to the world of observable fact. The fact is a particular item of information. It is a fact that chlorine is a gas at room temperature and normal atmospheric pressure. It is also a fact that chlorine is yellow green under these conditions. From facts such as the normal gaseous state of chlorine, its change under pressure and low temperature to the liquid or solid state, its ease of diffusion, and its decrease in volume under pressure, it is possible to derive a theory that chlorine is composed of particles (molecules) which are in rapid motion.

Theory defined

Theory may be defined as a report of an unlimited, perhaps infinite, number of events. A fact is a particular item of information, whereas a theory is general, a higher order of abstraction from experience. The scientist can change chlorine from a gas to a liquid under the proper conditions. This can be done anywhere, with all chlorine, and the theory of the molecular composition of chlorine applies to all chlorine molecules.

Theories explained

Not only must theories relate facts coherently and meaningfully, but they must also predict and explain these facts. Theories, however, are not automatically and effortlessly extracted from experiment and observation. In Nagel's words, theories are "free creations of the mind" which are conceived by a relatively small number of creative scientists. Theories are not accepted because scientists believe that the ideas associated with them are necessarily "true" but because the theories relate, explain, and predict the greatest variety of facts in the simplest and most economical ways.

Inventing concepts

For example, consider the concepts symbolized by the word *molecule*. A molecule is not directly observable, and in this sense it is not a fact of experience. It *is* an assumption that cannot be confirmed by human perception. But the conception of *molecule* as it is used in molecular theory "explains" many seemingly unrelated events such as diffusion, pressure–volume changes, different states of matter, and differences in the nature of chemical substances. Even the familiar *electron* is an idea, a concept, a mental construct rather than an actually existing bit of matter. It may well exist, but there is no proof other than in its value as an abstraction in explaining many phenomena which *are* observable. The *vacuum* is also an idealization because pure vacuum exists nowhere in the universe. Force, mass, energy are ideas, "creations of the mind," but they are also powerful tools, which in the hands of scientists have led to practical results of the greatest usefulness.

The meaning of a scientific theory was concisely expressed by Joseph J. Thomson, one of England's great physicists:

> [My] new theory was not to be regarded as an ultimate one; its object is physical, rather than metaphysical . . . from the point of view of the physicist, a theory of matter is a policy rather than a creed; its object is to connect or co-ordinate apparently diverse phenomena and above all to suggest, stimulate, and direct experiment.[31]

Theoretical Models

Thinking with models

Another way to understand a scientific theory is to think of it as a model with which scientists may make certain testable predictions. The picture of the atom created by Niels Bohr in 1913 is well known to all who have studied elementary science. The atom was pictured as a miniature solar system; a positively charged nucleus played the part of the nuclear sun, and electrons (whose total charge neutralized the nuclear charge) revolved around the nucleus in fixed orbits. Electrons were restricted to these orbits unless the kinetic energy of the atomic system changed by specific quantities. This was a model (theory) of the atom from which was drawn an astonishing number of predictions that could be tested. Although it was soon changed to accommodate new data, the Bohr atom is still useful to physical scientists.

Hierarchies of theory

A theory is not a simple, all-inclusive statement. It usually exists as a part of a hierarchy of theories. A relatively simple theory is apt to be a piece of a more comprehensive theory. For example, Kepler's three laws of planetary motion, Galileo's law of free fall, and the laws of the tides all became special cases of Newton's world system, which he described in his famous book *Principia*. This system in turn may be derived from Einstein's general theory of relativity. Each higher theory is more inclusive, predicts more effectively, and is more widely applicable than its elements.

Interpretation of Facts

Facts as building blocks

Theories clearly are mental constructs, but so are facts. An event as it is perceived is filtered and interpreted through a screen of theories of which the beholder's mind is often unaware. What one sees through the eyepiece of a microscope, for example, does not necessarily correspond to what is "actually" on the slide. The frame of reference the biologist brings to the microscope is not the same as that which guides the layman; neither sees exactly the same things. The botanist who identifies a certain plant as a species of primrose is clearly making a statement of scientific fact. But this act of classification depends on abstract ideas of taxonomy and species, which shape his identification. The conception of absolute and verifiable *fact*, whatever meaning this concept may have for philosophers, is meaningless in science.

Hypothesis

Educated guesses

The term *hypothesis* has been used frequently in this chapter. How does a hypothesis differ from a theory? For the purposes of this discussion, *hypothesis* is defined as a tentative idea about certain relationships which connect observable events. A theory may be described as a fairly well-confirmed hypothesis, although many hypotheses are not sufficiently interpretative or explanatory to be accepted as theories. The hypothesis may be wholly or partly incorrect, but it must offer a relatively simple explanation and prediction of the phenomena involved. The invention of pertinent hypotheses is exceedingly difficult; their verification, given the necessary facts, is usually less difficult. The creation of hypotheses is the lifework of the scientific theoretician.

A logical expectation

Evangelista Torricelli, a pupil of Galileo, invented the mercury barometer. In the course of his work, he hypothesized that the change he observed in the height of his barometer was caused by changing atmospheric pressure. This hypothesis was confirmed by Blaise Pascal, who arranged for a barometer to be carried to the top of a mountain to test Torricelli's hypothesis. He reasoned that if the air is thinner at the top of a mountain, the column of mercury in the barometer should fall. This is the simplest and most logical expectation. The height of the barometer did fall, in accordance with Torricelli's prediction, and his hypothesis has since attained the status of theory. This and other theories have been incorporated into the kinetic-molecular theory. Using the kinetic-molecular theory, it is possible to explain why a column of mercury stands approximately thirty inches under normal conditions and why the height of the column changes from day to day.

Law

No fines for scientific law breaking

A frequent source of confusion in many textbooks arises from different meanings of the term *law*. *Law* is sometimes defined as a theory which has been extensively tested and found valid.[32] For the purposes of this book, however, *law* is defined as a description of a regular natural occurrence; it is "no more and no less than a careful record of what actually happens, [therefore] there is no possible way of violating it."[33]

In 1858 Rudolf Virchow, the great German biologist, proposed this biological law:

> Where a cell arises, there a cell must have been before, even as an animal can come from nothing but an animal, a plant from nothing but a plant. Thus in the whole series of living things there rules an eternal law of continuous development, nor can any developed tissue be traced back to anything but a cell.[34]

It summarizes many hundreds of observations and experiments; and it is still generally valid today, even though Virchow extended his law to all eternity. A law of biology, however, may be much less inclusive. The "all-or-nothing" law states that an excitable fiber such as nerve or muscle will respond completely to a stimulus even if the stimulus is barely strong enough to excite. This law is valid because it is a record of what happens. It is a description, however, not an explanation.

In the realm of physics, accurate records of the distances traversed by falling objects, the duration of fall, and the acceleration due to gravity provide the data from which Galileo's law of free fall can be derived. This law is usually given as $S = \frac{1}{2} aT^2$, in which S is the distance fallen, a is the acceleration of gravity (approximately 32 feet per second per second), and T is the time in seconds during which the object falls. This law cannot be scrupulously exact because it is impossible to take every variable into account. For example, it is not exact if, as is usually the case, the falling object is slowed because of air resistance. However, the probability is high that $S = \frac{1}{2} aT^2$ will be obeyed within close limits as long as air resistance is relatively small. It is highly probable that falling objects will obey the law, but it is still only a probability, despite the previous statement that "there is no possible way of violating" a law. A law, then, is an account of a regular natural occurrence. It may be either quantitative or qualitative, but within the limits of human and experimental error it is a careful record which makes prediction possible.

Law—a consequence of theory

A scientific law is often derived from theoretical consideration. Laws are *explained* by theories. Boyle's law, which relates the pressure of a gas to its volume, may be deduced from the kinetic-molecular theory. It is therefore explained by the kinetic-molecular theory, which in turn is explained by the theories of statistical mechanics, elasticity, and molecular attraction—the higher levels of this hierarchy of theories.

A matter of sequence   Empirical laws are frequently proposed in science. These are laws lacking a theoretical base, and many years may elapse before they are incorporated into the conceptual framework of theory. Boyle's law was not firmly embedded in a theoretical structure for almost two centuries after its first formulation.

One historian of technology remarked that prior to 1850 the steam engine did more for the advancement of science than science did for the steam engine—meaning that the artisans and engineers who constructed steam engines our of their practical experience were able to do so without the science of thermodynamics. The science of thermodynamics, the theories of heat and heat transfer, could not have developed so rapidly without the empirical technology of the steam engine.

Theory—success and failure

What is the fate of a theory that satisfactorily explains and correlates all the pertinent facts of observation and experiment with only one exception? Suppose that this exception flatly contradicts a prediction derived from the theory? Does this destroy the theory, or is the contradiction so minor that it may be disregarded? An excellent example for consideration is the Copernican-Newtonian theory of the solar system, which in the early nineteenth century had been unsuccessful in explaining the strange behavior of Uranus. Despite repeated attacks on the validity of Newton's law of gravitation, most astronomers intuitively believed that the elegance and relative simplicity of Newton's ideas were such that they must be correct, and that some other explanation must be sought. When Leverrier extracted from the theory the prediction that an extra-Uranian planet was responsible for the deviations, the theory was once again confirmed.

Reconciling theory and fact   When, however, the disturbance of Mercury's orbit could not be reconciled with the theory, Newtonian concepts were not immediately overthrown because they were better explanations and better predictors than any other astronomical scheme. With the development of the theory of relativity in the early years of the twentieth century, a new, more comprehensive explanation of planetary motion was possible—a conceptual scheme which successfully predicted and thereby explained the deviations of Mercury.

The vision of perfect accuracy and perfect precision of observation and measurement is an illusion. Scientists approach but never attain this elusive goal. Therefore, their predictions are expressed in terms of probability. Deviation from prediction is possible and inescapable, but the value of the theory is not destroyed by such variation. Contradictory facts may render the theory more unlikely, but they do not cause its abandonment as long as it is possible to modify the theory to explain both the new and the old facts. Eventually, however, the theory may become so complex and difficult to apply that the

New theories   time is ripe for a new hypothesis. The phlogiston theory, which died in the early years of the nineteenth century, was such a theory. Its vogue of more than a century served chemical research well, despite the complications that chemists later encountered in attempting to adapt it to meet the demands of their new knowledge. Phlogiston was believed to be a substance of *negative* weight which was found in all combustible substances. On combustion, enough phlogiston escaped so that the final ash weighed more than the original substance. The phlogiston theory was destroyed by the theory of combustion advanced by Antoine Lavoisier a decade before the end of the eighteenth century. Lavoisier's ideas were not only in accord with all the chemical evidence, they were also simpler, less mystical, and more powerful.

Even today, the Ptolemaic vision of an Earth attended by a satellite sun and planetary system is not an impossible model. Ancient astronomers relied on Ptolemaic theory to predict the position of the known stars and planets because they found that the theory was reliable. It *was* complex. It had to be in order to correlate the numerous phenomena with which it dealt. Copernican ideas were somewhat simpler because Copernicus assumed that the sun, not the Earth, was the center of the solar system. But before the invention of the astronomical telescope in the seventeenth century, Copernican theory was little more successful in predicting planetary and stellar motions than was

A reason to change   Ptolemaic theory. Therefore the new astronomy was not accepted by most learned men, for there was no practical reason to change. Religious and philosophical ideas motivated some of the resistance, but less than is generally thought. Only when telescopic observation proved that planetary positions were not in accord with Ptolemaic predictions (and that the discrepancy was increasing over the centuries) did Copernican ideas begin to make rapid headway. Even the great Galileo, whose enthusiastic acceptance of Copernican ideas hastened the decay of the Ptolemaic scheme, was unable to demonstrate their validity.

Galileo was so impressed with the simplicity and elegance of the Copernican picture as compared with the complexity of the Ptolemaic picture that he felt emotionally that it must be true; and in the absence of a convincing physical argument, his method of discussion really amounted to little more than ridiculing the complexities of the Ptolemaic system.[35]

Scientific explanation

It is always possible to question an explanation, to ask Why? again and again. Sooner or later, no matter how knowledgeable he is, the person answering must admit that his ultimate answer is grounded on faith. Why does a magnet pick up a needle? Why does an apple fall to the ground? Why is the rainbow colored? These questions search for explanation. They may be meaningfully pursued up to a point at which they expire in the blind alley of unsupported assumption or are blocked by the statement that we do not know why. The meaning of *explanation* in science is different from the word's popular usage. The scientist explains a particular event, fact, or phenomenon by deriving it from theory; that is, he predicts a particular event must occur under certain conditions because of its logical relationships in a conceptual scheme. It is not necessary for the prediction to be a new, unexpected event. It is only necessary for the prediction (explanation) to emerge logically and systematically from theory.

It will be helpful to describe in further detail the factors that make up a scientific explanation. First the phenomenon in question must be included within the domain of well-validated theory or theories. In addition certain facts independent of the phenomenon must be known. Finally the explanation must follow logically from the theory or theories and the independently known facts. If there is no suitable theory, the explainer must either admit his ignorance or resort to imagination, myth, or fantasy.

A common elementary science experience is that in which a drinking glass is inverted in a water trough. As the glass is pushed to the bottom of the trough, the water level in the glass rises. How can this rise be explained? Is there a vacuum in the glass? If air fills the glass, does some of it dissolve in the water? Does the air leak out of the glass? Does the glass somehow cool off sufficiently to decrease the volume of air within it? What theories and what independent facts are required to explain the water rise? These questions are relevant to the answer, which is obviously oversimplified:

Theories

1. Fluids (air is a fluid) are composed of rapidly moving molecules whose attraction for each other is relatively weak.
2. Gases (air is a mixture of gases) are compressible because their molecules occupy a small part of the total volume of the gases.
3. The pressure and volume of a gas at constant temperature are inversely proportional to each other.

4. By definition, matter occupies space.

5. No two objects occupy the same space at the same time.

6. Pressure in fluids increases directly with depth.

7. Fluids move from regions of high pressure to regions of low pressure.

Independent verifiable facts and assumptions

1. Increasing the depth of the glass increases the pressure on the air in the glass, as shown by measurements with a manometer (pressure-indicating instrument).

2. No air bubbles escape.

3. The glass is a solid; no air escapes through it.

4. Temperature changes in the system are minimal.

5. No chemical reaction between the glass, air, and water is observed.

6. The solubility of air in water is low.

From these theories and facts it is possible to predict the rise of water in the glass and thereby to give a scientific explanation. The volume of air in the glass must decrease as the pressure on the air in the glass increases because air is compressible and cannot escape from the glass; therefore as the depth of the water increases, the pressure on the air trapped in the glass increases; the air becomes compressed, and the water rises in the glass because of the decrease in air volume, as water, a fluid, moves from regions of high to low pressure.

Value of conceptual structure

The value of a conceptual structure in science lies precisely in the degree to which it makes prediction (explanation) possible. The example of the glass is trivial, but it does illustrate how the structure of science is "fruitful," and why modern science education addresses itself particularly to the theme of "an interconnected series of concepts and conceptual schemes."

Summary

Science is an attempt to explain the universe by creating general theories which "predict" the observable facts of that universe. Theories are possible because scientists assume that there is an order in nature or, more appropriately, that man can create an order in nature from what seems to be chaos. In response to the belief of scientists that nature can be made intelligible, science has evolved into one of the dominant forces of this confused world. Although it is only one of these forces, and surely not the most important, its conceptual structure, creative vitality, and immense effect on society should demand of all literate individuals a determined effort to understand its twofold nature — the twin aspects of process and product, neither of which has meaning except in relation to the other.

Elementary school teachers of science should know both of these aspects, which together lead to the understanding of why science is important in the world today. With this knowledge they can provide their pupils with insightful science experiences to help them grow up to a world that is now, and that will in the future, be even more dependent on science and technology.

For further study

1. What is classificatory knowledge? Is it important? Is it necessary for the layman? How does it differ from "investigative" knowledge?

2. How does Simpson's definition of science differ from Conant's? Is it more relevant? Is it better? (See Simpson, George G., "Biology and the Nature of Science," *Science*, 139: 81–88, January 11, 1963.)

3. What conceptual schemes other than those described can you think of? Do they fit Conant's definition? (See Chapter 5.)

4. Is magic really as irrelevant to man as the authors suggest?

5. What are some of the technological changes which have occurred during the past decade?

6. Are the authors on firm ground when they assert that the nature of science can be understood only by active participation in science?

7. Leaf through a current issue of *Chemical* or *Biological Abstracts* in order to become aware of the volume of chemical or biological research.

8. What arguments, other than those cited, can you produce against teaching science from a technological orientation?

9. Are the authors justified in stating that traditional approaches to teaching science have failed? What is meant by traditional? Failure? Success?

10. What important goals of science education have the authors omitted or slighted?

11. Can you cite any major writers who integrate science and literature in their writing? Why do you think there are so many or so few?

12. In what kind of world would measurement be impossible? What are the possible consequences in such a world?

13. Will the domain of the social sciences be conquered by scientific techniques?

14. What is *your* image of the scientist?

15. Was the last scientist you saw on television or in the movies a stereotype? Whose stereotype?

16. Do artists experiment? Observe rigorously? Are they scientists?

17. What is a "statistical-probabilistic mode of operation"? Why is probability so important in the natural and social sciences?

18. How many times in high school and in college did you know in advance the answers to your laboratory experiments? How often was the laboratory an adventure?

19. Should science be "politicized"? Should scientists be concerned only with research that has no military or "evil" consequences? Is there any way of knowing the outcome of research?
(See the following papers for their honest and insightful treatment of the problems raised by questions 19–25.)

Weinberg, A. M., "In Defense of Science," *Science,* 167: 141–145, January 9, 1970; Morison, R. S., "Science and Social Attitudes," *Science,* 165: 150–56, July 11, 1969, and "Where is Biology Taking Us?," *Science,* 155: 420–33, January 27, 1967; Lorenz, K. Z., Chap. 7, "Pathology of Knowledge," in K. H. Pribram, ed., *On the Biology of Learning,* (New York: Harcourt Brace Jovanovich, 1969).

20. Should scientists as scientists, in contrast to their role as citizens, take leadership in the struggle against the difficulties now confronting society, which arise in large part from the rapid growth of science and technology? How do scientists and scientific societies respond to this demand by citizens and by some scientists themselves? (See Weinberg, A. M., "In Defense of Science," *Science,* 167: 141–45, January 9, 1970.)

21. Is science dehumanizing? Is its insistence on rationality and on order hostile to man's humanity?

22. Is it necessary for scientists to turn away from their usual research interests to socially acceptable and "relevant" research? Is there a place for such physical sciences as nuclear physics if this change occurs?

23. Are certain lines of research in biology so potentially dangerous that they should not be pursued? For example, are there sinister implications for molding man in the announcement that "pure genes" have been isolated? Should scientists "tinker" with man's genetic structure?

24. The building of nuclear power plants for generating electrical power is meeting increasing opposition. How can we provide more electrical power if nuclear power cannot be used?

25. Should elementary school children discuss the social and ethical implications of modern science and technology? If so, what specific examples could you use?

26. To what extent is experimental educational research valid?

27. Why can't a scientific hypothesis be proven, once and for all?

28. What examples of scientific prediction, other than those in this chapter, can you find? Which scientific theories have been discarded?

29. Is it possible for Vulcan to exist? Is the idea completely dead?

30. To what extent are the disciplines of psychology, economics, and anthropology sciences? Use the "Characteristics of Science" as criteria in your answer.

31. Experiences with magnets are often found in elementary school science. In a typical experience with a bar magnet, certain kinds of conceptual and factual information will be forthcoming. Which theories, laws, hypotheses, facts, and concepts are likely to be involved?

32. "Explain" each of the following phenomena:
    (a) Pouring air from one glass into another under water.
    (b) The fall in height of a barometer as humidity increases.
    (c) The light generated by an incandescent lamp.
    (d) The rise of a hydrogen-filled balloon.

Notes and references

1. Conant, J., *Science and Common Sense* (New Haven, Conn.: Yale University Press, 1951), p. 25.

2. *Ibid.*, p. 47.

3. For a discussion of the events leading up to this scheme, see Kuslan, L., and A. H. Stone, *Robert Boyle: The Great Experimenter* (Englewood Cliffs, N.J.: Prentice-Hall, 1970).

4. Conant, J., *Modern Science and Modern Man* (New York: Columbia University Press, 1952), p. 9.

5. Wilson, E., *An Introduction to Scientific Research* (New York: McGraw-Hill Book Co., 1952), p. 40.

6. *Ibid.*, p. 46.

7. Hanson, N., "Leverrier: The Zenith and Nadir of Newtonian Mechanics," *Isis*, 53: 361, September 1962.

8. *Ibid.*, p. 362.

9. *Ibid.*, p. 362, quotation translated from the French by L. Kuslan.

10. *Ibid.*, p. 363.

11. *Ibid.*, p. 374.

12. Sarton, G., *The Life of Science* (New York: Henry Schuman, 1948), p. 40.

13. Conant, J., *Science and Common Sense*, p. 17.

14. Bridgman, P. W., "The Prospect for Intelligence," *The Yale Review*, 34: 450, March 1945.

15. Conant, J., *Science and Common Sense*, pp. 43–44.

16. As cited in Cohen, I. B., *Science, Servant of Man* (Boston: Little, Brown and Co., 1948), p. 42.

17. *Ibid.*, p. 43.

18. *Ibid.*, p. 43.

19. As cited in Taton, R., *Reason and Chance in Scientific Discovery* (New York: Science Editions, 1962), p. 76.

20. Ratcliff, J., *Yellow Magic: The Story of Penicillin* (New York: Random House, 1945), pp. 16–17.

21. Taton, R., *op. cit.*, pp. 85–91.

22. Cohen, I. B., *The Birth of a New Physics* (New York: Doubleday & Co., 1960), p. 174.

23. Bronowski, J., *Science and Human Values* (New York: Harper & Row, Torchbooks, 1965), p. 13.

24. Mead, M., and R. Metraux, "The Image of the Scientist among High School Students: A Pilot Study," *Science*, 126: 384–90, August 20, 1957.

25. Gissing, G., *The Private Papers of Henry Ryecroft* (New York: Modern Library, n.d.), p. 227.

26. Einstein, A., *Out of My Later Years* (New York: Philosophical Library, 1950), p. 26.

27. Weinberg, A. M., "In Defense of Science," *Science*, 167: 142, January 9, 1970.

28. *Ibid.*, p. 145.

29. Adapted from Kemeny, J., *A Philosopher Looks at Science* (Princeton, N.J.: D. Van Nostrand Co., 1959), p. 87.

30. *Ibid.*, p. 91.

31. As cited in Conant, J., *Modern Science and Modern Man*, p. 91.

32. Wilson, E., *op. cit.*, p. 30.

33. Kemeny, J., *op. cit.*, p. 38.

34. Singer, C., *A Short History of Scientific Ideas to 1900* (New York: Oxford University Press, 1959), p. 413.

35. Hoyle, F., *Astronomy* (New York: Doubleday & Co., 1962), p. 126.

The Nature of Child Thought in Science

Developmental Psychology for Elementary Science: Two Points of View

Children Learning Science

Children Thinking Science

Motivational Factors in Learning and Thinking Science

Children's Science Concepts: Selected Cases

Chapter 2 discusses the ways children learn and think about science, the close relationship between cognitive and affective development, and the kinds of "sciencing" children can and will do. Teachers teach science, both product and process, to active children, each of whom is similar in many ways to his classmates. Yet each child is an individual, and because these children are different, because the science they can learn must be matched with their cognitive and affective status, teachers must become acquainted with the body of psychological knowledge that has relevance to the teaching of science. Curriculum development at the present time and during the next decade will be based on this knowledge of psychology and development.

For the reader's convenience we have organized this chapter into five separate but interrelated sections: Developmental Psychology for Elementary Science: Two Points of View, Children Learning Science, Children Thinking Science, Motivational Factors in Learning and Thinking Science, and Children's Science Concepts: Selected Cases. We have selected the content in each section on the basis of its pertinence to modern instruction in science and its power to enrich the teacher's skill and understanding. Because we wish to show the specific relationship of research in psychology and development to the teaching and learning of science, the description and analysis of studies is more comprehensive than is customary in science methods textbooks. Hopefully the studies will give prospective elementary school teachers insight into how children learn and think and will suggest useful techniques for motivation, instruction, and evaluation. However, beginning teachers should expect that they will have to blend classroom experience with this understanding of the cognitive and affective development of their pupils to achieve the exciting and enjoyable teaching experiences to which children are entitled.

Developmental Psychology
for Elementary Science:
Two Points of View

Overview

Piaget and cognitive development

Jean Piaget is probably the most potent name in matters of children's cognitive development. More than any contemporary researcher, he has extracted fundamental ideas about the ways in which children's mental processes develop. As the founder of a field of study called *genetic epistomology,* he has evolved stimulating ideas of concept formation, stages of cognitive development, and the approximate ages at which these developments are likely to take place. Piaget has provided a new foundation on which to study the nature of learning.

Gagné and hierarchical learning

Robert Gagné approaches the learning of science in a direct, organized, and pragmatic way. He deals with learning as a function of mental processes within the framework of specific description-oriented tasks. He sees learning as a matter of building hierarchies from their simplest elements to highly complex syntheses. Hence Gagné is a proponent of clear-cut planning and organization for learning; he sees that learning evolves from specific acts and experiences.

If we consider the learning models provided by both Piaget and Gagné, we will have an adequate psychological framework on which to base most science teaching processes and operations.

Learning and Developmental Models — Piaget

Learning is restructuring

According to Piaget, learning depends on the continual reorganization or restructuring of one's mental processes; it is not just a matter of adding new information and skills to earlier learning. In the course of the child's development, new categories of mental skills come into existence, skills which cannot evolve without variety and richness of experience and activity. In every sense learning is a transmutation of the child's mental framework into new and higher thought capabilities. This transformation, which takes place at roughly comparable ages for school children throughout the world, is contingent on a continual interaction of many internal and external processes.

As the child grows physically, his nervous system grows in complexity. He responds to experiences, each of which alters in some way the course of his development. He is living through a dynamic series of actions that Piaget refers to as *equilibration* or *autoregulation*. In equilibration the child reacts in two ways to experiences: He *assimilates* them—that is, he incorporates aspects of these experiences into his own frame of reference, subconsciously selecting those aspects that fit his mental scheme. He also *accommodates* to these experiences—that is, he alters his usual pattern of behavior because of these environmental encounters. Together, these complementary processes of assimilation and accommodation make up the self-regulating system of learning behavior Piaget christened *equilibration*.

Assimilation and accommodation-equilibrium

Assimilation and accommodation may operate in harmful ways as well as in helpful ways. The child who decides on the evidence of a single experiment that all plants carry on photosynthesis, or the child who does not recognize that there are important differences between static and current electricity, assimilates these errors into his behavior pattern. He also accommodates to these experiences because his behavior toward plants or electricity is no longer the same. These particular misconceptions and modes of response are rather trivial examples, but they are illustrative.

Periods of development

Mental operations

Piaget's hypothesis that children pass through a succession of mental growth periods, or stages, is not new. What is new is his careful delineation of these periods based on studies of thousands of children. Children who are twelve years old are entering a stage of mental operations in which they are obviously better at formal logical thinking than are children of eight. There is some question, however, about the existence of qualitative differences between these stages. Is the thinking of young children less "logical" because they have had fewer opportunities to think logically? One school of thought says that qualitative changes in thought processes—that is, to noticeably different levels of thought—do not occur, and the major differences between younger and older children lie in the increasing complexity of the situations to which older children can accommodate and from which they assimilate new and important elements.[1]

Do cognitive structural changes occur?

Most psychologists agree with Piaget that structural or qualitative changes do occur.[2] Part of the controversy undoubtedly stems from the techniques psychologists use to investigate cognitive ability. They rely heavily on problem solving and on questioning children about how they solve problems, a tricky path by which to gain insight into thought processes, for children (and adults) are often unable to explain how and why they came to a decision. Furthermore children often propose solutions that, although incorrect according to the investigator's solution model, are logical and completely rational from their own point of view. Children are often uninterested in the kinds of answers adults ask them to give. For example, a class of six-year-old children had been studying the change in temperature of cans of hot and cold water and came to a surprising conclusion. The answer expected by the teacher was that the two cans would gradually come to room temperature, the hot water cooling down and the cold water warming up. The children, however, proposed their own

Illogic may be logical logical explanation. They considered body temperature to be a standard of "warmth," and as the temperatures of the water in the cans changed and approached body temperature, they concluded that both cans had "warmed" up. These children had not assimilated the concept that a lowering in the temperature of the hot water means that the water is growing cooler. Their logic was impeccable, however, since they were comparing temperature change to their own arbitrary standard.[3]

The three major periods defined by Piaget are *sensorimotor, concrete operations,* and *formal operations.* The third period is not discussed in detail because elementary school children, as a rule, have not entered it.

Sensorimotor period

According to Piaget, the child remains in the sensorimotor period up to the approximate age of twenty-four months. During this time, his primitive responses and predominant motor reflexes gradually become better differentiated and generalized. He begins to distinguish between goals and the behavior necessary to attain those goals, and he responds much more readily to stimuli (at least these responses are easier to observe). He responds more quickly and effectively to changes in the location of objects, to the differences between fixed and movable objects, to the passage of time, and to changes resulting from his or someone else's manipulation.

Concrete operations period

From about the age of two years to eleven or twelve years, the child passes through the period of concrete operations, which is divided into several phases. The first is the *preconceptual phase,* in which the child begins to think sym-

Accommodation and
assimilation

bolically and to use symbols in an elementary way. Except in unusual cases he is unable to replace sensorimotor actions with operations. That is, instead of mentally translating the stimuli to which he is exposed into some kind of mental symbolic system, he more or less directly copies the actions he perceives. He is an imitator, and he learns rapidly by imitation. Simultaneously his language skills improve rapidly with continued use and his exposure to new events in his environment. As he is acted on by the many stimuli of this environment, *accommodation* continues, forced by the differences (the dissonances) between his own actions and the world around him. Through play and teaching, formal and informal, he *assimilates* his experiences into his mental fabric unless the dissonance is extreme. He is now consciously acting on and being acted on by his mental and physical world.

Preschoolers and
causal relationships

During the preschool years, children are unable to understand or to cope with most causal relationships,[4] in part because they have not worked out for themselves a consistent system for separating the effective variables of their environment and for relating variables to their effects. These children do change a single variable to see what happens as they try one thing after another in one-by-one tests. Five-year-olds identify the members of a particular class, but they are less successful in comparing a subset with the entire set—a class of animals with all living things, or green balls with a set of green and red balls. At this age the subset appears to be as big as the whole set—the part is equal to the whole. However, children at this stage can handle many new ideas because they have developed a certain symbolic fluency. They think in simple abstractions that divorce thought from physical action so that, for example, they may look ahead to what will happen if they add blue ink to water or if they fail to feed their pet turtles.

Operations

Intuitive Phase. From about the age of four years to seven or eight years, the child's ability to classify objects grows, as does his ability to coordinate relationships and to think quantitatively. Classification, quantitative skills, and measurements are examples of what Piaget terms *operations,* which are actions on concrete and relatively nonsymbolic objects. Before this age children respond to the quantity of matter (mass), volume, weight, and number according to the appearance, feel, and arrangement of objects. They are not "conservers"; that is, they do not realize that the weight, volume, or quantity of matter of a particular object is constant no matter how it is manipulated. They are unable to reverse a pattern of thought, to retrace an action they have taken or have observed. By the age of five and a half to six years, children first begin to see that their naïve expectations are often contradicted by reality.

Guided by their previously successful assimilations and accommodations, children are often disappointed as they attempt to manage a more complex environment. If their mental structure is discriminating enough to note these dissonances, they either accommodate to the change and assimilate it or retreat into emotion-charged failure. Especially during the earlier years of this phase, children are characterized by an egocentric frame of reference; they are the focus, the center for all they see and feel. For example, a child might think that clouds move because he moves or that clouds are pushed by the sun in the same way he pushes his wagon.

Dissonances and equilibration

Mental-Concrete Operations Phase. At the age of seven or eight years, children move into a new phase in which they relate their actions to the results of those actions much more explicitly than before. They internalize their actions; that is, they incorporate them into mental, visualizable images. They integrate new actions with already available sets of actions and reactions into more embracing action patterns. This integration is valuable because comprehensive thought–action patterns are more useful for predicting and coping than individual subsets.

Children grow more objective; they set aside to an ever greater extent their self-centered evaluation of the world. Their operations, however, even though more internalized and symbolic, are still tied to direct experience and to what are called concrete-empirical props, which are the physical objects they must handle: they manipulate objects that they see in their mind's eye. If they are asked to predict what will happen to a balance when a weight is placed on the pan, they "see" the weight added to the pan, and they can make their prediction without physically performing the weighing operation. At the beginning of this phase they are unable to predict consistently the result of changing experimental factors without actually performing the operation themselves, but toward the end of this phase they can often think through the effect of successively changing variables, although their predictions for simultaneous changes in two or more variables are much less accurate than predictions for one change. This ability to visualize objects and actions on the objects is particularly appropriate to elementary science because many scientists seem to operate in much the same way; that is, scientists too give abstract phenomena some kind of physical reality. Michael Faraday visualized the magnetic field of a magnet as flowing "lines of force," for example, and chemists depict molecules as three-dimensional space-occupying masses.

New cognitive capabilities

At seven or eight years of age children develop the ability to perform serial operations; that is, they can arrange objects according to size, weight, and

Serialization

color and show understanding of some aspects of conservation and classification. However, these children cannot follow a logical chain of ideas. They are unable to group classes of objects or ideas into more comprehensive classes with consistency. In experiments, they cannot mentally change variables while holding other variables constant to see what would happen, although they can do the actual physical manipulations and on occasion predict correctly by guess or by intuition. Reciprocals and inverse relationships are nearly meaningless to children of this age.

Thinking abstractly

Because their ability to use symbols is still narrowly limited, children are not able to use mathematics to simplify scientific phenomena. For example, they learn quickly that as weight is added to a coiled spring, the spring lengthens. However, Hooke's law, $F = kX$, means nothing to them because these mathematical symbols have no elements in common with their experience. Thus children turn to physical experience or to intuition (guessing) to predict what will happen when weights are added to a coiled spring.

Lack of experience with mathematical symbols

As they assimilate new experiences and accommodate to these experiences, children improve in their ability to deduce the properties of members of a class from the properties of the whole class. They approach formal, propositional thinking. They reason more effectively, recognize assumptions and hypotheses divorced from direct experience, and derive conclusions more effectively from these assumptions. Adolescents can see many more possibilities in situations than can younger children; they can mentally anticipate the effect of combining different variables. Younger children, on the other hand, must first learn what the variables are by testing them, one after the other; and even then they often fail to put the variables all together.

Formal thought

Readiness to think abstractly, to deal with concepts and ideas, seems to come somewhat earlier in science than in the social sciences or in other areas of child experience because children have already had or will soon have direct concrete experiences with such important concepts as weight, volume, velocity, and space. On the other hand justice and democracy, concepts of the utmost importance, are far removed from the immediate concrete experience of children. Concrete experience is a necessary antecedent to logical thought, and concrete experience obviously is the foundation of science.

Scientific ideas and concrete experience

These Piagetian phases in the evolution of logical thinking are, of course, not precisely age fixed, although they do appear in the same order in every child in every society.[5] The culture of the society and the intelligence, experience, education, and socioeconomic status of the child undoubtedly affect the ages at which the phases appear. For example, few educable retarded children are able to operate at even a concrete level of thought in science by the age of fifteen; they learn, but they do not understand.[6] Children also act on

Levels of operation

several levels at the same age, depending on the tasks they face. They may be completely logical in one task and illogical (according to adult standards) in another without self-contradiction. For example, one child who was not quite seven years old discovered that three boxes with which he was playing held equal volumes although their bases were of unequal size. He confirmed this discovery to his satisfaction by first filling one of the boxes with water, after which he poured the water into each of the other boxes in turn. To the question of whether it was possible for a box of small base area to hold as much water as a box with a large base area, he replied, "Oh yes, but it would have to be much taller."[7] Yet the same boy, when children planned to pour different amounts of water into bottles to play a musical scale, asked, "What's a scale?"

Completely developed logical stages

Each developmental stage comes into full existence only if its predecessor has been fully developed; an incomplete stage will weaken and distort the next stage.[8] Piaget argues that teachers should not correct "incorrect" explanations. Children, he says, do not deliberately make errors. Because their thinking is so often preoperational, they focus on factors that may not interest the teacher. By asking the right questions at the right time, teachers can guide children to consider factors they have missed.[9] An important task of the teacher is to provide the right kinds of experience so that children can learn the "right" answer for themselves.[10] To be so perceptive as to ask the right questions at the right time on all occasions is a fantasy, but it is, nevertheless, an ideal for which to strive. If teachers *give* answers, they force children to make improper accommodations. We should remember that "children always correctly answer the questions they ask themselves."[11]

Concrete experience

To master at a functional level the Piagetian operations of placing objects and ideas into appropriate series, of classifying them, of reversing these steps, of identifying variables, and of manipulating reciprocal relationships, children need many different experiences and alternate strategies. Not many preadolescent children understand a mathematical statement of the inverse square law. They can, however, achieve an equivalent understanding through firsthand experiences with magnetism, light, and static electricity that will help introduce this law. These concrete experiences are necessary in making the transition to higher levels of formal thinking.

Application of Piaget's Theory

The full application of Piaget's developmental theory to classroom teaching must be left to the future, although some new elementary science curricula (the Science Curriculum Improvement Study, for example, which is discussed in Chapter 5) have adopted many of his hypotheses. Piaget's work is difficult to translate into operational classroom terms. As he says, "The heartbreaking difficulty in pedagogy, as indeed in medicine and in many other branches of knowledge that partake at the same time of art and science is, in fact, that the best methods are also the most difficult ones."[12] The difficulty of incorporating these dynamic psychological principles into the classroom by traditionally trained teachers, even those who earnestly desire to do so, should not be minimized.[13]

Can learning be accelerated and improved?

Piaget has not produced a theory of learning or teaching; his theory is of child and adolescent development. There is no accurate way to identify stages that can be accelerated by special training. Celia Stendler remarks, "Sixteen-year-old thinkers can never be made of six-year-olds, no matter how carefully the educational program is planned."[14] Perhaps, however, seven-year-old thinkers can be made out of six year olds if this result is consciously sought. As J. Easley says, "For the first time, experiments of Piaget have revealed children operating at levels considerably 'above' the intellectual demands of the curriculum. . . . Teachers have generally been given little encouragement and practically no training in uncovering children's concepts, beliefs, and commitments. . . . Knowing that children are capable of thinking is surely a first step to discovering whether or not a particular child thinks of one of these ways."[15]

The visual image is not concrete

Piagetian psychology has led to some significant classroom advances in science curricula — improvement of methods and redirection of the goals of science teaching. Piaget has supplied solid evidence for much that teachers have intuitively believed for many years — that children should be immersed in an extended series of enriched experiences from virtually the beginning of life, that these experiences should be objective and concrete, and that children should not be inundated with verbal substitutes for real materials. Even the seeming reality of the motion picture falls far short of what is necessary:

The image, the film, and all the audiovisual methods with which any pedagogy anxious to persuade itself of its modernity is perpetually bombarding us at the moment, are precious aids as long as they are thought of as accessories or spiritual crutches, and it is obvious that they represent a clear advance on purely verbal methods of instruction. But there exists a verbalism of the image just as there is a verbalism of the word, and compared with the active methods, the intuitive methods — when they forget the irreducible primacy of spontaneous activity and of personal or autonomous investigation of truth — are merely substituting this more elegant and refined form of verbalism for the traditional kind of verbalism.[16]

The crux of learning is not just exposure to experience but active reaction, exploration, feeling, and experiencing. Piaget's insistence that each developmental stage must be properly formed before the next stage can be fully developed is a warning to all teachers. He also insists on group interaction; individual experience will not erase the child's native egocentrism. Piaget's pedagogy may be condensed into this oversimplified dictum: The child should structure his own curriculum.

Learning and Developmental Models— Gagné

Gagné and S–R learning

Robert M. Gagné has proposed an explicit psychological foundation for teaching the common school subjects. His model is a comprehensive stimulus–response theory of learning from which specific prescriptions for teaching and learning are quickly derived. It is the psychological framework for the American Association for the Advancement of Science K–6 science curriculum, which is probably the most highly organized (from a psychological point of view) of the new science curricula.

What is learning?

Gagné believes that children have learned when they perform acts they could not perform before a given experience.[17] Because these acts can be analyzed into subacts, Gagné argues that teaching requires the planning of a series of instructional sequences, each of which leads to mastery of a single subact. These subacts are then combined to form more comprehensive acts. Working backward from the total action desired, the teacher picks out the various subsidiary learning acts. Through such analysis Gagné believes it is possible to select the skills and conceptual understanding necessary to master each subact.

"Science" learning may be too narrow

Because many of these skills and understandings are useful in other school subjects, it is self-defeating to think narrowly of "science" learning, "English" learning, and "geography" learning. All young school children, for example, should learn to give an accurate description of an unfamiliar object. This skill is as indispensable in the language arts and in the social studies as it is in science. Distinguishing the relative length of two objects by superposition is a useful measurement skill in science, but it is surely as useful in many other aspects of school and in out-of-school living.

Concept hierarchies

Process skills, or operating skills, such as the aforementioned are to be contrasted with scientific facts, concepts, and principles, which comprise the "product" aspect of science.[18] The concept *magnet* is derived from simpler concepts such as magnetic field, attraction and repulsion, paramagnetism and diamagnetism, iron and steel (magnetic objects), nonmagnetic objects, inverse square law, bar, U, and horseshoe magnets, keeper. The young child's understanding of *magnet* will include some of these ideas, which he has gained from direct experience. Older children and adolescents will incorporate more of these ideas at higher levels of complexity in visualizing a more complete concept of *magnet*. A popular, although minor, objective of elementary science teaching is for children to become familiar with magnets, to make magnets, to use them to pick up certain metals, and to know how magnets are used. Process skills are important elements — indeed, "tools" — for attaining this product objective. Conversely, the study of magnets can become a learning focus for strengthening selected process skills to transfer to other studies.[19]

Gagné builds his learning hierarchies from a number of qualitatively different kinds of learning, of which the four described below are the most important in science teaching.

Stimulus–response learning

Names and objects

Stimulus–response (S–R) learning is characteristically observed in young children, but it is often relied on by adults who are learning new material. In S–R learning the learner concentrates on linking objects and events, names and objects, and reactions and actions. Teachers often seem to assume that sufficient S–R learning has already taken place, that their children already know a great deal about the characteristics of science objects, that their children know how cats and dogs differ, and that solid objects denser than water sink. Yet these assumptions are often unfounded. Children who cannot differentiate between textures, shapes, and colors, who do not know that objects may be soft or hard, red or black, have much to learn.

Multiple-discrimination learning

Improving perception

The next higher type of learning in Gagné's hierarchy is that of multiple-discrimination learning.[20] Because the focus of science is on "natural objects and events," children should learn at the earliest opportunity to discriminate such characteristics of objects and events as taste, weight, texture, smell, and pitch. In both the Piagetian and Gagnéian psychologies, learning depends on concrete props and rich, full experience. Mothers who routinely stimulate their children to observe the sights and sounds of their surroundings give them a priceless start in life.[21] Everyone, adults as well as children, misses much of what is around him. It is not that he ignores his surroundings, for ignoring implies awareness. The skilled naturalist on a field trip amazes his companions by the seeming ease with which he discovers interesting plants, animals, and geological formations even in places he has never been before. His untutored fellow walkers see only trees and grass. But children can learn to be better observers.

Concept learning

Importance of concepts   The ability to infer and create concepts is based on skill in separating and identifying the characteristics of objects and events. For purposes of this analysis, *concept* is defined as a unique quality common to a number of objects, processes, phenomena, or events, which are grouped according to this unique quality. To reach a more advanced conception of water, children must draw on experiences with glasses of water, rainwater, pool water, hot and cold water, and water encountered in other places and with applications. Water becomes more than the contents of a drinking glass; it imperceptibly merges into a class of properties — transparency, fluidity, taste, odor, color, convertibility to steam and ice, all of which are included in the concept *water.*

Concepts are essential   Concepts are not all-inclusive statements, nor are they independent of other concepts. They too can be arranged in hierarchies extending from simple to the most advanced and comprehensive. Until there is substantial mastery of these concepts at their appropriate levels, there can be no learning of scientific principles at any level. Many concepts, especially the most fundamental ones, probably cannot easily or conveniently be taught in a formal way. They seem to originate intuitively from the assimilation of and accommodation to concrete experiences. Force, gravity, magnetic field, and electric current are examples of concepts derived in this way. Once the elemental concept has emerged, it can be built into a more abstract and powerful organizing component within its hierarchy.

Principle learning (process skills)

Scientific principles are not process skills   Gagné distinguishes between scientific principles such as *the repulsion of like magnetic poles* and *the power of acids to neutralize alkalis* and another class of principles called process skills, which include: observing, using space/time relationships, using numbers, measuring, classifying, communicating, and predicting-inferring.[22] These skills are especially desirable for primary grade children. Five additional process skills are proposed for the intermediate grades: formulating hypotheses, controlling variables, interpreting data, defining operationally, and experimenting.[23] All the process skills are indispensable in the sciences, and they appear to be equally valuable to many other aspects of learning.

Improving observational skills

Observing. Observing begins early in life and on an informal level is part of association and multiple-discrimination learning. Observing, however, may systematically be taught and learned through a conscious search to identify objects and events. In this use, observation is raised to a higher psychological level than in multiple-discrimination learning, for it embraces understanding of the value of rigorous observation as a scientific tool. Formal activities for improving observational skills may include perceiving color, shape, texture, size, temperature, sound, odor, taste, as well as changes in color and state (from solid to liquid). These activities are not the goals of elementary science instruction, at least not in Gagné's scheme. However, they are preliminary steps in attaining the other process skills and in mastering important scientific facts and principles.

Time and space

Using space/time relationships. A large part of the content of the sciences, such as scientific principles and phenomena, depends on perception and analysis of movement, volume, and time. The seasonal changes, which so profoundly affect our lives, are dependent on time—the earth's motion around the sun and the regular changes in the apparent position of the sun. The increased distance needed to stop an automobile at faster speeds is a function of the kinetic energy of the automobile. Kinetic energy, in turn, depends on mass and velocity. The theory of evolution, one of the supreme scientific creations of the nineteenth century, encompasses a panoramic vision of immense spans of time, of shifting environmental conditions, and of the infinity of plant and animal adaptations to these vast changes.

Without a firm grasp of space/time relationships, children will be severely handicapped in science. Gagné suggests that these skills can be improved by experiences in observing movement, recognizing direction, measuring distances, timing motion, and recognizing time intervals. Children learn informally to cope to some degree with space/time relations, but planned exercises to develop competency make later learning even more effective.

No science without numbers

Using numbers. Although it is a staple of the elementary school curriculum, arithmetic is almost always a separate subject taught without reference to science. But science is also quantitative, for it seeks to reduce complex scientific phenomena to simple mathematical statements. The physical sciences in particular decrease the number of variables to a conveniently handled minimum. The social sciences, in their confrontation with the complex mixture of human variables, use statistical methods in an effort to make sense of their data. Elementary science curricula include a number of exercises with sets, the ordering of objects and relationships, counting, and for older children, graphing, decimals, and arithmetic means.

Measuring. Measurement, the comparison of one physical aspect of an object or event with a standard unit, is another of the essential process skills. Familiarity with measurement units is expected of primary grade children. They should learn that the standard units of measurement, including all the ones they use in elementary school science, are arbitrary. Conceptually the important meaning is not the length of an object in inches or the weight of a salt pile in ounces but rather that the length or weight is so many units greater than some agreed-upon standard. Manufacturers of chemistry sets discovered that children can more easily measure with such common units as "three spoons" of salt and "half a test tube full" of water than they can with technical units such as grams or milliliters.

Practice in measuring may begin with comparisons of the length of two objects that are placed one over the other; they, together with other objects, may be arranged into a hierarchy of lengths. This hierarchy, as a set, can be compared with another hierarchy that serves as an agreed-upon standard scale.[24] Exercises have been prepared in which children compare relative areas, relative volumes, find the length of objects with a metric scale, and eventually move on to describe motion by drawing force diagrams and to discover the rate at which a liquid evaporates. Children will as a matter of course develop some measuring skills in conventional science classrooms. But it is doubtful that they will master techniques of measurement to the same degree that is possible with special attention to process skills.

Basic to the sciences

Classifying. Classifying is a complex learning activity that embraces many subordinate skills and in which objects and phenomena are grouped according to their common characteristics. Deciding on the proper category may be relatively simple, as, for example, in comparing the class of cats with the class of dinosaurs. But at other times it may be difficult. For example, the class of trees is not sharply separated from the class of shrubs, and depending on environmental conditions, trees and shrubs may take on each other's characteristics.

Simple exercises in classifying leaves, nuts, shells, and other objects lead to more complex grouping exercises, such as classifying life forms in an aquarium, deciding which common substances fall into each of the three states of matter, and separating simple materials from mixtures of materials.

Communicating.   Science is a public pursuit, open to all who are qualified and evaluated by anyone who chooses to evaluate. The implication is that scientists are expected to describe what they do clearly and accurately so that it can be tested by other scientists. Children should be able to report their experiments, but they should also be prepared to recognize the assumptions and inferences that shape their communications. These complementary aspects of communicating are not often included in elementary school science, although communication is one of the primary developmental tasks of elementary schooling.

Exercises for improving communication skills might include bar graphing, written and oral accounts of, for example, the life forms of an area, frequency distributions for population, plans for testing variables that affect plant growth, and drawings that show the change in direction and length of shadows during the day.

The nub of the sciences

Predicting–inferring.   Predictability is one of the most significant characteristics of science. Scientists search for the underlying principles of operation of the phenomena they study, and they rely on these principles to predict what will happen under other conditions. The accuracy of these predictions, in turn, helps to validate their research. Predicting in the physical sciences is relatively simple because the pertinent variables are reasonably easy to control. For example, children who experiment with pendulums soon learn to predict what will happen to the period of the pendulum when its length is increased or if the weight of the pendulum bob is changed. With sufficient experience, they can predict what will happen if three dry cells are connected in series or if a magnet is moved closer to a pile of iron filings.

Inferring

Prediction is one kind of inference. We may infer that a particular action is caused by *A* instead of *B*, or we may draw a conclusion based on available evidence. We may infer that because different weights of sugar and salt dissolve in water at different temperatures, sugar is more soluble than salt in warm water. Children need practice in distinguishing between what they can observe and the conclusions drawn from these observations. There is a vast difference between knowing that all objects children throw into the air soon fall to the ground and inferring that the force of gravity acts to pull them to earth. Gravitation is an idea proposed many years ago to "explain" why objects fall. In a sense the reason why objects fall is not the pull of gravitational force, for in this case, one action is explained by another action, a mysterious pull that cannot be directly observed and can only be inferred.

Behavioral engineering   Gagné and his school of "behavioral engineers" argue that when the process and product skills are developed in the proper sequences, new levels of skill and knowledge are attained; young children succeed in learning scientific principles, and they are more likely to turn this success into successful problem solving. He believes patterns of behavior that reflect these skills can be strengthened by suitable experiences and children will then be ready for more advanced science. Gagné argues that "repetition or practice is not the major factor in learning." What is important is "the prior learning of prerequisite capabilities."[25]

> If one wants to insure that a student can learn some specific new activity, the very best guarantee is to be sure he has previously learned the prerequisite capabilities. When this in fact has been accomplished, it seems . . . quite likely that he will learn the new skill without repetition.
>
> Let me illustrate this point by reference to a study carried out by Virginia Wiegand. She attempted to identify all the prerequisite capabilities needed for sixth-grade students to learn to formulate a general expression relating the variables in an inclined plane. Without using the exact terminology of physics, let us note that the task was to formulate an expression relating the *height* of the plane, the *weight* of the body traversing downward, and the *amount of push* imparted to an object at the end of the plane. (Wiegand was not trying to teach physics, but to see if the children could learn to formulate a physical relationship which was novel to them.) The expression aimed for was, "Distance pushed times a constant block weight equals height of plane times weight of cart."
>
> Initially, what was wanted was explained carefully to the students; the plane and the cart were demonstrated. Thirty students (out of 31) were found who could not accomplish this task; that is, they did not know how to solve the problem. What was it they didn't know? According to the hypothesis being investigated, they didn't know some *prerequisite* things. [Examples were Identifying variables in symbolic expressions; Identifying the factors of numbers (up to 100); Systematic recording of values of variables."]
>
> What Wiegand did was to find out which of these prerequisite skills were

present in each student and which were not present. She did this by starting at the top of the hierarchy and working downwards, testing at each point whether the student could do the designated task or not. In some students, only two or three skills were missing; in others, seven or eight. When she had worked down to the point where these subordinate capabilities *were* present, Wiegand turned around and went the other way. She now made sure that all the prerequisite skills were present, right up to, but not including the final inclined plane problem. . . .

. . . Having learned the prerequisites, nine out of ten students were able to solve the problem which they were initially unable to solve. They now solved the problem without hesitation and with no practice on the problem itself. On the other hand, for students who did not have a chance to learn the prerequisites, only three of ten solved the problem (and these were students who had no 'missing' skills). This is the kind of evidence that makes [Gagné] emphasize the critical importance of prerequisite intellectual skills. Any particular learning is not at all difficult if one is truly prepared for it.[26]

Application of Gagné's Theory

Gagné's teaching–learning theory is directly testable in the classroom, and in a modest way, it has already been tested. The evidence suggests that children who miss parts of hierarchically organized science curricula do not do as well as the children who complete all parts in the proper order.[27] It is also obvious that a careful analysis of acts and subacts is necessary to include all important elements; otherwise the success Gagné predicts cannot be attained.[28] Nevertheless this theory offers educators a unified workable package that has already been adopted almost unchanged in the American Association for the Advancement of Science elementary science curriculum. In practice there are many difficulties to be overcome, such as the infinite number of variables operating on children, teachers, and schools, which hinder the consistent application of Gagné's theory. The psychological components of these variables are discussed at length in this chapter.

Recent studies indicate that a number of the Piagetian developmental factors are essential in mastering tasks on the higher levels of the learning hierarchies. Nevertheless it is too early to predict whether Gagné's or Piaget's theory will be more effective or whether they both present previews of a more comprehensive and useful theory that will eventually emerge.

Gagné's approach is that of the "behavioral learning engineer." It is remarkably like that advocated by B. F. Skinner, whose thrust is to arrange the "contingencies of reinforcement which expedite learning."[29] Skinner has proposed that much instruction be through programmed materials in which desirable behavior (that is, the right responses) is reinforced. Unfortunately, although reinforcement may be efficient, it appears to result in remarkably joyless learning.

Summary

Although his developmental theory is complex and in places obscure, Piaget has contributed the most important analyses of the cognitive stages of child thought. He insists that children learn by reinventing and reorganizing experience, not by merely stuffing new increments of learning on top of old knowledge. This reorganization in the child is a creation of the processes of biological maturation, knowledge, and autoregulation (assimilation–accommodation). Up to the age of two years, the child lives through what Piaget calls the *sensorimotor* period. From two to eleven or twelve years, he is in the period of *concrete operations,* which is divided into several phases; *preconceptual,* from two to four years; *intuitive,* from four to seven or eight years; *mental-concrete,* from eight to eleven or twelve years. As the child moves through these stages, he shifts from egocentric and animistic thought to probabilistic thought, to mastery of such operations as serializing and classifying, to simultaneous consideration of two or more variables, and to mechanistic causality.

Piaget argues for a free, unstructured, highly enriched learning environment for children. Robert Gagné, on the other hand, has profoundly influenced the new elementary science curricula with his concept of structured *learning hierarchies.* Each learning task in his hierarchies, whether it is reception learning or a sophisticated problem to be solved, is divided into a number of simpler learning subtasks, which in turn may be divided into still simpler tasks. To master the complex learning task most efficiently, children must first master the subtasks. Gagné has proposed what may be called *behavioral learning engineering.* Once the teacher has "properly structured" the learning environment, Gagné argues that the desired learning will follow. Gagné also pays particular attention to what he calls the *process skills.* These skills— *communicating, measuring,* and *observing,* for example—are necessary in science, but he believes they are just as useful in the social sciences and in the communication arts. These skills, he believes, are strengthened with suitably structured exercises.

For further study

1. To what extent should the emotional and physiological differences between children affect the teaching–learning process?

2. Justify Piaget's statement: "Learning, in reality, depends on development, contrary to the widespread opinion that development is a consequence of a series of learning experiences."

3. What are the implications for science teaching of Piaget's statement: "To comprehend is essentially to invent or to reinvent, and every time that one teaches too quickly an outcome of reflection, one hinders the child from discovering it or from inventing it by himself"?

4. Has Gagné oversimplified learning when he states, "Any particular learning is not at all difficult if one is truly prepared for it"? (See Chapter 2, p. 59). If this statement is true, why is problem solving so difficult even for those with extensive experience? (See also Chapter 1, pp. 17–20.)

5. What does Gagné mean when he says, "The teacher is the manager of the conditions of learning"?

Notes and references

1. Ausubel, D. P., *The Psychology of Meaningful Verbal Learning* (New York: Grune & Stratton, 1963), p. 115.

2. Wallach, M. A., "Development from Approximately the Third to the Eleventh Year," *Child Psychology,* Sixty-second Yearbook, Part 1, National Society for the Study of Education (Chicago: University of Chicago Press, 1963), p. 267.

3. Hawkins, D., *New York Review of Books,* 6: 25–26, June 23, 1966.

4. See a somewhat different interpretation in Shapiro, B. J., and T. C. O'Brien, "Logical Thinking in Children Ages Six Through Thirteen," *Child Development,* 41: 823–29, 1970.

5. Sinclair, H., and C. Kamii, "Some Implications of Piaget's Theory for Teaching Young Children," *School Review,* 78: 173, February 1970.

6. Lovell, K., "Developmental Processes in Thought," *Journal of Experimental Education,* 20: 18, 1968.

7. *Teacher's Guide 1,* Nuffield Junior Science (London: William Collins, 1967), p. 17.

8. Stendler, C. B., "Elementary Thinking and the Piagetian Theory," *The Science Teacher,* 29: 34, September 1962.

9. Kamii, C., "Piaget's Theory and Specific Instruction: A Response to Bereiter and Kohlberg," *Interchange,* 1: 36, April 1970.

10. Duckworth, E., "Piaget Rediscovered," in R. E. Ripple and V. N. Rock-castle, eds., *Piaget Rediscovered*, a report of the Conference of Cognitive Studies and Curriculum Development (Ithaca, N.Y.: School of Education, Cornell University, 1964), p. 4.

11. Sinclair, H., *op. cit.,* p. 170.

12. Piaget, J., *Science of Education and the Psychology of the Child* (New York: Orion, 1970), p. 69.

13. Kohl, H. R., *The Open Classroom* (New York: New York Review of Books, 1969), chap. 8.

14. Stendler, C. B., *op. cit.,* p. 37.

15. Easley, J. A., Some Pre-Adolescent Dynamic Concepts of Motion, unpublished paper, University of Illinois, March 1969, pp. 11–12.

16. Piaget, J., *op. cit.,* p. 74.

17. Gagné, R. M., *The Conditions of Learning* (New York: Holt, Rinehart and Winston, 1965), p. 172.

18. See Chapter 1 and Chapter 2 on concepts and on science process and product.

19. Gagné, R. M., *op. cit.,* pp. 183–85.

20. *Ibid.,* p. 182.

21. Pines, M., "Why Some Three Year Olds Get A's—and Some Get C's," *New York Times Magazine,* July 6, 1969, p. 4.

22. *Description of Program, Part A, Science—A Process Approach* (New York: Xerox Education Group, 1967), p. 3.

23. *Description of Program, Part D, Science—A Process Approach* (New York: Xerox Education Group, 1968), p. 3.

24. *Science—A Process Approach, An Evaluation Model and Its Application,* 2nd Report (Washington, D.C.: American Association for the Advancement of Science, Commission on Science Education, 1968), p. 202.

25. Gagné, R. M., "Some New Views of Learning and Instruction," *Phi Delta Kappan,* 51: 470, May 1970.

26. *Ibid.,* pp. 470–71.

27. *Science—A Process Approach, op. cit.,* p. 57.

28. Howe, A. C., and D. P. Butts, "The Effect of Instruction on the Acquisition of Conservation of Volume," paper delivered at the National Association for Research in Science Teaching Convention, Minneapolis, March 1970.

29. Skinner, B. F., "Teaching Science in High School—What is Wrong?", *Science,* 159: 707, February 16, 1968.

Children Learning Science

Overview

Knowledge of the ways in which children learn science and of the factors that effect learning is invaluable to teachers. To facilitate understanding, the treatment of learning has been separated from that of thinking. Obviously this is an impossible separation to make in reality; in the child and in the adult thinking and learning are not separated. Nor will they remain separated in this chapter, as the second and third sections relate learning, thinking, and the affective inputs that bring them together.

Learning in science depends on cognitive and affective growth, individual differences such as sex, the kinds of experiences children have had, their nutritional and biochemical status, their flexibility and readiness to adapt to new situations, and the extent to which they are able to transfer previous learning to new tasks.

Factors Affecting Cognitive Growth

Individual differences

Children really differ

Teachers know that the children they teach differ widely in intelligence, aptitudes, and physical characteristics. The children also come from homes whose cultural and educationally stimulating setting vary greatly. Despite this knowledge, differences that are clearly of educational importance are often ignored in the schoolroom. The almost unbelievable differences between individuals in gross organ structure, functioning of endocrine and enzyme systems, body metabolism, activity of the nervous system, and genetic apparatus are not sufficiently appreciated.[1] These variations surely have their cognitive counterparts; the biochemical actions of the brain and its complicated relationships with all aspects of learning and personality is now under intensive investigation.[2]

Maturation is one difference

The child's environment acts in subtle (and sometimes not so subtle) ways to influence biochemical and genetic structures. For example, different parts of the brain are known to mature at different rates; hence connections between hearing, speaking, and seeing are not effective until the age of three or even later, when the association area of the inferior parietal lobule of the brain matures. There is a good chance that integration of these areas is necessary before children are able to demonstrate Piaget's preoperational thinking. A four-year-old child may give an incorrect answer to a problem that requires a combination of speech, hearing, and seeing behavior because the necessary pathways are not sufficiently developed. If vision is not yet sufficiently integrated, the teacher may help the child by shielding him from visual cues and freeing him to use language and hearing alone. The teacher may also help children who do not learn well because of weak perceptive integration by encouraging them to try different kinds of learning responses.[3] Weak cognitive function should not be ignored, of course. On the contrary, "The practice of

Learn to think by thinking

complex thinking may promote the physical development of the brain itself. Such a possibility makes 'readiness' propositions seem even less defensible. Waiting until a child is 'ready' may substantially contribute to his permanent mental retardation."[4]

The complex interaction of brain chemistry, structural development, and genetics is illustrated by the apparent difference in the ability of black children and white children to cope with certain visual tasks that require synthesis of perception, language, and action. There is a possibility that dark-

Genetic differences

pigmented eyes may not respond effectively to certain visual stimuli for chemical and physical reasons, and therefore children who have dark pigmentation may be handicapped in reacting to visual signals. It has been suggested that black children be taught with "highly salient perceptual materials," materials that stand out, are easily noticeable, and are well organized.[5]

Malnutrition

It has been discovered that malnutrition is often a significant contributor to such symptoms as apathy, lack of curiosity, inactivity, diminished IQ, and susceptibility to illness. Teachers of disadvantaged children should especially watch for malnutrition.[6]

Sex differences, or "male chauvinist pigs"?

Many educators have not seriously tried to understand how the cognitive patterns of boys differ from those of girls or how to change these patterns. The extent to which differences are the result of environmental rather than genetic factors is unknown. Boys seem to be more analytical in their thought patterns than are girls despite the early superiority girls show in language skills.[7] Girls tend to talk, read, and speak in sentences at an earlier age; but by the fifth or sixth grade boys are at the same reading level as girls, although girls are somewhat more fluent. Girls appear to be equally proficient in elementary mathematics, although by adolescence boys are superior in spatial visualization and in analytical-deductive thinking. Girls seem to analyze problems in more global and general terms than do boys, apparently influenced more by the diverse elements of their environment.[8] Boys are somewhat less rigid and more curious than girls in their encounters with new phenomena and ideas. Curiosity, an indispensable characteristic of great scientists, is important in this context because children who are curious learn and retain more in a given time period than do children who are relatively incurious.[9]

The demands of society

The influence of the cultural environment on the maturation of curiosity must not be discounted. Male curiosity and power to think analytically may arise from society's approval of aggressiveness, ambition, and independence in boys. Girls, on the other hand, are expected to be passive, to respond positively to the needs and desires of others, and to help others at the expense of their own individuality. Elementary school science textbooks reinforce these stereotypes, because their scientists and engineers, the "doers" of society, are almost always pictured as men in illustration and text. Science, then, is obviously something that men do![10]

The fact that underachievers and poor readers in school are likely to be boys is at least partly attributable to environmental factors. Girls tend to receive higher grades in elementary school classes despite their failure to surpass boys in achievement on standardized test,[11] because the woman-dominated schoolroom neither evokes nor encourages action boys associate with masculinity. School rewards are for conformity, "good" behavior, self-discipline, and cooperation—qualities that do not appeal to boys.

The female-dominated school

Teachers must make a special effort to adapt schoolwork to the interests and capacities of boys. At the same time teachers must encourage girls to be independent and self-sufficient, to ask questions, and to reject implausible answers, if their scientific potential is to be fulfilled. Because they seem to be somewhat better in analytical thinking, boys should be given frequent opportunity to enhance this strength. The apparent deficiency in the ability of girls to think analytically is a strong argument for more analysis-oriented learning experiences for girls and a strong argument for science teaching that stresses such learning.

More science for girls

There are enormous variations between children in every phase of the mental spectrum. For example, no two children have equal ability to solve problems, to plan a course of action, to complete a specified sequence of activities, or even to respond to their teacher's stimulation and reinforcement. These differences affect both the teaching and the learning process, and for this reason rigid, group lockstep instruction in science is an invitation to mediocrity. The wise teacher knows that no single instructional method—whether

Children differ—so must classes

it is inquiry, recitation, or programmed learning—is sufficient to sustain interest, to develop cognitive skill, and to maintain "the responsive environment" that nurtures learning.

Activity

Activity for younger children

    Students of young children stress their restlessness, ceaseless activity, and short attention span; these characteristics are particularly noticeable in the restraining atmosphere of the classroom. The belief persists that this perpetual motion distracts from the daily business of the classroom, that the business of learning could proceed with dispatch if children would only sit still. But this belief is a misconception because the growth of logical thought depends on activity, on experiencing, on handling and manipulating. Activity should be encouraged, not just as an expedient by which to arouse interest or to allow children to "prove" a statement in the textbook but because thought in young children evolves from physical actions. This relationship between physical manipulation of things and growth in perception and image formation is well substantiated.[12]

Activity for older children

    Traditional ideas about the activity needs of older children have been challenged by recent research. Teachers often assume that fifth grade children are less likely to be challenged by abstract ideas than are eighth grade children. Robert Davis, in contrast to some interpreters of Piaget, describes fifth graders as "natural intellectuals" who enjoy abstract thinking, in contrast to children in seventh and eighth grades, who are more "practical." Seventh grade and eighth grade children seek to explore, build, move around, and take chances—activities that are essential in modern elementary science; they suffer because they are rarely "doers" in the science classroom. First grade and second grade children learn through action, and educators may seriously have underestimated the dependence of older children on activity-based learning.[13] This premise is supported by Edward Eaton's study of sixth grade achievement in astronomy.[14] Eaton found that the majority of children learned astronomy best from a text that provided many different kinds of activities.

Perception

Limited perception

    Young children are severely limited in what they are able to perceive; they are unaware of happenings obvious to older children. As they mature, however, their awareness of their environment grows, partly because of growth in the number and richness of mental images—a growth that comes from reading—

and partly from extended interaction with their physical world. They become better able to plan and anticipate future happenings. As their thought pattern becomes more flexible and less egocentric, and as their cognitive structure grows, they are better prepared to interpret complex stimuli and to sort out the relevant from the irrelevant according to recognized and meaningful criteria.[15]

Training to improve perception

Young children usually require special training if they are to distinguish differences among the properties of objects, the relationships of these objects, and the individual objects themselves—interrelationships that comprise what has been called the "natural history of material objects."[16] First grade children exposed to the University of California Science Curriculum Improvement Study unit on material objects were significantly better at identifying the similarities and differences among various forms of an object than were children who lacked this training.

In one lesson children separated different kinds of unpainted wood samples according to such properties as grain, color, and aroma. After this sorting, the children were asked to count the number of different kinds of wood represented by their test specimens. In a follow-up lesson children sorted eleven different kinds of minerals, again according to their physical properties. Similar experiences with common objects such as buttons, nuts and washers, leaves, and metals furnish the conceptual framework with which these children gained significantly in perceptual and analytical skills.

Specially trained children are better at observing experiments and describing what they see than are untrained children.[17] For example, in one of the Science Curriculum Improvement Study experiments, the experimenter filled a balloon with carbon dioxide generated by mixing vinegar with baking soda. Children who had received training were not only more successful in describing what they had seen and in explaining why the balloon was inflated, they were also more likely to conclude that the balloon was not filled with air.

Difficulty in testing hypotheses

Few of these first graders were able to invent an experiment to test the hypothesis that the inflated balloon was not filled with air. To this extent they were unable to apply their observations and previous knowledge. As Herbert Thier remarks, "They are not able to put together a conceptual scheme for solving this problem."[18] The problem was probably too abstract for their level of cognitive ability. However, the experimenters did not try to cultivate skill in testing assumptions, nor did they provide the children with early related physical and conceptual experience, although attention to this particular goal would probably have resulted in significant growth. Despite the characteristic immaturity of the young child's perception, experimental evidence, although somewhat contradictory, shows that ability to sort out environmental stimuli can be improved with suitable training.[19]

Distortion of what one sees

As they mature, children tend to rely less on immediate perception as the main source of concepts and relationships, provided their new experiences are closely related to previous learning. They become sensitive to new subtleties and to formerly invisible environmental patterns as the processes of assimilation and accommodation continue. At the same time they tend to fit what they see into preexisting patterns and biases. A contrary fact may either be ignored or be isolated in some mental compartment, neither accepted nor rejected. Children often bend and distort what they see according to their own logic. For example, in one experiment children insisted that objects of different mass fell at different velocities even though they were simultaneously released from the same height. Most of the children who predicted that the heavier of the two objects would strike the floor first were certain that they saw it happen. The desire to make their prediction come true was sufficient to distort what they saw.[20]

Concrete experiences

Children organize the complex world they see and experience into their own individual explanatory patterns. Their hypotheses and intuitions often grow out of a vision that is intensely vivid to them. Young children may hold so tenaciously to the idea that big things sink, because this is what they see, that they ignore the existence of such variables as the weight and volume of those objects. Time and both structured and incidental experience are required before the complexity of nature becomes more than a figure of speech to them. Insight into physical existence can never be achieved by telling children that there is more to the world than what they themselves see;[21] perceptual growth is inseparable from physical experience.

Rigidity[22]

One desirable result of science instruction is teaching children to examine different approaches to problems. Sooner or later children encounter situations that are so different, so dissonant, that established approaches either fail or are too time-consuming. The tendency to face new situations without changing responses, even if these responses are unadaptive, is called *rigidity*. Psychologists do not agree about the extent to which rigidity is a generalized personality trait in individuals. The situations people meet are obviously influential, but the responses evoked seems to depend to some extent on the child's adaptive capacity. Despite extensive research on rigidity the relationship between adaptive capacity and learning is still conjectural.

Children who cannot tolerate ambiguity—that is, conflict between alternatives—also show rigidity; yet in science the evidence is often insufficient for either accepting or rejecting conflicting hypotheses. In 1550, for example, the Copernican and Ptolemaic hypotheses explained the known data of planetary motion equally well, but it was not until late in the seventeenth century that the Copernican hypothesis was generally accepted. Children may become more rigid, more inclined to follow tested rules, if they are faced with situations that increase ego involvement and personal anxiety. There is security in retracing familiar paths, yet the more difficult and ambiguous the problem is, the less likely it is that the usual formulas will work. Some children who are forced to make predictions become rigid in perception and in action because they feel threatened. Thus they unconsciously narrow or distort what they see.[23] This distortion is not surprising—scientists of high reputation have been known to overlook or to minimize evidence that contradicts their hypotheses.

Ego-involvement and rigidity

Children who tend to think or act in constant patterns are often trying to avoid ambiguous stimuli. Rigidity, however, is not an either–or characteristic; the extent of a child's inflexibility depends to a great degree on the interaction between his personality and the particular circumstances. If there is a generalized tendency to rigid behavior, it is less likely to occur in relatively simple tasks that cause little anxiety.

Complexity of rigidity

Some psychologists argue that males are less rigid than females because males are less dependent and submissive. Children of high intelligence are somewhat less rigid than other children; they abstract and generalize more quickly and effectively. They think more comprehensively because they begin with more information and integrate into their cognitive structure a greater variety of facts and perceptions. Relationships between rigidity and age are not clear-cut. Older children appear to act more rigidly than younger children, but their apparent rigidity may result from school instruction, which emphasizes formal responses and narrow direction.

Permissive classrooms and divergent thinking

Divergent thinking, the search for new and different ways to do things, is more likely to flourish in permissive classrooms than in restrictive classrooms. Teachers should encourage children to try something different the next time, to look for more than one interpretation, for more than one way of judging, and for more than one way of acting.[24] The teacher should not push children, however; haste, despite good intentions, actually increases inflexible behavior because time and effort are needed to find and explore alternatives.

Rich experience

Children who have had many different opportunities to explore and experience their environment are more likely to develop intellectual strength

Experiences with the physical environment

than are less-favored children. Many learning problems that plague children from low socioeconomic groups seem to begin with the lack of cognitive stimuli in their home environment. The child changes through maturation and learning, but his learning environment must also become progressively richer.[25]

Mental images and environmental experiences

Through many experiences, planned and unplanned, the child begins to make finer discrimination between environmental stimuli, moving from gross perception and structural and functional classification.[26] Unfortunately experience in depth takes more time than is available in most classrooms. Abstract ideas and relationships are associated with a good supply of mental images, which begin to form as young children imitate desirable models in their symbolic play.[27] Concrete empirical experiences with objects — touching, smelling, tasting, lifting, throwing, weighing, bending, and twisting the objects — help to create the visual imagery necessary for the abstract, symbolic thought that gradually replaces its more primitive and less efficient forerunners.

Children in the early years of elementary school, in what Piaget has called the intuitive subphase of the concrete operations period, should have the opportunity to handle many different materials and engage in a diversified range of activities. Although they are able to classify, count, and arrange objects in order and reverse the order, children must still work from concrete materials because vocabulary and imagery are immature. From experiences with these materials such concepts as causality, probability, invariance, and conservation arise. Intellectual skills cannot be learned as abstractions. You cannot tell a child to measure, to infer, to "think," nor can you reasonably expect that he will use these skills unless he has already had experience in concrete situations with them.[28]

Transductive reasoning

Up to the age of four years, the preconceptual stage in Piaget's terms, children think transductively; that is, they skip from individual event to individual event. They focus on chance factors or obvious features to the exclusion of important but less obvious factors. These children reason that an object sinks because it is big, but a small pebble must be heavier than a large cork because it is made of stone. "Big" does not denote a class of objects. Big stones exist; therefore little stones are also described as big and heavy.[29] Only after many errors, questions, and experiences does image match reality. (Adults often respond transductively to new phenomenon. They reason that because X is like Y in some one respect, it must be like Y in all respects.)[30]

Environmental influence on rate of learning

The rate at which a child moves through the various stages of intellectual development is to a greater or lesser extent dependent on the richness of his environment. An intelligent child from an impoverished environment is handicapped because he has insufficient experience to develop successful strategies for school-related problem solving. J. McV. Hunt maintains that "the more new things an infant has seen and the more new things he has heard, the more new things he is interested in seeing and hearing; and the more variation in reality he has coped with, the greater his capacity for coping."[31] (This point does not refer to play experience alone, for play becomes boring, and in any case, it provides fragmentary learning experience.) These hypotheses imply that both curriculum and method must be directed at challenging the child's capacity to assimilate and formalize experience.[32] But experience, whether it comes from experimentation, teacher demonstration, or observation and reading, is in itself insufficient to quicken cognitive growth unless the child reacts to it, transforms it, thinks about it, and deals with it.[33]

Learning from interacting, not verbalizing

Direct transmission of science information from teacher and textbook results in verbal learning and prevents the child from making his own meaningful synthesis. In Piaget's words:

> Good pedogogy must involve presenting the child with situations in which he himself experiments, in the broadest sense of that term—trying things out to see what happens, manipulating things, manipulating symbols, posing questions, and seeking his own answers, reconciling what he finds one time with what he finds at another, comparing his findings with those of other children.[34]

This is a functional definition of the process methodology in elementary science.

False learning

The lesson described below, contrary in almost every respect to the preceding quotation, is fraudulent because it deprives children of the opportunity to do their own thinking and experiencing. To lead his class to infer the concept that sound is caused by vibration, the teacher planned his science lesson around a concrete activity. He showed the class a tuning fork but did not permit any of them to hold it, and only the few students who were sitting closest could see it vibrating. He asked the class, "What happens?", which was quickly answered by a child sitting nearby: "The fork vibrates." The teacher just as quickly said, "Yes, that is right," wrote on the blackboard "Sound is vibration," and asked the class to repeat it. The teacher acted as if the class now "knew" the word *vibration* because the children could say the words, but it is doubtful that most members of the class could connect the word with its concrete reference.[35]

Classification categories

It has been suggested that planned exercises in classifying, serializing, comparing, and finding likenesses and differences help children develop suitable strategies by which to reorganize their experience. Objects and events may be classified according to such pertinent characteristics as size, color, shape, weight; degree to which they possess certain characteristics in common; differences; changing characteristics; changing relationships—distance, aging, growth; motion, direction, velocity; and cause and effect changes.[36] (The curricula described in Chapter 5 include several primary level exercises planned for these purposes.) These experiences will provide practice in generalizing and in transferring to new situations the ideas and skills learned in measuring in as many ways as possible sizes, weights, shapes, and temperatures. Even if the growth of reasoning ability in young children cannot materially accelerate, the aforementioned experiences will help children to learn much about their world.[37] School and home together must provide interaction that helps children develop new and more comprehensive intellectual operations.

*Interaction for
intellectual operations*

Verbalism

As the child grows, his ability to manipulate abstract ideas also grows, because he continually adds to and enriches his store of symbols and abstract terms. He comes to think about wood as an entity—not a particular specimen but rather an abstraction with such characteristic properties as floating, slivering, showing grain, and being easily cut. As these ideas are integrated into his cognitive structure, they increase the power of that structure, because they are generalizable and predictive. But they also gain in power by being related to the child's general knowledge. As his vocabulary increases in size and precision, the number of relationships, distinctions, and refinements he can generate in his thinking also increases. With sufficient practice in building relationships between the conventional concrete props of early learning, the learner becomes more skilled. As his ability to manipulate words and ideas grows, he begins to separate the relationships from the concrete objects with which he began.[38]

This idealized sketch reflects what should happen and what probably does happen to most children, yet children have often not mastered the words they use. They perhaps have never made the transition from the concrete to the abstract meanings of their vocabulary. The teacher should beware of emphasizing verbalistic response. Mere verbalism—repetition of phrases, sentences, and clichés—does not guarantee understanding at any level.

Teachers can easily find in their own classrooms verbalistic statements similar to those reported in a published study of sixth grade children who had sat through many science experiences in school. These children were of above average intelligence, and they came from an economically and culturally favored segment of society. After performing several simple experiments, they were asked to explain what happened in their own words. The answers tended to be vague and empty; words were substituted for explanations. For example, they "explained" that a coin whirled about in a box held at arm's length does not fall out of the box by such statements as: "Air pressure pushes it [the coin]"; "The force of gravity [holds it in]"; "Pressure from above holds it in"; and "centrifugal force." They also used words such as *force, surface,* and *noise* without providing a meaningful explanation of why a wooden block makes a noise when it hits a table. They said, for example: "The surface of the block hit the surface of the table and made a noise"; "It hit with such a force it made a noise"; "The noise was caused by the block hitting the surface".[39] These children merely repeated words they had heard before in an unsophisticated, random attempt to supply correct answers, hoping that their guesses would be close enough to get them by. They failed to extract valid meanings for these words from school and home science experiences.

John Holt's comments about the children he taught are pertinent:

> All she [Marjorie] knew was that she had been told to start doing something and didn't know what to do. She was wholly incapable of analyzing the instructions, finding out what part of them made sense and what did not, where her knowledge ended and her ignorance began.
>
> Children like Marjorie get in the habit of waiting for teachers to show them how to do everything, so that they may continue by a process of blind imitation; they never learn how to get information out of verbal instructions. In fact, they do not seem to believe that verbal instructions contain information. They do not expect to be able to figure out from mere words what it is that one wants them to do. Nor can they distinguish between the goal and the route needed to get there, the job to be done, and the method needed to do it. If someone gives them a problem, they either know or don't know "how to do it." If they don't the problem itself is meaningless to them.
>
> And this is the great danger of asking children to manipulate symbols whose concrete meanings they do not understand. After a while they come to feel, like Marjorie, that all symbols are meaningless. Our teaching is too full of words, and they come too soon.[40]

This kind of verbalism is reminiscent of the Australian bushmen who attempted to start an automobile by imitating the sound of the starter. One morning the owner of the car heard many voices shouting in rhythm, "Ah-ooh, ah-ooh, ah-ooh-ooh-ah." He noticed that the medicine man, the chief of the tribe, sat with his hands on the wheel, nodding his head in response and shouting back at his tribesmen. They, in chorus, echoed the ah-ooha, ah-ooha sounds the owner had just heard. He realized that these people believed that the car would start if its starting noises were mimicked. The chief was scolding his followers because they had not yet hit on the right combination of sounds to start the car.[41]

Acceleration of Learning

Can we accelerate learning?

Educators and laymen have often advocated accelerating young children's learning, an idea opposed by those who interpret Piaget's developmental stages in a narrow, restrictive way. Piaget, however, is not a teacher. He made no attempt to teach the thousands of children he tested, and there is no substantial evidence to refute the proposition that well-planned instruction in science will help children to pass somewhat more quickly to the level of formal, abstract thought. Children have effectively learned many ideas once shunned as too difficult for them, although other ideas seem to demand too high a level of experience, mental structure, and expertise for young children to grasp even intuitively.[42] On the other hand proper training may be successful in achieving some presently unknown maturation limit. Research directed at accelerating Piaget's stages by well-planned, *long*-term teaching is almost nonexistent.

Perception hides abstraction

As long as he is dominated by perceptual clues, the child will miss the abstract ideas that make scientific experiences meaningful. For example, some young children who were trained to recognize the effect of the length of a seesaw in balancing the seesaw accepted the suggestion that the color of the weights at the ends of the seesaw affected its equilibrium. Older children reject color as irrelevant.[43] A three year old can probably be taught to use words that represent abstract ideas, but he will not know what they mean.[44] Preoperational children may be trained to assert the conservation of quantity, but as Jan Smedslund demonstrated, this concept is easily destroyed.

Generalized experience

Training children to perform specific tasks is unlikely to produce significant learning, because it has little effect on the child's general pattern of thought. Generalized experience seems to be more important than specific teaching in attaining concepts of conservation of number, mass, weight, and volume, which appear at about the same chronological age in both "schooled and unschooled subjects" in many different cultures and socioeconomic strata. Montessori training of young children does not naturally accelerate conservation, despite the many Montessori activities that are essentially sensorimotor experiences. Acceleration may occur if children are close to the average age at which these concepts develop and if they have already developed logical prerequisites, such as making double classifications (long and thin, short and heavy), thinking of two dimensions simultaneously, and visualizing reversals. If suitable experiences are presented so as to arouse conflict and if "situational relevance" is made clear by many experiences in classifying the factors involved, disregarding extraneous information, and thinking through the meanings of descriptive words, some acceleration may occur.[45]

Early teaching may be wasted

Tasks taught too early may waste time because they do not improve long-term learning. The teacher should be aware of the possibility that too early an exposure to a concept, such as weight conservation, may result in slower learning of other concepts, such as transitivity, and therefore the child may lose in general growth what he gains in specific growth.[46] Children learn in ways teachers do not expect, and teachers who impose adult logic on children may force them to skip the intermediate stages that are necessary for normal and maximum development.[47]

Children who encounter a wide variety of concrete experiences and are encouraged to respond imaginatively and analytically will be better prepared for abstract thought. But more time, not less, is required.

Problem solving in the first grade

Although most studies of accelerating problem-solving behavior in children have been discouraging, the important work of Richard Anderson is much more optimistic. Anderson sorted sixty bright first graders into control and experimental groups that were equated by sex, mental age, and chronological age. After a series of twenty-seven twenty-minute training sessions, these children were given a series of problems, some of which were similar to their training tasks, some of which were more difficult. The children were taught to change the experimental variables one at a time while holding the other variables constant, to "demonstrate that when presented with suitable training, children will acquire and transfer a rather advanced, complex problem-solving skill."[48]

Most children in the two groups achieved the criterion of mastery before moving on to the next training tasks. Ten children failed the most difficult training task, which was to select from eight leaves the leaf that exemplified a particular combination of three characteristics. Leaf characteristics chosen were pinnate or palmate, simple or compound, and smooth or notched margins.

Problem analysis

Two test problems were derived from science. One was a pendulum problem in which the variables were the pendulum length, the weight of the bob, and the angle at which the bob was released. The task was to "figure out what makes this swing the most times in ten seconds." The second problem, a variation of a Piaget experiment, was chemical. The children were required to find "which bottles you have to use to get yellow."[49] Only three of the five available bottles of reagents were necessary. The other problems were simpler in that they could be solved without combining or changing the materials, and they did not depend on a series of mental combinations. They were of the multiple-concept discrimination type—for example, selecting unsharpened, eraserless pencils from a group of twelve pencils of differing lengths, with or without erasers, sharpened or unsharpened. The experimenter pointed to each pencil in turn, saying, "This pencil shows my secret" or "This pencil does not show my secret." The children were then expected to select pencils with the proper combination of characteristics and to explain the reason for their choice.

The experimental group was significantly superior to the control group, except in the pendulum and chemical problems; but even in these two problems, the experimental group was more successful. There was no reason to expect significant transfer to these two problems, because they were on an entirely different psychological level. However, training directed at "conceiving combinatorial possibilities" will also possibly help children with such problems as these.

Transfer of skills

Because the skills that were successfully taught do not spontaneously occur in six year olds and seven year olds, it is reasonable to expect that with practice children "can acquire, retain, and transfer rather complex problem-solving behavior."[50] No sex differences were found, nor was the order of the tasks significant. There was no attempt to arrange tasks in any kind of learning and testing sequence.

Transfer of Learning

Two kinds of transfer of learning have been proposed: *applicational transfer,* which is the application of facts and principles to a new but related problem, and *aptitude gains,* which is a generalized way of looking at and dealing with ideas and phenomena in special contexts.[51] Both kinds of transfer can be achieved in science learning, and both are important objectives of science education, although aptitude gains are more likely to be of enduring educational value. Each type has a part to play in the child's continuing encounter with the structure of knowledge. When he says that "to learn structure . . . is to learn how things are related," Jerome Bruner refers to facts, concepts, and principles, and to the importance of relating them. When the meaning of the conceptual scheme "We live in an ocean of air" is understood at a high level, it is because concepts of pressure, buoyancy, force, density, volume, gas, liquid, and fluid have been interrelated. This richness of meaning leads naturally to explanations of why balloons are able to float in air and to comparisons with a ball floating in water. It confirms the scientific belief that man can explain his natural world with the procedures and conceptual framework of the sciences.

Importance of transfer

The new elementary science curricula pay a great deal of attention to cultivating intellectual skills and to the ways in which scientists approach their problems. They accept the hypothesis that these skills can be transferred. Richard Suchman has shown that this transferability can take place not as specific rules of procedure but rather as attitudes—for example, confidence in dealing with raw data, in proposing hypotheses, and in trying new ideas.[52] In addition, a considerable body of evidence shows that children who are trained to think analytically are more successful with new problems.[53] Even though an adolescent who is at a generally high level of thought must begin at a concrete level in a new situation, he moves quickly to higher orders of abstraction because of his intellectual style and competence. His stronger vocabulary and capacity to think symbolically, the larger body of facts and concepts at his disposal, and his previous experience in discovering relationships are factors that enhance generalized transfer.[54] The success, in physics courses, of students who are mathematically able is one argument for the validity of this proposition.

A transfer experiment

The problems of classroom teachers, however, are not appreciably eased by experimental proof that transfer to new but related situations is possible under special conditions. The phrase *new but related* is difficult to define in operational terms. How new? How related? May it be that there are no psychological associations in some phenomena that seem to be both visibly and logically related?

Susan Ervin's experiment in applicational transfer provides insight into learning when the psychological demands of the problem change. In this experiment, modeled after one of Piaget's, children play with a toy truck running on an inclined plane. The truck, drawn by weights, is affected by three variables: the weight of the truck, the weights that pull the truck, and the slope of the inclined plane. The children were trained to predict the direction in which the truck would move when two variables were changed. They were then tested for transfer when all three variables were altered at the same time. The children were in the third and fourth grades, and they had a median IQ of 120. Most of them completed the assigned training tasks successfully. However, only half succeeded with the three-variable problem. Children who had higher IQs and those who were more competent at spatial and verbal tasks were significantly better.

The investigator suggests that the two-variable and three-variable tasks were not really identical or even closely similar. The variations in the test, some of which were supplementary—that is, they all operated in the same

Difficulty in handling
three variables

direction—or complementary—with one variable opposing the other two—were more complex than in the training tasks. It was much more difficult for children with little or no experience in manipulating all *three* variables at once to pick out the opposing effects and to predict their interaction.[55] It is probable that there was too little time for many of these children to grasp the nature of their task and to achieve a high enough level of familiarity with the variables. As David Ausubel says, "Prior learnings are not transferable to new learning tasks unless they are first overlearned," and overlearning was obviously not incorporated in the experimental design.[56]

One day during an elementary science teacher's workshop, a participant was asked to find out if the period (the time for a complete vibration) of a simple pendulum was affected by changing the weight of the pendulum body. He tied a marble ball to one string and a steel ball of the same diameter to another string and discovered that the periods of the two pendulums were equal only if the strings were of equal length. He was then asked to substitute a metal cylinder for one of the balls and to equalize the periods of the two pendulums. Before he began his manipulations, he asked, "Let's see now, are they the same weight?" despite his just having demonstrated that weight was irrelevant![57]

> He as a learner seemed to have learned something quite straightforward. But this linear elegance simply had not served the purpose. Certainly he had learned something, but this one stripped down instance had not been sufficient for him to learn solidly, "Weight doesn't make any difference! Learning is messy!"[58]

Some teachers have the unfortunate tendency to present a fact or idea once, and then to assume that it has somehow been transformed into active knowledge. Experienced elementary school teachers are much too wise in the ways of children to count on immediate retention. They know that repetition, review, and diversified learning tasks, coupled with evaluative feedback, are important teaching tools. They know also that the fine line between motivational repetition and boredom is sometimes invisible even to the master teacher.

Overlearning

Children are not equally able to generalize to other contexts and propose multiple solutions to problems. No one knows the extent to which these inequities come from differences in knowledge and experience, or from hereditary factors, or from the interaction of both. The broader the concepts that have been learned and the more varied the experiences in which they have been encountered, the greater will be the probability of successful application.

When children have genuine mastery of the concepts, and the new problems are not beyond a conceptual match, the probability of transfer is increased. Previously assimilated learning is surely of great importance.[59] Ausubel insists that "the most important single factor influencing learning is what the learner already knows. Ascertain this and teach him accordingly."[60] Transfer cannot occur unless something has first been learned; but once something has been learned, the teacher must provide many opportunities for applying this learning. Science teachers must provide richness of experience—which has been previously recommended—not to provide experience merely for itself but rather to give children the chance to cope with experience, to analyze it, to interpret it, and to capitalize on it as completely as possible.

Summary

Children differ cognitively in creativity, in insight, in rigidity, and in analytical and synthetic patterns of thought, to cite but a few. They are limited in what they perceive, although perceptual ability appears to improve with training. With experience and maturation, logical thought is gradually transformed from confused, simple, and sometimes causal patterns into a mechanistic, formalized logic. These emerging causal patterns, which are particularly noticeable as children attempt to control experimental variables, may be somewhat strengthened by special training. Acceleration of this kind is particularly desirable because experimental science depends on the proper control of variables.

The dependence of intellectual development on rich experience with the broadest range of phenomena and operations is now well accepted. For example, young children profit from unhurried exercises in classifying objects and events into descriptive categories. Hence several of the new elementary science programs have incorporated many of these experiences for primary grade children into their curricula.

For further study

1. In what ways is perceptual growth dependent on physical activity?
2. Contemplate the design of an open classroom in terms of the ideas concerning rich experience.
3. What pitfalls might be avoided in attempting to modify the rate at which children learn?

4. What are the consequences likely to be for children who are relatively high in rigidity in a permissive classroom in which science tests are not routinely assigned?

5. Compare the kinds of science-related experiences that children from ghetto and from middle-class neighborhoods bring to primary level classrooms. To intermediate level classrooms.

6. From interviews with several children draw up a list of science verbalisms. Does the age and intellectual background of the child affect the quality of these verbalisms? Does concrete experience with a particular concept reduce the verbalistic level of a child's explanation?

7. Is acceleration of learning an important educational goal?

Notes and references

1. Williams, R. J., *Biochemical Individuality* (New York: John Wiley, 1963).

2. Pribram, K. H., ed., *On the Biology of Learning* (New York: Harcourt Brace Jovanovich, 1969); Mandell, A., and C. Spooner, "Psychochemical Research," *Science,* 162: 1441–52, December 27, 1968.

3. Farnham-Diggory, S., *Cognitive Synthesis in Negro and White Children,* Vol. 35, No. 2, Monographs of the Society for Research in Child Development, 1970, p. 5.

4. *Ibid.,* p. 4.

5. *Ibid.,* p. 79.

6. Eichenwald, H., and P. C. Fry, "Nutrition and Learning," *Science,* 163: 644–48, February 14, 1969.

7. Waetjen, W. B., "Learning and Motivation: Implications for the Teaching of Science," *The Science Teacher,* 32: 22, May 1965.

8. Rossi, A. S., "Women in Science: Why So Few?", *Science,* 148: 1200, May 28, 1965.

9. Waetjen, W. B., *op. cit.,* p. 23.

10. Gaetano, M. A., "A Study to Determine the Distribution of Male and Female Figures in Elementary Science Textbooks," *Journal of Research in Science Teaching,* 4: 178–79, November 3, 1966.

11. Waetjen, W. B., *op. cit.,* p. 22.

12. Stendler, C. B., "Elementary Thinking and the Piaget Theory," *The Science Teacher,* 29: 35, September 1962.

13. Davis, R. B., "The Madison Project's Approach to a Theory of Instruction," *Journal of Research in Science Teaching,* 2(2): 149–50, 1964.

14. Eaton, E. J., "An Investigation of the Relationship of Three Factors in Printed Materials to Achievement in Astronomy by Sixth Grade Students," paper presented to the National Association for Research in Science Teaching, February 13, 1965.

15. Ausubel, D. P., *Theory and Problems of Child Development* (New York: Grune & Stratton, 1958), p. 549.

16. Karplus, R., "The Science Curriculum Improvement Study," in R. E. Ripple and V. N. Rockcastle, eds., *Piaget Rediscovered* (Ithaca, N.Y.: School of Education, Cornell University, 1964), p. 115.

17. Thier, H. D., "A Look at a First Grader's Understanding of Matter," *Journal of Research in Science Teaching*, 3(1): 84–89, 1965.

18. *Ibid.*, p. 88.

19. See, for example, Allen, L. R., "An Examination of the Visual Classificatory Ability of Children Who Have Been Exposed to One of the 'New' Elementary Science Programs," *Science Education*, 52: 432–39, December 1968.

20. Cunningham, J., and R. Karplus, "Free Fall Demonstration Experiment," *American Journal of Physics*, 30: 656, September 1962.

21. Almy, M., "Discussion of Papers by Professors Atkins and Karplus," *Science Education*, 47: 184, March 1963.

22. The content of this section leans heavily on J. Cunningham, "Rigidity in Children's Problem Solving," paper presented to the National Association for Research in Science Teaching, Chicago, February 1965.

23. Cunningham, J., "Rigidity in Children's Problem Solving," *School Science and Mathematics*, 66: 377–87, April 1966.

24. *Ibid.*, p. 386.

25. Hunt, J. McV., *Intelligence and Experience* (New York: The Ronald Press, 1969), p. 272.

26. Ausubel, D. P., *op. cit.*, p. 549.

27. Hunt, J. McV., *op. cit.*, p. 198.

28. Gagné, R. M., "Process in Science for the Elementary Grades," paper delivered at the Sixteenth Annual Convention of the National Science Teachers Association, Washington, D.C., 1968.

29. Piaget, J., *The Child's Conception of Physical Causality* (Totowa, N.J.: Littlefield, Adams & Co., 1960), p. 294.

30. Hunt, J. McV., *op. cit.*, p. 192.

31. *Ibid.*, p. 262.

32. *Ibid.*, p. 279.

33. Duckworth, E., "Piaget Rediscovered," in R. E. Ripple and V. N. Rock-castle, *op. cit.,* p. 4.

34. *Ibid.,* p. 2.

35. Shumsky, A., *In Search of Teaching Style* (New York: Appleton-Century-Crofts, 1968), p. 36.

36. Heathers, G., "A Process-Centered Elementary Science Sequence," *Science,* 45: 204, April 1961.

37. Almy, M., "Wishful Thinking about Children's Thinking?", *Teachers College Record,* 62: 399, February 1961.

38. Ausubel, D. P., "The Transition from Concrete to Abstract Cognitive Functioning: Theoretical Issues and Implications for Education," *Journal of Research in Science Teaching,* 2(3): 263–64, 1964.

39. Brucek, J., et al., "Children's Verbalism and the New Curriculums," *National Elementary Principal,* 45: 23, April 1966.

40. Holt, J., *How Children Fail* (New York: Pitman Publishing Corp., 1964), p. 113.

41. Hunt, J. McV. "Conceptions of Learning with Implications for Styles of Teaching Young Children," in *The Craft of Teaching and the Schooling of Teachers* (Denver: Proceedings of the First National Conference, United States Office of Education—Tri-University Project in Elementary Education, 1967).

42. Ausubel, D. P., "The Transition from Concrete to Abstract Cognitive Functioning," *op. cit.,* p. 265.

43. Wohlwill, J. F., "Development and Measurement," in R. E. Ripple and V. N. Rockcastle, *op. cit.,* p. 98.

44. Ausubel, D. P., *The Psychology of Meaningful Verbal Learning* (New York: Grune & Stratton, 1963), *op. cit.,* p. 121.

45. Kohlberg, L., "Early Education: A Cognitive-Developmental View," *Child Development,* 39(4): 1031–32, December 1968.

46. Wohlwill, J. F., *op. cit.,* p. 100.

47. Anderson, R. C., "Can First Graders Learn an Advanced Problem-Solving Skill?", *Journal of Educational Psychology,* 56: 285, December 1965.

48. *Ibid.,* p. 289.

49. *Ibid.,* p. 293.

50. Kamii, C., "Piaget's Theory and Specific Instruction: A Response to Bereiter and Kohlberg," *Interchange,* 1: 36, April 1970.

51. Cronbach, L. J., "Course Improvement through Evaluation," *Teachers College Record,* 64: 680, May 1963.

52. Suchman, J. R., "The Illinois Studies in Inquiry Training," in R. E. Ripple and V. N. Rockcastle, *op. cit.,* pp. 107–8.

53. Hunt, J. McV., *op. cit.,* p. 286.

54. Ausubel, D. P., *The Psychology of Meaningful Verbal Learning, op. cit.,* p. 119.

55. Ervin, S. M., "Training and a Logical Operation by Children," *Child Development,* 31: 555–63, 1960.

56. Ausubel, D. P., "A Teaching Strategy for Culturally Deprived Pupils: Cognitive and Motivational Considerations," *School Review,* 71: 456, 1963.

57. Duckworth, E., "A Child's-Eye View of Knowledge," in *Reason and Change in Elementary Education* (New Orleans: United States Office of Education—Tri-University Project in Elementary Education, 1968), p. 36.

58. *Ibid.*

59. Ausubel, D. P., *Educational Psychology* (New York: Holt, Rinehart and Winston, 1968), p. 130.

60. Ausubel, D. P., and F. G. Robinson, *School Learning* (New York: Holt, Rinehart and Winston, 1969), p. vi.

Children Thinking Science

Overview

To learn science, children must think science. The older psychologies of child learning held that children were not able to think abstractly, to reason logically and causally, to apply conceptual learning to new situations; in short, children were condemned to learning without thinking. The research of Piaget and Bruner, among others, has proved that these ideas are incorrect: children can think on high levels if they have sufficient concrete experience and guidance to enable them to develop the necessary concepts and relationships.

Children's thinking resembles that of scientists in many ways, although not of course at the same level of sophistication. To think in causal terms, children seek answers to questions that puzzle them, and they often find intuitive and creative answers to these questions. They even create mental models (tied closely to concrete referents), and often, as in fantasy, these mental models are far removed from the child's real world.

Because an important goal of the elementary schools is to help children to think more clearly and more effectively, beginning teachers need to operate with a higher level of knowledge about children's thought processes than ever before. For this reason this section is concerned with the analysis and interpretations of children's thinking.

The Child's Logic: Causality

Out of a tangle of sense impressions, the child picks certain related visions, which, although meaningless to an adult, make sense to the child. The assortment of curios in the trouser pocket of a twelve-year-old boy, for example, is valuable to him. This collection of junk embodies associations, future uses, indeed, even wealth of a kind. To the adult (woman?) there is no logic in such a collection because the adult is applying (at least on this occasion) the formal logic of an exalted maturity.

Do children think in logical pathways recognizable to adults? To answer this question, let us examine the nature of cause-and-effect reasoning. If children do have an inherent capacity or ability for cause-and-effect thinking, it is obviously many-faceted and exceedingly complex. Many young children often think causally, whereas, adolescents and adults sometimes react with precausal explanations.

The large body of research in children's cause-and-effect thought patterns shows clearly that young children often propose reasonable explanations, whereas older children may fail with the same problem. An interesting study of causal thinking was reported by Donald Inbody, who asked fifty kindergarten children to answer a number of questions dealing with weather, buoyancy, and electricity. He grouped their answers into six categories:

1. Generally correct and causal.
2. Plausible, causal, but incorrect.
3. Correct, but verbalistic.
4. Incorrect, noncausal; animistic, or anthropomorphic, or religious.
5. Descriptions or restatement of observations.
6. No explanation of any kind.[1]

The order of frequency of response was 2, 4, 1, 5, 3, 6. All the children proposed several different types of explanations, although most relied on just one or two. About one quarter of the children gave predominantly causal explanations. Questions about freezing and wind, the phenomena with which the children had had the most experience, were most likely to be answered causally. With less common phenomena, causality was usually not invoked. For example, air trapped in an inverted tumbler in water meant that "nothing *kept* the water from entering the tumbler."[2] In their contact with nonempirical events or with indirect phenomena, some children confused cause and effect. Others resorted to animism or anthropomorphism, or appeared to think the phenomena were unique and without cause. Because of their limited experience, the children were unable to provide coherent explanations and could not detect contradictions that were apparent to older children. Explanation 3, "Correct, but verbalistic," meant that even though a scientific principle had been correctly stated, the child did not understand it because he was unable to use it in a prediction.

Inbody concluded that the ability of children to make cause-and-effect statements depends on a rich experience with many aspects of a phenomenon, and that overgeneralizing and failure to note similarities between events is the result of inexperience with these events and unfamiliarity with causal thinking.[3]

The role of experience in causal thought is illustrated by Marilyn Mogar's finding that children of five to six years old who had an opportunity to play with floating objects, and to whom the comparative buoyancy or lack of buoyancy of large and small objects was pointed out, were able to explain floating as a function of size more effectively than children in control groups. (The experimenter was aware of the distortion caused by equating size with floating for the sake of simplicity.) The children clearly improved the quality of their causal thinking by experience with floating objects.[4]

"Moral" explanations   Most of the recent work in children's causal thinking is contradictory to Piaget's conclusions, which are derived from his research during the late 1920s. Piaget hypothesized that young children explain natural events by combining free will on the part of objects with a "moral" attraction or repulsion between the object and the natural world. For example, he said that children think that rivers are attracted by lakes, rain attracts clouds, and rocks pull water to make it flow. At a later stage of development, they believe the attracting or repelling force arises from some kind of contact, but even then an object in motion is still the positive cause of the action. The sun, for example, is forced to move by clouds, but it also forces the clouds to move with it. Eventually these notions are replaced by the idea of purely mechanistic and nonliving forces. At the age of five, children believe that *they* make the clouds move with them as they walk. At six, clouds move because God and men make them move. At about seven, children say that clouds move by themselves, but that this motion is caused by a mystic compulsion exerted by the sun or the moon. At eight, they believe that the wind makes clouds move, but that the wind is itself a product of the clouds. Not until approximately the age of nine is cloud movement correctly explained.[5]

Piaget quotes one seven-year-old child as answering the question "What makes the clouds move along?" by saying, "It's the sun . . . with its rays. It pushes the clouds."[6] Piaget believes that *physical* determinism begins to have meaning for the child when the notion of chance appears, at seven to eight years of age. Prior to this age, the child attempts to eliminate chance factors. Because he thinks there is a reason for everything, the child tries to explain what he sees in moral and animistic terms, whereas older children and adults explain many of these events as chance occurrences.[7] With the acceptance of chance, the conception of physical law free of personal compulsion can develop.

The domain of children's causality is exceedingly complex and confusing. There is agreement that the kinds of experience, the extent to which children

What kind of science is indicated?

are free to interact with their environment—to push and pull, to test, to handle, and to experiment—are important factors in conditioning causal thinking. Only as children have the opportunity to deal with causality, to vary conditions, and to experience directly the changes resulting from these variations do they learn to avoid the fallacy of thinking that what occurs first is the cause. Here again one sees the importance of science instruction that permits children to encounter a wide variety of situations in a relatively unstructured setting.

Piaget also comments that the child of seven or eight does not reason inductively or deductively in adult fashion but rather transductively—that is, from particular instance to particular instance. He does not generate general ideas from individual facts or ideas, nor does he make use of more general propositions to validate specific ideas. Instead he moves from one item to

What children say and what they think

another that is unrelated by logical necessity. The child of seven who insists that the sun is alive because it moves does not also think that all moving things are alive because he knows that clouds, which are not alive, also move. The focus of reasoning is on individual cases, without recognition of logical necessity.[8] Of course, children who say something is alive may mean only that it is active; they do not necessarily impute feeling or purpose to it. They may not even know that not all things are alive.

Alina Szeminska asserts that three causal stages may be observed in children:[9]

I. Answers combining facts, concepts, or phenomena that are linked by their simultaneous occurrence or by physical proximity.

II. Reference to the causal relation but without comprehension of the passage from cause to effect.

III. Complete explanations with comprehension of the necessary conditions and of the part played by the various factors that enter into the causal sequence.

Causal thinking in personal, nonschool experiences improves more or less regularly in quality until, between the ages of fourteen and sixteen, it is predominantly stage III. The growth curve shows some gains after initial teaching in school, but the decrease that occurs in the following year leads Szeminska to conclude that "the acquisition of the knowledge was strictly mnemonic [by means of artificial memory aids]."[10] On the other hand information that is more pertinent to the children and therefore more readily assimilated on an intellectual level is not only better remembered but is better assimilated during the course of the next year.

Thinking in logical
steps

Young children are severely handicapped in dealing with causal relationships because they are unable to carry through a consecutive series of intellectual steps. In the operation of a pendulum, for example, because they do not
separate the length, the mass, the amplitude, and the material of the bob, they
do not change each in turn, holding the others constant. They do not think,
"If I use the same bob and the same starting point on the swing and if I make
the string longer, then the changes I see in the number of swings in a minute
must be because I made the string longer." The effect of teaching children to
analyze problems in this way has been the subject of some educational research, and the success of the new elementary science curricula, which stress
precisely this kind of process instruction, is an encouraging sign.

Certain causal relationships, particularly those involving multiple variables, are difficult for children to handle. The identification of relevant factors
is difficult even for adults with long experience, and the difficulties children
encounter are surely understandable. The young child can often grasp the
significance of some variables but fails to note the irrelevance of other variables, which must also come with experience.[11]

These and other difficulties were encountered by second and third grade
children in a Piagetian experiment conducted by Susan Ervin.[12] The children's task was to predict and explain the bending of a number of flexible
rods affected by four independent variables: (a) the composition of the rods,
(b) their length, (c) their thickness, and (d) the effect of weights attached to the
ends of the rods. A few second grade children and a larger number of third
grade children were consistently successful. Boys did better than girls in each
grade, but there was no difference in IQ between those who succeeded and
those who failed.

The four-variable
problem

A number of children who were successful with one or two of the variables failed with others, but no particular order in this failure or success was
discovered. Correct prediction of the effect of the first variable did not mean
that the second prediction would be correct, nor did failure with the first variable mean that the second prediction would be incorrect. The experimenter
assumed that failure would stimulate children (perhaps because of the resulting
dissonance) to reverse the direction of the chosen variable or to select other
variables, but this result did not always occur. Many children, including those
who sometimes used controls, often worked with two or more variables at the
same time (despite an injunction to the contrary), perhaps believing that they
would see a greater change. These children may have been unwilling to risk
short-term failure and therefore incorrectly tried to increase their chances of
success by changing two variables at a time.

When the children were asked to explain their failures, about half of their explanations cited one or more variables that had not been controlled. A number of the children knew that these variables existed and had referred to them in earlier explanations. Therefore the children were probably now focusing on a different aspect of the problem, or these variables now seemed to be unimportant. Many of the new hypotheses proposed after initial failures properly took these variables into account.

Many children acted as if they believed that a variable effective in one case—for example, a small weight bending a thin rod—would always have the same effect; that is, the weight would bend a thick rod an equal amount. The children who worked with two variables at a time often justified disregarding instructions by remarking that they just wanted to see what would happen. They may indeed have been curious, but it is likely they were uncertain and desired to avoid committing themselves.

Word meanings

Children failed for a variety of reasons. Many were puzzled by word meanings. For example, some children equated *length* with *thickness* and therefore did not attempt to control length, or they used *heavy* and *light* interchangeably when referring to the composition of the rods, their thickness, and the weights. Several children believed that the weight of the rod and the weight suspended from the rod were somehow connected. These verbal confusions are certainly not unexpected in children of this age. Misunderstanding of words whose meanings are apparently known is one of the most effective blocks to science instruction.

Systematic testing is not for children

Children frequently chose to test conspicuous variables but did not systematically test one after the other. Again this reaction is to be expected. Piaget suggests not until early adolescence does the pattern of systematic testing become dominant in the majority of children. The children in this experiment tended to repeat unsuccessful predictions and tests and to restrict their choice of hypotheses. Their most prevalent error was to disregard uncontrolled variables in their explanations.

When these children were confronted with new situations in which they had to make predictions, their choice of variables to test depended more on their verbal fluency in differentiating the variables and on the quality of their earlier explanations and predictions than on the types of training situations. Perhaps this result only means that children (the successful second graders, for example) who already think analytically or who are moving toward analytical thinking will solve these multivariate problems. On the other hand, even without instruction directed at improving the child's ability to solve these problems, many children were able to overcome errors and to achieve some degree of success. A knowledgeable teacher could probably help children increase their ability to think analytically by eliminating verbalisms, by providing many opportunities for children to experiment individually and in small groups, and by working cooperatively with the children in assessing the results of their experimentation. Millie Almy has pointed to the enrichment of primary grade instruction achieved by teachers who are thoroughly grounded in Piagetian insights and techniques.[13]

Concrete Operations and Causality[14]

Piaget remarks that the transition from concrete thought to formal logic begins when children first discover that much of what occurs in the world is a result of overlapping, independent factors; that is, a particular effect may have several causes, or a major variable may be obscured by several noncausal variables. The child is frustrated because he can no longer investigate each variable independently. If he is in the concrete stage of development, the child is unable to separate the variables by excluding or neutralizing them. For instance he may satisfy himself that most metal rods are flexible. Yet many are *not* flexible. At other times he may discover that despite a general lack of correspondence between the strength and the size of a magnet, the two qualities are sometimes related. The more vigorous his search for instances of how one behavior correlates with another behavior, the greater the chance that he will encounter the many exceptions that exist—because of experimental error and lack of information and because this is a natural characteristic of real objects. Botany is an extreme example of a field of science in which exceptions to the rules are commonplace and confusion is compounded.

Children of age eight or nine or even younger can isolate some variables and can test the effect of a variable by observing or by experimenting. However, they merely separate these factors; they do not exclude them. Separation may occur through simple observation—that is, by seeing what happens in the presence and absence of the factor—or by actively controlling it (for example, lengthening or shortening a pendulum). But children do not exclude as they observe and experiment; they do not mentally separate the variables and foresee the result if each variable is removed. If the variable cannot be physically separated, children come to a standstill. From the age of eleven, however, children are able to think ahead and even in relatively complex situations can predict the probable results.

When two or more variables act at the same time, the concrete-level child changes each variable to see what happens, not to find what it does to another variable. He tests brass rods and aluminum rods to see how much they bend, but he does not think to compare a long brass rod against a short brass rod to isolate the effect of length in bending. The older child eliminates length as he manipulates brass rods. He no longer concerns himself with different materials because he is able to neutralize them in his experiments.

Excluding variables

Once the child is able to neutralize and exclude variables, he is well on the way to formal thought. At this stage the child can generalize these operations to all combinations of the phenomenon in question. Consider, for instance, a long, thin brass rod that is more flexible than a short, thin steel rod. Unless he is able to exclude the kind of metal, the child cannot say that the bending is caused by the length of the rod or by the inherent capacity of the metal itself. Some concrete-level children can solve this problem if they meet enough instances of this kind to come to the conclusion that sometimes the metal is causal and at other times the length is causal. They do not simultaneously consider these two variables, because they are unaware of the possibility of coexistence. They move ahead, multiplying cases and confusing data, and thus diminish the chance of finding relationships. The formal-level child, on the other hand, compensates for differences in each variable by holding it constant while varying each of the others in turn. He is able to deal with possible combinations mentally, without direct resort to the objects, once he has a sufficient stock of accurate images to guide his mental operations.

Questions of Why[15]

"Why" and cognitive dissonance

Children as young as three or four years of age believe that their world behaves according to certain rules. This belief is one of the working models by which they cope with their world. When an unexpected or startling event occurs, a *cognitive dissonance* in psychological terms, the child's conceptual scheme may not be able to accommodate it because of his unfamiliarity with the situation or his lack of perception or because of the sheer complexity of the event. The child's scheme is almost always too fragmentary to reduce this dissonance, and he turns to adults for help. He asks "why?" because his own resources are insufficient to make sense out of what happened. (Some psychologists argue that children have an innate drive for competence and a desire to know. How this differs from the drive to reduce dissonance is not clear.) He must assimilate the discrepancy, decide if it is a fact, take time to verify it, and see if it happens when conditions change. If the discrepancy is too great, he has no mental model to handle it; if he can give an answer, there is no discrepancy. If the match is right, the child accommodates the event into his model, changing it and reaching a balance, a harmonious readjustment of model and event.[16]

Children's "why" questions tend to become less frequent as they grow older, in part because children fill in some of the gaps in their mental models with sufficient information to reconcile what they see and in part because what they do in school is unrelated to what they themselves want. "Why" questions disappear because they are smothered by an unresponsive environment in which effective stimuli and effective answers are infrequent and adults are often disinterested and impatient. These questions, with their potential for becoming active, dynamic interests, shrivel away when they are quickly answered to satisfy the child's immediate need. Adults and teachers must be understanding, patient, and resourceful, responding to questions in ways that encourage the child's exploration of his universe. Children want to know what makes things happen, but they will not bother to think of sharp, clearly focused questions unless they are convinced that it will benefit them to do so. The pioneering studies of J. Richard Suchman show that children can learn to ask this kind of question.

Children's "why" questions may be categorized as seeking either information or explanation.

Informational questions

The different "why" questions

Whys of purpose.   These are teleological or motivational questions, whose intent is to find out the purpose of an event—what it accomplishes or what role it plays. For example, Why is thunder so loud? may not be a demand for a physical explanation but simply a question of motives.

Whys of justification.   These questions seek the logical necessity for rules, customs, and modes of procedure. Their answers come from definitions and axiomatic postulates. Why is this an oak leaf? and Why is iron an element? are examples. Questions for justification tend to be relatively rare in the sciences, perhaps because children have never been told that the foundation of knowledge is definitional and axiomatic.

Explanatory questions

Whys of causation.   These questions ask for the particular circumstances or relationships resulting in the event (for example, What makes lightning? Why do the rivers run down to the sea?). The child may wish to know the reasons for the contradictions he observes or the chain of circumstances that inevitably results in the occurrence. He is seeking a certain kind of information. He is not looking for an animistic-moral set of rules, but rather for genuine mechanical causality—even though his own conception of causality is fuzzy and confused. As they grow older children learn to refine and to narrow these questions to such specifics as What makes this happen? What causes it?

The child, puzzled by the discrepancy between expectation and experience, turns to an adult for help. Nathan Isaacs suggests that the distinguishing characteristic of these questions is their implicit "whereas" clause.[17] The first time a child encounters silicone putty he may ask, "Why does this putty bounce . . . [whereas] clay doesn't?" An incorrect answer—for example, that it contains rubber—may remove this discrepancy. The adult, however, sees no discrepancy. He may answer that even though the silicone putty looks like clay and behaves like rubber, it is made of other materials and behaves in an unusual way. Or he may merely pass off the question.

What is behind the question?

There is always the possibility that the child does not really want to know Why is the sky blue? but if it is genuine, does the question reflect the child's expectation that the colors of the sky could be different? The child may not be able to differentiate a correct answer from an incorrect answer if he lacks proper criteria for judging answers, or the answer may be too abstract so that *his* question is not answered and an opportunity to draw the child into a problem-solving situation is lost.[18]

Mental Models

Importance of mental models

One reason why many young children are unable to propose mechanistic explanations of scientific events is that they do not have a sufficiently powerful series of theoretical structures and relationships (*mental models*) to help to organize thought and to give meaning to what they see. Piaget's famous experiments with concepts of volume reveal that children do not form a model or theoretical structure of space as a continuum until they are age eleven or twelve. "Space as a continuum" refers to the absolute quantity of space in a container (interior volume) as unchanged despite the volume of objects located in the container. Until children can visualize total interior volume and separate it from the internal volume of the objects and the volume the objects occupy, they fail to judge volumes correctly when the arrangement of objects is changed, even though these children may be conservers of interior volume—that is, they know that the interior volume of a container is constant. The recognition that the volume of the objects in the container is constant is necessary, but it is not a sufficient condition for success in complex volume judgments. The follow-ing protocol of Piaget's shows clearly how the young child fails:

> Jaq [eight years, 2 months] realizes that the water level will rise on the immersion of the tower of 3 × 3 × 4 [composed of cubes of 1 cm on a side]: Now what will happen if I turn it over? — *The water will go down a bit, be-cause the house is at the bottom now.* Well, will there be the same amount of room in the house itself if I put the bricks at the bottom? *Yes, there'll be the same · amount of room.* — And that means it's the same for the water? — No, *that's not the same.* — Well, supposing I split the house into two parts, will there still be the same amount of room inside? — *Yes, there'll be just the same amount, but in two parts.* — And then there'll be the same amount of space left for the water, eh? — *No, that changes. There'll be less room. No, more.*[19]

This child knows that the blocks maintain their interior volume, but he asserts that the volume of water (which is complementary to the interior volume of the blocks) is not only not conserved (held constant), but that the exterior volume of the blocks is changeable. To him, the interior and exterior volumes of the blocks are not necessarily equal!

However, a child who is three years older responds as follows:

> Dro [11 years]: Supposing I take these bricks and put them up this way [the blocks are arranged in units of 3 × 3 × 4] into the water, what will happen to the water? — *It rises. It's just the same if you put your hand in the water. It takes up a lot of room and so the water rises.* — And when I put them in this way [3 × 1 × 12] are they going to take up the same amount of space in the water? — *No* — Why not? *Oh yes! I was wrong, it stays the same.* — What about the space taken by the water all round? Is that the same too? — *Of course.* — Well, supposing we spread the bricks around? — *It's still the same. They'll always take up the same amount of room.*[20]

This child has developed a picture of "space as a continuum" on which he draws to give the correct prediction and explanation.

Models and explanations

Little research on children's formation of mental models has been at-tempted despite its obvious relevance to science teaching. In an excellent study Ronald Anderson selected 180 third grade through sixth grade children matched by age, intelligence, grade, and sex. The experimenter presented five demonstrations whose explanation, although not known to the children, could readily be explained by referring the children to an appropriate mental model. He defined *mental model* as "a theoretical form or structure which is hypothesized on the basis of observation of natural phenomena."[21] It is a theory, a set of assumptions, and the conclusions that are derived from these assumptions. At the end of the demonstrations, the children were asked to create a mental model to explain what they saw.

The demonstrations were intended to illustrate the following principles:

1. A mixture of alcohol and water occupies less space than the sum of their separate volumes.
2. Surface tension is present in water.
3. An appropriate increase in temperature causes ice to change to water.
4. An appropriate increase in temperature causes water to change to water vapor.
5. An increase in temperature causes (the volume of) water to expand.

Only one molecular model was necessary to explain all the demonstrations except the first, for which a mental model of alcohol as a liquid was required. Children were asked to answer such questions as What is water like so this happens? to "force" them to give explanations in terms of the structure of water.[22] Following the five demonstrations, a mechanical model of "alcohol as a liquid" was presented. This concrete model was a container filled with marbles. After each child was satisfied that no more marbles could be added to the container, the experimenter showed that small steel shot could pass through the spaces and asked why the shot could be added. After a brief review of demonstration 1, the child was asked if the marble and shot demonstration "gives you any idea about why alcohol and water take up less space when they are mixed together?"[23] A mechanical model of this kind is sometimes called an analogue model because it attempts to present a principle by analogy. The analogy here is between marbles and invisible molecules and between spaces between the marbles and spaces between molecules.

Excluding those demonstrations for which no explanation was forthcoming, the children proposed three kinds of models:

Surprisingly high-level thinking

1. Atomistic, in which such words as "molecules, atoms, little pieces, particles, and cells" were used. Most children who gave this response thought that the liquid was only partially atomistic.
2. Nonatomistic, in which water was considered to be magnetic, or sticky, or in which air pressure was causative.
3. Magical and animistic, in which the liquid was partly alive, or acted as if it were living, or "it just vanishes."[24]

Several of the eight atomistic models are given below:

1. Particles are different sizes.
2. Particles hold together or attract each other, freeze together, or lock together.
3. Particles come together because of electrical attraction, magnetic attraction, gravitational attraction, or because they are sticky.
4. Heat makes particles move faster.[25]

Ten percent of the children explained surface tension of water by a magnetic-particle model. At the third grade level 16 responses were atomistic, 33 nonatomistic, and 4 magical or animistic, and there were 169 nonexplanations. At the fifth grade level there were 48 atomistic responses, 32 nonatomistic, 1 magical or animistic, and 139 cases of no explanation. At the sixth grade level, 74 explanations were atomistic, 32 were nonatomistic, 7 were magical or animistic, and 111 were nonexplanations.

The number of atomistic models hypothesized increased considerably following the presentation of the sixth demonstration. Thirteen percent of the children gave atomistic explanations prior to it; 30 percent afterward. Sixty-four percent could propose no explanation for demonstration 1 at first; only 40 percent had no explanation for demonstration 1 after the sixth demonstration. However, the intervening demonstrations could possibly have served as learning experiences that led to more atomistic explanations when they were coupled with demonstration 6.

Despite the limitations of this experiment many of the children, including some third graders, were able to construct mental models. This number increased rapidly with age and grade level, perhaps reflecting some classroom instruction in science. As one would expect, children of higher intelligence were more successful, and the consistency with which mental models were applied increased with age. Boys seemed to be somewhat superior, but this inference is unsupported by solid evidence. Other studies present much the same kind of picture for certain mental models.

By grade four, many children are able to use a kinetic molecular theory of matter in explaining expansion, change of solid to liquid or gas (as well as the reverse), contraction, and diffusion at a "descriptive or classification" level.[26] Mental models are important for transfer of learning because they enable children to apply a consistent explanatory scheme to apparently unrelated phenomena. Until they form appropriate mental models, children are unable to understand the logical reasons for the phenomena they encounter. The many kinds of models children can formulate, the difficulties in their development, and the extent to which these models are more than word repetition are unknown at the present time. John McNeil and Evan Keislar's experiment in developing a kinetic molecular model with first grade children is a case in which working models were not formed.[27] It is difficult to decide from the report of their experiment whether concepts of molecules, molecular motion, and molecular attractions have real meaning to children or whether children have once again demonstrated their capacity to manipulate meaningless symbols.

Problem Solving

The development of mental models has implications for solving simple science problems through reasonable, analytical thought processes. Without cognitive structures to which to relate the various aspects of the problem, problem solving is left to the vagaries of trial and error. Hence teaching that strives to analyze and to apply scientific knowledge to problem situations can only succeed if the appropriate facts and theories have been assimilated by children.

Improvement of problem solving abilities

Much has been written about the ability of children to solve problems. The psychological dimensions have been outlined, but applications of this outline to science education are still vague. What kinds of science experiences will generate in children a generalized ability to cope with problems that are not exactly like previously solved problems? The precise answer to this broad question is not known. Educators are still exploring the differences children at any one age level or at different age levels show in problem solving. The time-honored debate as to whether problem solving is a constellation of specific skills or a generalized ability has not yet been solved.

Is experience the important factor?

David Ausubel believes that the most important difference between the problem solving of children and that of adults lies in the complexity of the problems that are successfully handled.[28] Older children and adults, he believes, are merely more sophisticated; they draw on more experience and are better at verbalizing and symbolizing. Older children are more aware of the problem, more systematic in tackling it, more persevering, less stereotyped in approach, and better able to profit from past error. Younger children focus on only one part of the problem at a time, are more easily frustrated, tend to stray from the problem, and are less successful in generalizing to other situations. For them, the problem must be directly connected with physical objects and concrete imagery. They are less competent at verbalizing solutions and at transferring them to other problems, whether the solutions have been verbalized. They are also less able to defer the satisfaction of knowing where they are in their task and how well they are doing.

Before they can effectively incorporate problem solving into their teaching, science teachers need to know how problem solving is affected by the child's rigidity, impulsiveness, and anxiety, and the effect of the teacher's warmth and receptiveness on the child's desire to solve problems. Some children hypothesize impulsively, accepting the first answer that comes to them. Others, slower and more thoughtful, are more likely to be correct the first time. These children may be better at drawing inferences than are impulsive children; they read with fewer errors and are sometimes thought of as "inhibited."[29] Some children fear to guess and be wrong; others guess too freely:

"Answer grabbers"

> How often we have seen our answer-grabbers get into trouble. The fact is that problems and answers are simply different ways of looking at a relationship, a structure, an order. A problem is a picture with a piece missing; the answer is the missing piece. The children who take time to see, and feel, and grip the problem, soon find that the answer is there. The ones who get in trouble are the ones who see a problem as an order to start running at top speed from a given starting point, in an unknown direction, to an unknown destination. They dash after the answer before they have considered the problem. What's their big hurry?[30]

Strategies for problem solving

Problem solving refers to some unexpected or perplexing occurrence that must be explained, and it is not likely to be successful through hasty investigation. If children's ability to think in critical, reflective, cognitively structured ways is to grow, they must have sufficient time for exploration, for asking questions, for poking around, for just thinking. The ability to solve problems as a goal of science education can be achieved only if children encounter many different kinds of problems; from this variety an attitude to apply and adapt tested strategies can arise. Ample evidence shows that children who have learned the appropriate ground rules and have been trained to use information can employ more sophisticated strategies for solving problems than one would expect.[31]

Children usually do not know how to solve a scientific problem, even if it is as simple as finding the effect of temperature on the rate of evaporation of water or on the rate at which their hair grows. Their questions are too vague to gather the pertinent information, such as the number of objects in the system and their properties. The inconsistency of their questions and actions demonstrates that most children are unfamiliar with tactics for problem solving. Not only are they unaware that planning is necessary to obtain suitable information, they have no idea of what "suitable information" is. They disregard or miss pertinent factors, concentrating instead on one or two prominent but not necessarily important aspects. With no idea of how to find out for themselves, they either ask someone for answers or experiment aimlessly. Part of the difficulty, of course, is that they are inexperienced in expressing, both to themselves and to their teachers, what they want to know or what they have found.

The tasks most children have been required to perform are:

> . . . too easy, too repetitive, and seem meaningless and trivial to [them], where [they are] often rewarded for low-level performance on these tasks, where [they] can often just passively listen instead of actively trying out the skill, where [they get] incomplete and delayed evaluative information about how well or poorly [they are] doing and little specific information of just what [they are] doing right and what wrong.[32]

That these fumblings can be remedied has been demonstrated by J. Richard Suchman at the University of Illinois. Suchman prepared a series of films of such physical phenomena as the bending of a heated bimetallic blade. At the end of the film the children who had watched were asked to explain what they saw by asking questions of the teacher, who would guide them but not supply answers. In explaining why the strip bent, the children often said that it had been heated. This answer is partly correct, but it is misleading because it assumes that causality is a simple one-to-one relationship and that the only change in the experiment was a temperature change. Even the incorrect explanation—that the metal bent because it was softened by heat—is not a scientific explanation because it fails to associate an external set of conditions with a scientific theory. The bending must be shown to occur as the natural result of a certain set of conditions and operational principles (see Chapter 1).

Suchman tried to shift children's explanations from simple, naïve sequences to a realization of the multidimensionality of causation in which several conditions operate simultaneously. The correct explanation for the bending of the blade, for example, must include the difference in expansion of the two metals. When the metals are held rigidly together in a blade, the blade will bend because one metal expands more than the other when heated. This expansion, in turn, results from increased molecular motion.[33]

Suchman described the chief characteristic of the experimental group as it appeared to him during the first stages of his instructional program:

> To begin with, there was a marked lack of autonomy and productivity, stemming—we believe—from children's dependence upon authorities, teachers, parents and books, to shape their concepts. When given new data, or a situation in which such data were available, the children rarely organized what they had, rarely gathered more data, rarely raised and tested hypotheses or drew inferences. Instead they blocked completely, began to offer unsupported conclusions, or produced a string of stereotyped probes that led nowhere. Accustomed to having concepts explained to them in discussions, pictures, films, and textbooks, the children were unwilling or unable to plan and initiate action with the purpose of discovering new concepts for themselves—even when all the data necessary for such discovery were available on demand.[34]

This inexperience of the fifth grade children with whom Suchman worked in framing questions is clearly reflected in the following extract:

Better questions

Examiner: What made it [the bimetallic blade] go up?
    I'm here to answer questions.
Mark: Yes, I know. I can't think of any to ask.
Examiner: I see. Think. Try.
Mark: [Pause] Well, I can't think of any questions.
Examiner: What is it you want to know? What would you want to know?
Mark: Why it bended upwards.
Examiner: What could you do to find out what things were necessary?
Mark: Try it. Ask someone who knew.
Examiner: Yes, you could ask someone that knew, but that would just be getting someone else to tell you, wouldn't it? I mean finding out for yourself.
Mark: Just try different things.
Examiner: What?
Mark: Well, you could get the materials and things, and then try holding the thing at a different angle.
Examiner: What do you think would happen?
Mark: I don't know.
Examiner: Can you ask me some questions to find out?
Mark: No, I can't ask you any questions.
Examiner: You're completely stumped? You have any ideas now for any rules at all that would explain it?
Mark: No.

Examiner: None at all. It's a complete mystery to you? No hunches? And no ideas as to what you could ask me to get some hunches?
Mark: No.[35]

Many children were distressed by the challenge of this strange teaching technique. Some remained quiet, unwilling to guess; others spoke but asked no questions; some asked the first question that came to mind. All were unable to think of a plan for systematically studying the problem. Their questions were ambiguous, incapable of clarifying or eliminating, of fixing precisely, or of changing conditions. Most of the children thought of the experiments they had watched as a repetition of events or a series of manipulations. Before their training, none knew why controls were necessary or why they should try to identify the pertinent variables in a systematic way. Because they did not approach the problem with a general plan that required the identification of the objects, conditions, and events of the demonstration, the children failed to note the variables and to specify the conditions under which the variables operated. For example, when they asked Was the blade hot? the children did not specify *how* hot, at what stage in the experiment was the blade heated, or what part of the blade was heated.[36]

Hypothesizing

Improving hypotheses   Suchman found that "even a very small amount of experience and training under less than ideal conditions can produce measurable improvements in the question asking of sixth-grade children. . . . The technique [Inquiry Training] in its present form has a marked effect on the motivation, autonomy and question-asking fluency of children.[37]

The training, limited to one or two hours a week for twenty-four weeks, is suggested by the following protocol of a child who is beginning to gain some confidence in his ability to frame questions. The child is asked to explain why a metal can that is partially filled with water heated to the boiling point and then sealed collapses when cooled:

S: I know that because there wasn't any air in the can, so when you poured the water on it, it cooled off and it contracted. So it collapsed.
T: You have a theory about contracting?
S: Yes. The can contracts when you pour water on it.
T: How can you tell when the can contracts?
S: It gets smaller.

> *T:* If you take this theory about contraction, can you carry out an experiment to see if this idea of contraction really explains — can you find out if the can did get smaller?
> *S:* Did the can get smaller?
> *T:* No. What are you going to do with your theory?
> *S:* I don't know.
> *T:* Are you going to keep it?
> *S:* No.
> *T:* Why?
> *S:* Because it's not right.
> *T:* How come?
> *S:* Because you said so.
> *T:* What do you mean, I said so?
> *S:* When I asked you, did the can contract, you said, no.
> *T:* Did I say that your theory was not right, though?
> *S:* No.
> *T:* Who did decide that your theory needed some looking at?
> *S:* Me.
> *T:* Do you see how you can come up with an explanation, and then you can gather some information, and then depending on the information, you can see if your theory checks with the facts, and keep your theory; if it doesn't, look for another.[38]

(Note that the use of the word *theory* in this dialogue is not in keeping with its scientific meaning.)

The teacher here is helping the child to visualize what happened and to propose logical ways of testing his ideas. In the course of this process the child realizes that his mental model of contraction is contradicted by the facts and he should therefore propose another model.

Creativity

Creativity in science

Creativity is a catchword of contemporary education. With the realization that creativity is not confined to the arts alone, educators have seriously begun to consider its educational implications. At the present time, however, the meaning of creativity has not been standardized. To some educators creativity accompanies free activity and is something of which all children are capable — for example, painting, poetry, fiction, or perhaps an unusual form with building blocks. Others believe that only a few children can be creative. It may be that creativity can be the same in all kinds of endeavor — in art as well as science —

and there is no certainty that creativity, however it is defined, can be taught. Many questions about creativity remain unanswered at present. Does creativity in art and music begin before creativity in science? Is it possible for a child to be creative in only one field? Are internal or external factors more important in generating and releasing creative potential?

E. Paul Torrance, a leading investigator in this field, defines creativity as:

> The process of becoming sensitive to problems, deficiencies, gaps in knowledge, missing elements, disharmonies . . . identifying the difficulty; searching for solutions, making guesses, or formulating hypotheses about the deficiencies; testing and retesting these hypotheses and finally modifying and retesting them; and finally communicating the results.[39]

Novelty

In itself, this statement appears to be another version of the scientific method. Surely, creativity is not problem solving in another guise! As Torrance notes, the missing element in this definition is that the product must be novel. The outcome of a creative act may be valuable to its creator or even to his society; it may force a change in the child's normal patterns of thought or behavior. But these outcomes, significant though they may be, are overshadowed by the element of novelty, even if the novelty exists for the creator alone. There is some agreement that creativity also calls for high motivation and concentration on a course of action to the exclusion of distracting influences.

Torrance found that children who ranked high on his creativity tests proposed more hypotheses and original ideas to explain how unfamiliar "science toys" worked. When matched for intelligence, sex, race, and teacher, creative children in grades one through six "had reputations for having wild and fantastic ideas, produced drawings and other products judged to be original, and produced work characterized by humor, playfulness, relative lack of rigidity, and relaxation."[40]

Improving creative capacity

Torrance was able to stimulate primary grade children to think of new ideas by leading questions. In an experiment on improving science toys, he used eighteen such questions: What would happen if we made it larger? What could we add? What would happen if we gave it motion? What would happen if we changed the shape? Children who were asked these questions and urged to think of "clever, interesting, and unusual ideas" were more successful than those who were told to think of as many things as possible. This second group, in turn, was more successful than children without training, suggesting that children who are encouraged to propose new ideas tend to produce more novel ideas. When children are trained to think up new questions, to reword problems, and to propose their own ideas about these problems, they become better able to deal with "entirely new and different problems."[41]

Creative children are better at coping with difficult, frustrating, and open-ended tasks than are noncreative children because they enjoy the challenge, the aura of discovery, and the uncertainty of these problems. They dislike closed tasks with a more or less well-defined path to their solution.[42] Creative children will be challenged by discovery (inquiry) tasks. For noncreative children, the challenge will be to the teacher, who must provide a responsive environment in which the curiosity of children about science and their willingness to study it will equally be fulfilled.

Although more than twenty intellectual factors of importance in scientific creativity have been identified, the following seven factors are perhaps the best demonstrated:

Creativity factors

1. Ideational fluency—the relative ease of proposing ideas without regard to quality.
2. Spontaneous flexibility—the generation of many different ideas and approaches to a problem.
3. Originality—the unusual, uncommon, novel responses to a problem.
4. Curiosity (questioning)—a positive response to the unknown elements of the environment.
5. Causal hypothesizing—the ability to devise cause-and-effect statements.
6. Consequential hypothesizing—the ability to conceive of the consequences of changing conditions.
7. Constructiveness—the ability to devise a more or less practical method of solving a problem.[43]

The capacity of children to demonstrate these factors grows from the first to the third grades. Boys are superior by the third grade, although girls move ahead rapidly in the fourth and fifth grades, a finding that is in harmony with the facts of developmental psychology. The ability to propose causal hypotheses develops slowly but consistently, without the regression that is observed in the other factors in the fourth grade. The ability to form hypotheses of consequence appears to be less stable than causal hypothesizing, begins at an earlier age, and is more strongly affected by sex differences.[44]

Creativity and sex

Sex-linked stimuli strongly affect the creative responses of first graders. Girls, for example, are more creative with a toy nurse's kit than boys; boys are better than girls with a fire truck. Little difference in performance is observed with a toy dog. In the second grade boys begin to assume superiority with the nurse's kit, and by the third grade they are "clearly superior" with all three toys. Many of the boys, however, shun the nurses's kit; others call it a doctor's kit, and with that fiction they become more productive. In addition manipulation is a significant factor in productivity. Boys consistently handle toys more than the girls do, particularly from second grade on. Manipulation of toys by girls does not increase from grade to grade.

Creativity and intelligence

Teachers often assume that creativity and intelligence go hand in hand. There is a modest correlation, but only a third of the highest 20 percent of children in IQ score in the upper 20 percent on tests of creativity. Research reveals that elementary school children can be grouped in four broad creativity–intelligence categories:

1. High creativity–high intelligence: These children can exercise within themselves both control and freedom, both adultlike and childlike kinds of behavior.

2. High creativity–low intelligence: These children are in angry conflict with themselves and with their school environment and are beset by feelings of unworthiness and inadequacy. In a stress-free context, however, they can blossom forth cognitively.

3. Low creativity–high intelligence: These children can be described as "addicted" to school achievement. Academic failure would be perceived by them as catastrophic, so that they must continually strive for academic excellence in order to avoid the possibility of pain.

4. Low creativity–low intelligence: Basically bewildered, these children engage in various defensive maneuvers ranging from useful adaptations such as intensive social activity to regressions such as passivity or psychosomatic symptoms.[45]

Some psychologists hypothesize that the creative thinking of children, especially boys, is likely to be most effective when their emotional state is somewhere between unconscious anxiety and high overt anxiety:

Anxiety

Those psychological processes associated with creative functioning require, for their optimal operation, a context free from or minimally influenced by the stresses that arise from academic evaluation and a few of the consequences of error. To further this kind of goal within education, then, is to fashion a learning and teaching environment that will permit children to minimize the bind produced by negative sanctions for error.[46]

Psychologists support process-centered instruction because it combines divergent (creative) *and* convergent (accepted) modes of thinking, and "therefore such a method is of relevance for both creativity and intelligence."

Intuitive Thought[47]

Can intuition be bad?   It has been said that when they think like creative scientists, children propose intuitive solutions to problems. The difference between these two kinds of intuitive thought is immense. The vague, formless intuition of children is tied to concrete-empirical evidence. Their lack of power in using abstract symbols, coupled with unsophisticated problem-solving strategies and ignorance of general and specific knowledge, is hardly comparable to the expertise of scientists, who in full cognitive maturity bring deep knowledge and experience to the study of new problems. Despite an initial fumbling and imprecision, scientists can usually deal with new problems on a highly formal and propositional level, although they do not necessarily approach these problems intuitively in coming up with solutions that are likely to be creative. They still may not succeed in solving the problem, even though they are better prepared than the layman.

Intuition versus guessing   Children who propose intuitive answers may not necessarily be creative, and their answers may be both wrong and illogical. Ausubel believes that a child who is creative in some general sense thinks intuitively and creatively without possessing the tools for rigorous thinking. The child's answers, although incorrect, will be plausible. The intuitive child who lacks the perspective of factual and methodological knowledge must resort to guessing. If he is creative as well as intuitive, he will add the elements of originality and plausibility.

Skill in inquiry   Some children are much better than others at proposing significant hypotheses and at testing and deciding whether to reject them. These are surely both creative and intuitive behaviors. There is no doubt that the intuitive capacity of many children improves with age, presumably because children are also growing in knowledge and in ability to think in general terms and to use symbols in testing hypotheses. A cognitively mature adult confronted with a problem in an unfamiliar field is also forced to attack it intuitively, but because he can call on transferable elements of his previous knowledge and can manipulate this knowledge on an abstract–symbolic level, he shortens the time required for the solution. He has already mastered a style of inquiry, and general techniques of gathering and evaluating the necessary information. Scientists such

Encouraging intuition

as Harold Urey, Linus Pauling, and George Gamow (who are probably not representative of the great body of scientists) have achieved success in more than one scientific field because of cognitive maturity.

In the classroom the teacher must try to harmonize intuition–creativity, where it exists, with the developmental stages of the children. Pure guessing leads to error; unless he tests intuitive ideas, the teacher gains little by proposing them. Therefore the teacher should frequently propose problems that can lead to verifiable solutions. Guided discovery is important in preventing the loss of class time in fruitless search. Verifiable information is vital: hypotheses are worthless unless they can be checked. (Classroom limitations may preclude experimental testing, and therefore verification must come from other sources.) The teacher should encourage unorthodox approaches, but whenever possible they must be directly testable.

Summary

Successful science teaching in the elementary school demands of the teacher an understanding of how children think and particularly of how they think in science. Children's logic is somewhat different from that of adults, but in many significant ways it is surprisingly similar. Young children are able to do cause-and-effect thinking if they are dealing with aspects of concrete experience. Overgeneralization and causal errors result because they have had little opportunity or training in causal thinking.

Children's "why" questions are signs that they need help in reducing a dissonance between their conceptual schemes and their environmental situations. As they grow older their "why" questions become less frequent because they have already answered some of these questions to their satisfaction and because they may have given up trying to get answers.

As a result of suitable guided learning, children's mental models become more adequate, and they are better prepared to give scientific explanations that depend on problem solving. This preparation, combined with a generalized approach to problems leads children to become more confident in their own intellectual strength.

Nonrigid, highly creative, intelligent children are generally considered ideal for inquiry teaching. Creativity is not a simple, intelligence-anchored capacity, however, for it coexists in varying degrees with high and low intelligence. Children who differ in creativity–intelligence ratios may be surprisingly dissimilar in cognitive, social, and emotional classroom behavior.

For further study

1. What is the evidence for the statement "Logical thinking is the outcome of many experiences and physical activities"?

2. What is the relevance of Suchman's work on inquiry to elementary school science?

3. How adequate is the evidence that young children can formulate mental models to explain natural phenomena?

4. In what ways may the teacher foster creativity in the classroom? How is creativity to be assessed?

5. Analyze a science learning task into its subtasks and compare the ease with which this subdivision may be accomplished for reception learning with problem solving.

Notes and references

1. Inbody, D., "Children's Understanding of Natural Phenomena," *Science Education,* 47: 276, April 1963.

2. *Ibid.,* p. 276.

3. *Ibid.,* p. 277.

4. Mogar, M., "Children's Causal Reasoning about Natural Phenomena," *Child Development,* 31: 59–65, 1960.

5. Piaget, J., *The Child's Conception of Physical Causality* (Totowa, N.J.: Littlefield, Adams & Co., 1960), pp. 61–62.

6. *Ibid.,* p. 65.

7. *Ibid.,* p. 275.

8. Piaget, J., *Judgment and Reasoning in the Child* (Totowa, N.J.: Littlefield, Adams & Co., 1959), p. 233.

9. Szeminska, A., "The Evolution of Thought: Some Applications of Research Findings to Educational Practice," in P. H. Mussen, ed., *European Research in Cognitive Development,* Vol. 30, No. 2, Monographs of the Society for Research in Child Development, No. 100, 1965, pp. 55–56. No. 1 is reworded.

10. *Ibid.,* p. 56.

11. Huttenlocher, J., "Development of Formal Reasoning on Concept Formation Problems," *Child Development,* 35: 1241, December 1964.

12. Ervin, S. M., "Experimental Procedures of Children," *Child Development,* 31: 703–19, 1960.

13. Almy, M., et al., *Young Children's Thinking,* (New York: Teachers College Press, 1966), pp. 135–36.

14. Much of the content of this section is based on Inhelder, B., and J. Piaget, *The Growth of Logical Thinking from Childhood to Adolescence* (New York: Basic Books, 1958), pp. 278–89.

15. The content of this section is based on Isaacs, N., "Children's Why Questions," in S. Isaacs, ed., *Intellectual Growth in Young Children* (London: George Routledge, 1938), pp. 291–349.

16. Fischler, A., "Implications of Structure for Elementary Science," *Science Education,* 52: 278–79, April 1968.

17. Isaacs, N., *Early Scientific Trends in Children* (London: National Froebel Foundation, 1960), p. 13.

18. Arnstine, D., "Curiosity," *Teachers College Record,* 67: 596–97, May 1966.

19. Piaget, J., B. Inhelder, and A. Szeminska, *The Child's Conception of Geometry* (New York: Harper & Row, Torchbooks, 1960), p. 376.

20. *Ibid.,* pp. 382–83.

21. Anderson, R., "Children's Ability to Formulate Mental Models to Explain Natural Phenomena," paper presented to the National Association for Research in Science Teaching, 1965, p. 2.

22. *Ibid.,* p. 5.

23. *Ibid.,* p. 6.

24. *Ibid.,* p. 7.

25. *Ibid.,* p. 8.

26. Pella, M. O., and R. E. Ziegler, "Use of Mechanical Models in Teaching Theoretical Concepts," *Journal of Research in Science Teaching,* 5: 149, 1967–68.

27. McNeil, J., and E. Keislar, "An Experiment in Validating Objectives for the Curriculum in Elementary School Science," *Science Education,* 46: 152–56, March 1962.

28. Ausubel, D. P., *Theory and Problems of Child Development,* pp. 568–70.

29. Kagan, J., "Personality and the Learning Process," *Daedalus, Journal of the American Academy of Arts and Sciences,* 94: 559, Summer 1965.

30. Holt, J., *How Children Fail* (New York: Pitman Publishing Corp., 1964), pp. 46–47.

31. Bruner, J. S., et al., *Studies in Cognitive Growth* (New York: John Wiley, 1966), p. 150.

32. Crutchfield, R., "Sensitization and Activation of Cognitive Skills," in

J. Bruner, ed., *Learning About Learning* (Washington, D.C.: United States Office of Education, 1966), p. 65.

33. Suchman, J. R., "Inquiry Training: Building Skills for Autonomous Discovery," *Merrill-Palmer Quarterly of Behavior and Development,* 7 (3): 154–55, 1961.

34. *Ibid.,* p. 155.

35. *Ibid.,* p. 156.

36. *Ibid.,* p. 158.

37. Suchman, J. R., *Elementary School Training Program in Scientific Inquiry* (Urbana, Ill.: College of Education, University of Illinois, 1963), p. 81.

38. *Illinois Studies in Inquiry Training,* March 1965.

39. Torrance, E. P., "Scientific Views of Creativity and Factors Affecting Its Growth," *Daedalus, Journal of the American Academy of Arts and Sciences,* 94: 663–64, Summer 1965.

40. *Ibid.,* p. 672.

41. MacDonald, J. B., and J. Raths, "Should We Group by Creative Abilities?", *Elementary School Journal,* 65: 137–42, 1964.

42. Gagné, R. M., "Elementary Science: A New Scheme of Instruction," *Science,* 151: 53, January 7, 1966.

43. Guilford, J. P., "Intellectual Resources and Their Values As Seen by Scientists," chap. 8, in C. W. Taylor and F. Barron, eds., *Scientific Creativity* (New York: John Wiley, 1963), p. 111.

44. Torrance, E. P., *Rewarding Creative Behavior* (Englewood Cliffs, N.J.: Prentice-Hall, 1965), p. 298.

45. Wallach, M., and N. Kogan, *Modes of Thinking in Young Children* (New York: Holt, Rinehart and Winston, 1965), p. 15.

46. *Ibid.,* p. 323.

47. This section owes much to Ausubel, D. P., *The Psychology of Meaningful Learning* (New York: Grune & Stratton, 1963), pp. 122–23.

Motivational Factors in Learning and Thinking Science

Overview

Rewards

To help children think and learn science, the teacher must understand what makes Johnny and Mary tick. How can the teacher capitalize on a child's desire to know without inhibiting the child from finding out for himself? How can a child's interest be channeled and supported so that he can satisfy his search for understanding? How can minimal or passing interests be used as a basis for lasting, intense studies of natural phenomena? How can the school experience of studying be made an exciting and enjoyable enterprise for the child?

These questions should be approached with the understanding that children have intrinsic interests in the phenomenal world around them and that the teacher can often help children see exciting facets of what superficially appears rather plain and uninteresting. Finally a significant set of ideas suggest that more learning and thinking occurs when interpersonal interaction among children is maximized.

Desire to Learn: Problem of Motivation

Many teachers rely on extrinsic motivation, on rewarding children for their contribution, but such motivation is shallow and unsatisfactory for encouraging independent learning. To be sure, one's life is often strongly influenced by the desire for promotion, for increased salary, for the esteem of one's fellows, or to serve humanity, but these extrinsic stimuli are too weak to influence many adults to be interested in science. Although few adults will pursue scientific careers, there is hope that adults will become literate in science if they continue to read and understand science. If they are apathetic or hostile toward science because they were bored or repelled by inferior science teaching, they will achieve neither autonomous learning nor scientific literacy.

Children themselves are the agents of active learning. Children, not teachers, must ask more questions. Instead of an endless one-way stream of questions whose purpose is only dimly perceived by the children, the search for answers must begin with the learners. What depth of meaning can children extract from statements that are submissively accepted but never grasped? To talk about atoms without putting them into a meaningful framework is to waste time. In John Holt's words:

> Children cannot learn much from cookbooks, even the best cookbooks. A child learns, at any moment, not by using the procedure that seems best to us, but the one that seems best to *him;* by fitting into his structure of ideas and relationships, his mental model of reality, not the piece we think comes next, but the one he thinks comes next. This is hard for teachers to learn, and hardest of all for the skillful and articulate, the kind we often called "gifted." The more aware we are of the structural nature of our own ideas, the more we are tempted to try to transplant this structure whole into the minds of children. But it cannot be done. They must do this structuring and building for themselves. I may see that fact *A* and fact *B* are connected by the relationship *C,* but I can't make this connection for a child by talking about it. He may remember the facts and what I said about the relationships between them, but he is very likely to turn my words into three facts, *A, B,* and *C,* none of them connected to any other.[1]

Importance of early schooling

Once the individual is past the elementary school years, it will take educational surgery of the highest order to cut away formalistic and hardened learning attitudes and to replace them with more desirable principles of action. The evidence is indisputable that in the first few years schools can establish (or confirm if previously formed) a disposition for intellectual activities. Children who have not demonstrated a drive for intellectual mastery by the age of eleven or twelve are not likely to change even if confronted by excellent high school instruction. It has even been suggested that the most important intellectual contribution of the kindergarten is in the arousal of interest, desire, and enjoyment in learning rather than in actual formal thinking.[2]

Factors That Affect Desire to Learn[3]

Important motivating forces

Psychologists have isolated some factors that affect learning motivation from the bewildering tangle of environmental, personality, and intellectual interrelationships every child shows. The following list of factors, although not complete, is a helpful guide to the psychology of learning motivation.

Desire to be accepted by adults or peers

Acceptance

Although adult acceptance may be effective with young children and with girls, it tends to be a relatively weak, extrinsic force. Peer acceptance is a stronger force, but it is more likely to act negatively. The effect of adult or peer acceptance is to diminish the importance of learning; learning is important not because of what it can do for the child but because it is important to those he respects.

Desire to be different

Uniqueness

The child seeks group acceptance, but he also tries to be different from his friends, a device by which the child gains unique identification. Intellectually and emotionally strong children may choose the path of intellectual achievement, which, although rewarded by adults, is likely to isolate them from other children. The compulsive striving for uniqueness, despite its effects on personal relationships, is characteristic of creative adults.

Desire to emulate an admired model

The model

The child may admire another child or an adult so strongly that he tries to be as much like him as possible. The absence of an intellectual model in some homes can be a cause for a child's lack of intellectual drive. Many parents do not oppose intellectual striving; but if they have not exemplified the intellectual life, the likelihood that their children will want it is diminished. "Do what I say, not what I do" is an exhortation doomed to be ignored. Hence teachers who seek to inspire children to learn must themselves be worthy models.

The opposing forces of differentiation and emulation are strong in most children. Human beings tend to leave groups that have little to offer them and to identify with more potent groups. "Psychological development has a spiral form in which a child identifies with a group commanding desirable goals and, after maximizing similarity to that group, differentiates from it and passes on to the next identification, in an almost neverending seesaw struggle between maximizing similarity to one model and differentiating from another."[4]

Anticipation of failure

Success

Early in his school career, the child becomes aware of the possibility of failure, which is often sufficient to discourage him from pursuing his school tasks and to withdraw into himself. Young children know or think they know what they can do, and they try to avoid the anxiety of failure or of competitive pressure to succeed. The strong extrinsic motivations of school sometimes increase withdrawal because they increase pressure on children to do what they cannot do.

Anxiety arising from learning conflict

Competition

Overcompetitiveness, passivity, or sex-role conflict may affect the child's learning. Classrooms are typically competitive, and girls in particular may develop guilt feelings, become anxious and inhibited, and perform at low levels. In the primary grades boys already identify with men and resist the passivity their female teachers expected of them. Many school subjects are sex-linked in that children think they are more appropriate for one of the sexes. The physical sciences and mathematics are male-centered, and therefore girls are less likely to want to study them. The girl who fails physical science is not disgraced; indeed success in science may be defeminizing to adolescent girls.

In the early school years girls are much more successful than boys in school tasks. This difference decreases as children grow older, and by adolescence boys tend to be superior in mathematical and physical tasks and are certainly not inferior in reading. Young boys may think of reading and arithmetic as part of the female-centered environment, which they resist. Not until they are age ten or eleven do they begin to see relevance between what is done in school and future vocation, which, coupled with the fact that they suffer relatively little competitive anxiety, may help to explain how their learning behavior changes. Whereas girls seek approval from their teachers, boys think of task mastery as a symbol of their ability.

Work standards

Goals

Children soon set standards of achievement for themselves that maximize security and minimize anxiety. Children who are intensely competitive and strongly motivated to achieve may set impossible standards for themselves; those who are able but less intensely motivated often settle for a median position in the class. The authoritarian teacher who demands high levels of achievement is not likely to stimulate these children to change their work standards voluntarily. On the other hand the teacher who through personal warmth and interest encourages children to raise their own standards of achievement minimizes the tensions that arise from the opposite pulls of security and adult standards.

Attention

Naturally attention-getting

Learning is rarely easy *and* enjoyable. The teacher must maintain the class's attention, even of those members who are unmotivated to learn or are intellectually unable to learn, because unless each child's eyes, ears, and mind are open, nothing will be accomplished. Attention is not captured by admonition, however, for children learn to present an attentive facade without interrupting their own interesting daydreaming. The science teacher is helped by the novelty of science activities and the genuine appeal of experimentation, which can quickly cut through this facade.

Curriculum structure

Organizing curriculum properly

According to Gagné, a suitably structured curriculum is essential because new learning and motivation for additional learning arise from the proper presentation and sequence of ideas. Previously acquired knowledge must be restructured in a variety of contexts and combined with new knowledge if genuine integration of experience is to occur. Gagné believes that content and its order are the two most important factors in learning, and both must be appropriate for the learner.[5] He assumes that a child will want to learn if he knows exactly what new skill or knowledge he will have when each task has been completed. Compare, for example, the motivational force of the statement "We will now study magnets" with its functional counterpart "Learning the principles of magnetic action will enable us to understand how electric motors work, how doorbells operate, and how a compass indicates direction."

Promise of process science learning

One strength of process learning in science is that the burden of motivation shifts from the teacher to the student. In a problem-centered, nonauthoritarian environment, cognitive motivation will be sustained as long as solutions can be found. This motivation is twofold: (1) to solve the problem, to match what is observed with what is known or can be found; (2) to continue to experience in a free situation the pleasure and excitement of manipulating and of obtaining data and to discover the power of reason and experimental design in finding answers.[6] Success in science thus provides a self-renewing desire to continue learning.

Curiosity

Curiosity, inquisitiveness, and interest are strong motives, but they are erratic and unsystematic, easily satisfied, and incapable of providing informa-

Alleviating boredom tive feedback. Teachers of primary grade children are fortunate because their children have not yet learned to be bored by school. Feedback is instantaneous and curiosity is quickly aroused (and perhaps as quickly lost); children's questions, comments, and attentiveness (or its lack) are direct indicators of instructional quality. This lively curiosity is obscured in older children by a "show me" attitude; older children seem almost to challenge teachers to interest them.

The teacher as motivator Motivation, after all, lies in the child; the teacher merely stimulates that motivation. Teachers should therefore use few heavily teacher-directed, teacher-centered activities. They should shun the customary relentless pressure of finishing all activities on time; children cannot be totally immersed in activities without opening to them large blocks of time and some freedom of choice. One developmental psychologist speaks of "intellectually burned" children, who have been so frustrated by interruptions in their intellectual activities that they refuse to become involved again.[7] Teachers should rule out days whose routine never seems to change. Surprise and novelty are essential, yet they must be embedded in the familiar and the comfortable. If children know exactly what to expect, or conversely, if they have no basis for predicting what will happen, they will have no reason to be curious. There is evidence that the teacher's personality and expectations have an important motivational role. Teachers who rely on intrinsic motivation, who are warm and personally interested in their students, tend to raise the level of student interest in science. There need be no conflict if a high expectancy level is balanced by tension-reducing personal warmth and teaching that encourages intrinsic motivation.

Questions and children's needs The idea that science activities should be chosen *only* if they satisfy the needs revealed by children's questions is without merit, except in the hands of a great teacher. Questions do not necessarily indicate interests or needs; they may serve only to gain attention, to confirm fixed ideas, or to remove fears instead of providing intellectual probes. What is "relevant" for children may act to negate intrinsic motivation because it devalues learning as a value in itself.

Freedom in decision making Before he enters school, the child is relatively free to make his own decisions, to build his own concept systems, and to do whatever he wants to do when he wants to do it. In school he is no longer autonomous. He is under pressure to accept a program of learning into which neither he nor any other child quite fits. His interests are not those of the teacher; the direction of class activity may be contrary to what he wants, even if *his* questions are welcomed. Interests and curiosity are dissipated by teacher-originated tasks whose purposes are unknown to the child. He is told to follow certain rules, but the rationale for these rules is rarely presented and even less often cooperatively discussed by the class. The reasonable compromise by which the child is permitted some freedom to propose his procedures and to decide the basis for accepting or rejecting answers is not always permitted, even though the challenge of this kind of freedom is sometimes sufficient to motivate learning.

Whether active or latent the child's intellectual ability is not necessarily a motivational force. Not until the child realizes that he can gain some desirable end by hard, careful thinking will he transform potential capacity into reality. It is thus important to provide a rich classroom experience through which potential interest is transformed into actual interest.

Children's Interest in Science

Teachers who provide rich experience and prepare the child's environment for cognitive learning minimize the problems of motivation.[8] Children are or can become intensely interested in many aspects of science. Teachers who are aware of these interests and who are ready to capitalize on this intrinsic motivation will find that their battle is half won.

Interest and motivation

Children's interests in science have been studied intensively during the past half century. Almost always the range and intensity of these interests was ascertained by collecting from children lists of things they wanted to know about or questions to which they sought answers. The conclusions tend to be unreliable guides to classroom action, however, because of contradictions in the ranking of interests and because interests change quickly. A more important type of research is still virtually unreported in science education— analysis of the function of interest in effective science teaching. Is interest necessary for motivation?

Without a guiding theory of "classroom interest," each teacher is forced to rely on intuition to create challenges to which her children will respond. Creating challenges in this manner is not a difficult task in science; there is evidence that disadvantaged elementary school children are more interested in process-centered science than they are in mathematics or in the language arts and that discipline is less often necessary in this kind of science instruction then in conventional instruction.[9] Studies in elementary science education confirm the deep interest of children in physical and biological science.[10] In one study of the "sharing periods" of 1,860 children in thirty-four communities and fourteen states, the category of nature and science was the most popular, comprising 25.9 percent of all "sharing" topics. Such topics as plants, animals (pets), space, astronomy, geology, weather, chemistry, and energy were included. As one would expect, children were more interested in aspects of the environment they could experience directly.[11]

Instruction centered on children's expressed interests is often difficult to manage in the classroom. Children's insightful questions are frequently impossible to pursue because their answers require resources and knowledge that are either unavailable or too difficult for children to understand. Interests may disappear in the course of instruction, or they may be so divergent that science becomes incidental and accidental. Some children may suppress their curiosity because they imagine that answers to their questions may threaten their security. Other children may not care to show that they are knowledgeable about a topic discussed in class because they are reluctant to participate actively in discussion. Some psychologists derogate the importance of interest as a drive to mastery and insist that teachers should rely on extrinsic rewards rather than on an innate and somewhat nebulous motivation in the child.[12] Good teaching capitalizes on children's interests, but it also leads to new interests, to new lines of search and action. Interest is important in science, but teaching cannot and must not be content to rest with interest alone.

Problems with interest-centered instruction

Enjoyment

Some psychologists attempt to counterbalance the rather romantic statements on motivation of some contemporary writers by reminding us that children do not "develop an affection for learning" in the natural course of events. They argue that children do not want to learn new skills and new ways of thinking unless it makes them "more like an admired person or brings them affection, praise, or promise of tangible rewards from the admired model."[13] They are soon bored, no matter how stimulating a particular technique or idea is, for they (and adults) adjust quickly to stimuli.

Should science be fun?

The remedy suggested for boredom is to increase the complexity of the child's environment. On the other hand, if the child is frustrated his environment may be too complex. The challenge and the children should be so closely matched that they will be pleasurably and positively involved. This involvement may be accomplished with puzzling or surprising demonstrations or experiments. The wise science teacher knows the value of the element of surprise, and the simpler the demonstration, the more striking it is likely to be. For example, tell a child to touch a rubber band at room temperature to his lips so that he will know whether it is hot or cold. Next tell him to stretch the band quickly, to touch it to his lips again, then to release it, and test its tempera-

Challenges

Value of dissonance

ture a third time. The unexpectedly dramatic changes in temperature may set the stage for a study of the laws of conservation of energy.

Experiences with reversible phenomena often lead to stimulating dissonances. One teacher, for example, showed his class two containers of water, each of which contained an egg. One egg floated, the other had sunk to the bottom. The children, not knowing that there was salt in one of the containers, guessed that the egg that sank was heavier than the other egg and that the egg that floated contained more air than did the other. The teacher then exchanged the two eggs. The children were completely surprised by the results and demanded to know why the eggs behaved in such a contrary way. The first demonstration had not disturbed them at all. They had been able to assimilate the action into their mental models of floating, either in terms of greater weight or in terms of trapped air. When the experimental conditions were reversed, however, the children could no longer assimilate the result in the same way, and a cognitive conflict led them to seek new solutions.[14]

Discovery and dissonance

Not all science can or should be taught in this way, but it is surprising how many novel (to the children) and interest-arousing science experiences need only simple materials. Children, at least the younger ones, are naturally interested in exploring and learning why. Even such seemingly trivial tasks as finding likenesses and differences, measuring, and counting can be happy experiences as long as they are not busywork.

School science *can* be a deadly bore to both children and teacher if it functions only to communicate information. It is difficult to see how the motive of competence or the need for self-fulfillment through achievement will maintain interest in recitation science. It may seem naïve to insist that science can be fun, but it *can* be, and it should be. Science should be enjoyable not only because so much of it is directly apprehendable to children but because children like to manipulate and to experiment. There may even be a manipulative drive that experience in science can satisfy. In a sense science is toy-play.

Discovery approaches to science instruction are exciting from a motivational point of view because they begin with a conceptual dissonance. Children strive to eliminate this dissonance by fitting it into a dissonance-reducing framework. Even though this framework is incorrect, it may be perfectly acceptable to the child and perhaps the best one that can be proposed at the time. But to think that an electric bulb lights because electricity is flowing through the bulb like water flowing through a faucet may lead him to think that he really understands. This erroneous model, even if it is convenient, must eventually be transformed into a more accurate and fruitful conception. The resolution of these difficulties will result in pride of accomplishment as the child successfully measures himself against the task, but guidance is essential; no child by himself can discover the laws of electromagnetic induction or invent the theory of evolution.

Surprise, doubt, perplexity, bafflement, and contradiction stimulate action. This assertion is in harmony with the principle of cognitive dissonance, provided the challenge and the children are matched. Frustration occurs if the challenge is too great, but if the challenge is too easy, there is no task. When the match is close, the child will be pleasurably and positively stimulated. Matching the child with the right classroom experiences is difficult not only because of the physical limitations of the classroom but because no two children are at exactly the same psychological stage.[15]

Socialization

Group learning   For practical reasons modern elementary schools encourage children to work and learn cooperatively. But group learning also fosters intellectual growth. As children work with other children and with adults, the other points of view they encounter help them restructure their ideas and lead them to a more critical point of view, to a different way of looking at their environment. Young children are egocentric; they judge others without pretense or objectivity. The discovery that other children see things differently helps them to accommodate, to rebuild their idea structure, and thus to come close to an effective operational scheme.[16]

Robert Davis has commented that the children to whom he taught the "new mathematics" were relatively unsuccessful when they were alone or in small groups. He attributed their difficulty to lack of communication of ideas and comments and to the loss of reinforcement that comes from showing "the whole class how clever you are."[17] Sharing ideas and cooperative evaluation will improve learning as long as the facts and ideas to be learned are not already predigested and immovably organized. Children are often taught by

Teaching by peers   their peers, perhaps more often than teachers realize. They are stimulated by the better students, they adopt better strategies, and they are better motivated.

Summary

The desire to learn is an important force in education. Unless children want to learn and actively work to restructure what is presented to them, learning will be inefficient and superficial. The desire to learn is strongly affected by anticipation of failure or success and by the extent to which the classroom provokes anxiety. Young children are attracted to experimental and observational science; they are strongly interested in science. The need for children to eliminate discrepancies, dissonances, conflicts, in their experience is a powerful argument for science instruction.

Elementary school teachers are fortunate in that children enjoy science. If they capitalize on this enjoyment, the teachers will avoid many of the problems they encounter in teaching other elementary school subjects.

For further study

1. Do the factors that affect the desire to learn operate in the daily routine of teaching? How can classroom teachers adapt them to help children to learn?

2. From casual talks with children, find out what science-related interests they have.

3. Plan several science activities with the major criteria being that of maximizing the child's enjoyment in the tasks.

4. Select an area of science and suggest ways in which it could be taught so that socialization is maximized.

5. Is enjoyment a legitimate goal of science teaching? Should children enjoy learning? Is there a moral issue in learning when it is enjoyable?

Notes and references

1. Holt, J., *How Children Fail* (New York: Pitman Publishing Corp., 1964), p. 127.

2. Almy, M., "Wishful Thinking about Children's Thinking?" *Teachers College Record,* 62: 404, February 1961.

3. Much of the content of this section is based on Kagan, J., "Personality and the Learning Process," *Daedalus, Journal of the American Academy of Arts and Sciences,* 94: 554–59, Summer 1965.

4. *Ibid.,* p. 555.

5. Gagné, R. M., "A Psychologist's Counsel on Curriculum Design," *Journal of Research in Science Teaching,* 1(1): 30, 1963.

6. Suchman, J. R., "The Illinois Studies in Inquiry Training," in R. E. Ripple and V. N. Rockcastle, eds., *Piaget Rediscovered* (Ithaca, N.Y.: School of Education, Cornell University, 1964), pp. 106–7.

7. Elkind, D., "Piagetian and Psychometric Conceptions of Intelligence," *Harvard Educational Review,* 39: 334–35, Spring 1969.

8. Reed, H. B., "Implications for Science Education of a Teacher Competence Research," *Science Education,* 46: 473–86, December 1962.

9. Rowe, M. B., "SCIS in the Inner City Schools:, *SCIS Newsletter,* No. 11, Winter 1968, pp. 6–7.

10. Blanc, S., "Critical Review of Science Interest Studies," *Science Education,* 42: 162–68, March 1958.

11. Byers, L., "The Interests of Space-Age First Graders," *Elementary School Journal,* 64: 237–41, February 1964.

12. Friedlander, B. Z., "A Psychologist's Second Thoughts on Concepts, Curiosity, and Discovery in Teaching and Learning," *Harvard Educational Review,* 35: 26–27, Winter 1965.

13. Kagan, J., "On Children and Learning," *Today's Education,* 57: 23, December 1968.

14. Palmer, E. L., "Accelerating the Child's Cognitive Attainments Through the Inducement of Cognitive Conflict: An Interpretation of the Piagetian Position," *Journal of Research in Science Teaching,* 3: 324, 1965.

15. Hunt, J. McV., *Intelligence and Experience* (New York: The Ronald Press, 1961), p. 272.

16. Duckworth, E., "Piaget Rediscovered," in R. E. Ripple and V. N. Rockcastle, *op. cit.,* p. 4.

17. Davis, R. B., "The Madison Project's Approach to a Theory of Instruction," *Journal of Research in Science Teaching,* 2(2): 151, 1964.

Children's Science
Concepts: Selected Cases

Overview

The final section of this chapter provides specific examples of science concept formation and of the difficulties children have in science conceptualizing. The examples illustrate some of the ways in which the ideas and conclusions of the previous four sections are applied to concrete, science-related learning.

Concepts, in the sense in which Bruner uses the word, are ideas built from many facts. They are essential in thinking and learning because discrete facts do not provide a basis for any kind of intellectual action. Concepts maximize remembering and learning because they include what is important in a mass of information and exclude what is of lesser value. Teachers should thus know a great deal about how children form concepts and the effective ways of optimizing science learning through concept development.

Concept Formation

Accurate verbal and mental images are necessary if children are to understand their world. By the time they enter nursery school, they have acquired a large number of concepts of varying degrees of accuracy that act as filters in interpreting everyday experience. For the purposes of this book, *concept* is defined as a unique quality common to a number of objects, processes, phenomena, or events, which are grouped according to this unique quality. To form concepts, children must be able to draw these unique qualities, these abstractions, from the raw materials of experience. To a young child a rock may be a large, solid, gray, heavy substance. As he grows older his conception of a rock becomes more sharply defined—a rock is now "a natural material which is a component of the earth's crust"; at still another level, he sees the rock as an aggregation of one or more different minerals that may occur in varying proportions.

The literature of education provides many examples of the increased efficiency and retention of learning through generalizing and conceptualizing, which contrasts sharply with the shortcomings of learning individual facts. *"The effect of concept learning is to free the individual from control by specific stimuli."*[1] He is no longer forced to remember the mass of events from which the concept emerged. The test of whether a concept has been mastered at any level of complexity is the ability of the learner to identify a new event as an instance of concept, and thus endow the event with the general properties of the concept.

Examples of concepts

The idea of energy—in its electrical, chemical, mechanical, and thermal forms—as the ability to do work is an important concept because it leads to vastly increased understanding of the physical universe. The learner cannot sample all the individual events in which energy is involved. If he has created an image of energy from his experience, however, he is better prepared to recognize its presence and pertinence in other phenomena. The word *energy* now summons up a host of related meanings that the child can use fruitfully because others will understand it as he does.

The ability to repeat a definition of energy orally or in writing does not imply that a child has mastered any of these meanings. Many college students complete a physics course and are still not certain of the differences between kinetic and potential energy in the simplest cases of energy phenomena. This kind of verbalism is a sign that the individual's concrete-empirical experiences have been inappropriate or inadequate. Once the concept is formed, however, it can be coupled with additional concepts and facts to form a scientific principle (such as the principle that the potential energy of a falling body is changed into kinetic energy).

Concepts and experience

The assertion that direct experience is necessary to the formation of scientific concepts and principles has been verified many times and is accepted by educational psychologists. Important scientific concepts will not be discovered and identified by unguided children, however. David Butts demonstrated that unguided children of superior intelligence, socioeconomic status, and scientific awareness fail to pick out the important concepts and generalizations from simple scientific experiments. He devised four concrete experiences that were planned to give enough knowledge to permit children to develop the concepts of displacement (two objects cannot occupy the same place at the same time), inertia, and action–reaction and depth–pressure relationships. They made some progress, but few gained more than a sketchy understanding.[2]

Let us suppose, however, that a skilled teacher had planned these experiences in cooperation with the class, that they had been discussed as they were being performed by the class and after they were over. We would reasonably expect more efficient and meaningful learning from this kind of guidance than if the children had been left to discover for themselves. The Piagetian belief that manipulation of concrete materials paves the way for concept formation is pertinent here. The necessary skills, so to speak, are stored and are combined at the right time. J. McV. Hunt points out that the roots of space, time, and causality, to cite but three concepts, lie in the infant's testing of motor skills as he throws, climbs, walks, and plays.[3]

Concept hierarchies

No single statement of a scientific concept is completely correct because concepts exist in hierarchies of meanings that range from the very simple to those that are expressed in abstract and theoretical symbols. Teachers should work for a gradual growth of sophistication as individual concepts are enriched and transformed by new learning. They should not expect children to learn the concept in its entirety at one time. There is a rapid increase in the depth of meaning of the concept of animal from the picture of animals as living, growing, reproducing creatures dependent on food, air, and water to their classification as vertebrates and invertebrates.

Concept stability

Once it is established, an abstraction is more or less stable. It can be used without any further need to refer to its concrete-empirical referents, and it is much less likely to be forgotten than is learning of isolated facts or principles. As they grow older, children become less and less dependent on direct experience for the formation of concepts and principles. Their knowledge is increasing so enormously that verbal learning becomes more effective as long as this learning is based on clearly understood concepts. However, it is doubtful that many scientific concepts will ever have meaning without some kind of tie to concrete experience. The concept of the atom, for example, may be formulated intuitively and with little or no reference to the facts of the physical world that must be explained. But if it is merely intuitive, the concept will bear little resemblance to the atom of modern physical science, which, although far removed from direct experience in many ways, explains many diverse facts of the physical world.

Teachers must always be alert to differentiate between verbalism and the ability to apply concepts to explain physical events. Children who use the terms *atom* or *energy* may be thinking of something that has little or no connection with the atom or energy of science. These images may be pure fantasy. Millie Almy writes of the bright kindergarten child whose logic in explaining why objects adhere to a flannelboard was impeccable. He said that the covering of the flannelboard was rough and that the material on the back of the object that adhered to it was also rough and therefore the object stuck. However, when asked whether a piece of paper would also stick to the flannelboard, the child replied transductively that it would not because it was round, whereas the objects that stuck were not round.[4]

Conservation concepts

Conservation—a basic scientific concept

Piaget believes that children must attain a broad concept of conservation before they can attain formal, logical thought. *Conservation* may be defined as the awareness that many kinds of physical changes are reversible and that nothing is lost by these changes. By the age of seven to eight years, according to Piaget, children without being aware of it have accepted conservation of quantity (mass) and are confident that the amount of material in an object will remain constant, no matter how it is distorted. They are conservers of quantity because they have earlier mastered the complementary operations of reversibility and compensation. *Compensation* means that what is taken off from one place is neutralized by what is added at another place. Children of this age perform these operations mentally.

Difficulties in developing conservation concepts

In one experiment in an English elementary school, about one third of the seven to eight year olds were "conservers," and another third were in a transitional stage (that is, their judgments were inconsistent). This experiment replicated the experiment in which Piaget changed a plasticine clay "sausage." Two thirds of the eight to nine year olds, three quarters of the nine to ten year olds, and nearly all of the ten to eleven year olds were conservers. Yet with an alternately stretched and unstretched rubber band, a third of the nonconservers were consistent conservers. Some nonconservers conserved the quantity of liquid poured from one container into another of different shape. The kind of stimulus is obviously an important variable. The early experiences of children seemed to exert a significant effect on conservation judgments.[5] Children must compare a simultaneous change in *two* aspects of matter, and make *two* judgments to compensate for the changes they observe. They must also accept or invent the idea that matter is formed of particles that change position when an object is distorted. This is a sophisticated "atomic" hypothesis with which the concept of reversibility must be united.[6]

Conservation and familiar situations

Children act as conservers whenever the situation fits their mental models and can be explained by these models. They become nonconservers in situations that lack familiarity. They predict, for example, that there will be the "same amount to drink" when liquid from a low, wide glass is poured into a hidden glass. Only when they are shown that the hidden glass is tall and narrow and that the level of the liquid in this glass is higher than in the first glass do they change their prediction. Their model of liquid volume rests on the height of a liquid column, and when the situation changes, they become nonconservers.

In another experiment under Piaget's direction or inspiration, equal-sized lumps of sugar were dropped into identical glasses filled with the same quantity of water. The rise in the water level and the increase in weight of the solution were pointed out. The belief by young children that the sugar simply disappeared is a nonconservation concept. They expected that the level and weight of the water would somehow return to the original state and that its sweet taste would remain, unaccompanied by other physical attributes. Older children, however, were aware that the increase in level and weight was a necessary and "permanent" consequence. Their thought pattern appeared to depend on these ideas:

1. Smaller pieces of sugar are formed, but there are more pieces (compensation).
2. These pieces could be seen if their eyesight were sufficiently sharp.
3. These pieces can be reconstituted into their original shapes.[7]

*Weight conservation
after mass conservation*

Weight conservation develops later than conservation of mass. It is not until they are nine or ten years old that a large number of children can conserve weight. This point is shown in an experiment with two plasticine clay balls of different densities. The smaller ball, filled with lead, was obviously heavier. After the experimenter rolled the lighter ball into another shape, children were asked to compare the weights of the two objects. Only 4 percent of the seven to eight year olds were weight conservers; that is, they still believed that the rolled-out ball had the same weight. This percentage increased to 74 in the ten to eleven year olds. Many children who failed to conserve weight were able to think reversibly, however, because they remembered that the two balls were not equal in weight in the beginning. Kenneth Lovell suggests that reversibility of thought, although necessary for conserving, is not sufficient for its mastery.[8]

Conservers of weight in this experiment were not as successful in predicting weights when water froze or when a ball of clay hardened. Most conservers, however, predicted that butter would retain constant weight as it hardened—additional evidence that different situations with different perceptual and environmental stimuli are important variables affecting the thought processes of children.

*Acceleration of
conservation*

Other experimenters have compared the effect of stimulus–response training (including immediate feedback) with equilibration training on children in second and third grades. In these experiments children who participated in stimulus–response training were permitted to ask questions but perform none of the physical actions. Equilibration children were not allowed to ask questions or to have feedback, but they were permitted to handle and weigh the materials used. The experiments were otherwise quite similar to Jan Smedslund's. The stimulus–response group gained significantly more than did the equilibration children, who in turn gained more than the controls. After a few weeks, however, there was no significant difference between the two experimental groups in the ability to conserve weight.[9]

Relationship of weight and mass

It is justifiable to say that younger children do not conceive of weight as a function of the quantity of matter; that is, they do not visualize weight as a measurable property of matter that changes if the quantity of matter changes. (The physics of this statement is somewhat inaccurate.) Some children believe that squeezing a clay ball somehow changes its weight. The kinds of experience children have had seem to be important. Their success with butter is probably the result of many experiences with butter, such as buying it by weight, whereas few children who play with plasticine clay notice its weight. As Lovell says, "Until the child has learnt from experience that warming, cooling, squeezing, hardening, ageing, lengthening and so on do not alter the weight, he will not conserve weight in the widest sense."[10] It will be interesting to see what effect the experience of the astronauts will have on the phenomenon of weight conservation.

The influence of perceptual stimuli in judging weight is significant because the child thinks of weight as a downward push, and the push produced by the weight of a ball is greater than that of the same weight flattened out.[11] The internal, muscular sensation of concentrated push is disregarded only after many different weight–volume experiences reinforced by physically weighing many objects.

Volume conservation after weight conservation

Conservation of volume develops still later. Children younger than six years do not recognize conservation of volume, and even at ten or eleven years many children cannot predict that equal volumes of water are displaced by equal volumes of different shapes or what will happen when small and large displacers are lowered into water-filled jars. Many children expect a heavy object to displace more water than a light object of the same volume. They are confused by the location of the displacer or the shape of the container, or they sometimes think that a displacer at the middle of a container displaces less water than if it were at the top or bottom. These variables are irrelevant, but nonetheless, children must learn to sort them out and to discount them.[12] The difficulty that children have in holding all variables but one constant are seen in volume-conservation learning.

Theoretical models and conservation

The displacement-of-water experiment is confusing to children. In the usual experiment of this kind they are required to compare the volume of an object with the volume of water it displaced. The logical necessity that these two volumes be equal is not apparent to them. Their primitive "atomic" ideas may compound these difficulties if their "atoms" change size according to their position and the number of atoms that push on them. If children rely on this atomic model, they cannot give "correct" explanations.[13]

Acceleration of conservation again!

Many educators have discussed the possibility of accelerating the attainment of conservation. If this were possible, such important ideas as buoyancy and density could be taught before children are eleven or twelve years, the age at which buoyancy and density first seem to make sense. However, children have not achieved stable learning when this attempt has been made. For example, Smedslund tried to teach weight conservation to nonconservers by demonstrating light and heavy objects. These were of equal volume, but their weights were so markedly different that their size had no apparent relationship with their weight. Smedslund hoped to eliminate quantity as a determiner of weight, but he was unable to increase significantly the rate at which children became weight conservers. This result does not mean that acceleration is impossible but rather that it may take more time and planned experience than was given.[14]

In another experiment with five to seven year olds, Smedslund was somewhat more successful with weight conservation. He weighed objects on a balance and demonstrated that even when they were deformed, their weight was unchanged. Some children transferred this conservation to situations in which the objects were not weighed. At first sight these results appear to support acceleration of conservation.

It should be possible to erase a belief in conservation that is not the result of genuine maturational necessity, to see whether the children had truly acquired conservation of weight. Smedslund tried another experiment. Using a variety of plasticine shapes, he first presented two similar forms of equal weight to the children. He then changed one of these shapes and secretly removed a piece from it. The children were asked to compare the two forms, which were then weighed to reveal the inequality, and to explain the difference in weight.

None who had "learned" conservation in the earlier experiment believed that anything was wrong with the experiment, whereas half of these children, who were natural conservers, held fast to conservation of weight. The ones who shifted seemed to accept the weight change as a fact, explaining it by referring to different shapes: "rounder and fatter" or "bigger." The conservers asserted that clay must have been taken away or lost. Smedslund concluded that "conservation-learners" had really learned nothing more than "a relatively empirical law."[15] The preexperimental explanations by conservers and nonconservers were similar, and it was impossible to predict the later responses of children who gave preliminary explanations such as: "They [the objects] will weigh the same because they weighed the same in the beginning."[16] These words obviously did not mean the same thing to each child; it therefore follows that words alone are insufficient to assess understanding of conservation.

Kinetic molecular concepts

A kinetic molecular model

The formation of kinetic molecular concepts is of special interest to science teachers because so many scientific explanations are based on atoms in motion. In one interesting experiment with elementary school children, Ulrich found that they can profit from lessons on kinetic molecular theory. He presented several demonstrations of kinetic molecular phenomena to them in order to help them form a mental model of moving atoms or molecules and to become familiar with some of the variables. A day after the demonstration, Arthur Ulrich tested more than 400 children in grades three to six on why water evaporates. More than 40 percent of the third graders, 65 percent of the fifth graders, and 86 percent of the sixth graders achieved a mark of 70 percent or more. The experimenter concluded that these children had either known or quickly learned some of the elements of kinetic molecular theory, even though the lesson was given entirely as a lecture demonstration without discussion of any kind. These children successfully identified in a drawing the positions of molecules in a solid; they related heat to increased molecular motion; they explained that expansion of heated solids was the result of molecular motion; and they agreed that the three states of water were composed of the same kinds of molecules.[17]

Some objections

This experiment is open to the criticism that the children verbalized and lacked real comprehension. After all, by no stretch of the imagination had the demonstrations *proved* that water molecules are unaffected as water changes into gas. It *is* possible that the children merely repeated what they were told and were not conservers of molecular number. There was no evidence that they knew that the number of molecules in a given volume must remain constant, even when conditions of pressure and temperature change. This conservation principle is an important part of kinetic molecular theory.

In another study primary level children were taught kinetic molecular theory by a programmed teaching machine. A series of molecular drawings represented liquid, solid, or gaseous states, depending on the velocity of the molecules and their distance from one another. Each child sat through a number of twenty-minute, individually programmed lessons over a period of several weeks. Evaporation and condensation of water were explained as the result of the attraction of moving molecules for one another. The strength of this attraction was related to molecular velocity.

Following individual interviews with the children at the end of the formal instruction period the experimenters concluded that the behavior of most children changed as follows:

Another kinetic molecular model

[They gave] correct verbal responses to oral questions about molecular movement, which the controls could not. When facing problems during the instructional period, subjects were able to predict that a gas would tend to expand throughout the whole space available and to indicate that gases can be changed to liquids by reducing the speed of the molecules. In the formulation of the abstract concept of molecules, pupils discovered (a) identifying detail and (b) relations by which they classified a series of instances. For example, subjects were able to read and interpret symbolic diagrams by which they classified physical phenomena depicted for them. The finding is important in view of the belief that diagrammatic materials cannot be used to express science concepts to young children. . . . Differences with respect to the use of words by control and experimental subjects were also noted during post-test questioning, e.g.:

Question: "How does a balloon get big when you blow air into it?"
Answer: (control) " 'Cause it gets more air into it."
Answer: (experimental) " 'Cause lots of molecules are going into it."
Question: "How does the dew get on the grass?"
Answer: (control) "Smoggy in the night—little bits of rain come on the railing sometimes."
Answer: (experimental) "Water vapor in the sky falls down."[18]

Criticisms of the experiment

This experiment has been criticized vigorously on grounds that the children's explanations were animistic or magical expressed in a pseudoscientific vocabulary and because such concepts as molecules were not related to everyday objects in the first grader's life. The first item in the program of instruction was "Can you see water vapor in the air?" The child who answered No was told "Right! Of course not. . . . Molecules are too small to see." The critic wondered if children had had the opportunity to ask: "If molecules are so small that we cannot see them, how do we know that they exist?" He remarked that "it would seem reasonable to suppose that 'molecule' and 'fairies that trade dimes for baby teeth' mean about the same thing" to a six-year-old child. He also questioned some of the "correct" responses. For example, "molecular attraction" as an answer to the question "Why did a cold glass get wet?" is "not more scientific an answer than 'it perspires.' "[19]

Verbalisms!

The use of scientific words here is not equivalent to a scientific explanation. The productive scientist does not attach a stereotyped pattern of answers to a set of questions. On the contrary he is productive because of the kinds of questions he asks:

> It is important for the child to learn that science and scientific theory do not have all the answers. Perhaps behavior which approximates an experimental environment where the *child* must ask many questions and *do* many things to get *some* answers would be more appropriate.[20]

When do kinetic molecular models make sense?

Probably not until the third grade do kinetic molecular ideas become meaningful to children.[21] The influence of high intelligence in the mastery of kinetic molecular concept is shown in an excellent study by William Harris and Verlin Lee, who found that in a well-controlled, discovery-type series of lessons the bright fourth, fifth, and sixth grade children learned these concepts to an appropriate level of mastery, whereas those whose mental ages were less than eleven years were much less successful. Nearly all members of the experimental discovery group made a significantly greater gain than the members of the control group. The written tests were not the whole story, however, for children with lower mental ages "were able to express their understanding of science concepts more easily through oral and behavioral response than through responding to questions on the written test."[22]

Probability concepts

An important concept

If it were possible to rate scientific concepts according to their importance, the concept of probability would undoubtedly be one of the leaders. By *probability* the scientist means that "all knowledge of what we call the physical world is . . . spread out over a spectrum of probabilities with one end so highly probable that in our usual frame of mind we consider it as 'quite certain.' "[23] The idea that the only certainty is the certainty of chance is not easily grasped by children. Even in so apparently simple an action as measuring the length of a table with a ruler, the results under the best conditions are only estimates of the most probable length—for example, three feet, six and one-eighth inches plus or minus a sixteenth of an inch. Acceptance of the inevitability of chance in experience comes as a result of fundamental changes in the child's outlook.

Probability emerges in concrete operation stages

Piaget hypothesizes that the idea of chance emerges during the concrete-operation stage (ages seven to ten), when the need for things to happen begins to be separated from the probability that they will happen. In the presence of many possibilities, the child begins to distinguish between certainty, probability, and possibility. The higher thought processes, in which abstract and formal reasoning takes probability into account, come into being during adolescence. Only then are systematic combinations of the individual elements of environment arranged and their relative probabilities of involvement estimated.[24]

No "lawlessness"
without "law"

To identify events as the results of "chance," the child must first know events that are not the results of chance; that is, there must be some way for him to contrast *lawlessness* with *law, chaos* with *order*. John Flavell says, "A mind which knows no law can know no lawlessness." During the preoperational stage the child cannot differentiate between chance and nonchance, between order and disorder, between what is possible and what is necessary.[25] For him, nothing is logically certain or genuinely chance. As he enters the stage of concrete operations, the child discovers that he can only guess about the outcome of many events despite his best efforts. He also learns that he can make *reasonable* guesses about the outcome of many events because some outcomes are more likely to occur than are others. The concrete-operational youngster recognizes chance occurrences, but without the mental equipment of the adolescent he is unable to cope with them in a consistent, rational way.

Young children may
think probabilistically

This general outline of cognitive development as it leads to probabilistic thinking has generally been well accepted. Some investigators, however, argue that Piaget's tests depend on verbal skill, and therefore the existence of probabilistic thought in young children who recognize the effect of chance but are unable to express this awareness is disregarded. They point out that young children can anticipate other children will not always behave in the same way and their favorite toys will not always work properly.

To test the hypothesis that young children intuitively understand probability, Carolyn Davies conducted an experiment with children from three to nine years of age. She confronted these children with a mechanical device that would supply them with colored marbles if they could predict the sequence in which the marbles rolled out according to some sort of probability analysis.

Nonverbal
understanding

Older children were more successful with this nonverbal test than the three year olds were, yet even at this age 50 percent of the children selected the correct levers to press. Most five year olds responded correctly, although only a third were able to give oral predictions and to explain these predictions. By the age of seven virtually all the children expressed their explanations as probabilities. The experimenter concluded that nonverbal understanding of event probabilities arises before verbal statements.[26]

The effect of introducing probability-centered science experiences in the nursery and primary grades is not yet certain. It is reasonable to expect that this kind of enrichment will lead to earlier and better probabilistic thinking. Avoiding probability and chance experiences in the primary grades appears to be unwarranted because children seem to be able to assess event probabilities intuitively. Many new elementary science programs recognize this capacity and include several more or less structured experiences for the purpose of developing it further.

Earth science concepts

Some studies of children's scientific concepts have assumed that young children are too unsophisticated to distinguish between the possible and the impossible or imaginary. They assume that those concepts are naïve and useless in science instruction. Many investigators have demonstrated that this is not necessarily the case, however. For example, George Haupt questioned many children in an effort to learn what their concepts of the moon were. Some first graders, when asked about the size of the moon, replied, "as big as the town," "two inches around," "half a mile or a mile," and "big as the sun." A number said that the moon was "bigger than the world." Many made quite reasonable comparisons. Although most could not describe the moon's composition, several said it was made of "mountains." A number described it as "a great big boulder," "sand and rocks," "rock," and so forth.[27]

Moon concepts

William King asked more than a thousand children the question "What is the sky?" Ten percent gave answers that could be categorized as "fantasy." Thirteen percent answered "don't know." Six percent gave "false explanations"; 27 percent, "false descriptions." The remainder gave "true explanations" (12 percent) or "true descriptions" (32 percent). The percentage of explanatory answers increased with age, whereas the percentage of descriptive answers decreased.[28]

Sky concepts

Laura Yuckenberg studied the knowledge of first graders about the sun, its effects on earth, the causes of night and day, the moon, and gravity. She concluded that they were unable to visualize the immensity of the sun, but this task is difficult even for adults. Children compared the size of the sun to houses, to airplanes, to "ninety-one round pans you cook in." Although their conceptions of the sun's distance were also vague, they knew that it is far away. They also knew that it is hot but not that it is a star composed of incandescent gas. They were aware of some of its effects on the earth and were intuitively aware of its relationship to day and night. The following extract is typical of their answers:

Other astronomical concepts

Investigator: I wonder why we have night and day. Where was the sun when it
    was dark last night?
Answers: a. The sun turned off and the moon turned on.
          b. It's just sort of magic, the sun and moon move.
          c. The moon made the sun go into the clouds.

       d. The sun goes over to where the cowboys live when it is dark.

       e. When it is dark the sun is right on the other side of the world.

Investigator: Someone talked about gravity. What is gravity?

Answers: a. Gravity is plain dirt, only it is like a magnet.

       b. It is some kind of air that keeps everything on earth.

       c. It keeps us from going up into space.

       d. It's stuff that keeps you on the ground.

       e. If we didn't have gravity we'd never come back to earth.[29]

Many of the answers are thoughtful and pertinent. The children often gave genuine, although intuitive, explanations. In terms of their cognitive framework, their answers made sense. There is no reason to doubt that their interest increased as a result of the space explorations by the United States and the Soviet Union in recent years. Surely such children should not be denied the opportunity to learn more about astronomy when they are ready.

Mathematical botany concepts

The new insights that creative scientists bring to the emerging elementary curricula are illustrated by this account of botany instruction in the second grade:

An unusual experience

I must begin by teaching them the ordinary parts of a plant; the stems, the roots, leaves, and buds. After they have learned these, I call their attention to the fact that every leaf has a bud in the axil. This is called an "ordered" pair.

If you will look at a tree with ten or twenty thousand leaves on it you will find that every normal leaf has a bud in its axil. The leaf lies between the root and the bud, and the bud lies between the leaf and the tip. I asked the children to map that relation on a stick. All of them could do it. Thus they can map a concept on a stick. Then I call to their attention that the root precedes the leaf, precedes the bud, precedes the tip as you go up the stick to indicate an ordered formula. They had just been introduced to equations two weeks before. One little youngster said, "This is just like an equation." Of course, there are some differences, naturally, but none the less, it is a mathematical statement that they have become aware of.

Then we give them a notation to represent these things, *r* precedes *b*, precedes *t*. Next, we say "We want to use this little model, this little map you have made, to discover hidden knowledge." In the first exercise, we give them an ordinary willow stem about four inches long. We selected the stems so that they are just about as thick at one end as the other. We told them, "Place the sticks on your desk according to your model so that the base is on the desk and the tip is in the air." Two of them missed it; all of the rest of them got it and knew why they were right.

The next thing we gave them was an ordinary white potato and said, apply your formula now to the white potato and see what the potato tells you. The teacher was told she was not to ask them any questions except, "What else does the potato tell you?" The first question was, "Do you see anything that *True discovery* looks familiar?" One little girl said, "I think I see something that looks like a bud." A little boy said, "Oh, that's just an eye." He did us a very great service because he gave us a vocabulary to work with. Then a youngster frantically waved his hand and said, "If the eye of a potato is a bud, according to my model the eyebrow is a leaf scar." He was using his mathematical model to arrive at something that never occurred to him before. The next youngster said, "If the eye of the potato is a bud, and the eyebrow is a leaf scar, the potato must have a base and a tip." He made this deduction by being prodded only to see what else he could discover.

The teacher then said, "Place the potato before you on your desk so that the base is at your right hand, the tip on the left." There were 39 youngsters and 39 got it right. They could use this model in the second grade and reach effective answers.[30]

Here is concept learning linking mathematics and living things in a new and exciting way. The value of an experience model for predicting and verifying new observations and new relations is vividly illustrated. The twigs and potatoes are concrete objects, which contrast sharply with the molecules and atoms of many other concept-teaching experiments. This model, which organizes concepts of leaf, axil, bud, root, and tip in a serial order, led to the discovery of new knowledge by children so young that their success was completely unexpected. Direct experience with concrete materials seems to be absolutely necessary in forming models, but once the models are formed, they can be generalized to new situations. The previously described lesson is an example of guided inquiry teaching.

Some Problems with Concept Formation

Despite the hundreds of published research studies about scientific concept learning our knowledge about scientific concepts that are both meaningful to children and scientifically accurate is still somewhat fragmentary. The majority *Problems in teaching* of studies have been so narrow that their conclusions are not much help in the *concepts* classroom. However, data strongly support the belief that the ability of children to understand scientific concepts has been underestimated. The important questions for teachers are these: What levels of conceptual sophistication can we expect of children in the various grades? How much more abstract and generalized can a sixth grade concept be than a third grade concept? What kinds of experiences lead most efficiently to concept formation? For each series of concepts in the appropriate hierarchy of concepts, is there a corresponding experience sequence that is best? How should these sequences be organized to meet the needs of children who are so different in their preparation, intellectual ability, and motivation for learning? Even if second grade children are potentially able to understand what density means—and this ability is doubtful—is density so important a concept in science that excessive time should be devoted to it? Or should more easily grasped concepts be presented first, even though they are of lesser importance? The answers to these questions are not known, but there is good reason to believe that they are emerging from the intensive research in child development and learning now in process.

When should concepts be taught?

Summary

Concepts are ideas built from many facts. Because they are economical ways to summarize and abstract information, concepts are essential tools for both thinking and learning. Not only are they remembered much longer than the facts from which they are drawn but they can also be used without further reference to these facts.

There are many different kinds of science concepts that children should learn, such as conservation of length, mass, weight, and volume, density, kinetic molecular matter, and probability. It is important to realize that many different levels of meaning make up each of these concepts and that as children grow and learn, their understanding of these concepts should become broader *and* deeper.

Children pass through a series of conceptual stages, from direct, more or less unbranched thought to a complex, interrelated network of meanings. Most children at the age of five are nonconservers of quantity, weight, and volume; they are not able to think reversibly, nor can they compensate for weight and quantity changes. They begin to conserve quantity (mass) at the age of seven or eight; they conserve weight at the age of nine or ten; and they conserve volume at the age of eleven or twelve. Although short-term attempts to accelerate the acquisition of these concepts have not been promising, acceleration may be feasible given proper instruction and sufficient time.

For further study

1. Investigate a series of elementary science textbooks to learn the suggested grade level for the following concepts: density, velocity of light,

variability of living things, microbes and disease organisms, rocks and minerals. In your opinion are these suggested grade levels appropriate?

2. What are some reasons for the irrelevance of some of the research in educational psychology to classroom instruction?

3. Select a particular conceptual structure and trace its development through the age of adolescence.

4. Why is it important for children to develop functional concepts of conservation before they can understand many aspects of elementary school science?

5. Analyze a series of elementary science textbooks or one of the new elementary science programs to determine when and how probability concepts are introduced and developed.

Notes and references

1. Gagné, R. M., *The Conditions of Learning* (New York: Holt, Rinehart and Winston, 1965), p. 136. Italics his.

2. Butts, D. P., "The Degree to Which Children Conceptualize from Science Experiments," *Journal of Research in Science Teaching,* 1: 135–43, June 1963.

3. Hunt, J. McV., *Intelligence and Experience* (New York: The Ronald Press, 1961), p. 275.

4. Almy, M., "Wishful Thinking about Children's Thinking?", *Teachers College Record,* 62: 402, February 1961.

5. Lovell, K., *The Growth of Basic Mathematical and Scientific Concepts in Children* (New York: Philosophical Library, 1961), p. 63.

6. Wallach, M. A., "Development from Approximately the Third to the Eleventh Year," *Child Psychology,* Sixty-second Yearbook, Part I, National Society for the Study of Education (Chicago: University of Chicago Press, 1963), pp. 248–49.

7. *Ibid.,* p. 249.

8. Lovell, K., *op. cit.,* p. 71.

9. Stuck, G. B., and M. D. Wyne, "How Children Learn the Concept of Weight: S–R Training vs. Equilibration Training," *Science Education,* 373–78, October–December 1970.

10. Lovell, K., *op. cit.,* p. 73.

11. Wallach, M., "Development from Approximately the Third to the Eleventh Year," *op. cit.,* p. 250.

12. Lovell, K., *op. cit.,* p. 125.

13. Wallach, M., "Development from Approximately the Third to the Eleventh Year," *op. cit.,* p. 250.

14. Smedslund, J., "The Acquisition of Conservation of Substance and Weight in Children." III: "Extinction of Conservation of Weight Acquired 'Normally' and by Means of Empirical Controls on a Balance," in R. Anderson and D. P. Ausubel, eds., *Readings in the Psychology of Cognition* (New York: Holt, Rinehart and Winston, 1965), p. 605.

15. *Ibid.,* p. 605.

16. *Ibid.,* p. 605.

17. Ulrich, A. H., "A Comprehension Level Determination of a Basic Science Concept," *Science and Children,* 1: 12–13, April 1964.

18. McNeil, J., and E. Keislar, "An Experiment in Validating Objectives for the Curriculum in Elementary School Science," *Science Education,* 46: 155, March 1962.

19. Goldberg, S., "A Note Concerning Teaching Scientific Theory to First Grade Pupils by Auto-Instructional Device," *Harvard Educational Review,* 31: 452, Winter 1961.

20. *Ibid.,* p. 453.

21. Dennis, D. M., "The Introduction of Concepts in Kinetic Molecular Theory to Children," *Journal of Research in Science Teaching,* 4(2): 106–11, 1966.

22. Harris, W., and V. Lee, "Mental Age and Science Concepts — A Pilot Study," *Journal of Research in Science Teaching,* 4(4): 287, 1966.

23. Conant, J., *Science and Common Sense,* p. 161.

24. Flavell, J. H., *The Developmental Psychology of Jean Piaget* (Princeton, N.J.: D. Van Nostrand Co., 1963), p. 346.

25. *Ibid.,* p. 342.

26. Davies, C., "Development of the Probability Concept in Children," *Child Development,* 36: 779–88, 1965.

27. Haupt, G. W., "First Grade Concepts of the Moon," *Science Education,* 34: 226, October 1950.

28. King, W. H., "Studies of Children's Concepts and Interests," *British Journal of Educational Psychology,* 31: 1–20, 1961.

29. Yuckenberg, L. M., "Children's Understanding of Certain Concepts of Astronomy in the First Grade," *Science Education,* 46: 149, March 1962.

30. Mason, H. L., "Concepts in Biology," in R. E. Ripple and V. N. Rockcastle, eds., *Piaget Rediscovered,* (Ithaca, N.Y.: School of Education, Cornell University, 1964), pp. 125–27.

Elementary Science: Goals and Curricula

The Past Hundred Years

The Next Twenty Years

The Past Hundred Years

Overview

Science has been part of elementary school instruction for more than a hundred years, but for most of this time this kind of science was far different in philosophy, structure, and method from that described in Chapter 1. It was taught for many reasons: it would help children understand God's design for the world; it would prepare children for the world of work they would soon enter; and it would strengthen their reasoning ability. The elementary science programs of today have long since abandoned the first two goals. They have adopted the third, but not its original, naïve meaning. The new elementary science education (see discussion in Chapter 5) has taken the best aspects of traditional elementary school science and, in combination with modern conceptions of the nature of science and of the importance of scientific literacy for all citizens, has devised scientifically valid and psychologically meaningful science curricula and methods for elementary school children. Hence prospective elementary school teachers who have a historical understanding of the evolution of elementary science instruction will be better prepared to view in perspective the contemporary developments in elementary science education described in the remaining chapters of this book.

The Theological Goal

Science and religion

During the first half of the nineteenth century the most important reason for teaching elementary science was that science seemed to give a direct confrontation with the handiwork of the Lord. Through his vision of the order and rationality of God's world, which came from the study of science, the child achieved a deep and abiding understanding of God and God's purpose. From the clear evidence of God's purpose in the natural world, which was disclosed by science, children were to gain a proper ethical and moral sense. In the search for God's design, therefore, the child had to be introduced to his natural world—the environment right at hand in addition to the far-distant universe. This theological argument was perhaps more frequently proposed than any other in the long struggle to include the physical world in the narrow curriculum of the elementary schools. None of the proponents of science, however, rested their case solely on the claim that science instruction was indispensable in moral and ethical education.

The Utilitarian Goal

Vocational education

Educators often spoke of practical outcomes that appeared to be important. Surely, they said, the young boys who were destined to become farmers or mechanics would be superior farmers or mechanics once they had mastered the elementary principles of the pertinent sciences. This argument was often coupled with the statement that because technological change was so rapid traditional education could not meet the needs of the new society into which these boys would soon be thrust. This goal has survived in one form or another up to the present.

The Disciplinary Goal

Better thinking through science

Science instruction was also introduced because the content of the sciences was believed to be peculiarly suitable for training the mental faculties of perception and comparison in children. Faculty psychology, the doctrine of the serial development of individual mental abilities beginning with perception and comparison, guided educators during almost all of the nineteenth century. It was perfectly natural for Horace Mann to make this claim:

> The objects of nature are re-adapted to the development of the intellect. . . . The objects of natural history—descriptions of beasts, birds, fishes . . .— should form the subjects of the earliest intellectual lessons. A knowledge of these facts lays the foundation for a knowledge of the principles of sciences, which respectively grow out of them.[1]

This disciplinary or training function of science has been reincarnated in some of the newest curricula in elementary science, although the naïve assumption of individual powers or capacities has been abandoned along with the belief that young children are unable to reason. The role of the sciences in fostering a totality of intellectual skills is a noteworthy contribution of these new curricula (see Chapter 5 for a detailed analysis of these curricula).

Subsidiary Goals of Science Instruction

Two other arguments advanced in the nineteenth and early twentieth centuries for teaching science are worthy of mention. Because science, often equated with nature, was assumed to be close to the hearts of children, it seemed that children would learn science quickly. This belief is a doctrine of innate interest, whose functional value is questionable. In addition a "cultural" goal was frequently proposed. Because they assumed that the sciences were products of man's highest intellect, the proponents of science found it unthinkable that children could leave school without exposure to that thought.

The educated layman   No man, they argued, could be an effective citizen without that understanding of the facts and principles of the world around him which was (or should be) one of the measures of the educated layman.

The Reality

Despite these urgent appeals for the study of science in the common schools, science was not often taught. How, indeed, could it have been otherwise? The majority of schools, particularly those in rural areas, remained in session for only a few months, during which time instruction in reading, writing, and arithmetic necessarily took precedence. Graded schools existed only in the cities. The one- or two-room schoolhouse, inadequately heated and lacking even simple equipment, was characteristic of the schools in the nation. Scientific equipment, although readily available, was expensive and rarely purchased during these years, when such luxuries as blackboards, globes, and writing paper were scarcely commonplace. Many teachers had nothing more than a common school (elementary) education. In 1857, for example, fewer than 10 percent of the common school teachers in Massachusetts had attended a normal school; few were high school graduates. A mere handful had attended college, and this group was concentrated in Boston and in the other large cities of Massachusetts. If such was the professional education of teachers in the more populated centers, what could be expected of teachers in rural districts? Teachers who knew no science could not be expected to teach it. And, finally, teachers who did introduce science were unable to find appropriate texts or curriculum materials. In fact courses of study, with a few exceptions, date from William Torrey Harris' outline of 1871, which is described on page 149.

There were, to be sure, occasional reports of lessons in natural history or natural philosophy (physics and astronomy). In a few schools and in a few towns, science textbooks such as Thomas Hooker's *Books of Nature* were adopted, but they soon found their way to the closet. Science instruction for boys and girls of high school age *was* well accepted, and the common schools in towns without a high school frequently presented some of the sciences in the guise of "the higher branches." On the whole, however, before the Civil War the advocates of science had failed in their efforts to establish science in elementary school curricula.

Object Lessons

The Civil War decade witnessed a rapid growth in the number and influence of public high schools, and the small number of common schools that taught science abandoned the subject to the high schools. As the high schools took up the burden of the formal sciences, leading educators turned their attention to a promising new methodology, commonly called *Object Lessons,* as a natural mode of instruction in the lower grades. Object Lessons, vaguely derived from the precepts of the Swiss educator Johann Heinrich Pestalozzi, were the most widely publicized instructional method in the two decades following 1860.

Piagetian?

The psychological foundation of Object Lessons was the belief in the serial development of the mental faculties. The early years of childhood were to be spent in observing, perceiving, and memorizing. Children of grammar school age were believed to be capable of comparing and classifying; not until they reached the age of thirteen or fourteen were they permitted to infer, deduce, and generalize. With these assumptions the content selected for Object teaching is obvious. The primary grade teacher was expected to begin teaching with a suitable object (a rock, an orange, or a cube) and to lead the children by skillful questioning to report the color, shape, taste, weight, texture, and other physical features of the object. Much of this teaching turned out to be vocabulary drill, in which such technical terms as *amorphous, argillaceous,* and *excrescence* are typical.[2] With older children who had been "properly" trained in perception, the faculties of inference and generalization were to be developed by textbooks, charts, experiments, and, all too frequently, by verbalization. In Orra Underhill's words, "Although Object Teaching started out as a means of emphasizing the part played by experience in giving meaning to words, it degenerated into the worst form of verbalistic memorization."[3]

Object Lessons were originally a method drawn from all aspects of the environment to stimulate appropriate development of one or more of the mental faculties. Readily available materials, often of scientific interest, were selected for this purpose. For example, in the schools of Oswego, New York, which became internationally famous as a center of Object instruction, children from the ages of six to eight were carefully instructed in sorting and describing colored materials. Nine and ten year olds learned some of the scientific reasons for color phenomena and were taught to classify colors as primary or secondary. Henry Barnard witnessed one of the Oswego lessons on the chemical differences between acids and bases:

> A class of boys and girls were arranged . . . so that they could observe the vials of liquids and solids upon the table in the center. . . . The children were each given some cream of tartar to taste; they pronounced the taste *sour*. The name of the substance was written on the blackboard. Then they were given some sal soda to taste, and they said it tasted *bitter* and burning. The name of this was written on another part of the board. The teacher then told the children that we call those substances which taste sour *acids,* and wrote the word acids over cream of tartar. She then told them that the name for those substances which have a bitter, burning taste, is *alkalies*. This word was written over sal soda. Then the children were given some vinegar to taste.[4]

Unfortunately few schools were equipped with the necessary materials, and charts were frequently substituted for real objects. Teachers, unaware of the theoretical foundation of their lessons and untrained in the proper methodology, relied on "telling" to give information.

Object Lessons were never widely adopted by the schools despite the hundreds of laudatory articles that filled the educational press. The accepted methodology continued to be memorization and recitation from textbooks, and there were relatively few instances of even this unsound science teaching. The history of education is frequently distorted by the appearance of fads, which monopolize the literature. At first glance Object Lessons appear to have been successful. But investigation of actual classroom teaching reveals that this was not the case at all. A method or a curriculum is merely a collection of words and requires the active participation of teachers to make it educationally functional. Elementary school teachers were never convinced that Object teaching was worthy of their acceptance.

Because some of the most recent proposals for elementary school science are surprisingly reminiscent of much that the leaders of the Object teaching movement advocated a century ago, the preceding analysis is instructive.

A moral

These curriculum reforms, advocated by scientists and educators, are described in Chapter 5. Although history never repeats itself exactly, a cautionary insight into the collapse of Object Lessons may provide guidance for evaluating current schemes for solving the problems of teaching elementary science.

Verbalisms

One such problem has been described: The difficulty of providing a sufficient variety of objects forced teachers to depend on secondhand experience. In addition Object teaching called for unusual knowledge of the properties and characteristics of objects and an intuitive awareness of how best to guide children in incorporating the desired percepts into their thought structure. When all books are forbidden, uncommon skill in "oral" teaching is indispensable. Teachers who were inexperienced in this adventurous business relied on amazingly detailed, "step by step" manuals to generate what critics sarcastically called "mechanic drill." "Oral lessons," really lectures, inevitably replaced objects. In the words of one reporter, Object teaching was a "verbal drizzle at a small boy holding a dandelion."[5] For these reasons the Object Lesson idea never attained wide acceptance.

The Nature Study Movement

The pendulum swings

The inevitable revolt against Objects evoked the educational reform referred to as *Nature Study*. Beginning about 1884, Nature Study, in one guise or another, has remained in existence up to the present. The Nature Study movement is notable because, like Object Lessons, it became an educational fad, much discussed but relatively unsuccessful in infiltrating educational practice. Its spirit, full of Froebelian undertones of interest in and oneness with nature, was distinctly different from that of its predecessor. Liberty Hyde Bailey, one of the leaders in this dissenting science, explained its function:

> Nature-study is a revolt from the teaching of mere science in the elementary grades. In teaching-practice, the work and the methods of the two [science and Nature-study] intergrade . . . and as the high school and college are approached, Nature-study passes into science-teaching, or gives way to it; but the ideals are distinct—they should be contrasted rather than compared. Nature-study is not science. It is not facts. It is spirit. It is concerned with the child's outlook on the world.[6]

Numerous subspecies of Nature Study were advocated, some concentrating on the biological and earth sciences, whereas others included some physical science; but almost always there was the common denominator of stress on the biological. This stress was particularly noticeable in the courses for younger children. There were new overtones of emotion and sentimentality, which accompanied a massive insistence on the doctrine of interest. Many authorities were emphatic in their belief that children must be personally involved to achieve real understanding. They, therefore, continually stressed the importance of textbooks in arousing interest. In actual practice, however, children's interests seemed to be identified with those of the textbook writer or, on more or less hypothetical grounds, with nature, which was assumed to be "near and dear" to children.

An excellent Nature Study text

Undoubtedly no "typical" manual clearly defines Nature Study. Dozens of manuals and textbooks were published during the thirty-year period, approximately 1890–1920, in which Nature Study was so vigorously advocated. However, a book written by Lucy L. Wilson, who was an exceedingly well qualified author, is an excellent model to examine. This text, *Nature Study in Elementary Schools,* was reprinted at least nine times following its publication in 1897, and was adopted by many school systems. The four content areas of weather, plants, animals, and "stones," were arranged in a monthly sequence in the first four school grades. Calendar organization was common in Nature Study manuals. In September the autumn flowers, ferns, insects, weather phenomena, and weather records were recommended. In November the weather record continued along with an investigation of temperature, the sun and moon, falling leaves, buds, bulbs, fleshy roots, pigeons, cocoons, and the preparation of animals for winter. In March the weather record was maintained along with a study of buds, the food supply of seeds, earthworms, birds and bird migration, soil, mica, sand, clay, quartz, feldspar, and pebbles.

Detailed information for using the proper method was included along with the appropriate scientific background. Wilson took it for granted that her readers were scientifically unprepared: "The courses generally pursued in college and university do not necessarily equip the student for practical, everyday work with little children."[7] On this belief she left little to chance. Her prescription for effective teaching is still apropos. After forewarning teachers to prepare themselves by study of the factual content of her book, she encouraged them in these words:

Time, precious time . . .

Leisurely guide the child's observation, imagination, and reason to the most important truths with reference to the subject of the lesson . . . remember that the object is to lead the children to think. Their untrained minds cannot do this in an atmosphere of impatience, emphasis, and hurry . . . [the teacher] should not have anxiety to cover a definite ground.[8]

Wilson, who focused the attention of children on easily perceived characteristics, encouraged them to answer such questions of function as "How does the earthworm move?" She made no real attempt to elucidate principles; her emphasis was on the primacy of observation as the major source of factual information. She omitted physical science because she assumed that teachers were more interested and better prepared in the biological and the earth sciences and that firsthand experiences were more readily available in these sciences. In addition she believed that the kind of quantitative understanding demanded in the physical sciences was inappropriate for children.

An important characteristic of Nature Study as it evolved was the Herbartian principle of correlation with such studies as drawing, modeling, reading, writing, and music, which often resulted in ridiculously farfetched combinations. In actual classroom practice, however, teachers, lacking knowledge of science taught mechanically, remorselessly covering the textbook or manual. The visible outcomes of this kind of instruction were collections of leaves, rocks, insects, and twigs.

Nature Study, at its best, is still a significant force in the teaching of science. Unfortunately its potentialities for the education of children have seldom been fulfilled. Many men and women struggled valiantly to capitalize on the scientific value of Nature Study. Wilbur Jackman, one of these pioneers, wrote these provocative words when the misteaching of Nature had become evident:

> The spirit of nature-study requires that the pupils be intelligently directed in the study of their immediate environment in its relation to themselves; that there shall be, under the natural stimulus of the desire to know, a constant effort at a rational interpretation of the common things observed. . . . This plan . . . will lay a sound foundation for the expansive scientific study which gradually creates a world-picture, and at the same time enables the student, by means of the microscope, the dissecting knife, and the alembic, to penetrate intelligently into its minute details.[9]

Nature Study in the elementary schools failed to meet the expectations of its founders. Despite the assurances of Wilson and the other writers, teachers needed to know a great deal about nature and the study of nature. Even though the courses were arranged seasonally, the difficulty of obtaining materials was a perennial obstacle. Field trips, recognized for their educational value, were ignored because of administrative and methodological hazards. Perhaps the most effective hindrance lay in the silent resistance by the rank and file of classroom teachers and the vociferous opposition by high school and college teachers of science. One of the latter expressed his antagonism thus:

> High school teachers of science must protest against a mass of so-called nature study, more or less sentimental and worthless . . . and must not be content simply with treating lightly this farcical science teaching, or passing it by with silent contempt.[10]

Elementary Science

Big science writ small During the Nature Study period a different school of elementary science instruction also attained some prominence. At first, as a simplified version of high school science, this instruction was nothing more than textbook recitation, which systematically surveyed the sciences and was occasionally punctuated by an exciting demonstration. Hooker's *Child's Book of Nature* and David Wells' *Science of Common Things* were among the texts commonly selected for this purpose. These books transferred the organization of the sciences into the elementary curriculum. Like their more sophisticated prototypes, they gave priority to the practical values of scientific laws and principles.

In 1871 Harris, then superintendent of schools in St. Louis, published a science curriculum for the elementary grades, which tried to show how scientific ideas were interrelated. Although not the first published elementary science curriculum, it is notable for its attention to relationships. Harris, one of America's most influential educational philosophers, placed the sciences in a subordinate role to the humanities. He assumed that mastery of "the material world" could occur only after certain social and humanistic principles had been mastered. "It is more important," he said, "for man to know human nature than material nature. But it is not necessary for him to be ignorant of either."[11]

He expressed his curriculum outline in the concepts and structure of the formal sciences:

> The first year, lowest grade, in the schools began with lessons on the plant; the second year was taken up with animals, and especially the structure of the human body; while the third year initiated the pupil into the physical forces in various familiar applications, and made some progress in considering the geological and meteorological elements, such as earth, air, fire, and water. In the fourth, fifth, and sixth years, the course took a more practical turn.

While in the first three years, it had dealt chiefly with the rationale of the child's playthings and such phenomena as excited his astonishment, in the second course he was to learn to understand what is useful to man in these departments. In the sixth and seventh years the maturity of the pupil allows him to investigate with some degree of scientific interest and hence the more general form is adopted.[12]

Although he emphasized the factual nature of the sciences, Harris grouped these facts and principles according to their relationships. He resisted overemphasis on facts. He urged his teachers to show how principles were logically derived from simple facts and urged them to draw on the background of experience children possessed. Harris advised teachers to limit the number of concepts presented to avoid superficiality. To this end he devised a three-year teaching cycle to ensure depth of learning.

In the schools the Harris course of study suffered from the same sterility and rigidity that afflicted Object Lessons and later paralyzed Nature Study. There could be no real achievement because children were left to the verbalizations of the *Child's Book of Nature* or the other texts Harris suggested. The single hour per week Harris recommended was absurdly inadequate for the teaching of even one concept in depth.

Herbartian Influences

Gagneian?

The rise of Herbartian psychology shifted emphasis to the generation of intelligent social behavior as the child came to understand his environment. The goal of good citizenship superseded the goal of practical usefulness. Educators assumed that well-organized ideas meshed with the child's own knowledge best stimulated the child's interest. They believed that "correct" ideas in the "proper" sequence caused the desired behavior to occur. Unfortunately none of the Herbartians knew what these ideas were or how they could effectively be organized. As a result the texts and methods in elementary science remained essentially the same—a large body of facts that were recited and quickly forgotten.

The Big Ideas

Many other proposals for the improvement of elementary science curricula were publicized during these years of educational ferment. Space limitations permit discussion of only the few that are still significant.

Wilbur Jackman was particularly influential in building a solid foundation for the present program of science instruction. Jackman's elementary science curriculum sought to fuse an understanding of scientific concepts with a functional grasp of scientific methods. He made scientific generalizations — the "big ideas" — his organizational framework, although he did not always state these principles precisely. For example, he suggested that the concept of "energy acting through the atmosphere" should guide the study of the physical properties of air.[13]

Jackman stressed firsthand observation and experiment. His major work, *Nature Study for the Grammar Grades,* is a series of questions that direct observation, experimentation, and interpretation.[14] Although this book was not the first of its kind, its publication prompted the appearance of several manuals designed to achieve the same ends. None of these manuals was effective in changing educational practice, but their thesis continues to influence contemporary thought.

The Scientific Method

As a kind of counterpoint to these proposals, many scientists and educators argued that understanding of "the scientific method" should be the major goal of science instruction. This Baconian ideal was expressed by such notables as Herbert Spencer and Hermann Helmholtz, who commanded an international audience. Many men responsible for the education of teachers believed wholeheartedly in its value. The best learning, they said, comes from the application of "the scientific method" to the raw data supplied by experiment and observation. Therefore a scientific curriculum pervaded by "the scientific method" provided the best preparation for life. They recognized that rapid expansion of scientific knowledge effectively barred encyclopedic mastery and that obsolescence was an inevitable result of fact-centered instruction. It was self-evident to these men that children who mastered "the scientific method" simultaneously created their own path to continued learning.

In 1895 the National Education Association Committee of Fifteen asserted that science was indispensable in the elementary schools because mastery of the scientific method was a key to success in life. This attitude is quite different from the belief that the study of the sciences is the best training for the mental faculties. One criticism of Nature Study was that it deliberately suppressed the analytical approach of the sciences to inculcate moral and aesthetic values. Nature Study was an attempt to change children's values by confronting them with their world; science, on the other hand, enabled children to change that world.

The advocates of the scientific method indulged freely in the educational game of "claim and counterclaim," sometimes overstating their case in polemics as unscientific as those of the Nature faddists. In 1910, for example, John Dewey wrote:

> The future of our civilization, depends upon the widening spread and deepening hold of the scientific habit of mind . . . the problem of problems in our education is therefore to discover how to mature and make effective this scientific habit.[15]

As Chapter 1 points out, this conception of the scientific method was somewhat deceptive. Its validity, however, was unimportant because no concerted effort was made to develop children's ability to think scientifically. Proponents assumed that the mere presentation of scientific facts, accompanied by observation of the objects of nature and by experimental verification of scientific fact, was sufficient to develop the "scientific habit of mind." The growth of laboratory instruction in the secondary schools during the last three decades of the nineteenth century was almost entirely based on the belief that the path to mastery of the scientific method led directly through the laboratory. The realization that examining plant stems through the microscope and collecting oxygen from heated potassium chlorate are insufficient by themselves to foster problem-solving abilities is of recent origin.

Teacher Preparation

Oversimplified teaching of teachers

By 1890 a number of the normal schools that prepared elementary school teachers had incorporated into their curricula exercises in the scientific method. They relied on a strangely distorted version of the method of science, in which students were supplied with brief instructions to "do" something, then commanded to "observe," and finally to "infer" a cause for the observed phenomenon. The experience of one young normal school student, whose laboratory task one day was to examine a rusty piece of iron, aptly illustrates the technique. The observation that the brownish substance covering its surface was iron rust led her to infer that atmospheric oxygen "unites with iron and forms rust."[16]

This impossible extension of a single observation characterized the "method" manuals written for prospective teachers. Granted that oxygen is a component of the atmosphere, that it is an active chemical element, and that iron rusts when exposed to air, the conclusion that the union of iron and oxygen causes rusting is completely unwarranted. This inference is justifiable only after controlled experimentation has isolated the pertinent dependent and independent variables, after an analysis of rust has determined its chemical composition, and after there is experimental proof that the chemically combined oxygen in rust is of atmospheric origin. In the classroom this version of the scientific method failed because students somehow discovered the required information; not, of course, from their observations and experiments but from the references with which their manuals were so copiously sprinkled. In short the pleaders for the scientific method in the classroom were themselves almost absurdly guilty of violating their own philosophical beliefs.

Teachers who endeavored to teach the scientific method were hamstrung by the assumption that only experimentation and observation were necessary. Even though verification was the sole outcome, students were somehow expected to perfect their understanding of the scientific method. By some mystic osmosis they emerged from elementary science instruction purified, exalted, and scientifically select, ready to take their places in the new technological society.

The Heuristic Method

A pioneer science teacher

Fortunately not everyone who espoused the scientific method was so trusting. Henry E. Armstrong, a leading English chemist of the late nineteenth century and a crusader for science in the schools, was convinced that the recitation was an abomination. He proposed that children find out for themselves and devised a heuristic method for this purpose. This conception has recently reemerged as *inquiry* or *discovery*. Armstrong pictured the teacher as a guide, a planner of problems for children to investigate, an organizer of the proper conditions for the solution of these problems. He believed the heuristic method was nothing more or less than "placing students as far as possible in the attitude of the discoverer—[using] methods which involve their *finding out* instead of being merely told about things."[17]

This vision of the teacher's role was so different that Armstrong was belabored as a mystic who, by laying out impossible and unimportant tasks for children, was impeding science in the schools. The notion that children were able to plan their own mode of attack on problems was inadmissible in both England and the United States. It was axiomatic that children, because they were children, could learn only with the most rigid direction.

Not only did Armstrong insist that children should be unaware of the outcome of their experiment, he was also convinced that each child should be a detective, hunting down the clues (the hunt itself serving as motive), sifting them, and eventually coming to a conclusion of his own. (Bruner's insistence on the importance of shifting from extrinsic to intrinsic motivation is a modern statement of this provocative idea.) Perhaps because of his own superlative scientific talents, Armstrong erred by giving too little help and by complicating the problems children encountered with technical difficulties. He was, however, well aware that the laboratory alone could not develop the traits of thinking and the attitudes he prized; free discussion and informative lectures were also required. He fully realized that children could not possibly rediscover all scientific knowledge and that they must learn much of science in other ways. Nevertheless he continued to insist on the heuristic approach:

> The facts must always be so presented . . . that the process by which results are obtained is made sufficiently clear as well as the methods by which any conclusions based on the facts are deduced. And before any didactic teaching is entered upon to any considerable extent, a thorough course of heuristic training must have been arrived at and the power of using it acquired; scientific habits of mind, scientific ways of working, must become ingrained habits from which it is impossible to escape. And as a necessary corollary, subjects must be taught in such an order that those which can be treated heuristically shall be mainly attended to in the first instance.[18]

He described his methodology of teaching young children thus:

> As soon as they can write, children will be required themselves to make out lists of the things they have collected, and as they systematically study these, to note down their origin, colour, and other properties obvious to them. And then they will go on to make experiments to ascertain properties which are not quite obvious. For example, they will be provided with a simple anvil . . . and with the aid of this, will find out that metals are more or less soft and may be bent and beaten out; that other substances are hard and brittle. . . . Then by measuring and weighing regularly shaped blocks, slabs, or plates of wood, stone or metal, the differences in density of different stuffs will be discovered. . . . Each day let some simple task be set; insist that this be carried out with scrupulous care and equally carefully be recorded in a very few lines of clear simple language.[19]

The Teaching of Scientific Method and Other Papers is profitable reading today. Much of what Armstrong asserted then is fully supported by modern theory in science education. The emphasis on individual activity, self-motivation, and genuine research is noteworthy. Armstrong was truly farseeing. He made no impression in the United States and hardly more than a disturbance in England, but the fresh note he struck in the education of children has magically survived as a summons to reform of elementary science teaching today.

A Study in Futility

Still no science teaching

The reams of printed courses of study, textbooks, manuals, and periodical pages that poured from the presses during the nineteenth and early twentieth centuries may not have been wasted, but they were futile. The national debate that compared Elementary Science with Nature Study (the names were often interchangeable) was a battle of ill winds with no anchor to reality. Neither program was functional. Teachers continued to teach what they had been taught—arithmetic, geography, reading, and writing—by the time-honored, although universally detested, recitation and drill. Undoubtedly those teachers who were devoted professionals and who were idealistically aware of their responsibilities, capitalized on the Froebelian and Herbartian themes of the nature of the child, interest, apperceptive mass, and correlation. But few teachers broadened the study of "fundamentals" to include the sciences, and fewer still taught science in accord with the best ideas of their times.

Commentators attributed this scientific vacuum to the lack of interest in science by teachers who characteristically knew little science and who were therefore fearful and insecure. Little or no equipment for teaching experimental science existed in the schools. True, there were some excellent manuals, which required the simplest home-made equipment, but they seem to have been almost unused. Even Nature Study, which required nothing more than some specimens from outdoors or as little as a clear view of the sky, was as likely to be neglected as were the physical sciences.

Revival of Elementary Science

Nature Study continued to dominate elementary school science curricula well into the twentieth century. It faded from the scene only when a new generation of dedicated reformers came to positions of national influence.

Such men as Samuel Powers and Gerald S. Craig at Teachers College, Columbia University, fought to revive Elementary Science, which to them was a systematic, conceptually organized, integrated program, embracing all aspects of physical, earth, and biological science. Their missionary zeal was so effective that by 1940 it was difficult to locate a school system in which Nature Study was said to be taught.

Craig's work is the major source for the structure of contemporary elementary science programs. In 1927 he published the single most influential research in elementary science curriculum construction. He analyzed hundreds of textbooks, courses of study, and journal articles to derive a long list of important scientific ideas. Each idea was rated by a panel of educated laymen for its importance to children. Craig's principal criterion for rating was that each idea must be sufficiently powerful, when understood, to modify both thought patterns of children and thought in other fields of knowledge.[20] These ratings were then compared with the frequency with which the same principles appeared in thousands of children's questions Craig had systematically collected. From these data he proposed a large number of generalizations, laws, principles, and concepts as the core of the elementary science curriculum.

Inspiration of elementary science textbooks

It is interesting to note that few of the ideas adults thought to be important were represented in any substantial way by children's reported interests. Indeed the role of scientific knowledge in maintaining health, a principle that headed the laymen's list, ranked forty-ninth in the children's list of fifty. Adults were obviously motivated by the social usefulness of scientific concepts and by the constructs of science. Children, on the other hand, were predominantly environment-oriented.

Grade placement of science principles

Many lists of principles have since been published, some of which place these principles at specific grade levels. But because placement has been more or less arbitrary, it has also been unsuccessful. There is no agreement on the proper age at which to introduce such important principles as "The earth is very old," or "Green plants make food by means of the process of photosynthesis." A cursory study of textbooks and courses of study quickly reveals how confusing and confused is the assignment of principles by age. And little improvement is likely in the near future, although research on cognitive structure and the intellectual maturation of children will eventually provide a sound foundation for placement.

In 1932 Craig published a series of graded elementary textbooks that embodied his research. This series, the direct ancestor of the many series now available, was structured on a framework of empirically distributed principles. Craig tried to provide a continuous and integrated curriculum by means of cyclical framework and by interrelated content units. Unfortunately few teachers were able to use these books as Craig intended, in part because of text limitations, in part because science teaching requires superior teacher training and experience. Indeed the many problems Craig attempted to surmount several decades ago are still very much in evidence.

The Thirty-first Yearbook

"Big ideas" again

In 1932 a committee of prominent science educators provided in the thirty-first yearbook of the National Society for the Study of Education an authoritative restatement of Craig's curricular research. Their reaffirmation of the potential of the "big idea" was instrumental in its adoption by prominent text-book and curriculum writers. Their point of view was that desirable "life enrichment" arose from the "functional" understanding of scientific principles. The committee defined *functional* as the capacity of the child to associate his own relevant experience with these principles and to apply them to new but related experience.[21] Curriculum, therefore, consisted of the relevant readings, experiments, demonstrations, and other activities that jointly created "functional" understanding.

In essence these curriculum reformers were striving to incorporate the same "structure of science" that still excites educators today. The centering of curriculum on principles presumably decompartmentalized the traditional distinctions between the sciences because the selected principles were universal in their scope. A generalization such as "The environment acts upon living things, and living things upon the environment" impinges deeply on the chemical, physical, and earth sciences.

Generalizations were memorized

In the classroom, however, the study of generalizations for their own sake converted a well-planned and potentially valuable design into a travesty. Many teachers never clearly understood the power of scientific principles to explain a complex nature, to predict physical phenomena, and to affect social life. The principles approach has failed to produce any substantial agreement in the organization of curriculum materials. Many texts and courses of study are arbitrarily divided into units with such titles as "The Earth's Changing Surface," "Life in the Past," "Machines," and "Aviation." In accord with sound practice the content of these units is drawn from environmental phenomena explained by the relevant principles. Unfortunately the units are often trivial, and, notwithstanding the implied integration of the unit organization, their study emphasizes the assimilation of facts.

Some texts, particularly those prepared for younger children, resort to much narrower centers of interest, such as grasshoppers, eggs, and trees. The

Overemphasis on biological science

dependence on Nature Study is evident. Indeed, there is still an overemphasis on descriptive biology, which is only partly overcome by the incorporation of physical science in the intermediate grades. The idea that children comprehend biological events and their associated concepts more easily than they do the principles of the physical sciences is unsupported by the available evidence. However, the same rationalizations proposed for the dominant role of biology in Nature Study are clearly evident in elementary science today.

A Modern Textbook

Analysis of a leading textbook series best illustrates the content and organization of such elementary science programs.[22] This series is impressively organized, and its potential for improving the quality of science teaching is obvious. Its ten areas include all the sciences; each area, with a few exceptions, is taught in every grade with varying emphasis from grade to grade.

Major areas

1. Health and Nutrition
2. Living Things
3. Conservation, Balance of Nature
4. Rocks and Soil
5. Atmosphere and Weather
6. Chemical and Physical Change
7. Motion, Mechanics, and Technology
8. Electricity, Magnetism, and Gravity
9. Energy from the Sun
10. Earth and Sky

Three areas are mainly biological, three are drawn from the earth sciences, and four are drawn from the physical sciences. A carefully planned repetition of scientific terms, concepts, and principles supplies an integrating mechanism. As an illustration of this planning, Book 3 presents such concepts as air pressure, atmospheric change in volume resulting from temperature change, condensation of water vapor, sound waves in air, and the oxygen content of the atmosphere. Book 4 adds the concepts of physical change, states of matter, melting point, evaporation, and freezing point. Book 5 describes the gaseous composition of the atmosphere, convection currents, and changes in the rate of evaporation of liquids.

The content of the "Chemical and Physical Change" area reiterates and strengthens these concepts by introducing them in different contexts. For example, Book 2 begins the study of the thermometer and of temperature change. This study is followed in Book 4 by abstract notions of states of matter, molecular motion, atomic and molecular structure, physical change, the role of oxygen in combustion, and chemical change.

The texts are copiously illustrated with challenging pictures intimately coupled with the written matter. The authors have earnestly tried to translate the goals of science education into practicable, achievable activities. They transcend the presentation of subject matter for its own sake by including many exercises that stimulate the child's creative imagination and enlarge his capacity to examine ideas critically. Their questions, more often than not, cannot be answered by mere repetition of the printed word. The authors strive to guide children to grow in understanding the structure of science by coordinating fact with concept and by raising questions that may be answered only when the unifying concepts have been mastered. Their *Teacher's Guide* is a minutely detailed source book for effective exploitation of the textbook. This series will undoubtedly enrich science teaching in the hands of the conventionally trained teacher.

Many other textbook series are similarly patterned. They are written for the elementary schools by experienced science educators and classroom teachers and, in their own terms, are truly on a high level. They share, however, in the weakness of curriculum rigidity. The design of science curricula depends to a large extent on informed opinion because valid research with children, which alone can provide the proper psychological foundation, is not yet sufficient itself. Although there is substantial research on the thought processes of children and on their cognitive growth, much of this research has not yet been translated into a serviceable guide for the grade placement of scientific concepts and principles.

The Rigid Curriculum and the Textbook

The dilemma that accompanies the rigid curriculum is not easily escaped. The mobility of contemporary American life assembles children of widely different intelligence, experience, and ability in the classroom. Curriculum planning, no matter how finished in principle, is ineffective in coping with these differences. Every teacher expects a number of pupils to be inferior readers, for example—a circumstance that creates difficulties because of the customary reliance on textbooks in science teaching. Children moving to a different school district may unjustifiably be penalized because the schools from which they came used a different series of textbooks. Consequently few children at any *one* grade level have a common background in science.

K–12 curriculum planning

Unless the system of education in the United States becomes highly centralized and therefore standardized, this quagmire of diversity will continue to plague us. For this reason, if for no other, the national and regional curriculum planning represented by textbook series and by courses of study cannot function effectively. The detailed kindergarten to twelfth grade program of science instruction, which is so widely advocated, can only operate efficiently in a society vastly different from our own. The textbook, by its very existence, tends to nullify operational understanding of the process of science because it treats science as a body of knowledge despite the efforts of its authors. In the hands of the unwary teacher the textbook becomes a series of reading lessons in which the illustrations take the place of firsthand experience.

Verification is not searching

Another related weakness of some texts for new science education arises from their dogmatic presentation of firsthand experience. Their activities are written to prove a statement in the book. For example, children may be directed to perform a minutely detailed experiment to verify the generalization that "heat causes metals to expand." The illustration that accompanies the directions all too often provides the answer so that children lose the opportunity to find out for themselves. Children undoubtedly enjoy this experience, but its educational value is questionable. Textbooks rarely provide situations that lead naturally into cooperative planning or give the teacher the opportunity to evaluate growth in ability to propose hypotheses, gather data, measure, compare, infer, and generalize.

Certainly, textbooks and their variants are not *all* bad. Good texts, such as the series previously described, can be used intelligently and effectively by teachers who are aware of the weaknesses described previously. There is, however, justifiable doubt about the extent of true learning of scientific principles that comes with text-based teaching, just as there is little reason to assume that many textbooks promote understanding of the scientific process. A sound case, however, may be made for increased reliance on authoritative presentation of facts and explanations as children grow in ability to think formally, as they are better able to deal with multiple variables on a semi-abstract level, and as their knowledge of the world expands.[23]

Economy of time and thought is a sufficient reason for deriving a large part of secondary school science learning from expert sources. The situation is quite different in the elementary school. This is the time for children who are intensely curious, and for whom vocational preparation and the content of the individual disciplines are of little concern, to approach science as inquirers, as discoverers. The tasks of finding out what, why, when, and how, without insisting on the memorization of facts and generalizations, are in themselves worthy goals for these children.

At best, a textbook is a tool; no text, despite the excellence of its accompanying teacher's manual, can achieve its postulated aims unless teachers are sympathetic to these aims and determined to achieve them. In practice, therefore, textbooks are often stultifying, limiting, and inflexible.

The Unit Book

In an effort to minimize dependence on a textbook, schools frequently provide multiple copies of several different texts in each classroom. Used in this way, books become a resource from which teachers and students may extract pertinent information. This approach is useful if instruction is focused on problems arising from cooperative teacher–pupil planning. Unfortunately textbooks are rarely complete enough to supply information in depth or to direct children to the proper sources. Such questions as "If the Earth has gravity, why doesn't the Moon fall?" or "How do we know that everything is made up of molecules?" are likely to be unanswered in the text because it is not the function of the text to anticipate such questions. Texts are not designed as scientific compendiums but rather to supply a carefully selected minimum core of scientific facts and principles for classroom instruction.

Textbooks cannot supply answers to questions

Publishers who recognize the inherent inflexibility of the textbook have prepared paperbound "resource" pamphlets that treat individually and in depth such topics as weather, animals, the planets, and machines. Some publishers bind each textbook unit separately so that a selection of appropriate units may be made. The obvious methodological advantages are balanced by these disadvantages. Multiple copies of these unit books are more expensive than a single set of books; they are also less resistant to normal wear and tear. But, in addition, if a unit book purposefully integrates concepts first presented in another volume, the difficulty of learning is inevitably increased because these concepts are assumed to be part of the learner's experience. In an attempt to avoid this outcome, short recapitulations of important ideas are often provided either at the beginning of the unit book or at strategic intervals.

Unit book problems

These summaries merely reemphasize the devotion of textbooks to the "rhetoric of conclusion." A two-hundred–word explanation of the electronic structure of the atom interpolated into a unit on static electricity is a conceptual roadblock of some magnitude.

The growth of genuine understanding of static electricity, or of any other complex phenomenon, is time-consuming and unlikely to be stimulated by brief outlines. Surely even the traditional model of atomic structure deserves a better fate than its acceptance as dogma. Ought not children to have the opportunity to become familiar with scientific models and the justification for accepting this particular atomic model? Is it not possible for intermediate grade children to discover by experiment, demonstration, animated film, and inductive reasoning why scientists propose such conceptual schemes? Only youngsters who are fortunate enough to experience this kind of teaching will profit from the two-hundred–word summary of atomic structure. A summary of atomic structure then makes a meaningful contribution to the unit on static electricity.

The Fact-centered Curriculum

All too often students must study the textbook from beginning to end; the children participate actively in all the demonstrations and experiences suggested, but the outcome is "almost entirely in facts rather than process. . . . The purpose of these experiments . . . is always to prove a fact, which is *not* the point of scientific inquiry."[24] Martin Mayer astringently summarizes this fact-dominated curriculum:

Strong criticism of fact-dominated curriculum

Throughout their school career, children prove that beans grow higher in fertilized soil than in unfertilized soil, that a metal police badge placed between the poles of a switch will make an electric bell ring while a plastic police badge will not, that a piece of lead falls to the bottom of a glass of water while a piece of wood floats on top, that mercury rises in a thermometer when the bulb is heated. Once the fact is proved, school science is through with it, and unless the child has the luck of an extraordinary teacher he cannot learn in school that a fact is merely a beginning, that there are always questions of causation, of condition, of verification, of prediction by analogy. School science simply presents a hypothesis and a recipe for an experiment which will "prove" it, and then the books are closed and we can all move on to something else, thank God. It is hard to find the right word for this procedure; "fraud" seems too strong because it implies intent, and everyone's intentions are honest. But its results are decidedly fraudulent.[25]

It is not unusual to find a description of controlled experiments; but it is novel to discover suggestions by which such experiments may be carried out or outlines of multiple probes by which to obtain valid, generalizable data. Explanations of the kind described in Chapter 1 are almost never encountered. The implications of experimentation, the limitations of knowledge, and the tentative nature of much that we know are ignored. Is it any wonder that the "cultivation of inquiring minds," so eloquently described by Laura Zirbes, is still only a rhetorical phrase?[26]

The Interest-centered Curriculum

Science has often been taught incidentally. In incidental teaching the immediate interests of the class generate content. For example, the resourceful teacher is quick to draw upon a butterfly brought into class, either as subject matter for a brief lesson on butterflies or as a point of departure for a comprehensive unit on insect life. Such teaching, however, is fraught with complexities of commission and omission. Significant areas of science are often overlooked, or, on the other hand, overtaught. The major problem arising from this narrow environmental approach is that the potential for a valuable learning experience is insufficiently realized because time for planning and preparation is unavailable. The mere exhibition of the butterfly, with perhaps a hasty glance at its parts and a statement that the butterfly is an insect with complete metamorphosis, cheats both children and teacher. The opportunity to learn how the butterfly is adapted to its ecological niche and how scientists study butterflies is never seized. Our indictment is perhaps unfair, but teaching of this kind has not been uncommon.

Curricula structured around the expressed interests of children are unsound because these interests are notoriously unstable. It may be laboring the point to remind the reader that children tend to be interested in those aspects of science that they know or that are sufficiently bizarre or unusual to be inherently fascinating. Children's lively curiosity about the life history of prehistoric animals is a case in point. Few girls, on the other hand, are anxious to know about machines, familiar or unfamiliar, nor are they ordinarily concerned with the scientific principles that explain how they work. Interest, of itself, is too weak a prop for the science curriculum, although the master teacher is astutely successful both in capitalizing on interest and in arousing interest in unfamiliar phenomena. Methodology and content do not create a master teacher of science; the master teacher reshapes and reconstructs methodology, content, and interest to suit his own educational purposes and strengths.

Summary

The teaching of science in the elementary schools has had a long and exciting evolution. Its early proponents argued that science was peculiarly suitable for achieving the theological, utilitarian, and disciplinary goals of nineteenth century education. Before the end of the nineteenth century, however, these goals had shifted to mastery of "the scientific method" and appreciation of "nature."

The purposes underlying contemporary science education include competence in problem solving, which is closely related to the scientific method of earlier years, as well as understanding of certain important generalizations that can change the learner's behavior patterns. In keeping with this progression of educational purpose, educators have moved from one curricular panacea to another. The dependence on textbook recitation a century ago was converted to the verbal drizzle of Object Lessons, which, in turn, succumbed to the emotional blandishments of Nature Study. A dissident group of educators argued vigorously for a structure that prepared children to think scientifically.

During the 1930s the "big ideas" of the sciences emerged as the dominant content and methodology of contemporary elementary science. However, this relatively inflexible curriculum is now changing to an inquiry-centered methodology in which process is more important than product.

Despite the almost kaleidoscopic fluctuations that mark the evolution of elementary science, actual classroom instruction in science has been relatively rare. When taught, science has almost always been in the form of textbook recitation. The educational propaganda of each era seems to exert a negligible effect in the classroom. The centrality of the textbook is almost as pervasive today, when science is accepted in many elementary classrooms, as it was in the poverty-stricken one-room schools of our distant past.

It is unwise to disregard the potential of curriculum guides, syllabi, textbooks, and manuals as instruments for effective teaching of elementary science. Their time-tested activities ease the struggles of the eager, conscientious teacher, who looks to them for suggestions instead of prescriptions. In accord with the philosophy of this book we recommend that teachers use commercially published texts as sources of data and explanations that are otherwise unobtainable from either firsthand experience or other vicarious means. Unfortunately few textbooks meet these criteria, and therefore, inquiry-centered instruction is unlikely to flourish when tied to texts. Textbooks are conservative perhaps because of their users. The routine, the security of knowing exactly what materials are required and what answers are expected, may make for heavy sales, but it also inhibits the exciting investigation of the world of science.

For further study

1. Contrast the aims of elementary school science one hundred years ago with those of contemporary elementary science education.

2. How have elementary science objectives changed because of changing conceptions of the child, society, and technology?

3. How has the goal of mental discipline been transmuted in modern education?

4. Contrast the purposes and outcomes of Nature Study, Object Lessons, and the early Elementary Science movement.

5. What reasons can you suggest for advocating the scientific method as the mode of teaching elementary school science? Is belief in the scientific method justifiable as a way of analyzing the world?

6. How does Armstrong's heuristic method differ from other proposals for teaching elementary science?

7. Examine a series of contemporary elementary science textbooks to discover the extent of their dependence on Craig's curriculum proposals of 1932.

8. Trace the evolution of curriculum ideas in the National Society for the Study of Education yearbooks of 1932, Part I; 1947, Part I; and 1959, Part I.

9. Write a critique of an elementary science textbook series that deals with its adequacy for meeting the demands of contemporary science instruction.

10. Are the authors justified in their comments about the relationship between textbooks and the rigid curriculum?

11. What are the alternatives to a curriculum that is centered on the textbook?

Notes and references

1. Mann, H., *Annual Report of the Secretary of the Massachusetts State Board of Education*, 1840, p. 73.

2. Underhill, O. E., *The Origins and Development of Elementary School Science* (Chicago: Scott, Foresman, 1941), p. 86.

3. *Ibid.*, p. 86.

4. Barnard, H., *Pestalozzi and His Educational System* (New York: Bardeen, 1854), p. 415.

5. *National Journal of Education,* 12: 185, 1880.

6. Bailey, L. H., *The Nature Study Idea* (New York: Doubleday & Co., 1903), pp. 4–5.

7. Wilson, L. L., *Nature Study in Elementary Schools* (New York: Macmillan Co., 1897), p. 2.

8. *Ibid.,* p. 5.

9. Jackman, W. S., *Nature Study,* The Third Yearbook of the National Society for the Study of Education, Part II (Chicago: University of Chicago Press, 1904), p. 9.

10. Brownell, H., "Science Teaching Preparatory for the High School," *School Science and Mathematics,* 2: 253, November 1902.

11. Harris, W. T., *Fifteenth Annual Report of the St. Louis Public Schools,* 1867–1869, p. 111.

12. _____, *Seventeenth Annual Report of the St. Louis Public Schools,* 1870–1871, pp. 174–75.

13. Jackman, W. S., *op. cit.,* p. 189.

14. _____, *Nature Study for the Grammar Grades* (New York: Macmillan Co., 1899).

15. Dewey, J., "Science as Subject-Matter and as Method," *Science,* 31: 127, January 28, 1910.

16. Dean, G. F., *Manuscript Chemistry Notebook* (Bridgewater State Normal School, 1884), p. 394.

17. Armstrong, H. E., *Teaching Scientific Method and Other Papers on Education* (London: Macmillan Co., 1913), p. 236.

18. *Ibid.,* p. 255.

19. *Ibid.,* p. 262.

20. Craig, G. S., *Certain Techniques Used in Developing a Course of Study in Science for the Horace Mann Elementary School,* Teachers College Contributions to Education, No. 236 (New York: Teachers College, Columbia University, 1927), p. 12.

21. *A Program for Teaching Science,* Thirty-first Yearbook of the National Society for the Study of Education, Part I (Bloomington: Public School Publishing Co., 1932), pp. 42–43.

22. Jacobson, W. J., C. Lauby, and R. D. Konicek, *Thinking Ahead in Science,* Vols. 1–6 (New York: American Book Co., 1965).

23. Ausubel, D. P., *The Psychology of Meaningful Verbal Learning* (New York: Grune & Stratton, 1963), chap. 2.

24. Mayer, M., *The Schools* (New York: Harper & Row, 1961), p. 223.

25. *Ibid.*, p. 224.

26. Zirbes, L., *Spurs to Creative Teaching* (New York: G. P. Putnam's, 1959), p. 238.

The Next Twenty Years

Overview

The direction of elementary science teaching in the next twenty years will undoubtedly be toward achieving more child-centered goals than those of the past. Because of the increasing role of process-centered science teaching, much of what has traditionally been accepted as a proper and essential kind of science will no longer be in harmony with this new goal. Therefore science teachers should be fully aware of what is meant by process-centered science and why this new focus (although with a long and honorable historical parentage) is necessary. Because goals give both teachers and children focus, direction, and a functional evaluational base, teachers must analyze, criticize, and either accept or reject these goals through conscious and deliberate intellectual action.

The goals of elementary science instruction described in this section are in keeping with this newer science. Despite their special relevance to evaluation, performance (behavioral) objectives are discussed because they give specific direction to teaching and because several of the new science programs discussed in Chapter 5 rely extensively on them. The reasons for accepting certain educational goals, such as the "cultivation of the inquiring mind," are considered in some detail together with a description of the consequence for science curricula, which must follow if these goals are accepted.

Goals and New Directions

The "inquiring mind"

Of the goals of science education mentioned in the first section of this chapter and in Chapter 1, the "cultivation of the inquiring mind" is given precedence. Science is one of the few branches of knowledge whose wealth of phenomena is open to direct observation, to the test of experiment and logic — invaluable operations in developing scientific thought.

In science teaching the phrase *inquiring mind* refers to the predisposition to find out what makes things happen. The inquirer is critical, reluctant to accept an *a priori* explanation, whether authoritative, without applying to it the tests of experience, experiment, and reason. The inquiring child is not content with the answers of the textbook and the teacher; he is not ready to accept what he sees around him without question.

One of the functions of elementary science is to help children to recognize a hypothesis, to discover its strengths and weaknesses and its implicit and explicit assumptions. The teacher should not be concerned with teaching the distance of the planet Mars from the Earth and the law that the strength of a magnetic field decreases inversely with the square of the distance from the magnet. Instead the teacher should try to teach how scientists have learned the distance of Mars and the application of the inverse square law. Throughout their school years children should grow in ability to recognize whether a statement is based on good evidence and whether an inference is justified. They should be able to decide that a particular relationship is cause and effect and to judge that the data have been properly interpreted.

Process thinking

These complex skills, traits, and abilities are brought together into the overall framework of "tacit" knowledge and skill called "the inquiring mind."[1] In short teachers may justly concentrate on fostering intellectual processes that lead to better thinking and use subject matter chosen because of its pertinence for developing these skills and habits.

Performance Objectives

Are behavioral objectives a panacea?

A frustrating problem confronting science educators is whether performance (behavioral) objectives are desirable and applicable because of the difficulty of specifying behavior in science. Many educators argue that only by specifying desired behavior patterns for children, as in the new elementary science program "Science—A Process Approach" (SAPA), can we assess how well teaching objectives have been attained.[2]

Science objectives have often been expressed in vague, imprecise terms; so general, in fact, that all teachers could profess these objectives without being committed in a functional way. Because they were so diffuse, the objectives gave little guidance. The disparity between what teachers believed they were striving for and the means they used in the classroom were all too often completely incongruous. As a result many educators have urged that performance objectives be substituted for the much disliked broad goals. These objectives should be written to describe the learner's overt action. Therefore

Specify actions

teachers should no longer be content when their children understand that the volume of a gas increases as the pressure on it decreases. Instead they should strive to have their students be able to predict what will happen to the volume of a balloon as it rises thousands of feet into the air and what will happen if it descends rapidly. They should no longer be happy with a statement that children will appreciate good conservation practices but insist that the children show certain specified kinds of behavior or performance. Performance objectives are unquestionably useful in the teaching–learning interaction, particularly if the children accept these objectives and genuinely try to achieve them. Robert Gagné argues that children will be much readier to accept learning if they know what they will be able to do with what they have learned.[3] Learning is more likely to take place if the learner has some compelling reason for it. Although new science programs have made extensive use of performance objectives, there is, nevertheless, a well-established and growing opposition

Performance objectives and motivation

to these objectives. Programmed science instruction depends heavily on performance objectives and seems to reflect a spirit of "training" instead of education because this type of instruction is forced to use explicit knowledge questions and answers.[4]

Because much behavior sought in process-centered science is on the higher cognitive and affective levels, it is almost impossible to specify in the necessary detail and sequence the kinds of behavior that indicate learning. The following behavioral objectives fall into the lower cognitive categories:

Low-level objectives

1. Distinguish between two temperatures without the aid of a thermometer where large differences in temperature exist.

2. Distinguish between the temperature in one place and that in another place with the use of the color-coded thermometer.

3. Identify various sets of objects when given the names or characteristics of the members.

4. Separate or classify the objects according to characteristics specified by the teacher.

5. Construct a classification of a set of objects into two or more groups depending on whether the objects can or cannot be used in a stated way.

6. Distinguish among certain objects by odor characteristics.

7. Demonstrate that some body forms of animals can be described in terms of three-dimensional shapes.

8. Identify from a group of materials those that can support the growth of molds and those that do not support such growth.

9. State and demonstrate which of two angles is larger by superimposing one angle upon another.

10. Demonstrate the measurement of the *same distance* in two ways, using different measuring instruments or units (for example, number of steps in a stick).

11. Distinguish and name an unseen three-dimensional object from two-dimensional projections (shadows) of it.

12. Demonstrate and state, in appropriate units, the speed (distance traveled per unit of time) of objects placed at different distances from the center of a rotating disk.

13. Identify the single variable under study, given a statement to be tested.

14. Observe an object of a certain length or width and name a known object of approximately the same length or width.

15. Distinguish between a statement based on direct observation and one that is an inference from observation.[5]

Behavioral objectives reflect a philosophy that has been called behavioral engineering. All children in the class are expected to attain the same behavior levels although they may achieve these levels at different rates. Furthermore the specified behavior is not usually the behavior sought but an approximation and sometimes a very rough approximation. Classroom behavior is not necessarily identical to behavior in open, more dynamic, and less controlled situations.

Writing performance objectives takes time

The teacher who accepts the principle and value of performance objectives may use a previously prepared set of objectives or must write his own and develop activities, evaluation, and resources every day for each curriculum area taught. However, because behavioral objectives in the higher cognitive and affective categories are difficult enough for experienced writers, it is not feasible for the classroom teacher to write his own objectives.

Performance objectives are subject to the criticism that they are too narrow and that they discourage attention to individual differences, to the higher intellectual acts, and to the importance of improvisation and creative teaching. James MacDonald and Bernice Wolfson sum up the disadvantages thus:

> Performance objectives imply that (1) Knowledge is certain—that it can be laid out and specified. (2) Knowledge is absolute—that only one answer is appropriate. (3) Knowledge is impersonal—that it is the same for all, no matter what—once you begin study.[6]

Performance objectives are criticized as the products of a primitive behavioristic psychology and theory of knowledge that treats education as the

Behavioral engineering process of retrieving certain inputs to the learner after much change.[7] These objectives have also been said to ignore "tacit" knowledge — interpretive, associative, inferential, integrative knowledge that comes from transforming what has been learned into many different contexts, into general schemes, into a mental framework of higher thought patterns. In the educated individual the "scholastic inputs — facts, principles, terms, formulas, experiments, problems [are transformed] into a frame of interpretation, a cognitive net, so to speak, that organizes and makes intelligible certain classes of phenomena."[8]

"Tacit" knowledge Consider the example of the physician and his use of the chemistry he learned in college and in medical school. He has forgotten the thousands of chemical facts and most of the principles he once knew. He cannot remember these details and simultaneously make use of the interpretive framework essential for his practice. He cannot know the facts and their higher synthesis simultane-

Either details or the ously. The doctor's knowledge is not forgotten, but it has been absorbed into a
big picture new and higher integration that enables him to read an article on a new drug and its applications with understanding. Here he relies on tacit knowledge gained from college, medical school, clinical practice, and other experience, all of which is combined to allow him to read and evaluate the article with an expertness and understanding impossible for an individual with a doctorate degree in chemistry.

Performance objectives for the integration, interpretation, analysis, and synthesis of science learning, with its affective elements, are not applicable,

Affective objectives at least in the present state of the art. Trying to write a behavioral statement
must be broad for holding to "the humanistic values of truth, freedom, independence, and tolerance" is something like writing such a statement about riding a bicycle. Bicycle riding is a highly integrated physical action comprised of many subsidiary muscle tensions, nerve impulses, delicate balances, and action–reaction responses, which cannot, at least at this time, be analyzed into the Gagnéian learning hierarchies and therefore organized for attainment.[9]

Despite these criticisms behavioral objectives will continue to have an important role in science instruction because some important process aspects of science can be so specified (see pp. 54–58). Once these objectives have been attained, teachers can then turn to the integration of these process skills with the other aspects of science instruction into tacit knowledge.

Despite the difficulty and sheer number of performance objectives in science (not to mention in arithmetic, social studies, language arts, music, art, health, and so on), there is much to be said for the learning experience from writing and testing one's own behavioral objectives. This experience will expose once again the meaninglessness and triviality of much elementary school science.

In addition to the aforementioned reasons performance objectives have been justified on these grounds:

Some values of
performance objectives

1. The process of specifying performance in measurable terms forces [teachers] to break content into manageable, meaningful terms.

2. When the smaller pieces are visualized, the process of constructing logical instructional sequences and hierarchies is facilitated.

3. [Teachers] develop greater expertise at determining the performance capabilities of their students.

4. Their greater expertise in determining performance capabilities of students facilitates the selection of the methods and media of instruction.

5. And, because terminal performance is stated, evaluation is simplified. It can be reduced to the random selection of test items from the stated performances.[10]

Many practical suggestions have been made to assist teachers in writing and in following these objectives in the most insightful and effective way:

1. Listing the goals we want to have students accomplish. The student will understand *x, y,* and *z.*

2. Analyzing these goals into smaller tasks and translating these tasks into specific descriptions of student behavior. If the student understands *x, y* and *z,* what will he do?

3. Selecting those learning activities which seem to us to be most efficient in aiding the student in acquiring the behaviors described in the second step.

4. Revising our plan in the third step, based on experiences with students. These experiences may also result in our first revising the task analysis in the second step when we discover tasks that need to be added to the list.

or

1. Doing the task ourselves.

2. Specifying what individual parts we had to do and in what order.

3. Describing the goals for doing this task and analyzing these into individual performances. Why do this task at this time?

4. Specifying the instructional activities, using the list of performance objectives as a basis of giving focus to the activity. How well does this activity lead to the expected student performance?

5. Revising our plans based on experiences with students.[11]

Related Goals

There are many valid reasons for including science in the school curriculum. Many facts and principles of the sciences affect modern life, from both a consumer's and a producer's standpoint. Concern for safety requires that children be scientifically literate about current electricity, combustion, kinetic energy of impact, and nutrition. True, the average life may be lived in an average way without recognizing the interplay of scientific and technological knowledge in modern society (with the exception of health and safety). One need know little science to start, drive, and park an automobile; to go shopping; or even to raise a family. The appeal to the practical value of scientific knowledge in the learner's experience is a weak reed on which to lean, for the facts of science often change quickly, both in their actual "truth" and in their usefulness. A child who learns how a motor operates may soon find that he is technologically obsolescent because invention confronts him with new types of motors whose mechanical arrangement is different.

Safety as an objective

Manipulative skill is probably not an important objective of itself, because few important manipulative skills emerge from elementary science instruction. The ability to heat liquids in a test tube without scorching one's fingers is useful, but this skill is easily acquired and too trivial to be worth striving for. For psychological reasons, however, manipulation has a vital role in inquiry teaching.

Manipulative skill

There has long been a call for teaching "the scientific attitude," which generally is held to include such habits (attitudes?) as lack of bias, objectivity, accuracy, suspended judgment, and avoidance of superstition. These attitudes, surely worth striving for, are probably best acquired within the scope of inquiry. Related to this "scientific attitude" is "appreciation of science and scientists," which means recognition of the contributions of scientists (individually and collectively) to the evolution of science and to the incorporation of the results of scientific discovery into the economic fabric of society; the phrase may also be extended to include the place of science, with its characteristic set of criteria, procedures, tools, and disciplines, in the realm of the subject matter disciplines.

Scientific attitude

Few of these reasons for teaching science in the elementary schools are trivial. Unfortunately the least important goals are the working goals, which, because they are easily assessed, are the practical outcomes in the schools — the learning of facts and generalizations as ends unto themselves, from books and from vicarious experiences. The focus of science education has been on the product component of the sciences. If a shift to the process component occurs, process must not be taught as a product; that is, process must not be

Too often, goals are trivial

given to children in a printed set of directions equivalent to "the scientific method" but instead discovered and explored anew by each generation of children.

There are, of course, critics of the goals set forth in the preceding argument. Some believe that a complete change to process science has been long overdue and that little or no justification exists for organized science content in the elementary schools. Others argue vigorously that it is time to return to the security of content, to scientific facts and principles, because process teaching is not science teaching. John Newport, a prominent science educator, asserts that both groups are wrong, that they have missed the crucial and, in the last analysis, the governing fact, that elementary teachers and parents are unconvinced either goal is sufficiently valuable to justify serious attention to science. He believes that parents and teachers *will* accept the proposition "that science can make a unique and highly valuable contribution to the elementary school program" if they can be convinced that science has special value in developing the intellectual competence of their children, thus raising their IQ.[12] The new elementary science programs seem to meet the psychological requirements for such growth. Research may be able to show convincingly that these programs contribute materially to such development. Although available research is not convincing at this time, it has not focused on testing Newport's hypothesis. The mass of Piagetian-type studies described in Chapter 2 provides strong supporting evidence. Within the next five to ten years studies of the new programs over the whole span of the elementary years will allow educational researchers to determine whether the programs do, in fact, improve intellectual development as claimed. If this proof is forthcoming, will elementary school teachers be convinced at last that *they should* make science as much a part of their instruction as reading and mathematics?

Goal Achievement Through Activity

Precisely because the major goal is that of the inquiring mind, we should seek to achieve this goal by relevant inquiry-centered activities. Although the inquiring mind may emerge from a diet of educational passivity, probably only an innately gifted child will break out of the prison walls of mental rigidity.

Albert Einstein, in an autobiographical note, comments on his frustrations with teaching rigidity:

> I soon learned to scent out that which was able to lead to fundamentals and to turn aside from everything else, from the multitude of things which clutter

up the mind and divert it from the essential. The hitch in this was, of course, the fact that one had to cram all this stuff into one's mind for the examinations, whether one liked it or not. This coercion had such a deterring effect [upon me] that, after I had passed the final examination, I found the consideration of any scientific problems distasteful to me for an entire year.[13]

Children who are taught at, told at, questioned at, who have never enjoyed the opportunity of finding out for themselves, who never realize that there is (or should be) a social climate that accepts individual investigation, are unlikely to mature into the scientifically literate adults our society needs. Therefore much, perhaps half to three quarters, of the total elementary science experience should consist of investigative activities. These are not traditional laboratory experiments, of course. Depending on the problem valid procedures, such as observing, questioning, viewing, or reading, for inquiring into what is not already known (unless verification is specifically desired) is appropriate. However, teachers *must* remember that unless children are given continual and sequential opportunities to use their senses, their minds, and their skills, they will inevitably be forced back to the convenient simplicity of traditional science instruction.

How do we select a curriculum?

In a sense laboratory experiences *are* the content of elementary science; as a result of these experiences pertinent behavioral changes occur. We have previously remarked that encyclopedic treatment of the facts, principles, and concepts of science is an impossible kind of elementary science. Curriculum makers *always* select content although their criteria are dissimilar. It is self-evident that an infinity of facts and ideas exists. Which ones shall we choose and why? We are critical of the cyclic or spiral curriculum organization as it presently exists because its major goals are the inculcation and development of scientific principles. If habits of thinking and ways of analyzing problems are the important goals, then these habits and skills should be used in tasks that will strengthen them. Activities should be chosen because of their relevance to inquiry and not because of their potential for learning facts and concepts. According to this interpretation the content of elementary science is its process—how scientists work, the criteria that direct this work, and the evolution of the scientific structure. Mastery of traditional content, although unobjectionable of itself, is not the most important reason for studying science.

Goals and the Open Curriculum

The physical act of focusing the curriculum on the process of science is no guarantee that the teaching act will be process-centered. The process-oriented

Process may be taught by rote

curriculum may be outlined from grade to grade, as it is in the program of the American Association for the Advancement of Science, or it may be informal, incidental, and unstructured. We believe that the professional teacher will be happiest with a relatively unstructured curriculum that suggests rather than dictates. He alone knows the relative maturities, reading abilities, quantitative strengths and weaknesses, interests, and socioeconomic status of his class, and therefore he is the best judge of the children's capacities. With the proper guidance he will select activities in harmony with his goals, his class, and his teaching environment. The teacher who is unprepared for this challenge is unlikely to be successful with even the most minutely planned curriculum.

A syllabus is not the curriculum

The child's *real* school curriculum is the sum total of all classroom activity. Moreover this curriculum is dependent on innumerable factors from outside the classroom, not the least of which is the experiential background of children and teachers, which inevitably affects what is done in the classroom. Courses of study, elaborated endlessly on countless sheets of paper, are *not* the curriculum. The school's philosophy, its physical facilities, the conditioning to inquiry learning on the part of both children and teachers, the teacher's intellectual and personality resources are the vitals of the real operating curriculum. A third grade teacher may be unaware of what the second and the fourth grade teachers are up to but only if she prefers ostrichlike isolation. Teachers in most schools try to know what their colleagues are teaching, what skills and habits of thinking they insist on. A course of study planned by and for an individual school makes more sense than a townwide or statewide course of study because of the inevitable diversity and separation from the planning center. A comprehensive curriculum is most suitable as a resource from which teachers may draw conceptual assistance, experimental plans, and evaluative aids. Teachers who know both the prior educational achievements of their children and the demands the future will make on these children will be ready for a program of science instruction that capitalizes on past strength and endeavors in overcoming revealed weakness.

The third grade teacher who knows that most of the children have already planned simple investigations of rainfall, of the flow of electric current, and of the balanced aquarium will be more confident (and more successful) in guiding new investigations. Research in the realm of cognitive structure assures us that necessary skills and habits can be learned but only if they are continually sought and watchfully practiced in activities planned for the purpose. In this sense the curriculum must have a structure. Each school is responsible for selecting, on some order of priority, the skills, habits, and attitudes it wishes to develop and for planning the total framework (and many of the experiences) for this purpose.

If this idea is valid, there is no reason for "covering" all areas of scientific knowledge. The rationale for the traditional curriculum arises from the belief that children should have some understanding of their environment and there-fore should be introduced to concepts (perhaps entire fields of science) of which they have neither knowledge nor interest. This philosophy carries with it a necessary superficiality because it presupposes a need to "cover" the text-book. It is surely desirable for children to learn as much as they can about everything known; but because of the hydralike growth of knowledge, selec-tion is necessary. For this reason it is better to allocate to any one grade a small number of scientific phenomena to be explored through time-consuming investigation. Here, too, intraschool planning will ensure that the children have been exposed to concepts from each of the many fields of science by the time they leave the school. This idea is a subspecies of the block-and-gap approach, which some critics of modern education have long advocated for high school and college instruction. These blocks consist of limited portions of knowledge, such as genetics and respiration; the corresponding gaps may be the omission of the systematic survey of the animal kingdom, which has tradi-tionally been the major content of biological education. The block is treated in depth, and its implications are rather fully explored on the assumption that what is learned well is more significant than a skin-deep exposure to a vast body of facts. Eric Rogers summarizes well the philosophy of the block-and-gap approach:

"Block and gap"

> "This is *your* class," I would like to say to my colleague. "Make your own choice of topics and do not try to copy mine. Be careful not to choose too many, and to make a selection which will show interconnections, making some kind of framework of science. Then you and your class can go ahead and think and argue and discuss and learn about science. At the same time, the class will learn some scientific material. Though you choose only a few topics, and though much of your attention and theirs is concentrated on methods and ideas, they will learn some facts and learn them well enough to seem well educated in the old-fashioned sense. And they will be happy to con-tinue reading and learning for the rest of their lives."[14]

If this point of view is valid, then teachers should choose the proper blocks, those curricular segments offering the maximum promise for goal achievement. In the more open classroom and with a less structured style of teacher operation, the blocks chosen will be based either on teacher choice, predominantly in response to the needs and interests of the children, or on children's choice, in response to the needs and interests of their teacher.

Admirably suitable blocks for this kind of process-based science teaching in many different informal classrooms are currently available in the Elementary

Science Study materials (see Chapter 5). These blocks are independent of one another. Children and teachers can take up one or more a year without the need to develop certain essential skills in a sequential order. In contrast SAPA (see Chapter 5), a process-oriented curriculum in its entirety, is so highly structured that blocks depend on preceding blocks, which must be experienced in a prescribed sequence in the primary and intermediate grades. Although many SAPA materials (blocks) can be drawn on with great profit in open and unstructured classroom instruction, the organizational structure of this curriculum is out of harmony with the goals and philosophy of informal and free-choice learning. Between these two extremes of process instruction — the open, child-centered curriculum on the one hand and the rigidly structured, prescribed curriculum on the other hand — there is a vast range of instructional possibilities from which children and *their* learning styles and teachers and *their* teaching styles can select effective science blocks.

Teachers who work comfortably and effectively in a highly structured process mode should continue to do so, although many criticisms applied to the rigid curriculum seem to be just as valid for the regional and national curriculum imposed on schools as for a textbook-based curriculum. The value of the block-and-gap approach as exemplified in the Elementary Science Study, and to an even greater extent in the British informal primary schools, lies in the flexibility, the freedom, and the opportunity for both teachers and students to choose blocks that allow them to assert their interests and abilities in non-threatening, process-centered ways.

Summary

Of the many goals proposed and adopted for teaching elementary school science, those goals associated with process-oriented science seem to be most relevant for the next twenty years. In particular the goal of the "cultivation of the inquiring mind," is stressed because it represents a whole philosophical style of thinking about what science is, how it should be taught, and what curricular structure (or lack of structure) is appropriate.

For further study

1. What is the role of specific scientific information in the nurture of the inquiring mind?
2. List and describe the behavioral objectives in the water–glass–card experience presented in Chapter 4.

3. Contrast the adequacy of these statements as behavioral objectives:

    (a) To be able to formulate a simple scheme for classifying leaves.

    (b) To show an appreciation for the work of the scientist.

4. Rewrite these statements as behavioral objectives:

    (a) To appreciate cause-and-effect relationships.

    (b) To be aware of the need for practicing conservation.

    (c) To be able to use mathematics in understanding science.

5. What are the weaknesses of the block-and-gap curriculum.

6. Pollution is a serious problem in contemporary society. Formulate goals that will help you deal with this problem in your elementary school classroom.

Notes and references

1. Zirbes, L., *Spurs to Creative Teaching* (New York: G. P. Putnam's, 1959), p. 238.

2. See, for example, Walbesser, H., "Science Curriculum Evaluation: Observations on a Position," in L. I. Kuslan and A. H. Stone, *Readings on Teaching Children Science* (Belmont, Calif.: Wadsworth Publishing Co., 1969), pp. 40–48. See also the important statement by P. Hurd, "Theory Into Action," in Kuslan and Stone, *op. cit.*, pp. 15–23.

3. See Chapter 2, pp. 52–53.

4. See Hedges, W. D., "Teaching Science by Programming," in L. I. Kuslan and A. H. Stone, *op. cit.*, pp. 210–16, or other examples of programmed science materials for confirmation.

5. Chosen at random from *Science—A Process Approach* units.

6. MacDonald, J. B., and B. J. Wolfson, *Elementary School Journal,* 70: 126, December 1970.

7. Broudy, H. S., "Can Research Escape the Dogma of Behavioral Objectives?", *The School Review,* 78: 46, November 1970.

8. *Ibid.,* p. 51.

9. *Ibid.,* pp. 43–57.

10. Anderson, H. O., "Performance Objectives: Panacea, Pandemonium, or Progress," *Addresses and Reports,* National Science Teachers Association, Seventeenth Annual Convention (Washington, D.C.: National Science Teachers Association, 1969), p. 24.

11. Butts, D. P., "Behavioral Objectives for Science Teachers," *Journal of Research in Science Teaching,* 1: 19, June 1963.

12. Newport, J. F., "Are Content and 'Processes' Salable Items?", *School Science and Mathematics,* 70: 308, April 1970.

13. Einstein, A., "Autobiographical Notes," in P. A. Schilpp, ed., *Albert Einstein: Philosopher-Scientist* (New York: Harper & Row, 1959), p. 17.

14. Rogers, E. M., "Science Courses in General Education," in E. J. McGrath, ed., *Science in General Education* (Dubuque, Iowa: William C. Brown, 1948), p. 16.

For additional reading on elementary science goals, see:

Hurd, P., ed., "Science Education for Changing Times," in *Rethinking Science Education,* Fifty-Ninth Yearbook, National Society for the Study of Education (Chicago: University of Chicago Press, 1960), chaps. 2 and 3, *passim.*

Hurd, P., and J. J. Gallagher, *New Directions in Elementary Science Teaching* (Belmont, Calif.: Wadsworth Publishing Co., 1968), chap. 5.

4 Process-centered Teaching

almost all elementary science textbooks and "experiment" manuals present this simple experience: The child is directed to fill a glass with water and to cover the glass with an index card. Then with the card carefully pressed on the glass the child slowly inverts the glass (over the sink), removes his hand, and lo! the card adheres firmly to the glass. Contrary to expectation the water obstinately remains in the glass. The result is startling (particularly if the experiment is carelessly performed), but the excitement fades quickly as the experience is explained:

The water remains in the glass because the pressure of air pushing up on the card is greater than the pressure of water in the glass on the card, and therefore the card is forced tightly against the glass and seals it. How would a child explain this phenomenon if, as is likely, his understanding of air pressure and fluid phenomena is extremely limited? Would he not say, "The paper sticks to the water," or "The water can't fall out—the card covers the glass," or more probably, "I don't know why. I can't figure it out." If his conceptual structure includes equilibrium of forces, the child may reply that the water remains in the glass because the forces pushing up must be equal to that pushing down. However, this response is too sophisticated for a child who is not science-oriented. Few children have had the kinds of experience with pressure and force that could lead them to think of the equality of forces.

In its usual form the glass-and-card experience is a convenient, interest-arousing visual aid for informing the child that air pressure pushes up as well as down and, by implication, that fluids also exert pressure up and down. The learner is told that the card prevents the water from falling out because the upward pressure of air overcomes the weight of the water in the glass. This experience is verificatory; that is, it visually demonstrates the principle that fluids exert pressure up *and* down. It adds little to the child's conceptual structure because the child does not understand the vocabulary, the assumptions, or the implications of what he sees. If verification is the main purpose of this experience, then the teacher would be wise to abandon it, time-hallowed though it is, and seek a more fruitful center of study. But verification need *not* be its sole function. There is much more to a glass of water and a card than is apparent. Suppose that the teacher demonstrates this experience but, prior to inverting the card and glass, asks the class what they think will happen and why it will happen. The expected response (if only to be contrary) is that the water will stay in the glass, but there will be few explanations. The teacher may then suggest that the class find out by referring to their textbooks or to other sources.

The teacher accepts the authoritative explanation, writing it for all to see on the blackboard. Then she changes the conditions slightly to see whether the explanation is still valid. She carefully pulls the card down slightly without spilling the water. She asks the children to look closely at the interface between the glass and the card. They see that the card does not press against the glass; that there is, indeed, no direct contact between card and glass and that a film of water extends around the rim of the glass. She then asks if the earlier explanation is completely correct. How does water remain suspended in the glass if the card no longer seals tightly against the glass? She then moistens a card

and applies it to a wet, empty (really empty?) glass once more. Does the card still adhere to the glass? What keeps it on? Is air pushing on it? At this point some children may guess that the wet card sticks to the glass and that the push of air has nothing to do with its adhesion. Can this be tested? Will a dry card adhere? Will a card covered with waxed paper adhere? Will the waxed card adhere to a glass filled with water? Is waxed paper wet by water? If not, must the waxed card be wet before water is retained in the glass? Will the card adhere if the glass rim is lightly coated with oil?

By this time many members of the class should have arrived at the idea that the card stays in place only if it is wet and that the water "connects" the glass and the card. Can this experience be carried out with materials that are not wet by water? If the class cannot suggest suitable materials, the teacher may use a polyethylene bottle (baby bottle, for example) and a polyethylene cover (freezer container cover). The results are enlightening. Does air push up only if a water-wettable cover is used?

The teacher may vary the original demonstration by filling the glass only half full. The card still adheres. In the first case the card adhered because the pressure of the atmosphere pushing up was said to be at least equal to the pressure of water pushing down. But in the second case (the partly filled container) the space above the water in the glass is presumably filled with air (how can this "fact" be shown?), and the pressure on the card within the glass should be equal to the pressure of the contained air plus the pressure of the water. The total pressure on the glass is now greater than the pressure outside, and yet the card remains fixed. Can we still maintain that external atmospheric pressure is sufficient to maintain the card in place? Or does air pressure in the bottle drop sufficiently to create a partial vacuum? What will happen if the closed end of the container is much larger or smaller in diameter than the end covered with the card? If the container is filled to different heights? The results are surprising and should lead to some doubts as to the accuracy of the textbook answer. For the present this experience is merely sketched; it is beyond the scope of this chapter to describe it in detail.

On the basis of these simple classroom activities the class should now be able to decide that the "sticking" force of the water between the card and the glass must have some effect. This answer, so briefly sketched, is more honest, pertinent, and functional than the usual explanation. Furthermore it arises from a process of investigation that questions the obvious and puts authoritative answers to the test of experiment.

Assumptions in experiences are often hidden

Few experiences described in elementary science manuals are as vulnerable to criticism as this one. But, all too frequently, even scientifically valid experiences are questionable, in that children are expected to accept a dubious inference or conclusion. The children can derive the same facts *themselves* as they use the methods of practicing scientists in learning scientific facts and principles.

Of course the elementary science textbook or "experiment" manual may embed the activity in an elaborate conceptual framework and thus promote growth in mastering the product component of science, although not necessarily its process. Experimental validity is a necessary but not a unique condition for good science teaching. The content of the sciences, of itself, can never be the growing edge of the new science education, no matter how many times that content is revised and updated. The new physics, the new chemistry, and the new biology may be taught, indeed have been taught, as dogmatically as their predecessors. Neither memorization of the structure and function of DNA and ATP nor verbalization of the terms *molecules* and *pressure* are reliable signs that the student knows what these terms mean and can apply them in different contexts. Traditional modes of teaching new content will not better serve the goals of science teaching. Increased rigor and greater demands on the student will not automatically result in more and better learning. Curricular changes must also be accomplished by changes in the spirit, methodology, and goals sought by instructors at all grade levels.

The most pervasive goal of science education in the elementary schools is the enhancement of the searching, inquiring, rational mind. The evidence is incontestable that elementary science curricula, textbooks, and teachers have neglected science as process and have consequently ignored those dynamic components of science that are the essence of scientific progress. American science education has too often substituted the letter of science for its spirit, and conclusions for its inquiries.

The "searching mind"

Fortunately impressive studies now under way are seeking new and better ways of teaching science. A variety of names have been coined in the attempt to describe the complex methodologies employed. Such terms as *enquiry, inquiry, discovery, problem solving, scientific thinking, process-centered* and *heuristics* have been proposed. The unifying thread is their dependence on gathering evidence for the solution of some simple scientific question by student activity. With the teacher's guidance children generalize these data into conceptual schemes that lead to new, fruitful understanding. Of course, inquiry is not new. Many scientists and science educators have long argued that science must be studied by the activities and thought processes of practicing scientists. But the effort to learn how children think and how science may most effectively be taught to children has been vigorously and effectively financed only in recent years.

Process-centered instruction

The authors define *process-centered teaching* as that teaching by which teachers and children study scientific phenomena with the approach and the spirit of the scientist. We also define it in operational terms as learning in which these instructional characteristics are consistently present:

1. Children and teachers habitually employ scientific processes such as observing, measuring, estimating, predicting, comparing, classifying, experimenting, communicating, inferring, analyzing, and drawing out inductions.

2. Time is unimportant. There is no urgency to complete a topic in order to meet a deadline.

3. The answers sought are not known in advance to children. Not only are these answers *not* often found in textbooks, but textbooks and manuals are chosen because they ask questions and suggest ways of finding answers, but do not *give* answers.

4. Children are genuinely interested in finding solutions.

5. The content of the inquiry is not necessarily related to what precedes or follows, although in some of the new elementary science curricula each activity is part of a learning hierarchy.

6. Teaching and learning are "Why?" centered. Questions such as "How do we know?" "Are we justified in this assumption?" and "Are we justified in this conclusion?" are characteristic of the inquiry style.

7. A problem is identified and narrowed until the class seems capable of solving it.

8. The class proposes hypotheses to guide the investigation.

9. Children take the responsibility for proposing ways of gathering the data from controlled experimentation, observation, reading, and other pertinent sources.

10. These proposals for action are cooperatively evaluated. Pertinent assumptions, limitations, and difficulties are identified whenever possible.

11. Children investigate in small groups, as a class, and as individuals to gather the data for testing the hypotheses.

12. Children summarize their data and come to tentative conclusions about the adequacy of their hypotheses. Every effort is made to formulate scientific explanations.

Inquiry is not restricted to the laboratory or to observation, nor is its success guaranteed. Children must become aware of the difficulties, the doubts, the false starts, and the labor involved in thinking up new ideas, which are soon altered and perhaps completely discarded. Children can learn *how* scientists learn, and in the process they can "learn" science. It is feasible for teachers to stress the "Whys" and the "How do you knows." They can provide opportunities for practicing how to phrase answerable questions, for isolating problems, inventing workable hypotheses, and deriving from data the simplest possible principles. In short the goal of process-centered teaching is not merely to understand the role of science in technological innovation or to better comprehend the scientific base of our world but to foster the child's ability to speak and use the language of science through cognition of its structure.

Special Values of Process-centered Instruction

Many science educators believe that inquiry, in one form or another, is the most promising approach to the unification of the process and product components of science in the schools. This is a bold, perhaps overoptimistic statement. Surely the history of educational panaceas is a warning that rhetoric, isolated from and unrelated to existing conditions in the schools, is insufficient. Therefore to make the attempt worthwhile what is the promise of process-centered teaching? How do the procedures and materials of inquiry differ from textbook science, from the "rhetoric of conclusion" described in Chapter 3, on which our children have been nourished?

In addition to philosophical and pedagogical reasons for stressing inquiry, there are a number of psychological, child-centered values. Jerome Bruner has proposed four major outcomes of discovery teaching:

1. It increases the intellectual potency of the learner.
2. The learner shifts from dependence on extrinsic to intrinsic rewards.
3. Mastery of the heuristics of discovery enhances its transfer value.
4. Learning by discovery expedites memory processing.[1]

Intellectual potency increases because students not only organize study procedures to discover relationships but also learn in ways that facilitate assimilation of data in general problem solving. The student who discovers that water expands when it freezes is better prepared to find out why ice floats on water or why a bottle filled with water cracks when the water freezes. The child who is aware of air pressure, equilibrium of force, and surface tension is in a stronger position to apply these concepts if they have been integrated into his own intellectual patterns.

Autonomous reward arises from confidence in one's ability to discover; that is, mastery becomes inner-directed. The child who successfully generalizes from his own observations and manipulations learns that he can predict certain consequences of his discoveries and in a limited way can control his environment. In every child's growth there is a period of intense curiosity, of desire to find out. For younger children this stage is a magnificent opportunity for the discovery of autonomous reward. Many children (and adults) never realize "intellectual happiness" because their learning experiences were never planned to provide the reinforcement that comes from the thrill and satisfaction of discovery.

Transfer value arises from the belief that the child strengthens his capacity to pursue inquiry only by participating in inquiry. He learns best how to phrase answerable questions by trying to phrase answerable questions. He develops a feeling for the significance of variables by testing variables for relevance. Children develop an inquiry "style" in somewhat the same way they become so adept at "Twenty Questions." This method of inquiry is not transfer in the older disciplinary sense, which supposedly helped the student of Latin to write better English; in this sense the sheer labor of translating Latin was believed somehow alchemically to transform and improve the student in all his intellectual endeavors. Neither is it strengthening common elements such as vocabulary, quantitative skills, or scientific principles in new contexts. It is mastery of a scheme of attack, of an analytical approach, which, more than subject matter, is the trademark of the scientist.

Memory processing means "learning by doing," a bromide of traditional educational psychology. The more children are encouraged to organize their learning in conceptual structures of their own devising, the greater is the probability that they can quickly and effectively retrieve that learning. Young children in particular must rely on concrete experience as the base for conceptualization from which there arises an increased probability of later retrieval. Although they must also accept much encapsulated, predigested information, children will more likely make better use of their own painfully acquired learning because it is their own.

Process-centered instruction is more effective in teaching general principles and concepts than it is in presenting large collections of facts that support these principles. This style of instruction encourages children to rely on their own resources and helps them attain goals that are more their own than those of the teacher. Learning through process-centered instruction also seems to increase the child's understanding of the content being studied and tends to increase his ability to remember principles and concepts. Although not as much content is taught through process-centered instruction as through more classical approaches, what is taught through process is better learned. However, as Frederick McDonald suggests, research on inquiry teaching may be too limited in technique and approach, and often too cursory, to produce clear-cut supportive evidence that process-centered teaching is a more effective approach to the mastery of content. He adds, however, that if discovery is "carefully programmed" and guided, "it proves to be an effective method."[2]

The "Eureka" complex

Psychologists have pointed out the additional involvement of children in problems concerning them, an interaction that increases attention and effort. For the genuinely involved child the importance of the task increases, and with it the need for intellectual endeavor. Success increases the child's confidence in his ability to think, gives him strength to be independent, and minimizes his inner conflicts because he is no longer passive. Of course, the often-cited "joy of discovery," which thrills both the child and the teacher, is an important incentive.[3]

Discovery procedures in harmony with Piaget's developmental theory

Discovery procedures for elementary school children are in harmony with the developmental theory of Piaget:

Basic understanding is a matter of active learning, which can be facilitated by constructing situations where the children can slowly build up their strategies in their own way. In the children's discoveries, each new idea must integrate what went on before and the activity of discovering itself must constitute the dynamic force which leads the child on to apply his newly-found knowledge to new situations.[4]

The demand for direct experience with nature and the need for children to act on and in turn to be acted on by natural phenomena are, if not uniquely a Piagetian revelation, fully in harmony with Piaget's psychology and are supported by many other psychologists.[5] J. Richard Suchman remarks that those children who are able to deal with raw data, who leap beyond data to generalize and hypothesize, and who are autonomous learners make the best inquirers. This conclusion does not mean that science taught by inquiry should be restricted to these children. If children begin with a concrete problem and know that with the assistance of the teacher they can find the necessary information and be guided to a solution without being *given* the answers, they will make significant progress toward the pertinent goals of elementary science instruction. In Suchman's words:

> When you present children with problems in very concrete terms, without the esoteric terminology, the definitions, the symbols, and the other conventions of a formalized science, the children begin to go to work on these problems in logical and productive ways.[6]

A sobering reality of education and educational research is that impressive gains as a rule do not show up in educational experiments. There is little chance that a few weeks of process instruction will produce gains of any magnitude, no matter how experienced or capable the teacher and her children. Benjamin Bloom remarks that at the University of Chicago two or three years of intensive effort by teachers and researchers are required to find evidence of significant growth toward newly formulated objectives.[7] Objectives as complex and significant as mastery of the spirit and strategy of scientists are surely dependent on teaching insight and on prolonged experience with many kinds of scientific activities. We should always keep these wise words of John Holt in mind:

A child's discovery is a real discovery

> We must recognize that children who are dealing with a problem on a very primitive, experimental, and inefficient level, are making discoveries that are just as good, just as exciting, just as worthy of interest and encouragement, as the more sophisticated discoveries made by more advanced students . . . the invention of the wheel was as big a step forward as the invention of the airplane — bigger in fact. . . . Above all, we will have to avoid the difficult temptation of showing slow students the wheel so that they may more quickly get to work on the airplanes. In mathematics certainly, and very probably in all subjects, knowledge which is not genuinely discovered by children will very likely prove useless and will be soon forgotten.[8]

The recent revival of interest in process learning, and its possible over-emphasis, has called forth a counterattack by many knowledgeable educators and psychologists. For example, Jerome Kagan argues that children of low intelligence or motivation cannot persist in tasks that are not immediately fruitful. He asserts that young children lack incentive to tackle problems because they have never experienced the fun and the ego boost of success. Furthermore, because of their intellectual and subject-matter limitations, these children are unable to tackle seemingly simple problems. Impulsive children, those who leap at answers, are likely to fail:

> The method of discovery is most appropriate for highly motivated older children who might have high dependency conflict and who are inclined to use a reflective strategy . . . least appropriate for younger children, especially those below the age of nine, who do not have high motivation to master intellectual tasks and who tend to be impulsive.[9]

Kagan also stresses knowledge of subject matter (a rich background) as a precondition for effective discovery learning.

Failure is also possible

Some psychologists also mention the greater possibility of failure in inquiry, which dampens the interest of the young investigator. They point to the lack of evidence that retention with discovery techniques is higher than retention with other teaching procedures. However, most psychologists agree that there are positive transfer effects. In David Ausubel's words:

> If learning by discovery promotes transfer in some unique way, it probably does so through the transferable experiences of independently formulating and testing alternative hypotheses and through the transferable attitude of independent search.[10]

Recent research has demonstrated reasonably well the following conclusions about discovery learning and teaching:

Some tentatively acceptable conclusions

1. Better transfer is obtained from discovery than from traditional methods of learning.
2. Discovery learning is relatively more effective as the period of time between learning and testing on a transfer task increases.
3. Discovery learning is relatively more effective when the learning task involves material such as that taught in schools.

4. There may be a tendency for discovery learning to be relatively more effective when the background of knowledge in a school subject is limited.

5. The discovery method is relatively more effective for low-ability groups than for high-ability groups.

6. In the discovery method, a reasonable degree of guidance is better than little guidance.

7. The inquiry process encourages an exploratory attitude on the part of the child, and the searching process is his own, resulting in questions generated within his own cognitive structure.

8. Inquiry strategy encourages an analytical mode on the part of the child that leads him beyond the overt perceptual phenomena inherent in our physical world. What is highly significant is the intuitive mode of behavior that the inquiry process brings out in children.[11]

Ausubel, a vigorous critic of this methodology, insists that there has not yet been a conclusive demonstration that discovery transfers across the various disciplines. However, the mere fact that transfer within the structure of elementary science is facilitated is sufficient justification for teachers to use inquiry procedures more frequently and for longer time periods.

Inquiring can and must coexist with content

Early success is necessary, but experienced teachers can select appropriate learning experiences. At first probably only a small number of children in each class will propose worthwhile ideas and will make the required inductive and deductive leaps, but the number of children will grow. The part conditioning and experience play, although obviously important, is still vague. Discovery is certainly not the sole instructional method for elementary science; the teacher will continue to present some kinds of information directly by reception learning. Yet, if problems are properly selected, direct instruction is less likely to be essential.

Difficulty in changing learning styles

If only older children are capable of inquiry, to delay the first contact with such instruction until the high school years would be foolish. Years of reception learning in the elementary school are not easily transmuted by a single course in high school biology or chemistry. The different patterns of thought and action required in discovery learning will not take place in a few high school years without long experience in the elementary schools. College teachers of science have long since learned the difficulty in convincing students of the possibility and desirability of learning for themselves. Students' expectations of how they are to be taught and of what is expected are often narrow and rigid, and few welcome the idea of self-direction even under considerable guidance.

The elementary school teacher *should* help children organize their data and should guide them in making the necessary inductive leaps and in evaluating their results. The teacher should help correct ambiguity, confusion, and misunderstanding. Bernard Friedlander states that "one of the goals of teaching and learning must be for students to accept the discipline of facts and skills as prerequisites for true understanding."[12] However, children will accept a discipline that is otherwise meaningless to them when they see for themselves the need for new facts, new information, and new experiments to find answers to the questions that interest them.

There is good reason to be optimistic about the values of process-centered instruction, if children are drawn into simple scientific problems presented through concrete experiences. The difficult vocabulary and symbolic structure with which children cannot grapple must be discarded for the children to develop a spirit of willingness and readiness to find out for themselves. If elementary school science is to cultivate "the inquiring mind," each elementary school teacher must face up to the task of strengthening the child's competence in recognizing and solving simple scientific problems.

Clear goals

Although learning by imitation is not impossible, and indeed it is necessary in many academic experiences, this particular kind of competence is hopeless if it is bookbound. On the other hand teachers who themselves learn science heuristically are prepared to guide their pupils through the pitfalls of illogical reasoning and invalid experimentation and can skirt the routine of rote recitation, which has long permeated science teaching. Children will learn to think scientifically and critically if their teachers both exemplify it *and* demand it of them in daily classroom activities.

Teachers as models

Obviously the millennium is not immediately at hand. The changes that authorities seek in instructional patterns can rarely guarantee positive results if teachers are not sufficiently prepared. In addition few teachers exemplify inquiry or customarily demand this kind of thinking in their classrooms.

Many widely known educational schemes of the past, such as Progressive Education, Object Lessons, the Contract Plan, and the Morrisson Unit, were based on more or less valid educational theories and were often successful in causing desirable behavior changes in the hands of ardent and skilled proponents of these plans. Unfortunately these programs were insufficiently tested before they were widely publicized so that the probability of their success in actual classroom practice was impossible to estimate. Even today inquiry methods have *not* adequately been tested although these methods are important in several successful new elementary science programs. Every educator is aware of the functional outcomes of the time-tested question-and-answer methodology that pervades many elementary and high school class-rooms in this country. He knows, or thinks he knows, the relative degree of success attainable by skilled and unskilled teachers, by bright and slow children, and by schools with good facilities and with inadequate facilities. But these rule-of-thumb, empirical data for inquiry teaching are not known. At present investigators are just beginning to learn the extent to which the "average" classroom teacher can use a nonroutine, time-consuming procedure whose outcomes are difficult to evaluate. Yet no matter what happens in the classroom as a result of these ideas, there will be little loss in either the net amount of science the children learn or the extent to which they attain the other goals of classroom science; and there is a high probability that overall science achievement will improve. Therefore teachers must continue in the struggle to achieve the essential goals of both science educators and scientists. Teachers have *nothing* to lose but the chains of rote instruction that bind elementary science to the nineteenth century.

Development of Suitable Attitudes

The methodology of inquiry is almost as strange and difficult for older children as it is for their teachers: neither have been trained in its procedures or have had successful experience with it. But younger children frequently learn by inquiry, although a crude, trial-and-error version, which by virtue of its difficulty and the relative lack of success (accompanied by an eternity of formal instruction in and out of school) is soon forgotten. Younger children spontaneously ask, "Why does the water bubble around in the bathtub when it's going out?" and "Why does my little metal car sink in the water?" The nursery school years provide frequent opportunities to introduce children to the joys of answering simple questions by means of scientific procedures. *Questions open doors* Young children overwhelm us with their questions, their insights, and their desire to learn, but their interests are frequently diverted into play or fantasy. A teacher sensitive to their implications may channel these interests into an investigation of pertinent phenomena to discover relationships of which the children are unaware. The experienced teacher is skilled in guiding the questions and the feedback of answers from a group of children into productive exploration. Each question answered, each interest satisfied, should ideally open a door to new questions and new interests in much the same way the research scientist finds that his field of research grows as he learns more about it.

Teacher-arranged situation

Success in inquiry depends on continual training in the skills and habits of observation, experimentation, and inductive and deductive thinking. The content selected (usually by the teacher in a formal teaching situation) must interest the learner sufficiently to present a problem rather than a puzzle. It must also be appropriate for the application of those habits collectively labeled "inquiry." How can the teacher arrange classroom situations in which children eagerly accept inquiry methods? One characteristic of the master teacher is that he is successful in devising challenging situations, statements and questions; he seizes on spontaneously occurring situations at the right moment. Suitable problems for the elementary school must not be abstract or the resulting verbalizations are likely to be meaningless. To attempt to present Copernican astronomy to a fourth grade class as a more efficient conceptual scheme than Ptolemaic astronomy is almost as immoral as teaching Copernican astronomy as the only astronomy. To attempt to explain the rusting of iron, the burning of a candle, and the formation of oxyhemoglobin as exothermic processes to a fifth grade class may be similarly unfortunate if the necessary conceptual structures and perceptual experiences are absent.

Understanding concepts requires many kinds of experiences

Concrete-empirical experiences, in the Piagetian sense, are essential for all children and particularly for younger children. The phrase *concrete-empirical* is not necessarily restricted to direct firsthand experience but includes such vicarious experiences as photographs, filmstrips, and personal knowledge. The idea of a vacuum, so sensible and meaningful a concept to adults today, is perilously difficult to grasp, as its slow and hotly disputed rise in the history of science testifies. Yet without some understanding of the vacuum how can one explain the phenomena that operate because of a vacuum? How can the lift of airplane wings, the card and water glass experience, the vacuum cleaner, the siphon, and the whole host of vacuum-related phenomena that are part of the world of the elementary school child be explained? To tell a child that an egg is forced into a bottle because of the partial vacuum inside the bottle is to present him with a semantic puzzle if all that he knows about a vacuum is a verbal link with vacuum bottles and vacuum cleaners. Only when children have experience with a variety of phenomena, when they feel for themselves the force required to pull a rubber "plumber's helper" from a wall, and when they see the height of a column of mercury sustained by "something," does the existence of a vacuum begin to make sense.

A prerequisite for the successful introduction of process-centered instruction in elementary schools is a carefully planned series of concrete-empirical experiences presented not as verification or as facts to be learned but as "something happens; how can we discover what makes it happen?"

Facilitating Inquiry

Success in inquiry is also based on an atmosphere more permissive than the atmosphere so often found in the traditional classroom. The essence of inquiry is freedom to pursue lines of thought unfettered by textbooks or by the necessity of learning certain facts, concepts, and principles for their own sake. A permissive atmosphere is not willed into existence; children are no better for being thrown into it suddenly. Children will accept permissiveness if they have come from classrooms where freedom was already accepted because of the teacher's orientation and because of the activities in which both the teacher and children were interested. But teachers and children accustomed to more autocratic and traditional ways of teaching and learning will best achieve freedom to investigate by taking it in relatively small doses at first. From a pragmatic point of view the teacher should select problems the children are likely to solve successfully as they attempt to find out what happened and why it happened with little difficulty. From a psychological standpoint frequent success is essential. In the elementary school years the teacher need not intentionally introduce the element of failure into the scientific enterprise, for many problems that seem appropriate for youngsters will end in unplanned and unexpected failures. In this respect the new elementary science programs described in Chapter 5 show great potential because their inquiry activities have been tested thoroughly in the classroom and are much more likely to be successful.

Some characteristics of the
nonauthoritarian science classroom

1. The questions and problems to be studied often originate in the class, either from earlier work or as a result of a chance occurrence.

2. Procedures originate in child–teacher discussion, and questions and problems are cooperatively analyzed.

3. Children frequently propose hypotheses that lead to experimentation, observation, and further logical analysis.

4. Children use texts and trade books as sources of information and later verification; these sources provide additional data, not authoritative answers.

5. The teacher conceives her role as that of guide, counselor, and consultant, not as "law-giver."

6. The data gathered from the various sources—experimentation, demonstra-

tion, reading, audiovisual aids, and personal experience—are cooperatively evaluated in testing hypotheses.

7. Children evaluate their success (or lack of success) in solving the problem with which they were concerned.

8. The teacher never hesitates to use more traditional procedures when they are better for her purposes; for example, she may need to explain a particular phenomenon, either because information is unavailable or because she can explain it more effectively.

9. Time is set aside for important activities. This time is available because there is no need to finish the textbook; there is no compulsion to complete a given number of units.[13]

Motivating Inquiry

Setting the stage for inquiry investigation with younger children is comparatively easy. Their curiosity about phenomena capable of stretching their frame of reference is frequently all that is necessary to begin an investigation if the phenomenon is exhibited (with or without teacher comment). For example, children who discover this piece of apparatus as they enter the classroom will raise a host of questions.

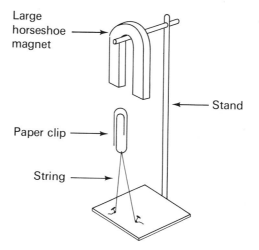

"What keeps the paper clip up?" "Will it fall if we poke it?" "Will it fall if the magnet is moved?" "How long will it stay up?" "What's between the clips and the magnet?" "Will a bar magnet work?"

The list of related concepts in this particular demonstration is startling: magnetic field, magnetic induction, forces in equilibrium, magnetic forces, gravitational forces, interactions, and the inverse square law. These concepts do not, of course, exhaust the list. There are problems sufficient for months of study should the class be so inclined.

Simplicity may be superficial

The problem of motivating investigation is more difficult with older children, and yet, paradoxically, it is simpler. Activities must be chosen more carefully because many problems demand knowledge and data too complex or too abstract for fifth or sixth graders. For example, a chemical process as familiar as the rusting of iron is too complex unless it is handled at a superficial, observational level. On the other hand the teacher does not need to depend as much on concrete-empirical materials for initiating problems or for gathering data with this age group as with younger children. Formal propositional thinking is more readily available along with greater maturity and informational understanding. Therefore analysis of data at higher and higher inductive and deductive levels is possible.

An innocent question may lead to sustained interest and scientific endeavor by primary and intermediate-level children. "Are all clouds the same?" "How do earthworms burrow into the ground? Do they go 'head' or 'tail' first?" "Do seeds grow if they are planted upside down?" "Do rocks look the same inside as outside?"

Introducing the Problem

Let science emerge from children's thoughts

Ideally problems are generated by the spontaneous interaction of children with the natural phenomena of their environment. The successful new elementary science programs in primary schools in England stress this point. The proponents of these programs believe that there is far too much science to learn. But more important they "do not believe that anyone can ask a completely significant question for someone else."[14] In actual practice, however, the teacher must introduce many challenging and worthwhile areas of study to his class because the child's world is so narrow. The teacher must set the stage in such a fashion that his children literally besiege him with questions in their eagerness to learn.

Devices for stimulating interest

Some teachers have discovered a simple device that will stimulate a surprising interest in the study of rocks and minerals: They write the following words conspicuously on a large slab of stone (a flagstone): "I am a rock. I am made up of minerals. Are there other rocks and minerals in this room? What is the oldest rock in the room?" To introduce buoyancy they prepare a Cartesian diver labeled: "Push down on my rubber top. What do I do? Do you know why?" The enterprising teacher often relies on a science corner as a focal point from which new questions and the answers to previous questions originate. No science corner is complete without a "curiosity box," an interest-arousing container whose contents should frequently be changed. During one week it may contain plant seeds, and it may be labeled: "How many kinds of seeds do I have? Are they all the same? In how many ways are they the same? Different? Are my seeds alike on the inside?" The next week it may hold a variety of leaves and be labeled with pertinent questions. The possibilities for stimulating desirable interests are endless. But the teacher does not have to depend on the science corner for the initiation of classroom science activities. The appeal of the science corner for informal investigation by children is one of its most rewarding features. Here volunteers maintain the salamanders, the aquarium, and the growing plants.

Novel demonstrations   A simple although striking and challenging demonstration is an effective method of introducing a problem. The more startling the outcome, the more the child's normal response pattern is shaken, and the greater is his drive to search for a solution without falling back on the secure clichés of daily explanation. There is no more provocative way to introduce children (and adults) to an investigation of static electricity than by rubbing a hard rubber comb on wool or fur (may other materials be used?), and placing the comb in close proximity to a thin stream of water. As the water curves dramatically toward the comb, the children will literally explode with questions. The stream of water almost seems to deny the law of gravity with this strange power.

What approach is more promising than being caught at the beginning of the school day in the act of preparing jars for studying insect responses to light? To the question, "What are you doing?" the teacher may reply, "I'm trying a little experiment. Would you like to help?" Is there a child who can refuse such an invitation? The resourceful teacher will find many opportunities to interest his children in activities that strengthen their ability to think independently and critically. On the other hand not every task in science is necessarily productive in the previously described sense. There *are* routine chores — feeding animals, cleaning the aquarium, and washing the glassware — which are necessary in efficient classroom management of inquiry. And there are many desirable learning activities that are not necessarily centered on scientific thinking. But as a more or less arbitrary rule of thumb, better learning is likely to result when learning activities are introduced with some provocative situation because of strong initial interest.

Science need not always be introduced in this fashion. It is not *necessary* to startle children into a learning situation, to fascinate, awe, and intrigue them, although there are some positive (as well as negative) values in this procedure. The mere opportunity to handle concrete materials, to do things for themselves, to "play" is sufficient incentive for many children to carry on teacher-structured activities, which are begun without a dramatic introduction. There are scientific domains in which spectacular demonstrations or provocative experiments are not feasible in the elementary classroom, just as there are fascinating phenomena too difficult to investigate. For instance, elementary school children rarely understand chemical reactions, and therefore the study of chemical reactions is best left to eighth or ninth grade children, as is the study of nuclear reactions and radioactivity.

Narrowing the Problem

Once his interest is aroused, the child must identify and analyze the problem. The analysis of the confusing mass of questions, half questions, vague statements, and unsupported assumptions of a group of youngsters inexperienced in discovery is a necessary although not a sufficient condition for success. Scientists agree that formulation of their problems is one of their most difficult tasks and that all too often their work is hard because they have failed to ask themselves the "right" questions. Therefore children will need much help in learning to formulate answerable questions that offer a reasonable promise of success with the materials available to the class. The question "Why do some things float?" is an invitation to disaster if addressed to second graders. It is too inclusive, too complex, and too general to be of directive value to them. The mastery of causal relationships and physical phenomena that it assumes is apt to be unjustified. A more effective restatement of the problem is the following: "How can we find out what things float? What things sink?" Or even more specifically, "Will this wooden boat float or sink? Will this piece of iron float or sink?" Children (and adults) rarely phrase such limited questions spontaneously, and therefore the teacher and class should cooperatively analyze the reasons for preferring the second questions to the first. They are not only more specific, but they are presented in the context of a particular empirical-concrete circumstance, which directs observation and experimentation.

The question as restated by the class may remain nebulous, or it may be made so specific that causal understanding fails to emerge. For example, the question of what kinds of things float is too limited for a group of fifth graders, who are prepared for a higher level of abstraction. On the other hand younger children will immediately propose such answers as wood floats, boats float, tin sinks, which thus furnish a base for further investigation. After the operational phrasing of the problem and the proposal of possible hypotheses, the class must pool its knowledge to provide the necessary data. An alert child may add the complicating fact that boats made of steel are able to float and that submarines (made of steel) float or sink at will. These contradictory observations are perplexing to most children. Few young children can distinguish the relevant from the irrelevant variables that complicate the analysis of floating bodies. Therefore if no child makes the suggestion, the teacher must suggest that the physical composition of the floating object is not necessarily the best guide for separating floating from nonfloating materials. Children may mention shape as another characteristic of floating bodies. Should this concept fail to emerge, additional play with floating and nonfloating objects should provide the necessary perceptual experience. Eventually the children will propose the proper hypothesis. They must now test their hypothesis on as many different materials, shapes, and liquids as possible. However, before they can think about floating on a high level of abstraction, specific concepts of density, specific gravity, weight, volume, displacement, equilibrium, and force must emerge. Because younger children have not formed clearly defined, unequivocal weight and volume concepts, the teacher must devote a large part of class time to developing these concepts. Not until children can manipulate these ideas with some skill will they be able to understand *why* a submarine sinks when its tanks are filled with water and *why* it floats when these tanks are emptied. Many third graders *can* comprehend on a relatively abstract level the meaning of density and volume and *can* propose a reasonably adequate explanation of floating, but this meaning will not emerge from a verbal explanation or from rote memorization of the textbook. It will come from *many* firsthand experiences with floating and nonfloating objects, experiences directed at eventually tying together these conceptual relationships.[15]

> *Teachers must guide*

> *Necessary prerequisite concepts*

Although the teacher may ask a question that makes sense, gives direction, and means much the same to both teacher and children, a child may often answer a question that is not the one he was asked. Questions designed to direct the child's attention to important aspects of his environment may actually distract him. A successful teacher can diagnose these zigzags and unintentional errors. A teacher trained in the new elementary science programs tends to ask questions that avoid recall as a goal, substituting instead more emphasis on the higher cognitive skills of analysis and synthesis and requiring children to demonstrate command of these process skills. Indeed such a teacher will ask many more questions than does the traditionally trained teacher who does too much telling.[16]

Proposing Hypotheses

*The important but
difficult task of
hypothesizing*

   If a problem is properly defined, that is, operationally limited, children will suggest intelligent hypotheses. The hypotheses may not be correct, but with continuing experience they will at least not be absurd. Although their hypotheses may not be testable in the classroom, the children do not necessarily need to terminate the investigation. Children unpracticed in thinking up hypotheses and in assessing the validity of hypotheses of others will need direct guidance and kindly but critical assessment directed at improving their probes. Young children must learn (or be taught) to distinguish fact from fancy, the possible from the impossible, the natural cause from the animistic and teleological cause. Time, in unrationed doses, is a requisite. Sympathetic discussion and critical evaluation of their hypotheses and other statements, by both teacher and children, is not possible in a period of ten or fifteen minutes once or twice a month.

   Older children (as well as many adults) often give unrealistic explanations when confronted with puzzling situations, particularly if they cannot find answers within their own accumulated knowledge. With practice and maturation children reduce the number of nonnatural explanations. Yet many responsible adults continue to believe that flowers are colored to attract bees or that evolution occurs to bring about more successful forms of life.

   Hypotheses should be relevant; but relevant to what? They should be naturalistic, stated in terms that lead to analysis and verification. They should be expressed simply and embody the fewest possible variable factors. Children can propose relevant hypotheses, but time, practice, broad experience with many phenomena, and a somewhat rare intuitive power are factors that promote hypothesis formation.

   The teacher who attempts to coax hypotheses from the class when he and the students are inexperienced in inquiry is apt to become discouraged quickly. The formulation of reasonable hypotheses is a difficult task for adults; indeed the mark of the great scientist is his ability to propose testable hypotheses. The teacher's first attempts at inquiry should be with simple observational or experimental problems, well within the grasp of the class. Even then the pace will surely be too rapid for many children, and the rate of the entire group is likely to be unexpectedly slow when contrasted with the traditional methodology of recitation.

Testing hypotheses

   The teacher must continually encourage the class to test each of the hypotheses with questions such as these: Is it reasonable? Does anyone in the class know of any facts that confirm or deny its validity? How can we find out?

What experiments are suitable? Does anything in the textbook help us test the hypothesis? Are other helpful materials available in the library? At home?

Most of the time, with a problem the children generate or one the teacher structures, unless the problem is purposely narrow, answers will not come from page turning in the textbook because textbooks are not written to supply information about an infinite number of investigative concerns. They are, after all, textbooks, not compendia. Should the problem be a relatively simple, observational question (Are all kinds of clouds the same? Do all the leaves on a tree have the same shape? What will happen if I drop a crumpled piece of paper and an uncrumpled piece of paper at the same time?), the alternatives are few, and suggestions for testing these hypotheses will soon be forthcoming. For a well-defined question (Why does a pencil in a glass of water appear to be bent? What makes the rainbow?), children may propose many hypotheses at a high level of conceptual complexity, but unless their background of experience is rich with the pertinent facts and principles, they are unlikely to propose fruitful hypotheses. Strategically it would probably be better to approach the rainbow problem after children have handled lenses and have learned that light is refracted in passing from one medium into another of a different refractive index.

Suitable problems for younger children require little related information and can directly be solved with experimental or observational data. With older children the question "Why does a pencil in a glass of water appear to be bent?" may evoke, in addition to the "I don't knows," the statement that "the water does something to the pencil." Except for those who already know about the refraction of light, children will rarely formulate a more specific hypothesis. The teacher must once again set the stage for evoking the desired hypotheses, after discussing the shortcomings of the hypotheses advanced by the class.

Varying observational conditions

Does the class believe that the pencil is actually bent? He may suggest varying the conditions of the demonstration to see whether the bending still occurs. Will the pencil be bent as much if it is observed from a different angle? The children should examine the pencil from many angles. Does immersing the pencil completely make a difference? Does the pencil "bend" in other liquids such as rubbing alcohol, glycerin, salad oil? By this time, a number of observations concerning the angle of view and the media will emerge. The children will probably never make spontaneously the statement that the pencil is bent because of the refraction of light; they will, however, come to this conclusion from the cooperative discussion between teacher and class, as they assess their data and attempt to find a simple, natural explanation.

With practice over a lengthy period of time children improve markedly in their ability to formulate and evaluate hypotheses, but this practice must be with concrete, directly grasped problems affected by a relatively small number of variables. Were the kindergarten to twelfth grade curriculum built on an inquiry methodology instead of on scientific concepts and principles, there would be ample opportunity for children to apply continuously, from month to month and from grade to grade, the skills and habits of learning to learn science. The pressures to complete the syllabus must inevitably be weakened when there is no longer the compulsion to cover air, water, health, electricity, growing things, and prehistoric animals during the nine teaching months.

Authority   Older children fall back on authority in proposing and testing hypotheses more frequently than do younger children, perhaps because of their indoctrination in authoritarian procedures. Younger children must rely more on direct perceptual knowledge and guessing, although children of all ages frequently attempt experimentation.

Rather limited research in elementary schools indicates that children in permissive classrooms in which discovery procedures are practiced are less dependent on authority for proposing and testing hypotheses than are children in nonpermissive rooms. Their hypotheses, although more numerous and ingenious, may not necessarily be more accurate. They are, however, better able to suggest tests for their hypotheses by experimentation and observation. There seems to be no positive correlation between intelligence and ability to test hypotheses empirically; in fact, measures of intelligence may be unrelated to the abilities required for critical thinking.[17]

Analyzing Assumptions

As they propose and evaluate relevant information, children have an opportunity to identify and assess the assumptions, implicit and explicit, on which their answers depend. They will make such statements: Light things don't push aside as much water as heavy things do. Heavy things sink. Things can float only on water. These statements are obviously based on partially or completely erroneous assumptions. However, elementary school children are not uniquely unskilled in analyzing the assumptions they bring to problem solving. Analysis of assumptions is not ordinarily part of the daily thought processes of either adults or children. Some of the hidden assumptions in the tumbler–water–card demonstration at the beginning of this chapter have been described. Almost every scientific experiment or demonstration rests on a number of assumptions that must be clarified (or at least recognized) if the experiment is to have any meaning.

The teacher must continually assist children to recognize and resolve the assumptions underlying inquiry procedures. Terms must be carefully defined, pertinent variables selected, and problems of measurement, control, and technique carefully examined. There is no shortage of source material to promote skill in analysis of assumptions. For example, a popular text for teachers suggests that to answer the question Can mushrooms and other fungi make their own food? children remove some mushrooms or bracket fungi from their habitat and, after placing them in water, compare the survival of these fungi with that of the fungi in their original locations. The conclusion given is that the fungi die because without chlorophyll they cannot manufacture food. There are a number of questionable assumptions in this experience, however. For example, the fungi may have been so severely damaged by their forcible removal that death was inevitable.

There is also the traditional demonstration that air exists in apparently solid materials. If a lump of soil is immersed in water, bubbles of "air" are soon trapped in the container. These bubbles are usually said to come from the soil, and therefore soil must contain trapped air. But this conclusion is not certain. For example, has the gas been tested and conclusively identified as air? If it is air, may it not have arisen from a reaction of the organic acids and other materials of the soil with water? Perhaps it is the air dissolved in water that escapes as the water warms up. Many unwarranted assumptions may be accepted, resulting in an answer of dubious worth.

Questioning assumptions is also important when additional data are required. Questions that, on the surface, are rather simple (What makes the sky blue? Why are there so many earthworms on the ground after a rainstorm? How long can a fly fly without stopping?) are in reality exceedingly complex. The simple demonstration at the beginning of this chapter was anything but simple because of its many hidden assumptions. Many problems will call for ingenuity in formulating hypotheses, a prolonged search for data from a wide variety of sources, and a sympathetic yet demanding teacher as a guide, if children are to formulate satisfactory answers. For this reason, the tested inquiry experiences in the new elementary science programs are of great value in science teaching.

Controlling Experiments

The most common and at the same time the most flagrant violation of the elements of scientific experimentation is the uncontrolled manipulation of variables. Controls must be used whenever possible. If the class is studying the growth of plants and the germination of seeds, for example, one of the questions inevitably posed, either by teacher or children, is Will seeds begin to grow in dry soil? To answer this question, a number of pots of dried soil, each planted with some quick-germinating seeds such as radish seeds (each pot is exactly alike as possible), are placed in the same environment. After a few weeks half the pots are watered and kept moist, although not saturated. The growth in the watered pots will be sufficient to result in the more or less valid generalization that radish seeds apparently do not germinate in dried soil in the time period, but do germinate in moist soil. All conditions are the same (within the limits practicable in the classroom) with the exception of moisture, and the limited generalization is valid, whereas if dry soil alone had been used, the lack of growth could be ascribed to defective seeds.

How else can children test experimental validity?

Ingenuity is frequently necessary in planning suitable controls, and adequate controls are often impossible to maintain in the classroom. Observations of many phenomena call for little or no experimentation, but eventually despite the obvious effect of certain variables final confirmation must be left to controlled experiments. Suppose that in examining an ant trail, a pathway from an ant nest to a source of food, a child rubs his fingers over the pathway. Some ants may become confused and lose the trail. Does this confusion result because the trail was erased or because a human odor was added? Is there any simple way to tell? Can you propose a controlled experiment that will lead to a valid conclusion?

Whatever the data, they must not be overgeneralized! Conclusions must be limited to the data, unless the specimens or samples, as well as the conditions, are known with great certainty to be typical; that is, selected from a general population. Could one legitimately conclude from the card and inverted glass demonstration that all glasses, all cards, and all liquids behave in the same way? Of course not; no more than we could say that all seeds fail to germinate in dried soil. It is an overgeneralization to say that children will always overgeneralize. But they often do, and the wise teacher carefully limits the conclusions of the class to their legitimate and appropriate realm.

Planning and Evaluating Process-centered Teaching

The teacher should frequently ask himself questions such as these in planning and evaluating the potentialities of science experiences:

1. Is it possible for my children to formulate the problem in operational terms?

2. Does the problem lend itself to a thorough but simple analysis that is not excessively superficial?

3. Do my children know enough science so that with various sources of information they will be able to propose intelligent hypotheses?

4. Are there enough firsthand experiences to sustain interest, develop skills, and provide the necessary direct contact with reality from which concepts grow?

5. Are classroom (and home) facilities adequate for gathering data and for testing hypotheses?

6. What scientific concepts and principles are included? Can they be fitted into a coherent structure?

7. Do the experiences lend themselves to critical analysis; to the evaluation of hidden and half-hidden assumptions; to the growth of skills that are essential to success in scientific thinking?

8. Is enough time available for exploration in depth?

9. What is the relationship of these activities to the great ideas of the sciences?

10. Do the children have a reasonable expectation of success without excessive fear of failure?

Some Examples of Inquiry

A class inquiring experience

Let us now examine a teacher-initiated problem more closely to illustrate and summarize the points previously made. Assume that a fifth grade teacher has set up a simple pendulum, constructed of a length of string and a lead sinker so supported that the pendulum swings freely. This may be a single demonstration, unrelated to previous learning, to serve as a motivational instrument, or it may be one component of a series of activities on gravitational force. If the teacher asks a child to pull the sinker to one side and then asks the class, "What will happen when Susie lets the sinker go?" the class will come up with several answers. The most probable is that the sinker will swing back and forth. The teacher may enlarge on the question by asking how long the pendulum will continue to swing and how high it will swing at each end. After the pendulum has swung several times (how many are desirable?), the teacher may ask how the rate of swinging can be changed. How can the speed of the pendulum be measured? Children will suggest different weights, string materials, string lengths, and arcs. The discussion may center on this question: What variables change the time of swing of this pendulum? Subsidiary problems of length, arc, and weight (someone invariably suggests pushing the sinker) are quickly proposed. Children propose hypotheses for each subproblem: Making the string longer makes the pendulum swing more slowly. The teacher and class must be alert to the need for keeping all factors constant except the experimental factor. The teacher then leads the class to propose controlled experiments to test their predictions. The data gathered by the class should be entered on a data sheet designed for the purpose. Small groups may carry out these experiments and then report to the class.

The assumptions underlying the experiments must be extracted and analyzed. Does it make any difference where the weights are tied on the pendulum string? Does the air affect the pendulum? Do the vibrations of the pendulum stand affect the period of the pendulum? What about deviations from the plane of the swing? Does changing the location of the pendulum affect the results? What other assumptions about the conditions of the experiment may be proposed?

Predictions as tests of hypotheses

The data should be adequate for a decision on the alternatives. The children's hypotheses are either right or wrong, or the data are not yet of a quality to permit decision. If the hypotheses are right, that is, if they appear to be valid, the children should be able to make two predictions. First, what will happen if each variable is altered in turn? Second, how can this knowledge be used to make other predictions? That is, what general predictive power comes from knowing the effect of changing the pendulum variables? As an example of the first prediction, the teacher may ask, "What should the length of the pendulum be for a one-second (or two-second) pendulum period? If the period (the dependent variable) and the length (the independent variable) are plotted graphically, the pendulum length for a period of one second is easy to find. Graphical analysis is particularly valuable because it bypasses the formal mathematical treatment of high school and college physics. The questions Can we make a pendulum with a baseball bat? and How can we speed up or slow down a pendulum clock? are examples of the second kind of prediction.

Systematic analysis

The teacher must continually point out the need to identify pertinent conditions, significant objects, and relevant procedures. He guides the class in assessing the value of the suggestions and questions proposed and in ascertaining essential variables. He must help children identify changing factors that thereby affect the results. Few children have had the opportunity or the desire to vary experimental conditions systematically to learn what may happen. If they do tinker with the variables, the children are apt to do so unsystematically, changing two or more simultaneously (see Chapter 2). If children alter both the length of the pendulum and the arc through which the pendulum swings, the results will be confusing. To cite another example, in the "bent pencil" experiment a simultaneous variation of the liquid used and the angle of viewing will give meaningless results.

The work of Suchman at the University of Illinois confirms the belief that children can propose and test hypotheses (see Chapter 2). They can learn to phrase their questions more narrowly so that specific answers may emerge. There is no dearth of opportunity for training in good habits of logical thought if children are not restricted to dull memorization of the textbook or to a routine course of study. The teacher should let children predict the results of a particular action; he should *not* supply the answer in advance or allow children to turn to authority before their own analytical schemes are found wanting or before additional verification is required. He should continue to ask Why? How do you know? How can we test this? Are you sure? How can we find out? What will happen if we do what you say? What do we need to do it? Where can we find out? What do we do next? As a variation of this procedure the teacher might quote some scientific fact, (for example, pressure of water increases as the water depth increases) and then ask the class to find some procedure to verify this fact. A teaser demonstration, such as the card and inverted glass demonstration described earlier or the evolution of oxygen from *Elodea* when sunshine falls on the plant, is even better.

The teacher may also present a few facts, either verbally or experimentally, and then cooperatively draw from these facts the fullest possible set of inferences. For example, if the teacher rubs a hard rubber comb with wool and quickly touches the comb to a simple "Rice Krispies" electroscope, the two bits of cereal are attracted to the comb and then quickly fly apart. If he then rubs the comb with a sheet of polyethylene film (a dry-cleaner's bag) and brings the comb closer to the electroscope, the bits are attracted to the comb, touch it, and then fly apart again. The comb repels the cereal kernels, which move closer to one another (although they do not touch) when the comb is taken away. What hypotheses about the behavior of the cereal kernels may be derived from these experimentally observed facts?

Summary

The process-centered approach to science teaching is neither a panacea for the infirmities of contemporary science instruction nor an infallible guide by which the aims of science teaching will be attained. It is, however, the most promising direction for elementary school science because it offers a unique opportunity for children to grow in mastery of both the processes and products of science. Inquiry *is* more difficult to plan, sustain, and evaluate than conventional, textbook-centered teaching, and many educators are not convinced that it is feasible in most elementary schools, but its psychological and conceptual strengths are such that elementary education would be remiss in not venturing boldly into a teacher-education program in science centered on inquiry.

The essence of process instruction is genuine experimentation with many phenomena to answer questions without relying on the crutch of a textbook or other authority (see Chapters 6 and 11 for examples of such experiments). Concomitantly a permissive, cooperative atmosphere in the classroom encourages both children and teacher to examine the evidence they find, assess their hypotheses and assumptions, and come to the most reasonable and logical conclusions consistent with the evidence.

These requirements demand far more from both teacher and class than traditional science instruction, but the potential rewards are so attractive that it would be folly to delay training elementary school teachers in the habits and procedures of inquiry. Little is to be lost by this shift—the past record of elementary science teaching speaks for itself. However, teachers who have been taught science as a rigid hierarchy of facts, laws, and principles cannot be expected to master inquiry procedures overnight. The simple scientific experiences described in this chapter will help to orient teachers to the kinds of doing and thinking that will help them teach process-centered science successfully.

For further study

1. Select an experiment from an elementary science textbook and rewrite it for inquiry. To what extent is it psychologically and pedagogically functional? To what extent are its outcomes in harmony with Bruner's postulates for discovery teaching?

2. How do conventional curricula attempt to solve the process–product dichotomy?

3. What are some of the important elements in successful inquiry teaching?

4. Ideally problems are generated by the spontaneous interaction of children with the natural phenomena of their environment. Is this idea a workable guide to practice in the classroom?

5. What are some of the important assumptions on which these experiments or events are based?

   (a) A metal expands when heated.

   (b) An inflated balloon shrinks when heated.

   (c) The rate of chirping of crickets increases as the temperature increases.

   (d) An electric current decomposes water into hydrogen and oxygen.

(e) The probable appearance of dinosaurs may be reconstructed from fossil remains.

6. Think of as many hypotheses to explain these phenomena as you can:

   (a) Water expands when it freezes.

   (b) The growth of animals or plant populations sooner or later levels off.

   (c) Silt and gravel carried by water may be deposited to form a delta.

   (d) The eye of a hurricane is relatively calm.

   (e) Dry cells that stand for long periods of time corrode.

7. To what kinds of scientific problems is graphical analysis applicable? [See Blackie, J., *Inside the Primary School* (London: Her Majesty's Stationery Office, 1967), pp. 91–92.]

8. Describe an experiment in a children's science book, which is not valid because controls are omitted. Can you think of a way to use controls to improve the experiment?

9. How do you know that a conclusion is valid? Overgeneralized? Give some examples from firsthand experience. Can you find examples in this book?

10. When a four-year-old child is shown two rods superimposed, one on the other, he would probably say the rods are equal in length. When the rods are no longer aligned, the child would probably say the one that hangs over is the longer. Yet the child does not really think one rod has grown longer. To him, the word *longer* here means the one that sticks out, and not until much later does he learn that the question was to be interpreted as "If you line them up at one end, which one sticks out at the other?" The question is meaningless to a child until he knows the procedure.[18] Can you find examples of equally meaningless questions in elementary science textbooks, including this book? How can these questions be made meaningful?

11. This book obviously promotes inquiry–process–discovery-based science teaching. Is this position justified sufficiently on the basis of the evidence presented? (For additional discussion see Newton, D. E., "The Dishonesty of Inquiry Teaching," *School Science and Mathematics*, 67: 807–10, December 1968; Tanner, R. T., "Discovery as an Object of Research," by Kochendorfer, L. H., and H. C. Penn, *School Science and Mathematics*, 68: 655–57.)

Notes and references

1. Bruner, J., "The Act of Discovery," *Harvard Educational Review*, 31, Winter 1961, pp. 21–32.

2. McDonald, F. J., *Educational Psychology* (Belmont, Calif.: Wadsworth Publishing Co., 1965), p. 214.

3. Kagan, J., "Personality and the Learning Process," *Daedalus, Journal of the American Academy of Arts and Sciences*, 94: 560–62, Summer 1965.

4. Sinclair, H., and C. Kamii, "Some Implications of Piaget's Theory for Teaching Young Children," *School Review*, 70: 182, February 1970.

5. Hunt, J. McV., "Conceptions of Learning with Implications for Styles of Teaching Young Children," in *The Craft of Teaching and the Schooling of Teachers* (Denver: Proceedings of the First National Conference, U.S. Office of Education – Tri-University Project in Elementary Education, 1967), p. 18; Sinclair, H., and C. Kamii, *op. cit.*, p. 175; Gage, N. L., "Can Science Contribute to the Art of Teaching?", *Phi Delta Kappan*, 49: 402, March 1968; Estvan, F. J., "Teaching the Very Young: Procedures for Developing Inquiry Skills," *Phi Delta Kappan*, 50: 393, March 1969; Lovell, K., "Developmental Processes in Thought," *Journal of Experimental Education*, 37: 19, Spring 1968.

6. Suchman, J. R., "The Illinois Studies in Inquiry Training," in R. E. Ripple and V. N. Rockcastle, eds., *Piaget Rediscovered*, A Report of the Conference on Cognitive Studies and Curriculum Development (Ithaca, N.Y.: School of Education, Cornell University, 1964), p. 108; Suchman, J. R., Inquiry Training: New Roles and Goals in the Classroom, mimeographed, University of Illinois, n.d., pp. 3–5.

7. Bloom, B. S., "Testing Cognitive Ability and Achievement," in N. L. Gage, ed., *Handbook of Research on Teaching* (Chicago: Rand McNally, 1963), pp. 390–91.

8. Holt, J., *How Children Fail*, (New York: Pitman Publishing Corp., 1964), p. 25.

9. Kagan, J., *op. cit.*, p. 561.

10. Ausubel, D. P., *The Psychology of Meaningful Verbal Learning* (New York: Grune & Stratton, 1963), p. 161.

11. Conclusions 1 through 6 are from Herman, G., "Learning by Discovery: A Critical Review of Studies," *Journal of Experimental Education*, 38: 66, Fall 1969; conclusions 7 and 8 are from Scott, N. C., Jr., "The Strategy of Inquiry and Styles of Categorization," *Journal of Research in Science Teaching*, 4(3): 153, 1966.

12. Friedlander, B. Z., "A Psychologist's Second Thoughts on Concepts, Curiosity, and Discovery in Teaching and Learning," *Harvard Educational Review*, 35: 26–27, Winter 1965.

13. Adapted from Atkin, J. M., "A Study of Formulating and Suggesting

Tests for Hypotheses in Elementary School Science Learning Experiences," *Science Education,* 42: 414–22, December 1958.

14. Westnedge, R. T., "Science in Primary Schools," *School Science Review,* 49: 346, March 1968.

15. Eccles, P. J., "Teaching Behavior and Lesson Effectiveness for a Specific Science Objective," *Journal of Research in Science Teaching,* 5(4): 397–404, 1967–68.

16. Wilson, J. H., Differences Between the Inquiry-Discovery and the Traditional Approaches to Teaching Science in Elementary Schools, unpublished doctoral dissertation, University of Oklahoma, 1967, pp. 68–69.

17. Atkin, J. M., *op. cit.,* pp. 414–22.

18. Holt, J., "A Little Learning," *New York Review of Books,* 7: 10, April 14, 1966.

*Elementary Science
for the Seventies*

elementary school science teaching is undergoing dramatic changes. For the first time the dream of a new elementary science to meet the challenges of modern society has stimulated the educational establishment into constructive action. Many scientists, teachers, and science educators have organized into independent teams and with massive government funding have been developing exciting and innovative programs of science curriculum. In recent years more than two dozen elementary science programs of national significance have produced science curriculum materials for school use. Some of these programs are no longer in existence, having completed their mission of experimenting with new elementary science materials. No two programs have proposed exactly the same goals, methods, curricula, firsthand experiences, or evaluative content. However, they have followed similar strategies in designing their programs:

1. A team of well-known scientists, together with elementary school teachers and educational specialists, usually under the leadership of one of the scientists, meets jointly to prepare objectives and a curriculum rationale. This meeting is followed by workshop sessions to write texts and teachers' guides, devise laboratory and other firsthand experiences, and prepare audiovisual aids and evaluative materials.

2. "Experimental" teachers are specially indoctrinated in the program during a summer or an inservice institute.

3. The "experimental" teachers test the preliminary curriculum materials and innovative methods at various grade levels in as many different schools and regions as can be secured for this trial.

4. Consultants sent out from the program headquarters visit the teachers regularly. The consultants seek to learn from the teachers and children what difficulties teachers and children are encountering. They attempt to work out ways to overcome the problems.

5. Teachers send regular reports to program headquarters about their successes and failures.

6. The field testing often takes three or more years and involves many dozens of teachers and thousands of children. Following the testing the "final" edition, which incorporates the many revisions, is published. It is accompanied by a detailed teacher's guide, kits of equipment, audiovisual aids, and other supplementary materials. These published materials then become available to any school system that wants to adopt that program.

7. Additional revisions are made as feedback from the teachers and children in the adopting systems is received, and new editions are published.

Pretesting makes the difference

Although major programs may vary these steps and their sequence they invariably include step 3. This pretesting and "bug elimination" is a significant departure from earlier efforts at developing curriculum materials. The older science curricula were textbook based. Because textbooks were seldom pretested in the same way, reading difficulties, unworkable experiments, misunderstood concepts, and impracticable teaching suggestions tended to be built into these curricula. Many changes in the teaching of elementary school science (see Chapter 3) have taken place in the long history of public school education. But with few exceptions they were the products of one teacher or a group of teachers—rarely including scientists—who decided on the basis of informed opinion what children should be learning in science and how that science should be taught. These curricula, composed of arbitrarily chosen and untested bits of science together with certain kinds of firsthand experiences, were imposed on teachers. The teachers, untrained in the content and methodology of these curricula, were unwilling and unable to give them the commitment necessary to make them work. In contrast the new elementary science programs vigorously recruit teachers sympathetic with their goals. Through workshop and inservice institutes, which are often federally funded, and with continuing feedback and the supportive services of elementary science consultants, the programs strive to gain willing acceptance for an elementary school science that differs in many fundamental ways from the rather traditional elementary science of the first half of the twentieth century.

Currents of change

Elementary school science is not the only content field in education affected by bold new ideas. The Biological Science Curriculum Study (BSCS) in high school and the School Mathematics Study Group Curriculum (SMSG) in the elementary school are only two of the hundreds of innovative curricula. Without doubt the curricular and methodological currents presently found in thousands of elementary and secondary schools will continue to inspire the teaching of science in elementary schools. For many years science education has sought to open to children in the elementary grades the opportunity to learn at firsthand what science is about, what scientists do, and simultaneously to provide many opportunities for the cognitive stimulation so necessary for the development of children.

Many fresh, ingenious, and functional materials have changed the face of elementary science. Classroom teachers can draw on a large body of stimulating and suggestive science materials successfully tested in many classrooms similar to theirs. The teachers' guides help teachers anticipate likely points of difficulty. They suggest ways of avoiding these difficulties and techniques for making maximum use of available resources. The combined insight, experience, and skills of the teams of scientists, teachers, and science educators have given the schools science teaching expertise never before available.

New versus old   The new programs tend to stress the processes of science and the formation of sound conceptual structures[1] in contrast with the traditional curricula that emphasized learning scientific facts and principles. In the new science children learn almost entirely from firsthand, concrete experience. The reading of science materials sometimes seems to be an afterthought. The programs introduce rather sophisticated concepts once assumed to be far beyond the grasp of children. Teachers are encouraged to be open, informal, and indirect in their teaching. They learn to work cooperatively with children in developing solutions to problems, instead of delivering answers.

The science programs for the seventies are each different in many ways. Some programs concentrate on one science, such as astronomy or physics. Some draw on the physical sciences, whereas others seek to integrate science and mathematics or science and conservation. Some are sequentially organized so that to succeed in the higher grades children must first master basic skills and content in the earlier grades. Other programs are used independently or as supplementary materials.

This chapter cannot possibly treat all the programs in detail, but three programs with quite dissimilar philosophies and structures are rather fully described: *Elementary Science Study* (ESS), developed by the Education Development Center, Newton, Massachusetts, beginning in 1960; *Science Curriculum Improvement Study* (SCIS), originated at the University of California at Berkeley under the leadership of Robert Karplus, a physicist, beginning in 1962; *Science—A Process Approach* (SAPA), instituted by the Commission of Science Education of the American Association for the Advancement of Science, beginning in 1962. They have been selected because (1) they are representative; (2) they are in use nationally and internationally; (3) they were experientially developed (4) they have many teachers and science consultants trained in their philosophy and procedures; (5) they have been used in schools long enough for experience and feedback to have accumulated from teachers without special training; and (6) they use materials that are all commercially available.

The Elementary Science Study

An open design

One of the most significant facts about the Elementary Science Study (ESS) is that, unlike SCIS and SAPA, the writers of this program have not proposed a formal psychological structure. They have avoided any kind of prestructuring, which they feel will inhibit freedom and initiative in the classroom. The units incorporate many psychological and developmental principles, which tend to be Piagetian in emphasizing the importance of firsthand experiences (see Chapter 2): Children are encouraged to do what they want to do with materials instead of doing what someone else tells them to do. The ESS materials are planned to involve children deeply and emotionally; materials that do not excite children are either revised or dropped from the program. Mastery of science concepts and conceptual schemes is not an ESS objective.

ESS planners have been guided by this point of view:

> Children use materials themselves, individually or in small groups, often raising the question themselves, answering them in their own way, using the materials in ways the teacher had not anticipated, and coming to their own conclusions . . . we tried to create situations where the children are called upon to talk to each other.[2]

This method, in ESS terms, is called "messing about," which was further defined in David Hawkins' account of some of his experiences as ESS director:

"Messing about"

> Simple frames, each designed to support two or three weights on strings, were handed out one morning in a fifth-grade class. There was one such frame for each pair of children. In two earlier trial classes, we had introduced the same equipment with a much more "structured" beginning, demonstrating the striking phenomenon of coupled pendula and raising questions about it before the laboratory work was allowed to begin. If there was guidance this time, however, it came only from the apparatus—a pendulum is to swing! In starting this way, I, for one, naïvely assumed that a couple of hours of "Messing About" would suffice. After two hours instead, we allowed two more and, in the end, a stretch of several weeks. In all this time, there was little or no evidence of boredom or confusion. Most of the questions we might have planned for come up unscheduled.

Why did we permit this length of time? First, because in our previous classes we had noticed that things went well when we veered toward "Messing About" and not as well when we held too tight a rein on what we wanted the children to do. It was clear that these children had had insufficient acquaintance with the sheer phenomena of pendulum motion and needed to build an apperceptive background against which a more analytical sort of knowledge could take form and make sense. Second, we allowed things to develop this way because we decided we were getting a new kind of feedback from the children and were eager to see where and by what paths their interests would evolve and carry them.[3]

The proponents of ESS insist that these explorations with concrete objects will lead children to develop attitudes of *wanting* to find answers to their questions.

The need for guidance

In all ESS units, depending on the children, teachers at times must give specific help, perhaps to guide children through a series of complex operations or to help a group work out an experiment. But on the whole children should be left to their own devices. An assumption of the ESS program is that the two aspects of science—the logical and highly structured and the intuitive, imaginative, and humanistic—will be brought together through this permissive, occasionally directive, methodology.

ESS—nonsequential

The writers of ESS have not prepared specific sequences of units because they believe that too little is known about the role of sequence and content in facilitating the growth ESS hopes to see in children. They also assume that the local school system or the individual school itself is responsible, rather than ESS, to determine a functional sequence for children and teachers. Some schools and school systems have worked out their own curriculum sequences and assigned certain units to particular grade levels, even though the logical and psychological interrelations are too weak to justify these sequences. Rather they assign their sequences to facilitate planning and alleviate equipment problems.

Throughout the units an important thread of science process exists although not formally stressed. Because in all firsthand discovery-oriented science, children make measurements, classify, observe, and infer, they will also develop proficiency in these process skills in ESS units. But they develop these process skills informally and as needed.

The units

More than fifty classroom-tested units, together with supporting equipment and audiovisual aids, have been published. They cover a broad range of subject matter in biology, chemistry, physics, geography, logic, astronomy, and mathematics. Some are rather narrow; *Bones* and *Ice Cubes* are examples. Some are designed to develop spatial coordination through imaginative play with geometrical forms; *Geoblocks* and *Tangrams* are examples. Some roughly approximate conventional elementary science units or perhaps parts of such units, for example, *Pendulums, Behavior of Mealworms,* and *Growing Seeds.* In keeping with ESS philosophy, the units are difficult to classify into grade levels. The majority of these units may be used in several grades, depending on the interests and proficiency of teachers and children. *Behavior of Mealworms,* for example, has been successful from the upper primary grades to college science education courses. *Attribute Games and Problems,* which is not a science unit, is useful from kindergarten to junior high school. Some units are best suited for individual or small group research, again depending

Richness of experience on the children and their teachers. The time required to complete most of the activities in ESS units varies according to the level and length of the science periods. As an approximation, five to twelve weeks are usually taken for most units provided at least three forty-five–minute periods each week can be scheduled. Other ESS units are the following:

Name	Grades
Batteries and Bulbs	4–6
Budding Twigs	4–6
Animal Activity	4–6
Clay Boats	2–6
Eggs and Tadpoles	K–6
Light and Shadows	K–1
Microgardening	4–6
Pendulums	4–6
Mystery Powders	3–4
Optics	4–6
Pond Water	3–7
Primary Balancing	K–4
Sand	2–3
Sink or Float	2–7
Whistles and Strings	4–5
Where Is the Moon?	3–7

Introducing an ESS unit   Teachers usually begin ESS units by asking questions about an object all the children have seen or handled. In *Peas and Particles,* a unit on large numbers and estimations for grades four through six the teacher introduces the unit by showing a large photograph of a child holding eight inflated balloons all tied together in a row. After each child has enough time to study the photograph, the teacher covers the picture and asks, "How many balloons do you think there are in the picture?" He then shows the class a handful of beans and asks for guesses about the total number in his hand, after which he lays the beans down in a pile on a square of dark paper so that the children may examine them closely and guess the number once again. A group of children count the beans and the children compare their guesses. The teacher then introduces several additional activities to help the children make better estimates of numbers and sizes. This unit, which has been successful from third to eighth grades, takes about fifteen class periods.

Science, mathematics, and social studies

ESS stresses the links between improving understanding of numbers in science and the positive effect on understanding numbers in social studies. Teachers are reminded that many number concepts in the social studies are meaningless to many children. For example, what do statements or questions such as these mean to intermediate grade children: The population of Scotland is equal to the population of Massachusetts. How many people lived in America at the time of the Revolutionary War? Such statements or questions mean little unless children know what they imply and have had meaningful experiences in handling large numbers. *Peas and Particles* will help them in this task. Many other units provide opportunities for children to develop other important social studies concepts.

The introduction to *Behavior of Mealworms* exemplifies the discovery spirit of ESS:

See for yourself

Behavior of Mealworms stimulates children to ask questions about the observable behavior of an unfamiliar animal and then directs them to ways of finding answers for themselves. As children observe and experiment, they learn some things about the process of scientific inquiry and about the sensory perception of the mealworm. How to carry on an investigation is the most important thing that children learn from the unit; the factual knowledge about mealworms is comparatively incidental.

The pupils begin their study of mealworms with undirected observations that lead them to elementary experiments on mealworms. A multitude of questions arise, such as these: Can a mealworm see? How do mealworms follow walls? How do they find a pile of bran? How can a mealworm be made to back up? In their attempts to solve these problems, the pupils devise experiments, observe, measure, keep records, design and build equipment, and draw conclusions. As they go on, they usually become aware of difficulties resulting from their inability to control pertinent variables. After studying *Behavior of Mealworms,* children may realize that they still don't know much about the animal which at first seemed so simple. [4]

Teachers sometimes worry that they are not properly prepared to teach this kind of science, which is so different from conventional elementary school science. ESS seeks to ease these teacher fears:

> You do not have to be a mathematics or science teacher to teach this unit. It can be taught without reference to other studies in order to give children a basic tool they can then apply wherever they need it; or it can be used in connection with other elements of a more formal curriculum, as a technique in science or math, or as an application to social studies.[5]

Every teacher can do it   The teacher's guide furnishes helpful suggestions for everyday activities, such as questions for the teacher, discussions of potential difficulties, suggested readings, optional activities, techniques for culturing mealworms, information about the mealworm's anatomy and behavior, and typical children's responses.

The ESS teacher does not give the material to her children, allow them to play with it for a few minutes, and then put it all away with a neat summary; traditionally closed and highly directed teaching does *not* meet the methodological demands of this program. The teacher acts as a guide and consultant; she allows the children to discover on their own for extended periods, but she also knows when to step in. The right kind of ESS teacher, at least from one child's point of view, has been described as follows:

Right!   The teacher is a person who:
   is not too busy to listen to your ideas;
   helps you find exciting things to do, and then lets you do them;
   helps keep others from bothering you—when you want to think;
   gets excited with you about your ideas and your discoveries
   encourages you to work on different problems, without ruining your work
      by telling you the answers all the time;
   is a helper when you need an extra pair of hands and all the others are busy;
   helps you realize what you've learned.[6]

Wanting to is a start   Teachers who operate in this style will naturally fit into ESS, but they will be ready to *capitalize* on ESS science only *when* they know *how* to use ESS units. Even though many teachers have been successful with only the published teacher's manual and the necessary equipment, the majority of teachers will probably need to know *how* ESS classes work, *how* the materials are handled, stored, and inventoried, and *how* the different roles of guide, consultant, and teacher of individual children, small groups of children, and the class as a whole are effectively carried out. In many school systems, particularly those systems that adopt the program entirely or partially, in-service workshops are usually scheduled for this purpose. In addition science consultants are often available to help teachers. Many, if not most, of the teachers who participate in innovative programs of any kind no doubt will need long-term supportive services, which must include moral *and* psychic support:

Need for support

It is very difficult for an isolated teacher to go it alone in an innovative endeavor, irrespective of his commitment to the innovation. He needs the continued philosophical and material support of his superintendent, principal, and supervisor, as well as the good will of his teaching colleagues. Real and lasting curriculum change comes only when it proceeds on a broad front and when personnel at all levels are actively committed to the same goals.[7]

Help for the teacher

In the following extract from the teacher's guide for *Behavior of Mealworms*,[8] notice the number of helpful suggestions for teaching this section and the ways the process skills are elicited. Mealworms are used because their behavior is relatively simple and consistent, and they easily grow and survive in good condition. Whenever possible the questions that arise from observations are investigated by simple experiments. The teacher may also ask such questions as these taken from the teacher's guide: Do you think mealworms can see? How are mealworms different from earthworms? Are mealworms very smart? The unit provides many opportunities for children to observe systematically, plan, and perform controlled experiments.

6. Making a Mealworm Back Up

Observation

The work on backing up gives the children a chance to observe how a mealworm reacts to various stimuli. Here they may begin to see how measurement by counting can refine qualitative observations. Because backing up is an obvious and clear-cut response, it is an easy one to begin with. Perhaps you or your children will find some other suitable question for study also.

Various ways to make mealworms move backward

If your students have ever seen mealworms backing up, they can probably describe examples of this somewhat unusual behavior. Then you can ask the question, "How many different ways can you find for making a mealworm back up?" Students can work on this problem at home and give their results in the following class.

The various methods which have been found to make mealworms back up should then be listed on the board. Some of the ways mentioned in trial classes are listed below:

Suggestions

flashlight	turpentine dropped with
smoke	medicine dropper
burning match	touching with pin
vinegar on Q-Tip	electric shock with battery
hot iron	touch with pencil
loud noise	color
bumping into something	blowing on it through a straw
ammonia	spinning on phonograph table
water dropped on head	wet ink from felt pen

If the list becomes too long, it might be convenient to have the children group some of the similar ideas together into larger categories. In the list above, the use of vinegar, turpentine, and ammonia might be combined under the heading of odor.

Selecting the best way to
make a mealworm back up

Quantitative data

The question can be raised: "Which is the best way to make a mealworm move backwards?" Guesses can be heard, but there will probably be little agreement. "How can we find out which is best?" Some child may say that everyone should try all the different ways. "Would it be better if everyone tried each way more than once?" "Why?" Perhaps the students can be led to see the desirability of *quantitative results* obtained by testing each method a large number of times. They usually do not realize that this may permit more precise statements to be made about certain observations.

*Defining the
problem*

Some ideas for making a mealworm back up might be considered poor by a majority of the students, and these can be eliminated through discussion. The class should then select for more study the four or five methods it thinks most promising. You can suggest that a definite procedure be established to test each method.

One class had the following ideas for hot things to use in testing heat:

a piece of glass heated on the radiator
steam from a steam iron
a nail heated by a match
short circuiting a dry cell battery with a wire and wrapping the wire
around the mealworm

The hot nail was selected because it was thought to be the most uniform source of heat and would be readily available.

Since the improper use of a hot nail can injure a mealworm, you could suggest that the heated nail be held far enough away so the mealworm would not get burned, but close enough so it could feel it. The children can experiment with one another to find what this distance would be for their own hands. Such a measurement may help to establish a practical distance even though the small size of mealworms probably makes them more sensitive to heat than we are. A hot nail could burn a mealworm's sensory hairs long before it could be painful to a child's fingers.

Each student can be asked to make a chart for recording his observations. Some of the better of these can be reproduced on the chalkboard. You might then take the best ideas and design a final chart. This can be copied by the students and used at home for recording the results of their experiments. It is not important how many times each method is tested. The students should make as many trials as they can.

The lesson which follows the experimenting might be initiated by asking the children which was the best way to make the mealworm back up. Despite the quantitative evidence, there will undoubtedly be no complete agreement. "Perhaps it would be better if we added together everyone's results." One way to tabulate class totals is to list, at separate places on the chalkboard, the different methods tested. The students can then go to the board and write their figures in the appropriate columns. When the columns have been totaled, they can be summarized on a master chart. The final figures will show that some ways are better than others. You might ask the children to rank the methods from best to worst. The results from one class are shown in Chart 1. Touching the antenna with a pinhead was best, but what is next best? Shining a flashlight made the mealworm back up 198 times in 334 tries, and the hot nail worked 247 times out of 330. Clearly this is an ideal example to show the value of computing percentage.

Chart 1. The best way to make a mealworm back up.

What was done	Times tried	Times backed up	Rank from best to worst
Hot nail	330	247	2
Flashlight	334	198	3
Blocking with hand	242	131	4
Touching antenna with pinhead	268	212	1
Mealworm at edge of paper	223	19	5

Some additional work on backing up

Analysis of results

"Why didn't everyone get the same results?" A variety of possible reasons may be suggested by the class. One answer to this question might come from the realization that there were still differences in the techniques employed, in spite of the precautions to avoid this. Also, students may have noticed differences in the reactions of the same mealworm to a particular stimulus, and differences between different mealworms. Such things as rough or repeated handling, hunger, age, and environmental factors can affect the responses of a mealworm.

The class totals could be compared with those of other groups of children. You can use the results shown here or ones from classes you have taught in the past. Some mention might be made of what the observations on backing up tell about those things which mealworms can detect. "Would mealworms back away from an unlighted flashlight?" "Do you think that mealworms can feel heat?" "Why do you think so?" "When you use a hot nail, do mealworms back up because of the heat, or because they see the nail, or for both reasons?" "Would cool air make a mealworm back up as much as would the warm air from your mouth?" "What other things (like smells, smoke, and wind) can mealworms detect?"

Enriching experiences

Perhaps interested students could attempt to measure the sensitivity of different parts of a mealworm's body to some of the stimuli. "Can he feel air on his tail as well as on his head?" "How would you find out?" (It is a curious thing that mealworms seem to back up regardless of the wind's direction.) Some other children might want to experiment to see how dim a light can be detected by a mealworm. "How could you find this out?" A bright light could be shined at a mealworm and made a little dimmer on each successive trial. (Dimming can be accomplished by moving the light progressively farther away or by covering it with various thicknesses of cloth or paper.) "What might it mean when the mealworm no longer backs up?" "Would it make any difference if you started with a dim light and made it brighter each time?" In one class some children became interested in the effect of poking mealworms gently with sharp and smooth objects. They found, to their surprise, that more mealworms backed up when touched with smooth things than when touched with sharp ones.

Evaluation

The writers of ESS purposely did not develop evaluative materials for teacher use because ESS has sought to foster an inquiring spirit—an attitude of curiosity, interest, and willingness to find out for oneself—and these affective aspects of science are difficult to assess objectively. For this reason,

ESS tends to rely on informal teacher and observer estimates of behavioral response based on such criteria as these:

Informal yet valuable

1. Do the children enjoy working with the materials?
2. Do they come up with a large number and variety of questions?
3. Do they take the apparatus home?
4. Do they think about the problems out of class?
5. Do they try to answer questions by working with the materials?
6. Are there conversations in the class—discussions or arguments?[9]

In one study conducted in a Washington, D.C. ghetto school, approximately 80 percent of all teachers, many of whom were uncertified, were successful in ESS, as judged by this evidence:

1. An increase in informal talk in the classroom.
2. An increase in the number of open-ended questions asked by the teacher.
3. A higher tolerance on the part of the teacher for working out solutions slowly.
4. The breakup of the class into small groups.
5. The evidence of pleasure and involvement on the part of the children.
6. Children hard at work on something so that they scarcely notice a visitor.
7. An increased output in student writing and storytelling.
8. Teachers showing an increased interest in other materials.
9. Teachers reporting they had developed new approaches on their own.[10]

The increased interest of the children in science seemed to lead to better learning in other subjects as well, perhaps because the childrens' self-image became more positive as they sensed their ability and success in science. Other studies confirm many of these findings. Children in ESS classes participate more actively in science activities, produce more high-level contributions such as inferences, judgments, and opinions, give more voluntary responses, and work harder and with more purpose than do children in conventional science classes. Teachers also ask more questions, rely far less on recitation and dictation, and call on children by name much less often for answers than do teachers in regular science classes.[11]

Science Curriculum Improvement Study

*Combining process
and content*

The Science Curriculum Improvement Study (SCIS) has maintained its status as one of the most highly developed and popular of the elementary science programs. Its major goal is the attainment of "scientific literacy." SCIS considers that scientific literacy includes knowledge and understanding of biological and physical concepts, which are essential for full participation in modern society, as well as "a free and inquisitive attitude and the use of rational procedures for decision making."[12] Each unit seeks to help children fuse understanding of these concepts with certain skills and attitudes that will lead them to scientific literacy.

Dependence on a formal psychological base is more apparent in SCIS than in ESS. Although both programs rely heavily on Piagetian principles, each SCIS unit is specifically planned to accomplish the following:

1. Make available a widely diversified program which relies to a great extent on concrete experience.
2. Relate these concrete experiences in such a way that a conceptual framework emerges with teacher guidance.
3. This framework will be more valuable to [children] than any generalizations they would make for themselves without guidance.[13]

Psychological framework

In defining the psychological framework for its unique methodology, SCIS has drawn liberally from many sources. Piaget's conception of equilibration (the harmonious balance between the child's assimilation of his world and his accommodation to it) is joined with selected aspects of Gagné's learning hierarchy (conditioning) and Piaget's, Bruner's, and Hunt's emphasis on discovery learning. The introductory, or *Exploration,* phase of SCIS units combines discovery and equilibration learning. The child's preconceptions as he investigates his materials affect the way he accommodates and assimilates these experiences. Sometimes he will move ahead to new ideas and to successful equilibration, but more often he will become confused and muddled, unable to remove the cognitive dissonances he has discovered. When the child becomes confused, the teacher steps in with the *Invention* phase to suggest ideas, procedures, and a resolution of the dissonances. In the culminating *Discovery* phase equilibration and learning-hierarchy conditioning consolidate the new concepts through repetition and application to new contexts.

This repetition and application must be *self-directed* so that learning will be cognitive rather than verbalistic.[14]

The old strengthens the new

In accordance with these principles each lesson supplies new, concrete experiences and simultaneously introduces or strengthens one or more scientific concepts.[15] In Exploration children individually or in small groups work with materials supplied by the teacher. They are to find out as much as they can; on their own they discover that they will need additional information to explain what they saw and did. In Invention the teacher usually introduces and explains a concept that will help the children make sense of their explorations. The concept is named, defined, explained, and clarified by teacher demonstrations and repetition of the exploration experiences if necessary. The term *invention* does *not* mean that children "invent" the concept but rather that scientists once "invented" the concept to help explain certain experiences. In Discovery the teacher guides the children through a set of experiences that apply the Invention concepts to new situations. The teacher spends more time on this part of the lesson than on either of the other two phases because SCIS emphasizes the importance of transfer learning for cognitive development. However, the teacher need not always follow this sequence: The Discovery lesson may be combined with the exploratory phase of the next lesson, and other shifts may be made.

The three phases

The teacher

Working hard with SCIS

The SCIS teacher, like the ESS teacher, is guide, catalyst, and observer. She must be effective in open, indirect classrooms and supportive of her children. She is a source of feedback to her class; she works actively to involve her children in manipulating, doing, observing, talking, questioning, and thinking. But at the same time she is expected to direct them to learn and apply certain scientific concepts. For these reasons SCIS lessons are much less open-ended than ESS lessons. Teachers will keep busy:

1. Asking questions which encourage students to extend their observations and experiments.
2. Asking, when necessary, questions that focus student attention on a specific object or event.
3. Involving students in discussion and review of their laboratory experience.
4. Suggesting possibilities for extending old or new experiments.
5. Selecting a variety of appropriate activities and providing materials.

6. Using the student activity pages (children's guide sheets) or manuals, games, and other learning devices to illustrate the meaning and application of a concept.[16]

The teacher's changing role
During Exploration children are relatively free; the teacher acts merely as observer and guide. In Invention the teacher becomes more directive in introducing children to a generalized way of thinking that will help them make sense of the Exploration questions and activities. For example, in one Invention phase of *Interaction and Systems,* described in detail on pages 241–42, the teacher, after the children have played with magnets (these magnets are placed on toy cars so that they can move freely), explains that the repulsion and attraction of the cars are examples of "interaction-at-a-distance" (the children are already familiar with the word *interaction* from other experiences) because the magnets did not touch although they interacted.

You may elect to do this while once again pushing one cart gently so as to make the other one roll away. Before proceeding further write the phrase *interaction-at-a-distance* on the chalkboard so the children may read it and repeat it after you. You might then point out how much distance there is between the two magnets while these are interacting. For contrast, call the children's attention to the hand and cart which interact only when they are touching and have no distance between them. Invite the children to coin a name for this relationship—perhaps "touching interaction," "interaction-without-a-distance," or a similar phrase. Write this name on the chalkboard beside interaction-at-a-distance.[17]

In Discovery the teacher returns to a nondirective stance. Her questions are more open-ended to encourage children to think of new ideas and new applications. She asks questions such as: What is your evidence of interaction? Will the objects interact without touching? The teacher is instructed not to give answers but rather to phrase questions so as to lead children to find out for themselves. She answers their questions with other questions, such as: Can you think of another way to check what you think? Have you tried to change the distance?

Supporting the teacher
Few beginning teachers will be prepared to move directly into SCIS programs without special workshop training and supportive services. Teachers are not expected to be science specialists, but they will be functioning in a

nontraditional science teaching role. For this reason SCIS has arranged for a national network of consultants and training programs. Teachers from school systems that plan to adopt SCIS may be trained in one- or two-week workshops, after which they will be prepared to serve as trainers in their own system.

The units

SCIS takes time

Twelve SCIS units are commercially available for the elementary grades. Teacher's guides have been prepared for each unit, together with a student's manual or student activity worksheets, equipment, and a number of supplementary films that may be purchased or rented. The schools schedule two units a year, each to run about four months, with two forty-five–minute science periods each week. One of these units is from the physical sciences, the other is from the biological sciences. The titles of the units are nearly self-explanatory:

Grade	Physical science	Biological science
first	Material Objects	Organisms
second	Interaction and Systems	Life Cycles
third	Subsystems and Variables	Populations
fourth	Relative Position and Motion	Environments
fifth	Energy Sources	Communities
sixth	Models: Electric and Magnetic Interaction	Ecosystems

These units are not suggested for grades lower than those assigned, although they may profitably be taught in the next one or two higher grades. The units are sequenced to a much greater extent than the ESS units in that the children are to master certain concepts and process skills in each grade. Children without previous SCIS experience will be handicapped in SCIS science, and teachers will have to give them extra help in bringing them up to the level of the class.

Objectives of the units

The first grade units *Material Objects* and *Organisms* seek to "sharpen children's powers of observation, discrimination, and accurate description." In these units children study such properties of objects as color, shape, and texture. They use concepts such as *objects, properties, change,* and *evidence,* and learn the needs of living things. They also meet the terms *birth, growth, death of organisms,* and *habitat.*

Beginning with the second grade the children are introduced to the important concepts of *physical interactions* and *organic plant and animal development*. In succeeding years these concepts are used again and again in different contexts and at higher levels of abstraction. The children also meet new concepts, such as *population, food web, reference frames, spatial relationships, environmental requirements, energy transfer, communities of plants and animals, life systems, electrical and magnetic phenomena,* and *scientific models.*[18]

The following extracts from the teacher's guide for *Interaction and Systems* are illustrative of SCIS methodology.[19] Notice how each of the three phases Exploration, Invention, and Discovery is introduced and carried forward by teachers and pupils following closely the SCIS principles.

Overview [of Part Two, "Objects Interact"]

In Chapters 4 and 5 children engage in exploratory experiments that can be carried out with assorted objects. During this work their attention should be focused on their objects and on the changes that occur during an experiment. The children make simple records of the objects they use.

Suggestions for teachers　　The invention of interaction in Chapter 6 is based on the definition stating that interacting objects influence each other. You will find directions for demonstration experiments in the teacher's guide and review problems and activities for your pupils in the student manual.

The evidence-of-interaction concept is introduced as the class experiments with light-sensitive papers in Chapter 7. Additional problems are posed in the student manual.

The concepts introduced in Part Two are further developed later in the unit. Therefore, we suggest you leave extensive review, clarification, and application for the discovery activities in Parts Four to Seven. Be patient in awaiting the children's spontaneous use of the terms *interact* and *evidence of interaction*. Even though a child may understand these terms, he usually requires several weeks of hearing them used by others before he uses them freely himself.

This section follows a review of the first grade unit *Material Objects* and is followed by five other sections: "Systems," which introduces the important systems concept in the SCIS units; "Pulley Systems"; "Dissolving," which discusses systems in solution; "Interaction-at-a-Distance"; and finally "Electrical Interaction."

4. Experimenting with Common Objects

In this exploratory activity, children experiment with simple objects and observe changes that are produced. At the same time, they spontaneously describe their observations to classmates or to you in small-group situations. This chapter will require one class period.

Teaching materials

For each team of two children:

    1 cardboard tray (Drawer 1)
    1 tumbler (to be partly filled with water—Drawer 1)
      colored candy balls (Drawer 4)
    2 "mystery pictures" (Drawer 4)
    1 piece of aluminum wire (Drawer 4)
    1 small magnet (Drawer 5)
    1 flashlight bulb (Drawer 5)
    1 battery (size D)*
    1 scissors*
    3 or 4 paper clips*
    1 rubber band*
    1 card (3" × 5")*
      plastic clay (1–2 ounces)*
    1 sharpened pencil*

    * provided by the teacher

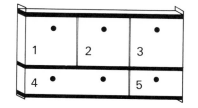

Advance preparation

Setting the stage

Each set of objects should include the items from the kit; in addition, the batteries, which are very important, must be purchased. It is not necessary that each team has all the other items. The kit items are provided in sufficient

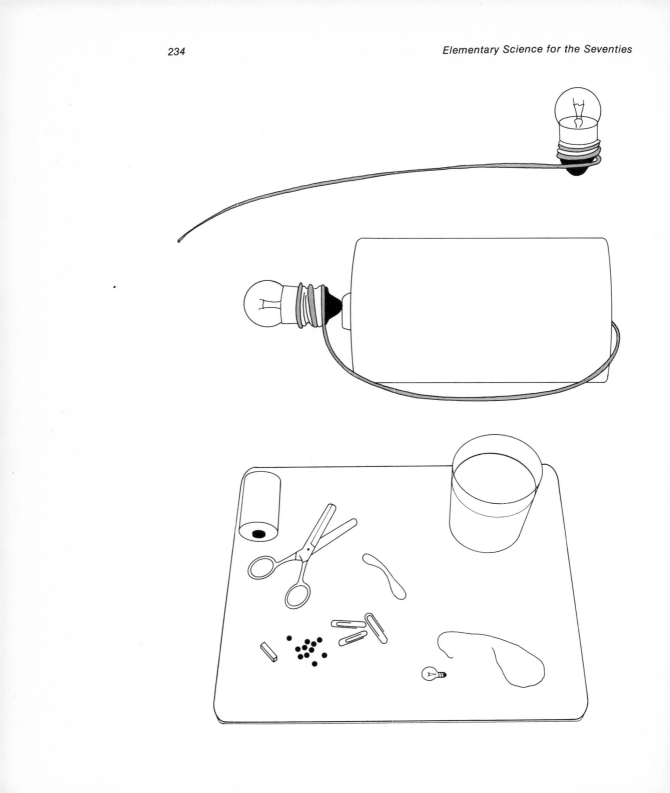

quantity to complete sixteen sets. The "mystery pictures," which are printed six to a sheet, must be cut apart. (When water is spread on them, colors appear.) Cut the aluminum wire into five-inch pieces and twist one end of each piece once around the base of a flashlight bulb. (When connected with a battery, as shown, the bulb will light.)

Prepare one set of objects for each team of two children. Partly fill the tumblers with water or plan to pour the water while the children work. You will be able to save time by asking two or three children to assemble the sets on the trays.

Teaching suggestions

Initiating activities

Distribute the trays and invite the children to experiment with some of the objects. They may add items from their pockets and desks but should not take more than three or four objects from a tray at one time. Encourage the children to use as many combinations of objects as they wish.

Individual children may want to show you their experiments. Encourage these children to discuss the objects they are using. You might also suggest that a child try another experiment with the same objects. If he can't think of one, you might suggest, "See if you can make the paper clip become a magnet by rubbing your magnet back and forth across it."

When the children have tried out their ideas, ask them to return the objects to the trays, so several sets may be used in Chapters 5 and 6. Postpone organized discussion until the end of Chapter 5, when the children will have recorded their experiments.

5. Picture Record

To begin developing skills in record keeping, children pictorially record the objects they used for experiments in Chapter 4. Some children describe and demonstrate their experiments. Later, they compare and discuss the changes that occurred. A single class period is adequate for this activity.

Teaching materials

Student-manual page 1

For the class:

several trays of objects (from Chapter 4)
drawing paper (optional—provided by the teacher)

Make a record of the objects you used in one experiment

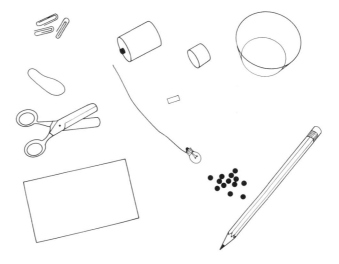

Teaching suggestions

Directions to children

Distribute a student manual to each child. Since this is the first time the children use their manuals, invite them to examine and discuss the pages among themselves.

Student-manual page 1. Tell the children that each of them will record the objects he used for one experiment during the preceding science class. He may choose any method he wishes to mark these objects on page 1. Even though the children have worked in pairs, each one should mark his page individually. If he used objects other than the ones shown in the picture, he may draw these freehand. If a child has difficulty remembering his experiment, give him a tray of objects and ask him to carry out a new one.

While the children are recording their experiments, observe their work and help those who are having difficulty. Look for interesting experiments that may serve as examples in a later discussion. If children ask you how to record more than one experiment, suggest that they draw others on a blank piece of paper. In order to avoid confusion, no more than two experiments should be recorded on one page.

Discussion. Invite a few children whose experiments were particularly interesting to demonstrate these for the class (they will need the trays of objects) and to show how they recorded them. Encourage the children to pay attention to the objects being discussed and to compare the changes that took place. We suggest that you spend only a short time discussing each experiment, since children quickly lose interest in the work of others. After the discussion, store the trays of objects for later use.

Optional activities

Further experiments. Especially interested pupils may carry out additional experiments using the same equipment. The children can draw pictures of the objects they used on a blank sheet of paper. By observing these drawings you can discover whether they were motivated to reproduce experiments that were demonstrated during the discussion period. If some are inspired to investigate more interesting object combinations, plan for them to report their discoveries to the class.

6. "Inventing" the Interaction Concept

Suggestions for teachers

A brief review of the children's earlier experiments sets the stage for the invention. You then introduce and illustrate the concept that objects interact when they do something to each other. Children observe and describe changes that occur during the demonstration experiments. They also interpret pictures of interacting objects in the student manual and later draw their own pictures. Plan to use one or two class periods. Optional activities by individuals or small groups may take extra time.

Teaching materials

Student-manual pages 2–4

For demonstration purposes:

    1 spring (Drawer 4)
    1 support stand (Drawer 4)
    2 carts (Drawer 4)
      vinegar in squeeze bottle (Drawer 4)
      concentrated bromothymol blue solution (BTB) in
        squeeze bottle (Drawer 4)
    1 large magnet (Drawer 5)

3 tumblers (Drawer 1)
1 pitcher (to be filled with water—Drawer 1)
1 pail (Drawer 1)
1 tray of objects (from Chapter 4)
  paper towel (provided by the teacher)

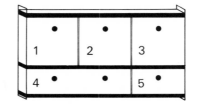

Advance preparation

Concepts to be reviewed

Prepare some materials from Chapter 4 for review demonstrations. You might use the light bulb, wire, and a tested battery; water and an unused "mystery picture"; and a 3″ × 5″ card and scissors. For the first new demonstration, you will need one cart, the spring, and the support stand. Set up the support stand and hang the spring from the screw eye.

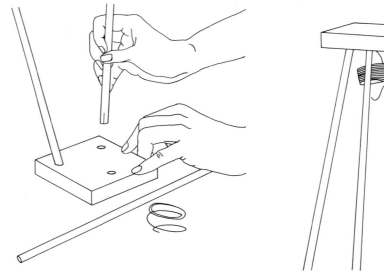

Assembling support stand   Support stand with spring

Another demonstration employs the large magnet and the second cart. Remove the keeper bar from the magnet by twisting it. Put the cart on a level surface. Practice attracting the cart with the magnet by holding the magnet above and in front of either end of the cart. Keep withdrawing the magnet

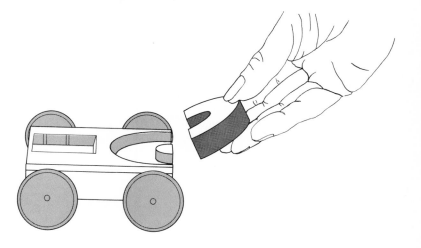

so the cart does not catch up with it as it rolls forward. You may also use the magnet to pick the cart up by its axles.

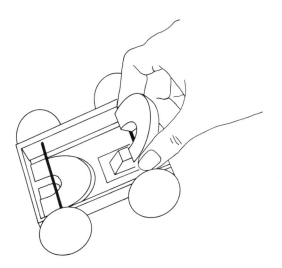

The last experiment is demonstrated after the interaction concept has been introduced. It employs separate, dilute solutions of bromothymol blue dye (BTB) and vinegar. The dilute solutions are prepared by squeezing three or four drops of each liquid into separate tumblers, each about one-third full of water. When these solutions are poured into a third container, the dye turns yellow. Try it. The BTB solution should be blue, but if your tap water is slightly acid, the BTB solution will appear green. In that case use distilled water for the experiment.

Teaching suggestions

Using the familiar

Review and demonstrations.   To establish a familiar context for the invention that follows, use a group of objects from Chapter 4 to demonstrate an experiment. Or, a child might demonstrate his experiment, using page 1 in his manual to remind him of the objects needed. Hold up the objects and ask the children what changes are occurring during the experiment. If they seem not to understand the question, describe the change yourself—for example, "The bulb is now lit." Then proceed to one or two other experiments and ask again about the changes that occur.

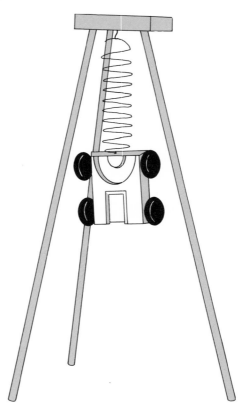

New demonstrations.   Next, you may perform one or two of the new demonstrations you have prepared. First, identify one cart and the spring as the objects to which the children should pay special attention. Ask the children to watch closely as you hang the cart from the spring. Remove and reattach the cart two or three times, so everyone has a chance to notice that the spring stretches. Briefly discuss the changes that occur and then set the objects aside, after taking the cart off the spring.

Second, pick out the magnet and the other cart and use the magnet to attract the cart several times as you did before. Again, ask the children what changes they notice.

Invention.   By now, you and the class have observed and discussed the changes that took place during several experiments. Tell the children, while indicating one set of objects with your hand, that you will use the word *interact* whenever objects do something to each other, as in the case of the cart and the spring. Write *interact* on the chalkboard and let the children pronounce it.

Illustrate the meaning of the word *interact* by repeating some of the earlier demonstrations. Ask the children to identify moments when the objects are

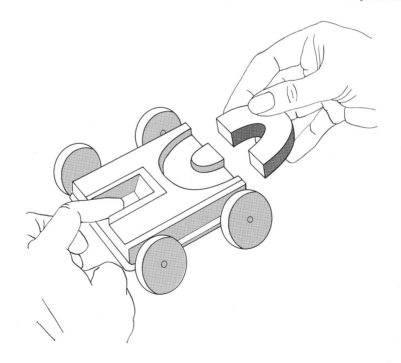

interacting and also moments when they are not interacting. Finally, invite them to describe their evidence. As an example of objects that interact, firmly hold the cart and the magnet so close to one another that you can feel the attraction even though you do not let them come together. Let the children see you "straining" to keep them apart as you ask them about interaction. (This example illustrates interaction-at-a-distance, which will be introduced by name in Part Six.)

After this explanation, tell the children that you will show them another system of objects that can interact. Display three tumblers on a paper towel and prepare separate dilute solutions of BTB and of vinegar in two of them.

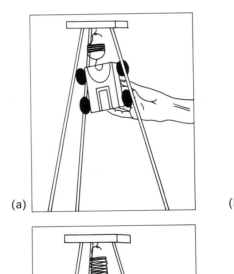

(a)

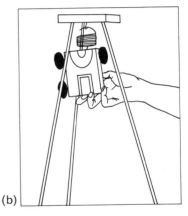

(b)

(c)

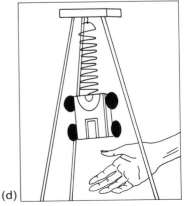

(d)

Ask the children to watch carefully as you mix the liquids by pouring them into the third tumbler. Let them describe the changes they observe. Do they interpret these to mean that the liquids interacted while you poured them together?

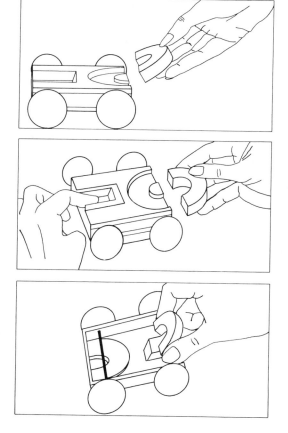

Follow-up experiments. Encourage all the children to experiment with the support stand, the spring, a plastic tumbler with a string handle taped on (to serve as a container for weighing crayons and other objects at the end of the spring), the magnet, and the cart. You may leave these on the class science table for a few days. (See the "Optional Activities" section for suggested experiments.)

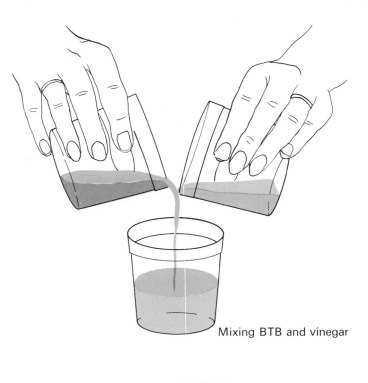

Mixing BTB and vinegar

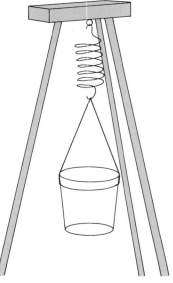

Student-manual pages 2 and 3. (You may wish to postpone this new activity to another day to avoid an overly long science session.) Let the children read about the experiments and study the pictures on pages 2 and 3. Your pupils must look closely and refer to their previous observations to answer the questions. If the children suggest that they should repeat the demonstrations to verify their hypotheses, encourage and assist them in doing so.

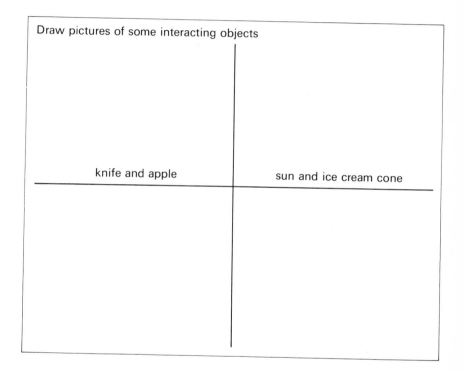

Draw pictures of some interacting objects

knife and apple   sun and ice cream cone

Student-manual page 4. The children may draw pictures, as suggested on this page. As you review the pictures, look for understanding of the interaction concept. If you find that some children draw objects after (or before), rather than while, the objects interact, ask them to describe the evidence that the objects interacted and add "after" (or "before") to their drawings. Children who make this kind of error apparently find it difficult to focus their attention on one instant of time in a quickly changing phenomenon, as when a bat hits a ball. They may need additional explanations emphasizing the time aspect by your calling attention to the "before" phase (the ball comes to the bat), the "during" phase (the bat hits the ball), and the "after" phase (the ball flies away).

7. Evidence of Interaction

At the beginning of this discovery activity, you introduce the phrase evidence of interaction to refer to the observed changes among interacting objects. Your pupils apply their understanding of this phrase when they investigate the interaction of light with photographic and Ozalid papers. They examine their student-manual pictures for evidence of interaction. Depending on the children's interest, plan to spend one to three science periods on this chapter. Encourage individuals to carry out optional projects.

Teaching materials

Student-manual pages 5–7

For the class:

        photographic paper (Drawer 4)†
        Ozalid paper (Drawer 4)†
2 tumbler lids (Drawer 4)
2 absorbent paper pads (Drawer 4)
        ammonia solution in squeeze bottle (Drawer 4)
2 tumblers (Drawer 1)

    †These materials must be used on a sunny day or under a strong light source.

Caution. Ammonia gas is highly irritating and should not be inhaled.

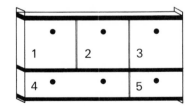

Advance preparation

If it is not feasible to take the class outdoors, your students will need a strong light source—an overhead projector, a 100-watt bulb, or a fluorescent bulb—for exposing the photosensitive papers. The children should be able to bring their papers to within one or two inches of the light source for the interaction to take place.

Cut each 4″ × 5″ sheet of Ozalid paper and photographic paper into two pieces. The papers should be kept inside their original wrappers until they are used. They will not be damaged, however, by being exposed *briefly* in a normally lighted room.

The photographic paper provided in the kit turns brown when exposed to bright light for some time and, unlike other kinds of photographic paper, does not need to be "developed" to show a picture. The Ozalid paper, however, only turns from yellow to white in light and must be "developed" by interaction with ammonia gas. To develop a small piece of Ozalid paper, squeeze five drops of concentrated ammonia onto an absorbent pad in a tumbler with a lid. Quickly insert the Ozalid paper under the lid. Keep the tumbler tightly closed to prevent the ammonia gas, which evolves from the liquid, from escaping. You may wish to try this procedure to familiarize yourself with it. Shortly before class prepare two tumblers with lids, absorbent pads, and ammonia for processing the exposed Ozalid paper when the children are ready.

Developing Ozalid paper

Teaching suggestions

Typical feedback suggestions

Feedback activity. An easy way to begin the lesson is to write or draw on the chalkboard. Ask "Are the chalk and the chalkboard interacting?" If the answer is "no" or there is no answer at all, try to discover the children's source of difficulty and review the interaction concept, using classroom objects such as the eraser wiping the board or your shoe stamping the floor.

Invention.   If the children answer "yes," continue with "How do you know they interacted?" Ask the children what they observed that made them think the chalk and the board interacted, and point out that "observing" means *feeling* and *hearing,* as well as *seeing.* (This will prepare them for the sensory activities in Chapter 11.) Carry out a few other activities such as tearing a piece of paper or sharpening a pencil. Each time, ask the children whether the objects interacted and what they observed to make them think so. In your responses repeatedly make use of the phrase *evidence of interaction;* you might also write it on the board for emphasis.

Photographic paper.   One way to introduce the photographic paper is to show an unexposed piece to the class. Then ask a few pupils to take some pieces of the paper outdoors, to a window receiving direct sunlight, or to the light bulb prepared in advance. Tell the children to bring their samples back when they observe some evidence of interaction. They will find that the paper darkens when exposed to light. Let them show this evidence to their classmates. Then send another group out with a small object, such as a paper clip or a key, to cover part of a piece of photographic paper while it is being exposed to the sunlight. Let them show their paper to the class and tell what changes took place. Eventually, all children can experiment with the paper, either during science class or at unscheduled times.

Alternatively, you may elect to take the entire class outdoors so everyone can investigate the photographic paper at the same time. Be sure that you observe exposed papers in a well-shaded spot so they do not darken further.

Ozalid paper.   When you introduce the Ozalid paper, point out that one side is pale yellow and the other side is white. Tape a small object, perhaps a leaf, to the yellow side and let a group take the paper outdoors or to the light bulb. The yellow side should be exposed to light in order to interact. (If you decide to go outdoors with the whole class, take along both prepared tumblers and the ammonia bottle for possible recharging, so you can develop the exposed papers in a shady place.)

In either instance, call the children back after a few minutes; they may not return of their own accord because they are waiting vainly for a spectacular change in the paper. Remove the object, and let them examine the paper and describe any evidence of interaction to the class. Then quickly open the tumbler, drop in the paper, and close the lid without letting much ammonia gas escape. While everyone watches, the once-covered part of the paper will turn blue or black. This change is evidence of interaction between the yellow material on the paper and the gas from the ammonia you put into the tumbler.

Take the paper out and let the children examine it. They will be able to see the changed color and smell the ammonia gas still clinging to the paper in a

Encouraging questions harmless but detectable quantity. After this introduction, some children may raise questions about what happened. Encourage all who are interested to experiment with their own papers. More suggestions are included in the "Optional Activities" section.

Something happens when objects interact.
Sometimes the objects look different.

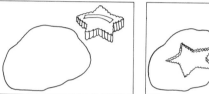

Sometimes the objects move together.

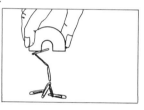

Sometimes the objects move apart.

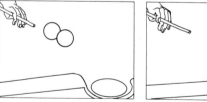
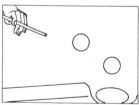

There is a change.
The change is evidence of interaction.

Avoid giving answers *Student-manual page 5.* (Use page 5 and the following pages in several short sessions rather than during a single, long science period.) Read page 5 to the class. It introduces the use of "first" and "second" pictures to show changes in interacting objects. Discuss the evidence of interaction shown in the photographs. Let the children also look at page 4 to describe the evidence they have shown in their drawings. They may compare the information conveyed by each of their single pictures with that conveyed by a pair of photographs.

Discussion is a
two-way street

Student-manual pages 6 and 7. Pages 6 and 7, intended for class discussion, extend the idea of using two pictures to present evidence of interaction. Here, however, not all the interacting objects are shown in the photographs. On page 6 the children are invited to speculate about what objects interacted to cause the changes. When there is no change in an object, as in the case of the banana, no other object interacted with it. Ask the class what objects (if any) interacted with those shown on page 7 in the manual.

Do these picture stories show evidence of interaction?

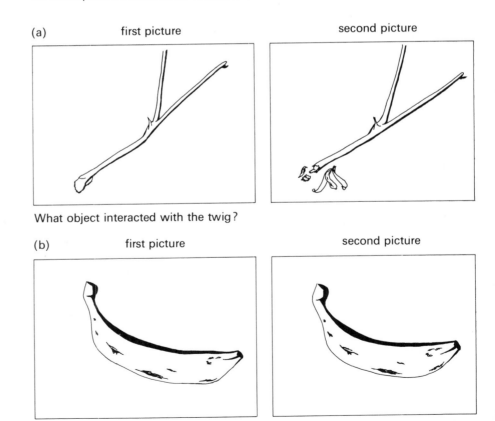

(a)   first picture   second picture

What object interacted with the twig?

(b)   first picture   second picture

Do these picture stories show evidence of interaction?

(c)   first picture   second picture   third picture

(d)   first picture   second picture   third picture

Limited formal evaluation

Evaluation

The SCIS program does not have special evaluative instruments for teacher use. However, teachers are encouraged to observe how well children respond to questions, generalize, apply concepts in new situations, and plan experiments. Students' responses provide information about how well they understand the concepts. Teachers also evaluate the written work in the student manuals and student activity pages. The teacher's guides suggest certain kinds of feedback experiences and the many optional activities also include evaluative suggestions. This statement from a teacher's guide expresses the evaluational philosophy of SCIS:

> Feedback is information that comes to a person in response to something that person did. As a teacher, you are collecting feedback from your pupils most of the time. An answer to a question yields feedback. So does a child who looks out the window during your demonstration. In this guide we have tried to alert you to feedback situations in which your pupils' responses are likely to influence your teaching plans. In addition, the "Optional Activities" sections in Chapters 7, 10, and 19 [of this manual] include suggestions for evaluation of feedback through special procedures designed for this purpose. Plan to examine the student manuals periodically, not to grade a child's work but rather to gather evidence of the quality of his understanding. If you confer with individual children, you may discover the reasoning behind some of the statements made in their manuals.[20]

Doing minimizes discipline

The SCIS program has had more descriptive and experimental studies published than has the ESS program, and therefore its strengths and weaknesses are better known. The results of these SCIS studies are generally encouraging. For example, in classes of disadvantaged elementary school children SCIS teachers were forced to use far fewer discipline moves in teaching science than in teaching mathematics or the language arts. The children were much more interested in science, and the teachers could act more permissively in science than in the other subjects. They could wait for answers to their questions, could give more neutral responses than before, and acted more like guides than directors.[21]

A second study compared the question-asking techniques of two groups of teachers. One group had been given special SCIS training and used SCIS materials in teaching science. A non-SCIS trained, but otherwise matched, group used traditional materials in teaching science. The SCIS teachers asked significantly more questions that required demonstration of skill, comprehension, analysis, and synthesis than did the traditionally oriented teachers, who asked mainly recognition and recall questions. Not only did the SCIS teachers ask different kinds of questions, they asked many more questions and relied far less often on "telling."[22]

There is, however, a negative aspect to these findings. Although they ask higher level questions, SCIS teachers also spend much more time giving directions to help their children handle the many SCIS materials effectively.

An irrational doctrine

Much class time seems to be wasted in distributing and storing materials.[23] One consultant who has worked with many SCIS teachers reminds them that SCIS never implies that all facts are subjective and that there are never *any* right answers. Teachers sometimes respond to the inquiry aspects of innovative science programs by accepting the philosophical doctrine that there is no ultimate authority and therefore, because truth is relative, the children's observations are as valid as anyone else's. Teachers who react in this way have made a serious error, for science *is* objective and its hypotheses can be tested.[24]

Improving questioning techniques

Despite these findings many teachers seem unable to "let go" of their traditional role in the classroom and allow children to explore and discover on their own. One observer has remarked that "In many of the . . . classrooms [she observed] the children were *not* interacting with the SCIS program simply because they were not given an opportunity to do so." She noted that as the school year wore on, the children's "spontaneity and freedom of expression" increased, although only in those activities the teacher permitted. The number of times the children disagreed with their teacher also increased, but the teacher made fewer discipline moves and spent more time with individuals. The children also shared their ideas with one another more frequently. The observer noticed further that although the teacher asked more questions, the questions tended to be convergent, perhaps because the teacher was not skillful in thinking up and phrasing divergent questions. However, the observer noted that within these SCIS classrooms was a "mutual contagion of interest and enjoyment." The children *and* the teacher enjoyed the lessons, and as the year progressed the teacher became even more positive as her SCIS skills developed more fully. Even an authoritarian, rigid teacher moved to allow more freedom to the children when she learned that she would not necessarily lose control of her class.[25]

Too little time

Another visitor to many primary grade SCIS classrooms discovered that the teacher spent excessive time in formal discussions and that the Exploration investigations "seldom lasted more than ten minutes" and were often not more than five minutes long.[26] The teachers seemed to value directive discussions more than firsthand experiences. The discussions in the physical science units, in particular, did not seem to help children form a more comprehensive and deeper understanding of the phenomena discussed, possibly because some teachers tended to value verbal facility more than learning from direct experience. They responded positively to "*who* participated rather than in terms of *what* was accomplished." The upper level units seem to offer somewhat less opportunity to stimulate intrinsic motivation because the unit goals are more subject-matter specific. As they worked through their assigned tasks, the children seemed to be enjoying themselves less than the younger children. If they are to profit from many of their planned and directed activities, the children will need to feel personally involved and "identify with the purposes of the experiments." Such involvement is asking a great deal of fifth and sixth grade children. For this reason teachers in upper level SCIS programs will undoubtedly need special training and support if they are to inculcate the SCIS spirit.

> The logistics and the social engineering required to set up a temporary lab (often with poor facilities) and to help six to twelve lab teams conduct an experiment is a most demanding task. To the extent that students are not motivated to perform the experiment well, the teacher must enter into the work of each lab team; to the extent that students are motivated primarily to have fun with the equipment and each other, the teacher will have a most stressful and unrewarding experience.[27]

The appeal of the SCIS program is through extrinsic motivation, whether by the achievement of marks, teacher approval or disapproval, or a "good science student" role. But if children must work "hard" for success the outcome will clearly be contrary to SCIS intentions.

Classroom-tested units The latest SCIS units have extensively been revised in accordance with the results of long-range evaluative studies. Effective teacher preparation and assistance programs are helping teachers to overcome their difficulties. This intensive evaluative revision will surely lead to much improved programs in the future. In the past feedback was nearly always informal and more or less impromptu. Textbook series rarely changed because of classroom experience; instead their content was updated, new illustrations introduced, and other format changes made. Their educational organization, however, remained essentially unchanged. For these reasons elementary science education using classroom tested, innovative programs such as SCIS will positively influence elementary schools and the preparation of elementary school teachers for these schools.

Science—A Process Approach

This elementary science curriculum is sometimes referred to as the AAAS curriculum because of its relationship to the American Association for the Advancement of Science whose Commission on Science Education secured sufficient funding to begin development in 1962. Science—A Process Approach (SAPA) has followed the customary writing path: A team of scientists, elementary school teachers, and science educators were brought together to write a new curriculum. Their tentative units were tested in elementary schools and then revised until they were ready for commercial publication.

A formal psychological structure

SAPA, to a much greater extent than either ESS or SCIS, is based on the idea of hierarchical skills developed by Gagné (see Chapter 2). The proponents of SAPA believe that children must master certain simple behavioral skills and acts before they can move on to "higher behavior acts." Gagné assumes that once they have mastered these simpler skills and behavioral acts, children will probably be able to master a higher behavior, which is a summation and integration of these subordinate behaviors. Based on this idea the SAPA curriculum is an elaborately outlined series of behavioral sequences, (with more than three hundred different behavioral objectives in the program). The many different behaviors included in the process skills are also interrelated insofar as possible.

This statement clearly describes the SAPA philosophy:

SAPA objectives

Science is more than a body of facts, a collection of principles, and a set of machines for measurement; it is a structured and directed way of answering questions. It is no mean pedagogical feat to teach a child the facts of science and technology; it is a pedagogical triumph to teach him these facts in their relation to the procedures of scientific inquiry. And the intellectual gain is far greater than the child's ability to conduct a chemical experiment or to discover some of the characteristics of static electricity. The processes of scientific inquiry, learned not as a set of rigid rules but as ways of finding answers, can be applied without limit. The well-taught child will approach human behavior and social structure and the claims of authority with the same spirit of alert skepticism that he adopts toward scientific theories. It is here that the future citizen who will not become a scientist will learn that science is not memory or magic but rather a disciplined form of human curiosity. From the start the child is an active participant in these scientific tasks. He does, indeed, observe, classify, measure, predict. He has the chance to work as a scientist by carrying out the kinds of tasks which scientists perform.[28]

The SAPA process

The basic process skills proposed for the primary grades are: Observing, Using Space/Time Relationships, Using Numbers, Measuring, Classifying, Communicating, Predicting, and Inferring. Process skills for the intermediate grades include these eight and an additional five that are more complex: Formulating Hypotheses, Controlling Variables, Interpreting Data, Defining Operationally, and Experimenting.

In pursuing these skills children engage in a broad range of science content, mainly in the biological and physical sciences. In SAPA, as in ESS and, to a more limited extent, in SCIS the facts, concepts, and principles of the sciences are given a lower priority. SAPA priorities are reserved for process skills; science content, to be sure, is important as the basis for the experiences from which children learn and through which they perfect Process Skills.

Content as raw material

The children examine and make explorations of solid objects, liquids, gases, plants, animals, rocks, and even moon photographs. But, with some notable exceptions, they are not asked to learn and remember particular facts or principles about these objects and phenomena. Rather, they are expected to learn such things as how to observe solid objects and their motions, how to classify liquids, how to infer internal mechanisms in plants, how to make and verify hypotheses about animal behavior, and how to perform experiments on the actions of gases.[29]

Nevertheless children will probably learn many scientific facts, concepts, and principles as they move through this program. An assumption of the SAPA program is that children who have had these sequential process units will be much better prepared for understanding science because they will have a better comprehension of the structure of the science and will be skilled in higher order scientific thinking.

SAPA—highly structured

SAPA, unlike ESS, and to a lesser extent, SCIS, is so highly sequenced that children who either have not attended SAPA classes or have been unsuccessful in these classes will be unable to participate effectively in advanced levels of this program without special remedial help. Because sequence is so important, teachers will find few opportunities to innovate and to add personal and creative touches. A high degree of teacher direction is necessary, even though the lessons include discovery. Open-ended investigations are rather few, and evaluative performance objectives and competency exercises serve as powerful directive forces. To complete a year's work of from twenty to twenty-six primary grade exercises, science must be taught daily from twenty-five to forty minutes, taking about five days to complete each exercise. In the intermediate grades, about thirty to forty-five minutes a day are required, with six days for each exercise. The teacher must devote several hours each week to planning, working through each exercise, collecting teaching materials, and giving and correcting the competency measures. Because of the necessity for specialized training, together with the time for lesson preparation, special science teachers or team teachers might best handle SAPA instruction in the intermediate grades.[30]

Method

Motivating lessons

Typically a SAPA teacher introduces each lesson by demonstrating experiments or showing interest-provoking materials. She asks interest-evoking questions to focus attention on the demonstration. The teacher follows the introduction with several activities integrated by a "Generalizing Experience," the purpose of which is to consolidate newly learned concepts and skills. Each exercise ends with an "Appraisal" exercise and a "Competency Measure," which assess the degree to which each child has attained the specified behavioral objectives. The lessons are teacher directed and initiated although children should complete the individual activities themselves. The teacher is active in class, moving around from child to child, guiding, asking questions, suggesting different approaches, pointing out errors, helping to make the equipment work better, and encouraging those who need psychic support.

The following extracts, *Observing Color Changes* (a kindergarten lesson) and *Loss of Water From Plants* (a more sophisticated third grade lesson), illustrate the nature of the work in the SAPA program.[31]

Observing 5: Observing Color Changes

Objectives

Performance objectives

At the end of this exercise the child should be able to

1. *IDENTIFY* and *NAME* a colored object by comparing it with a different kind of object that has the same color.
2. *STATE* that the color of an object changed from _____ to _____ after he has observed such change.

Sequence

A behavioral hierarchy

Rationale

Helping teachers plan

  In the first exercise on color the children learned to match similar colors and to name them. In this exercise, the children will again match and name colors. In addition, they will have an opportunity to observe and name colors in a situation in which colors change.

  In some of the activities the color changes occur as chemical reactions are taking place. Congo red, for example, is a substance which is blue in acid solution and red in basic solution. There is no need to make a point of this with the class, however. Here, simply emphasize observing the color changes and naming the colors.

Vocabulary

yellow	change
red	mix
blue	mixture
green	solution
color	

Materials

(Materials not with those provided for this exercise are with the general materials.)

*Three glass jars (about one-liter size) — One-quart canning jars will do.
*Yellow, blue, and red food coloring
*Six squares of construction paper approximately 10 × 10 cm — yellow, orange, red, purple, blue, and green
*Yellow and blue crayons for each child
*White paper
  Small plastic cups
*Baking soda solution (2 g/100 ml)
  Citric acid crystals (solution 2 g/100 ml)
  Congo-red dye
*Cotton cloth dyed with Congo red** (Use about ¼ gram of Congo red in 1 liter of water.)
*Cotton cloth dyed with Congo red, dipped in citric acid solution and dried (This cloth should be blue.)
  Paste sticks — one for each child
  Cobalt chloride
*Hot plate, or desk lamp with 100-watt bulb
  Congo-red paper — one piece for each child
*White vinegar
  Sheets of colored cellophane (red, yellow, and blue)
  Red and blue litmus paper

*Not supplied.
**If the concentration of the Congo-red solution is too high, the cloth will be dyed so deeply that it will appear black rather than blue when it is placed in citric acid solution.

Instructional procedure

Introduction

Put two glass jars in a place where all the class can see—one filled with water colored with 1 ml (20 drops) of yellow food coloring, and the other with 1 ml of blue food coloring. Put six squares of colored paper near the jars— yellow, orange, red, purple, blue, and green.

Ask a child to select a square of colored paper that is most like the color of the water in one of the jars. Tell him to put the square close to the jar it is most like. Ask another child to name the color. Repeat this process for the other jar.

Tell the children to observe closely while you mix some of the two solutions. Pour about one-fourth of the yellow solution into an empty glass jar. Then slowly add to it about one-fourth of the blue solution. The mixture should be green.

Ask the child to select a colored square that is most like the color of the mixed solution, and to put it near that jar. Ask another child to name the color.

Ask, What happened when I mixed the yellow water (or solution) with the blue water (or solution)? If the children do not say that the color of the water changed to green, say it to them.

Activity 1

Give each child a yellow and a blue crayon and a sheet of white paper, and ask the class if they think they might be able to make green by using the blue and yellow crayons. If they do not suggest trying to mix blue and yellow crayon marks on the paper, remind them how mixing yellow- and blue-colored water made green-colored water. Then ask them to try to do it. They might draw blue lines and color over them with yellow or vice versa. Tell them they can get a good green color by coloring an area uniformly blue and then coloring over it with yellow. They will get the best effect if they make yellow strokes crosswise to the blue strokes. Tell them, too, that light strokes give better results than heavy ones.

Ask them what happened when they made yellow crayon marks over blue ones. They should say that when they colored with yellow crayon over marks made with blue crayon, the color changed from blue to green.

Activity 2

Put three sets of two containers (plastic cups) on a table or on the floor in front of the class. Mark one of the containers of each set with a square and the other with a circle. Put about 100 ml of a sodium bicarbonate solution

(2 grams of baking soda to 100 ml of water) in the container marked with the square, and 100 ml of citric acid solution (2 grams of citric acid crystals to 100 ml of water) in the container marked with the circle. Put small pieces of cloth dyed with Congo red near each set of containers.

Ask three children to come forward and dip the piece of cloth in the container marked with the circle. Ask them to tell you what happened. (The red cloth turned blue when it was dipped in the bowl marked with a circle.) Ask three more children to come forward and dip some of the blue-colored Congo-red cloth (see *Materials*) in the bowl marked with the square and tell you what happened. You might let other groups of three children transfer the cloth from the bowl marked with the circle to the bowl marked with a square, and tell what they observe. (The blue color changes to red.) (See Figure 1.)

(Note: The citric acid solution is harmless, but it may be irritating to cut or scratched hands. For this reason, ask the children to transfer the cloth from the "circle" bowl to the "square" bowl by lifting it with a paste stick.)

Continue the activity until all the children have had a chance to dip cloth in the solutions and tell you what they observed. You might extend this activity by coloring the citric acid solution with red vegetable coloring so that red cloth dipped in the red solution turns blue. Similarly, you could color the sodium bicarbonate solution with blue vegetable coloring.

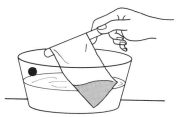

Figure 1

Activity 3

Before class, prepare a solution of cobalt chloride (about one gram of cobalt chloride in 50 ml of water); and use a paste stick to make letters, numbers, or patterns (circles, squares, triangles, and so on) with the solution on sheets of white writing paper. Prepare at least one sheet for each child and one for you. Then let all the sheets dry.

Ask the class to observe what happens when you warm one of the sheets over a hot plate. The pattern made with the cobalt chloride solution will change from white to blue. (A 100-watt light bulb will produce sufficient heat if you do not have a hot plate.) Help several of the children in turn to warm their sheets to reveal the patterns. In the course of the day each child should have a chance to see the pattern on his own piece of paper.

Show the class the colored squares that were used in the *Introduction*. Ask them which one is most like the color of the patterns on the paper. They should select the blue square.

Ask several children to tell what they observed when the paper was heated. They should say that the color changed from white to blue.

Generalizing experience

Putting things together

Give each child a piece of Congo-red paper and a paste stick. Provide each group of three or four children with a small bowl or jar containing some white vinegar diluted 1:1 with water (25 ml of vinegar and 25 ml of water). Tell the children to dip their paste sticks in the vinegar and then touch the stick to the Congo-red paper. Ask them what they observe. (Where the paste stick touches the paper, the color changes from red to blue.) Let the children draw patterns on the Congo-red paper with their paste sticks that they have dipped in vinegar.

Appraisal

Evaluation and reinforcement

Hold sheets of red, yellow, and blue cellophane in turn against the window, and ask the children to identify the colors. Ask them to predict what colors they will see if two of the sheets are combined. Try all possible combinations, and discuss the changes they see. If some child says he has a color wheel or top at home, ask him to bring it in for "Show and Tell."

When the time comes for dyeing Easter eggs, mixing the dyes will give added opportunities to reinforce learning about color change and to assess this learning.

Competency measure

(Individual score sheets for each pupil are with the general materials.)

Place on a table a jar containing weak citric acid solution colored with blue vegetable coloring, and a second jar containing sodium bicarbonate solution colored with red vegetable coloring.

TASK 1 (OBJECTIVE 1): Give the child a strip of blue litmus paper. Say, Point to the jar with color most like this piece of paper. Give one check in the acceptable column if the child points to the blue solution.

TASK 2 (OBJECTIVE 2): Say, Dip the end of the paper into the red mixture. Does the color change? Give one check in the acceptable column for a negative reply.

TASK 3 (OBJECTIVE 2): Give the child a second strip of blue litmus paper. Say, Dip the end of the paper into the blue mixture. What happens to the color? Give one check in the acceptable column if the child states that the color changes to red.

TASK 4 (OBJECTIVE 1): Give the child a strip of red litmus paper. Say, Point to the jar with color most like this piece of paper. Give one check in the acceptable column if the child points to the red solution.

TASK 5 (OBJECTIVE 2): Say, Dip the end of the paper into the blue mixture. Does the color change? Give one check in the acceptable column for a negative reply.

TASK 6 (OBJECTIVE 2): Give the child a second strip of red litmus paper. Say, Dip the end of the paper into the red mixture. What happens to the color? Give one check in the acceptable column if the child states that the color changes to blue.

Inferring 6: Loss of Water from Plants

Objectives

At the end of this exercise the child should be able to

Performance objectives

1. *CONSTRUCT* appropriate inferences about water loss from plants based on observations of investigations demonstrating water uptake and loss.
2. *CONSTRUCT* situations to test such inferences.
3. *CONSTRUCT* predictions from a graph about water loss from plants over a given period of time.

Sequence

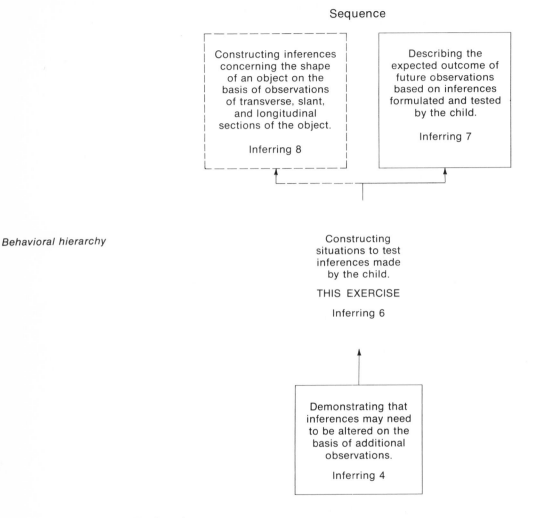

Behavioral hierarchy

Constructing inferences concerning the shape of an object on the basis of observations of transverse, slant, and longitudinal sections of the object.

Inferring 8

Describing the expected outcome of future observations based on inferences formulated and tested by the child.

Inferring 7

Constructing situations to test inferences made by the child.

THIS EXERCISE

Inferring 6

Demonstrating that inferences may need to be altered on the basis of additional observations.

Inferring 4

Rationale

Background for the teacher

Children already know that plants need to be watered. However, they may not know where the water goes after the plant is watered and they probably do not know how much water a plant uses. The study of transpiration in plants (a process in which moisture is given off through the porous surfaces of leaves and other parts) will give them an excellent opportunity to make careful observations, to make inferences, and to design situations in which they can test their inferences.

The activities here will also give them important background about the general phenomenon of water loss, which will arise frequently in the child's study of living systems, physical environments, and ecological relationships.

(Note: Two weeks before you expect to start *Activity 1,* plant a number of wax bean seeds—or have the children plant them—in two pots containing potting soil or vermiculite. Put the pots in a well-lighted area that is free from drafts, and water them daily. In two weeks the plants should be growing well.)

Vocabulary

transpire   stomate (STOW-mate)
transpiration

Related materials

Listed below are the materials required to conduct this exercise.

Some items cannot be supplied at all or are not supplied by Xerox in the Standard Kit. These are designated as *NS.* Note, however, that many items so designated are supplied in the Comprehensive Kit. A separate list of these items is included with the comprehensive materials.

It should be noted that some supplied items are expended in the course of this exercise. These expendable items are designated as *EXP.*

Items too large for the Exercise Drawer will be found in the Teacher Drawer and are designated as *TD.*

Bean seeds, 100 (EXP)
Flowerpots, 2 (EXP)
Vermiculite, 1 package (TD, EXP)
Geranium plant, 1 (NS)
Celery stalks, 30 (NS)
Dishpan, 1 (NS)
Single-edge razor blade, 1 (NS)
Red food coloring, 1 bottle (EXP)
Plastic cups, 30 (EXP)
Large pail, 1 (NS)
Leafy shoots of willow, pine, privet, sycamore, cottonwood, tomato, or
    geranium, 10, approximately 35 cm long (NS)
Flexible plastic tubing, 8 pieces
Masking tape, 1 roll (NS)
Cardboard, 10 pieces, 25 × 50 cm or larger (NS)
Modeling or florist clay (NS)
3-decimeter metric rules, 10 (found in Exercise "i" drawer)
Graph paper, 2-mm squares printed in green ink, 100 sheets (TD, EXP)

Plastic bags, 8 (EXP)
White petroleum jelly, 1 tube (NS)
100× microscope or a microprojector, 1 (NS)
Microscope slides, 6 (NS)
Cover slips for slides, 6 (NS)
Potted plants, 2, 15 to 20 cm high (NS)
Illustrations (as in Figure 3), 1 copy
Graph (as in Figure 4), 1 copy

Instructional procedure

Introduction

Suggestions for teaching

Show the class a healthy geranium plant and ask, What are some of the things a plant needs to live and grow? From their previous experience, the children will probably say that a plant must have air, proper temperature, soil, sunlight, and water. Ask if they have any idea what happens to the water when a plant is watered. Where does it go? Does all the water stay in the soil, or does it go into the plant? Will a plant live very long without getting more water? How long?

Activity 1

Designing experiments

Set the two pots of growing bean plants on a table in front of the class. Ask, How could we use these plants to discover whether plants require water? (Give water to one pot of plants but not to the other.) Tell the children to mark one pot "To be watered" and the other "Not to be watered," to put both plants in a well-lighted place, to schedule the daily watering of one pot, and to keep a simple record for a week or so, as in the following example:

Date	Time	Watered plants	Unwatered plants
Monday, 3/4	9:00 AM	Appear healthy	Appear healthy
Tuesday, 3/5	9:00 AM	Appear healthy	Appear healthy
Wednesday, 3/6	9:00 AM	Appear healthy	Becoming limp
Thursday, 3/7	9:00 AM	Appear healthy	Droopy leaves; losing color
Friday, 3/8	9:00 AM	Appear healthy	Bent over
Monday, 3/11	9:00 AM	Appear healthy	Leaves are dry

Discuss these observations with the children. Do your observations give you any information about where the water went? (No, they indicate only that plants will not live very long without water.)

Activity 2

Inferring

Remind the children of the potted plants they observed in *Activity 1*. Ask, Where did the water go that we gave the plants that remained healthy? (Into the plant, or it evaporated.) Are these observations or inferences? (Inferences.) Can we test these inferences? Discuss any ideas the children have. Then say you know one way they might like to try.

Put a number of celery stalks with leaves and a large dishpan of water on a table at the front of the room. Tell the children they are going to see what happens when you put a cut celery stalk in colored water and let it stand for a while. Say, You should observe everything that happens and write your observations down on a piece of paper.

Divide the class into groups of four children. Then give each group (or each child, if you have enough celery) a plastic cup about half full of water colored with red food coloring. Have each group or child, in turn, bring a cup (or cups) of red-colored water to your supply of celery stalks and water. As the group watches, submerge the lower part of a stalk in the pan of water; then, with a razor blade or a sharp knife, make a slant cut completely through the stalk about 2.5 centimeters from the bottom. Discard the small piece you have cut off. (You must make the cut under water to prevent air from getting into the conducting tubes in the stem. Also, the blade must be sharp enough to make a clean cut and to prevent the tubes from being crushed or pushed together and thereby closed.)

Ask a group representative (or each child) to quickly transfer the cut stalk with the leaves from the pan to his cup of colored water. Tell him to label his cup, put it in a brightly lighted place in the room, and leave it there for several hours.

Verifying inferences

As soon as they notice a change in the color of the leaves, have the children retrieve their cups. Tell them to remove the stalk from the water and observe the color in the stem and in the leaves. If they hold the leaves up to the light, they will be able to observe the color pattern more closely. Then cut across the stems in several places for the children and ask them to find the tubes in the stem that carry the water to the leaves. Also, tell them to break a piece lengthwise and to try pulling out the dyed strings (conducting tubes).

Ask the children to review their list of observations. Do your observations support and verify the inference that the water moves into the celery plant?

Activity 3

Before the class begins, cut one leafy shoot of a plant for each group of children. It should be about 6 millimeters in diameter and 35 to 40 centimeters long, and it should have several leaves. Branches of willow, pine, privet, sycamore, cottonwood, or tomato are all suitable, although branches with a woody, sturdy stem are better. A local greenhouse could supply them if you conduct the investigation in the winter and cannot find branches with leaves attached. Geranium plants also work well.

When the branches are cut from the plant, submerge the cut end immediately in a large pail of water. Then immediately make a second diagonal cut under water, 2.5 to 5 centimeters from the cut end. The purpose of this second cut is to remove any air bubbles that may be left in the water-conducting tubes of the plant after the first cut. Discard the small pieces of stem. Keep the cut end of each branch under water.

(*Start this activity early in the day.*)

Ask the children whether a plant draws up into its leaves and stem all the water that is put on the soil. From their previous experiences with evaporation and water vapor, some may suggest that some of the water evaporates from the soil. If so, tell them that this is true. Then ask, Does some water move into the plant itself? (Yes.) Does some water evaporate from the plant after moving into it? How much water does a plant take up?

Experimenting

Divide the class into groups of four children and give each group a piece of clear, flexible plastic tubing, 50 centimeters long. Have a child from each group, in turn, fill the plastic tube with water from a sink or a large, shallow pan. The child can put one end of the tube in the water and suck on the other end, or he can lower one end of the tube vertically and hold it under the water while the rest of the tube is gradually submerged, making sure no kinks or bends develop to prevent the water from filling the tube. After the tube is completely full, tell the child to put a finger over each end so that the water does not drain out and to submerge the entire length. If there are any large bubbles, the procedure has to be repeated more carefully. However, tiny pinhead-size bubbles that cling to the inner surface of the tube will not influence the experiment and can be ignored, and small bubbles can be pinched toward the end of the tube.

Now have all the children watch the next procedure. Quickly transfer one of the branches to the container of water. While the stem and tubing are still under water, fit the end of the branch into one end of the plastic tube. Again check to see that the tube is full of water and has no air bubbles. Carefully remove the branch and the attached tube from the water, and fasten each with cellophane tape or masking tape in a U-shaped position to a piece of cardboard already on the bulletin board. (See Figure 1.) To prevent loss of water at the connection between the tube and the branch, mold a little bit of modeling or florist's clay around the end of the tube. Then attach a ruler to the cardboard beside the plastic tube so that its zero end is in line with the water level in the tube. (You could also use a strip of lined paper or graph paper, with the divisions numbered.) Adding a drop of food coloring to the water will make it easier to read the water level.

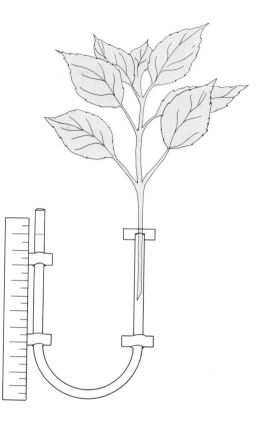

Figure 1

Quantitative skills

Have the children keep an hourly record of the water level throughout the day. The record might look something like this:

Time	Total distance (in cm) the water dropped in tube	Distance (in cm) the water level dropped from the previous level
9:30 AM (Start)	0.0	0.0
10:30 AM	1.0	1.0
11:30 AM	2.6	1.6
12:30 PM	4.6	2.0
1:30 PM	6.0	1.4
2:30 PM	7.7	1.7
3:30 PM	8.2	0.5

After the observations are completed (in five or six readings), discuss the data with the children. What total amount did the water level drop during the day? How much did it drop each hour? (Different amounts, probably.) If the data show it, point out that the amount of water the plant used each hour changed at different times during the day. (This may not be apparent, though, if the classroom temperature and lighting are relatively constant.) Now ask the children to graph their results. Discuss with them what they should plot

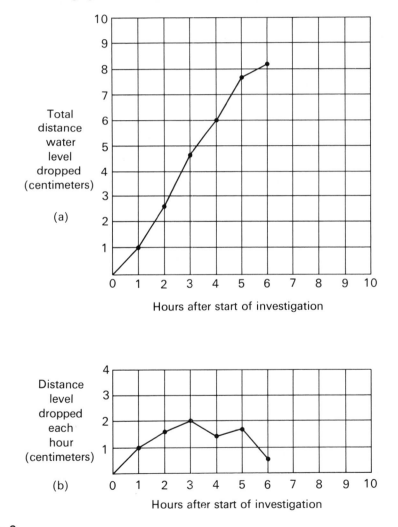

Total distance water level dropped (centimeters)

(a)

Hours after start of investigation

Distance level dropped each hour (centimeters)

(b)

Hours after start of investigation

Figure 2

on the horizontal and vertical axes. Then make sure that they label the axes appropriately, indicating the units of measurement (hours, centimeters). Afterward, you might reproduce some representative graphs on the chalkboard.

The graphs in Figure 2 show two ways to graph the data. The first one illustrates the *total amount* of water used as time passes. The second shows how the plant's rate of water uptake varied during each hour of the day. Although both graphs are based on the same data, they emphasize different aspects, and the children may have some difficulty seeing the relationship between them. If so, point out that the second graph shows the distance (vertical) between two successive points on the first graph.

Ask different groups to compare their results. They should conclude that although their actual measurements varied, the trends are similar: Large plants used more water than small plants, and all plants used more water during the warm, bright part of the day. Ask the children whether their conclusions are inferences or direct observations. You might point out that their measurements do not show the volume of water the plant uses. To find this, they could fill different lengths of tubing with water and then pour the water into a graduated cylinder and measure the volume.

Predicting

Ask volunteers to use their graphs to predict where the water level will be at 9:30 AM tomorrow morning. If they predict that it will be below the bottom of the scale, suggest that before they leave the setup for the day, they may add water to the tube so the level is up to the top of the scale. They can measure the water level at 9:30 the next morning. Their measurement probably will not agree with the predicted value, since the plant does not transpire as much water at night as it does during the day. The failure of the prediction should stimulate both discussion and disagreement. This is good, provided the discussion remains logical and is not random guessing. Persistent questioning of a child who has an explanation should reveal, however, whether his idea is based on thought or guesswork.

Save the experimental setups so you can use them again in *Activity 4*.

Activity 4

After *Activity 3*, various related questions may arise. The children should realize that they still do not know what happens to the water the plant takes up or why the plant continues to need water. They may ask if some of the water gets out of the leaves and stems somehow. They may want to know which loses more water, the leaves or the stems. Or they may ask if both sides of the leaves lose water. Try to elicit these or related questions if the children do not ask them first. Also, let them explore any ideas they have about finding answers to their questions.

Wherever possible, the children should use the equipment from *Activity 3* and the same technique to carry out further investigations. You will need to cut more branches as you did in *Activity 3*. If the children do not make any suggestions for tests, briefly propose the following procedures, but try to get them to work out the details themselves.

Where does the water from the plastic tube go? Tell them to add food coloring to the water in the tube. They should observe the change in the coloring of the plant parts and infer that the water went into these. Point out the similarity of this investigation to the one in *Activity 2*.

Does water get out of the leaves and stems? Tell them to wrap a polyethylene bag tightly around the plant and to examine this bag after a few hours. (They should see droplets of water condensing on the inner surface of the bag.) Where did this water come from? Have them draw inferences from their observations.

Testing hypotheses   Which loses more water, the leaves or the stems? Have the children cover the leaves with a waterproof layer of vaseline to prevent evaporation. Then tell them to compare the amount of water the plant used before and after the leaves were covered. What inferences can you make from these comparisons?

Generalizing experience

Have the children use the setup in *Activity 3* to test such questions as these:

Would another kind of plant use water as this one did?

Would the water in the tube drop faster or more slowly if the plant were in the dark?

Would the plant use water faster if a breeze from a fan were blown over the leaves?

Would the water level in the tube continue to drop if all the leaves were stripped from the plant?

Do flowers use water?

After each test, conclude by asking the children, What inferences can be made from an investigation such as this?

Appraisal

Evaluating process skills   Tell the children that you saw six carnations in a vase at the florist's shop and that three of the blooms were white and three were green. The florist told you that when he cut these carnations, all six were white. Ask the children to infer how the florist might have changed the color of the flowers.

Show the children a properly labeled graph, similar to one of those in *Activity 3,* that indicates the rate of water uptake during each hour, and the base line of which shows the hours when readings were taken. Say, Suppose one half of the plant's leaves had been removed before the study was begun. Pre-

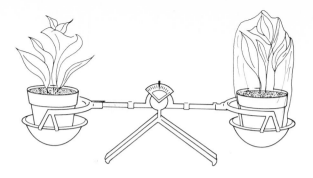

Figure 3

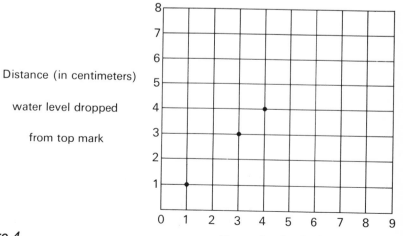

Distance (in centimeters)

water level dropped

from top mark

Hours after beginning

Figure 4

dict what the water level would have been at each of the designated hours, and mark points on the graph to represent your predictions. What observations did you use to make them? What inferences are these predictions based on?

Competency measure

(Individual score sheets for each pupil are in the Teacher Drawer.)

Show the child the following drawing (see Figure 3) and say, This drawing shows two potted plants, labeled *A* and *B,* that are the same size. Plant *B* was completely enclosed in a large, airtight plastic bag. At 1:00 PM, the two plants were placed one at each end of an equal-arm balance, which was then level. (Plant *A* balanced Plant *B*.) But by 3:00 PM, the balance was no longer level.

TASKS 1, 2 (OBJECTIVES 1, 2): Ask, What inference can you make to explain why the plant that was not in the plastic bag, Plant *A*, weighed less than the plant inside the plastic bag, Plant *B*, after two hours? Put one check in the acceptable column for Task 1 if the child says that water was lost from some part of Plant *A* (the soil, the leaves, or the stem), but that the plastic bag prevented loss of the water that evaporated from Plant *B*. Then say, Tell me a way to test your inference. Put one check in the acceptable column for Task 2 if he suggests an appropriate test.

Show the child a copy of Figure 4, which shows data from an investigation like the one described in *Activity 3.*

TASKS 3, 4 (OBJECTIVE 3): Say, Predict how far the water level measured in this investigation will have dropped after six hours. Put one check in the acceptable column for Task 3 if the child says "Six centimeters," or "About six centimeters." Then say, Predict how far the water level will have dropped after eight hours. Put one check in the acceptable column for Task 4 if he says "Eight centimeters," or "About eight centimeters."

Skill levels

At the kindergarten level the skills are quite simple. For example, "Observing 1," the first lesson on observing, calls for "Identifying and Naming the Primary and Secondary Colors"; "Observing 8," the eighth lesson on observing, calls for "Identifying and Naming the Taste of Objects as Sweet, Sour, or Salty." Each process skill is generally covered in a number of lessons: In kindergarten "Observing" is practiced in eight lessons, "Using Numbers" in four lessons, "Using Space/Time Relationships" in six lessons, "Classifying" in three lessons, and "Measuring" in one lesson.

At the third grade level "Inferring" has three exercises, building on three lessons from preceding grades. "Predicting" has two lessons, also building on work from previous grades. "Using numbers" has two lessons, following nine earlier lessons, "Measuring" has three exercises, following twelve earlier lessons. At the fourth grade level children should be ready to use these process skills; they then concentrated on more complex skills, such as "Defining Operationally" and "Controlling Variables."

In the SAPA program children learn through direct contact with scientific phenomena. Unlike the SCIS program there are no written materials for children, not even suggested readings, even though such materials would surely enrich the daily routine.

Evaluation

Appraising skill mastery

Children are expected to show a high level of proficiency in the performance objectives for each lesson. The "Appraisal" activity in each exercise is intended to show whether the majority of children have achieved these objectives. Although it furnishes general information about the entire class, the appraisal does not provide diagnostic information about individual children. The "Competency Measure," on the other hand, is best used with individual children or small groups, although several of these measures may be used with a large group. The performance of individual children and small groups generally indicates the success of the whole class. These measures are purposely different from those in the exercise so as to test the child's ability to generalize in new situations.

Successes and problems

The developers of this program have given much attention to evaluating its shortcomings as well as its successes. They have learned that primary grade children, whatever their socioeconomic status, can achieve the desired mastery of behavioral objectives about 80 percent of the time. This percentage of success decreases somewhat in the intermediate grades, perhaps because few children in these grades, when they were evaluated, had had the cumulative experience necessary to attain the higher behavioral skills. Children from high socioeconomic backgrounds were, however, more successful in the more complex verbal behaviors, such as communicating.[32]

As we might expect, field reports are somewhat mixed. In one "independent" evaluation of fifty-three elementary schools in New York and Pennsylvania, the observers were impressed by the fact that teachers gave more time to science after SAPA was adopted than before, that they accepted the SAPA program, that they tended to use more nondirective behavior, and that their children were averaging about 84 percent on the "Competency Measures." However, these teachers were beneficiaries of generous support from the Eastern Regional Institute for Education (ERIE), which undertook this installation as a research project.[33]

Even though SAPA does not stress scientific facts and concepts, children from this program do as well on the STEP tests (see Chapter 10) as children enrolled in the traditional curricula on which STEP tests are based. In addition the children from the SAPA program do significantly better on the "Competency Measures"; sex differences seem to play no part in success.[34]

Don't talk—do!

Teachers who have been oriented to the goals and techniques of SAPA are much more likely to introduce "doing" activities than are non-SAPA teachers. Nevertheless it is disturbing that as much as two thirds of time for both SAPA and non-SAPA science seems to be "teacher talk," although SAPA children spend significantly less time in verbal behavior than their counterparts in non-SAPA classes. SAPA teachers sometimes seem to spend too much time giving directions and procedures. Divergent and evaluative questioning seems to take up less than one percent of class time, a percentage slightly less than that of regular classes. The excessive time spent in direct teaching and the negligible time given to open-ended questioning may result from the restrictive effect of performance objectives, which do not allow much opportunity for divergent questions. On the other hand teachers may simply need better training for this innovative and unfamiliar way of teaching.[35]

Summary

Without question we must face the many problems that exist in installing and maintaining innovative programs. The problems confronting ESS, SCIS, and SAPA are typical. Different kinds of programs might well demand different kinds of teachers and teaching styles. Teachers who enjoy the openness and freedom of ESS are unlikely to be equally satisfied with the SAPA teaching model. One study of SAPA teachers reported that successful teachers in this program tended to be more submissive than those who were less successful or who had not volunteered for the program. They seemed to be more satisfied with their schools, more orderly in "setting and meeting goals for their students," more dependent on others. They looked upon their school environment as "controlled and restricted in its daily activities." Teachers who were "more verbal and aggressive in their personal relationships were more likely to be unsuccessful."[36]

The adoption of a new curriculum is a challenging and complicated task. Inservice preparation of teachers requires a series of workshops, not just a few days of perfunctory orientation. Teacher preparation, regular consultant visits, and administrative support at all levels will materially increase the probability of success. Teachers often consider the new programs to be supplements that reinforce the science they are already teaching. Because of this belief and because of their busy, normal school routine, teachers do not prepare themselves by reading the teachers' guides, by working through the experiences so that they know what to anticipate, and by obtaining the materials in advance. Insecure teachers may shun the advice and help of colleagues or consultants and supervisors. Teachers indicate that they have the most difficulty in obtaining the proper materials at the right time (particularly living specimens), getting experiments to work properly (keeping living specimens alive), and replacing material. The school principal must actively work to help teachers solve these problems.[37]

When everything is summed up, however, the new programs seem to be well planned and far superior to most past elementary science curricula. They represent an enormous effort to harmonize developmental and cognitive considerations — the structure of science and the values of science — into effective science for *all* elementary school children. These new curricula are scientifically, educationally, and psychologically sound. Despite the problems in implementing these programs the new elementary school teachers graduating from teacher-preparing institutions will be inculcated with the spirit of the new science education. They will know these programs and be prepared to give them a fair trial. "What *really* needs massive revision is not these curricula but the usual and current educational practice in our schools which is incredibly illogical, inappropriate, nonfunctional, and unconcerned with learning."[38]

For further study

1. Why has the federal government invested many millions of dollars in science programs for the public schools?
2. How do the ESS, SCIS, and SAPA programs differ in intent and procedure from conventional curriculum revisions?

3. Investigate some elementary school science programs not discussed in this chapter (see note 1 for this chapter). Are they significantly different from those discussed here?

4. Analyze a local science curriculum guide and contrast it with one of the three programs described in this chapter.

5. In view of the national studies, what function would you suggest for local curriculum development? What is the place for locally published science curriculum guides?

6. What are the implications of SAPA and its thorough K–6 planning for possibly increasing curriculum rigidity?

7. Do the programs described in this chapter require different kinds of preparation and commitment on the teacher's part?

8. Try a mini-teaching exercise with one of the programs. What problems do you encounter that you were not prepared for? How can you eliminate these problems?

9. Are these programs likely to meet the science educational needs of the seventies?

Notes and references

1. ESS and SCIS stress science process. SCIS is the only one of the three programs discussed in detail in this chapter that also seeks to develop understanding of the conceptual structure of science. Other programs such as the Conceptually Oriented Program in Elementary Science (COPES), Quantitative Approach to Elementary School Science (QS), and the Elementary School Science Project (ESSP) are more concept centered. For additional details see Lockard, J. D., ed., *Seventh Report of the International Clearinghouse on Science and Mathematics Curricular Developments 1970* (College Park, Md.: Science Teaching Center, University of Maryland, 1970).

2. Rogers, R. E., and A. M. Voelker, "Programs for Improving Science Instruction in the Elementary School, Part I, ESS," *Science and Children,* 7: 38, January–February 1970.

3. Hawkins, D. P., "Messing About in Science," in L. I. Kuslan and A. H. Stone, eds., *Readings on Teaching Children Science* (Belmont, Calif.: Wadsworth Publishing Co., 1969), p. 175.

4. *Teacher's Guide for Behavior of Mealworms* (Manchester, Mo.: Webster Division, McGraw-Hill Book Co., 1966), p. 17.

5. *Teacher's Guide for Peas and Particles* (Newton, Mass.: Education Development Center, 1966), p. 1.

6. From the *ESS Newsletter* as quoted in *Elementary Science Study ESS Program Report* (Berkeley, Calif.: Far West Laboratory for Educational Research and Development, 1970), p. 27.

7. Rogers, R. E., and A. M. Voelker, *op. cit.,* p. 42.

8. *Teacher's Guide for Behavior of Mealworms, op. cit.,* pp. 24–27.

9. Wolcott, C., "On Evaluation," *ESS Newsletter,* February 1965, pp. 1–2.

10. *Elementary Science Study ESS Program Report, op. cit.,* p. 32.

11. Honigman, F. K., and A. Smeraglio, "A Comparison of Teacher–Pupil Interaction Patterns in ESS 'Discovery' Classes with Those of Conventional Elementary Science Classes," *American Educational Research Association Abstracts of Papers,* 1969 Annual Meeting (Washington, D.C.: American Educational Research Association, 1969), pp. 204–5; Elgammal, A. A., "ESS Evaluation: Student's and Teacher's Reactions," in *National Science Teachers Association, Seventeenth Annual Convention Addresses and Reports* (Washington, D.C.: National Science Teachers Association, 1969), pp. 55–56; Bennett, L. M., "Experimenting with an ESS Unit—Growing Seeds in a Demonstration School Kindergarten Class," *School Science and Mathematics,* 64: 367–73, May 1969.

12. Lockard, J. D., *op. cit.,* p. 533.

13. Thomson, B. S., and A. M. Voelker, "Programs for Improving Science Instruction in the Elementary School, Part II, SCIS," *Science and Children,* 7: 30, May 1970.

14. Karplus, R., "Three Guidelines for Elementary School Science," *SCIS Newsletter,* No. 20, Spring 1971, pp. 1–2.

15. Thomson, B. S., and A. M. Voelker, *op. cit.,* p. 18.

16. *Science Curriculum Improvement Study SCIS Program Report* (Berkeley, Calif.: Far West Laboratory for Educational Research and Development, 1970), p. 18.

17. *Teacher's Guide for Interaction and Systems* (Chicago: Rand McNally, 1970), p. 83.

18. Lockard, J. D., *op. cit.,* pp. 534–38.

19. *Teacher's Guide for Interaction and Systems, op. cit.,* pp. 30–41.

20. *Teacher's Guide for Interaction and Systems, ibid.,* p. 18.

21. Rowe, M. B., "SCIS in the Inner City Schools," *SCIS Newsletter,* No. 11, Winter 1968, p. 7.

22. Wilson, J. H., Differences Between the Inquiry-Discovery and the Traditional Approaches to Teaching Science in Elementary Schools, unpublished doctoral dissertation, University of Oklahoma, 1967, pp. 67–69.

23. Moon, T. C., A Study of Verbal Behavior Patterns in Primary Grade Classrooms During Science Activities, paper read at the 1970 Convention of the National Association for Research in Science Teaching.

24. Troost, C. J., "S.C.I.S. and the Problem of Right and Wrong," *School Science and Mathematics,* 71: 522–26, June 1971.

25. Tresmontan, O., "SCIS in the Classroom—A Sample," *What is Curriculum Evaluation?* (Berkeley, Calif.: University of California, Science Curriculum Improvement Study, 1968), pp. 38–44.

26. Flory, D. L., "Dynamics of Classroom Behavior: An Informal Study of SCIS," *What is Curriculum Evaluation?* (Berkeley, Calif.: University of California, Science Curriculum Improvement Study, 1968), p. 24.

27. *Ibid.,* p. 35.

28. *Science—A Process Approach, Description of The Program,* Part D, American Association for the Advancement of Science (New York: Xerox Education Group), p. 14.

29. *Science—A Process Approach, SAPA Program Report* (Berkeley, Calif.: Far West Laboratory for Educational Research and Development, 1970), p. 7.

30. *Ibid.,* p. 36.

31. "Observing 5—Observing Color Changes," *Science—A Process Approach,* Part D (New York: Xerox Education Group, 1967); "Inferring 6—Loss of Water from Plants," *Science—A Process Approach,* Part D, *ibid.,* 1968.

32. *An Evaluation Model and Its Application,* 2nd Report (Washington, D.C.: Commission on Science Education, American Association for the Advancement of Science Miscellaneous Publication 68–4, 1968), pp. 91, 141. See also Torop, W., "Pupil Achievement in *Science—A Process Approach,*" paper delivered at the 1971 Annual Meeting of the National Association for the Advancement of Science.

33. *Research Into Process Curricula* (Syracuse, N.Y.: Eastern Regional Institute for Education, 1970), p. 128.

34. Partin, M., An Investigation of the Effectiveness of the AAAS Process Method Upon the Achievement and Interest in Science for Selected Fourth Grade Students, unpublished doctoral dissertation, University of Southern Mississippi, 1967, pp. 95–97.

35. Hall, G. E., "Teacher–Pupil Behaviors Exhibited by Two Groups of Second Grade Teachers Using *Science—A Process Approach,*" *Science Education,* 54: 333–34, October–December 1970.

36. *Research Into Process Curricula, op. cit.,* p. 187.

37. Anderson, R. D., and J. G. Horn, Evaluation of the Colorado Elementary Science Project, paper delivered at the 1970 Annual Meeting of the National Association for Research in Science Teaching.

38. *Research Into Process Curricula, op. cit.,* p. 99.

6

Tools of Learning:
Firsthand Experiences

We have assigned a high priority to science learning from first-hand experience with the phenomena of science. The testimony of modern experimental psychology, buttressed by the collective wisdom of generations of classroom teachers, strongly suggests that the development of scientific concepts and relationships is a direct result of interaction by children with all kinds of materials and situations, both structured and unstructured. This statement does not mean that children can only learn by direct physical contact. The modes of instruction described in Chapters 7 and 8 help to free children from the physical limitations of their classroom so that they may explore the farthest reaches of their world.

Abstract–concrete

Because elementary school children have not mastered the vocabulary or the formal logic required for purely verbalistic abstract instruction, the conceptual structure of science, which can easily become abstract and detached from "common sense," must be related as often as possible to a concrete physical reality. Why should a discussion of deserts, inadequate rainfall, and severe erosion be limited to far-distant regions when in the schoolyard there are small deserts whose aridity, surface temperatures, and limited life forms provide splendid examples, in miniature, of desert conditions? Why talk about magnets when children can conveniently study the characteristics of magnets for themselves?

Improving observational skills

Most children are not good observers, but they can learn to be much better ones. Traditionally, developing students' ability to observe has been one of the objectives of elementary science, but in practice this objective is almost completely ignored. Although classroom teachers concede that skill in observing is important, few teachers have taken enough time to achieve real growth in this area; they doubt that the diversion of time for this purpose is wise. However, they *can* make time available for direct experience with reality if they give precedence to this experience over the usual science content.

As a case in point think of the bewildering vocabulary that confronts the fifth grade child when he first reads his textbook on the classification of rocks.

He meets such words as *metamorphic, sedimentary,* and *igneous* — terms that are significant to the geologist but mean little to him. He reads about minerals, quartz, mica, feldspar, sulfur, crystals, magma, lava, crust, pressure, limestone, and marble. He sees diagrams and photographs, but he often fails to see the relationship of the illustrations to the topic at hand. He has difficulty translating the picture of a particular specimen into its three-dimensional referent. He may think that all specimens are like the superb museum samples in the color photographs.

Need for direct experience

The construction of reality through words, written or oral, is frequently impossible because of the differences between the images children visualize and the images the writer or speaker attempts to convey. There is, of course, no guarantee that physical objects, models, or field experiences will close this gap, for too much depends on the relevance or irrelevance of prior experience, the curricular and teaching emphases, and the availability of the associated concepts. However, the search for direct experience is psychologically a step in the right direction.

The Meaning of Firsthand Experience

Defining firsthand experience

Firsthand experience refers to nonverbal, nonsymbolic activities — direct, although not necessarily manipulative, contacts with a concrete situation. Experiments in which apparatus is manipulated so that a change may occur, demonstrations by the children or the teacher to elucidate a particular idea, and field trips to gather observational data are examples of firsthand experience. Obviously much of modern science is beyond the reach of firsthand experience. The structure of science rests on a complex foundation of assumptions, inductive reasoning, and mathematical formulations, which scien-

Experimentation plus

tists use to organize a chaotic world. Insistence that all science be taught by experiment or field trip is foolhardy and will only lead to a dead end. Other methods of instruction, such as motion pictures, diagrams, and models, must be used whenever and wherever direct contact is not feasible. On the other hand science instruction limited to secondhand or thirdhand learning, perhaps accompanied by verification experiments and activities, is meaningless and illusory.

Inherent Strengths of Firsthand Experience

Few children can resist the urge to try out experiments for themselves — to touch, to build, to change, to find out. Verification-type experiments are amazingly effective in maintaining the interest of children simply because these experiments keep children active. Their fascination with chemistry and microscope sets is direct evidence of children's "manipulative" drive. Firsthand experiences and opportunities surround children everywhere: In the home the kitchen is a convenient laboratory. A nearby field or city park is a nature study center. In those areas of the country still reasonably smog free, the evening sky is a planetarium.

Laboratories for all children

Science is one of the few elementary school subjects that children can and do learn on their own through firsthand experiences. A tragedy of high school science instruction is that laboratory work is usually available only to collegebound students, who, because of their socioeconomic environment and intellectual capacity, perhaps profit proportionally less from direct experience with the phenomena of nature than do those who, for one reason or another, are not in the college preparatory program. Perhaps the wrong youngsters are in the high school laboratories. Is there not an analogy in elementary schools that encourage the brightest children (the gifted?) to participate in special science-opportunity classes while excluding the other children?

Differences in interests

The differences in interests between boys and girls, well established in the elementary school years, appear to be culturally determined rather than inherent attributes of sex. No one knows whether these differences will disappear if a course of instruction insists that girls as well as boys participate actively in science experiencing and demands that girls investigate the world of science in the same way and with the same purposes as boys. But we might reasonably assume that such a program will diminish, if not eliminate, differences in interest. Boys typically deal with "boys'" things—machines, motors, construction—and therefore are more likely to have an attitude that facilitates further meaningful learning in the sciences and their concomitant technology. Girls lack these experiences and thus are handicapped in courses such as physics, which require both manipulative skills and physical–mechanical concepts.

These, then, are additional incentives for tying instruction in science to immediately accessible objects, phenomena, and relationships. But, more important, direct experience is essential to improve the ability of children to conceptualize and to make use of these concepts in relational and propositional thinking. Learning from reading, conversation, films, and all other sources of vicarious information will be more effective because of rich interaction with the immediate environment during the earlier years.

Positive aspect of verification

Firsthand experiences supply the raw data to be classified, measured, and interpreted, and in this sense they are part of the investigative or process-centered methodology. However, firsthand experiences are often used to confirm the accuracy of a textbook statement of principle or a textbook explanation. Investigatory experiences in elementary science textbooks tend to be supplementary, to explain further, to verify. Indeed most "experiences" can be omitted without appreciably altering either the intended use or the explanations of these books.

Activities that verify principles are often helpful. They may be intrinsically fascinating; they may open new paths; they may serve as a kind of drill, a repetition of previous learning that the teacher believes requires reiteration. To think that *every* firsthand experience must lead to new knowledge, or that *every* verifying task is deadening, is presumptuous. The teacher should select those "tools" that will accomplish her purpose; if she believes that an "experiment" taken directly from a textbook or manual provides the kind of thinking and practice she desires, she should feel free to use it. On the other hand, if her teaching focuses on the "inquiring mind," she should avoid activities whose main purpose is verification.

Limitations

Schools have always made a conscientious effort to include direct experience with nature, both in and out of the schoolroom. Educators were quick to sense the immediacy and power of direct contact with nature, but their efforts to root science education in the near-at-hand were usually frustrated. Schoolrooms, unequipped with even the simplest apparatus, sources of heat, or even running water, presented enough obstacles. Furthermore the community was apt to regard field trips as an evasion of the teacher's educational responsibilities. Perhaps the Puritan ethic—the belief that what is enjoyable must be frivolous—has forced teachers to equate teaching with recitation.

Practical problems

These inadequacies were compounded by the feeling of insecurity that afflicted teachers forced to teach science, and as a result science was tied to the textbook. Some of these difficulties still confront us today. Few elementary schools maintain a special science room. The unavailability of work space and science apparatus leads to constant frustration. Modern schoolrooms do have some counter space and running water, but the science corner, if it exists, is in competition with other space-demanding activities. Experiments may take days, weeks, or even months before reliable results are forthcoming. Children can rarely perform individual experiments because of these limitations (although for some children *individual* experimentation is not a wise use of time and resources). Many schoolrooms lack even minimal science teaching materials.

Even with these limitations the ingenious teacher can improvise and borrow. Science supervisors are anxious to supply the necessary materials. The local high school may be prevailed upon to loan special items. Improvisation, on the other hand, desirable though it may be, is time-consuming; and notwithstanding the genuine advantages of homemade equipment, it requires a certain ingenuity and mechanical facility. For example, few children are able to make a reliable electroscope because of the inevitable difficulty with the electrical contacts. Frequent failure, which so often happens with homemade apparatus, dampens the enthusiasm of even the most highly motivated children. And there is *no* substitute for the microscope or magnifier.

Need for proper equipment

Children have enough difficulty in interpreting what they see through a microscope without the additional complication of trying to use a toy microscope. A good microprojector, available for about 150 dollars, is more valuable than several inferior microscopes, which give good results only in the hands of an expert. Several useful, inexpensive microscopes are now available for about five dollars through the companies that supply equipment for the new elementary science programs. These microscopes are simple to operate and have been extensively tested under classroom conditions.

The teacher is not expected to dig out of the nearest clay bank enough clay for art and crafts instruction. Neither is she required to manufacture her own crayons. She can hardly rely on Pyrex milk bottles and homemade wooden stands in place of Pyrex beakers and iron stands with clamps. The gain in teaching effectiveness resulting from the versatility of commercial equipment pays for the additional cost.

Complexity in experimentation

Other limitations of firsthand experience affect its use as a learning tool. Young children are awkward in their manipulative ability, and their immaturity significantly limits the nature and extent of direct experimental activity. Class size also affects the number and variety of such experiences. Many natural phenomena are not open to elementary investigation because the necessary equipment may be too sophisticated. Also, because experimental results acquire meaning only from a chain of inferential reasoning, chemical experimentation, although fascinating and often easily performed, has little meaning except in terms of abstract theoretical structures. Therefore the study of chemical phenomena is generally unsuitable for children below the fifth grade level. Biological experimentation is even more difficult than chemical experimentation. In fact experimental biology is not often found in college laboratories because of the peculiar demands of living systems and the number of control variables. Only in physics—the science of heat, sound, light, electricity, and mechanics—are elementary studies relatively uncomplicated and reasonably clear-cut. For all these reasons the vicarious learning experiences of motion pictures, filmstrips, television, and trade books must be readily available to both teachers and children.

Elementary school children unfamiliar with experimental procedures and unskilled in cooperative work must gradually be brought into experimentation. They will need to learn when experiments are feasible, how to manipulate equipment to produce reliable results, and how to plan and work together. This learning takes time, effort, and patience. It will occur only if each teacher in the school provides suitable training and experiences so that children are gradually brought into higher levels of scientific investigation. The millennium will not arrive overnight; it must be planned for and struggled for in every elementary grade.

We have stressed the obstacles to experimental activity in the elementary schools. These limitations are more or less severe, depending on the community, the teacher, the principal, and the physical facilities. It has been said that the teacher who is sincerely interested in providing firsthand science experiences will, by imaginative struggle, somehow be able to incorporate these experiences into her teaching. All too often, this is moralistic, wishful thinking. The genuine obstacles that many teachers face are sufficient to quench the experimental fervor of a Faraday. Nevertheless in recent years many new tested science materials have become available to help teachers overcome these difficulties (see Chapter 9), and these materials are rapidly finding their way into the schools.

Inquiry by Inquiring

The idea that one learns to inquire by inquiring is a provocative although an unproven notion. Frequent opportunities, both incidental and intentional, for process instruction are therefore indispensable. The more frequent the opportunities the greater the probability that process skills will develop. Touching, feeling, handling, and looking furnish the rich experiential background from which questions originate and their testable consequences flow. We do not mean to imply that inquiry teaching is limited to the raw data of the senses; immediate scientific phenomena provide the crude, easily accessible facts.

Once again, however, we must point out the pitfalls for the inexperienced practitioner. Recognizing and controlling variable factors, perceiving relevant changes, and choosing proper conditions are complex, frustrating processes. The judicious teacher guides children along paths she knows so that the children are likely to attain the rewards of reasonable success.

Group Work

The difficulties of experimentation in the elementary school inevitably limit classroom investigation to group or class problem solving. The teacher must choose between small groups or the entire class, for she alone is aware of the task and each child's maturity level, manipulative skills, and ability to work both independently and cooperatively. In some first grades the children might be able to investigate magnetic field interactions by experimenting with magnets. Following a class discussion, which organizes their observations and develops hypotheses, the children may attempt individually to test the validity of these hypotheses. But in other first grades this procedure may lead to chaos. Small groups of young children can also explore the limitations and powers of their magnets, but their inexperience in working together is likely to lead to confusion. Children must learn to work effectively in groups; for this reason even young children should have an ever-increasing exposure to group assignments. With group involvement in an activity, such as the study of magnetic fields, the teacher can easily provide a few examples of many different experimental materials to the group; but she must now guide a number of diverse "researches" instead of one activity.

Learning to cooperate

The basis for grouping children in experimental science is different from the basis for grouping in reading instruction. The latter is relatively effortless because standardized tests in reading are reliable and because the task of the reading group is not that of working together but learning together. The diversity of skills, attitudes, interests, and abilities that children show in experimental investigation can lead the unskilled or unwary teacher to disaster. Therefore class activities are preferable for younger children, but the teacher should not exclude group and individual study.

Why small group and individual projects? Because other important objectives exist besides the improvement of cooperative working skills. Ideally a teacher meets with a few children at a time, and by questioning these children and listening to their answers, the teacher can guide and evaluate their progress more effectively.

Group learning is essential

Problem solving is materially improved for most children in groups because of the greater chance that one of the children will pose the right question or come up with a way to answer other questions. Children stimulate their classmates. Group consensus tempers extreme judgments and works to reduce anxiety and increase confidence, although it simultaneously tends to decrease individual responsibility and initiative. Each child, however, has a better chance to participate, to work, and to help in a group.[1] Early success is important because groups are quickly affected by lack of success. If all goes well, "a sense of solubility of the problem shoots through the classroom."[2]

Small groups, therefore, promise more effective individual learning. In addition groups can learn a great deal about the topics they select and can pursue those interests in depth because the children take different aspects of each topic. If each group grapples with a different part of a class problem, there should be a system for reporting so that the experiences and knowledge each group gains will be available to all. Effective as it is for problem solving in science, group work is not efficient in mastering facts and concepts. It is justifiable because mastery of science content is not one of the important goals of elementary science instruction.

One type of group with many advantages is the "ad hoc" committee, which is set up during the science period to find an answer to an unexpected problem. This committee is useful in many different situations. For example, a committee report on perpetual-motion machines will add interest in the study of forces; a report on rocket fuels will help clear away questions on how rockets work.

Acquiring teaching skills

The teacher who tries to enrich science instruction by means of individual and small group firsthand experiences will soon discover that success is never guaranteed. She and the children should take time to think through the questions for investigation, the means for finding answers, and the role of each child; and the groups should adhere to their accepted rules for group work and for reporting their results. The teacher should save time for conferences with each group so that she can keep up to date on their progress, and at the same time she should provide encouragement and assistance. Above all the teacher should realize that the group process in studying science is not a natural part of child nature. She will have to work hard to master the essential techniques.

Exploration

Taking enough time

With young children, those in primary and preprimary grades, science experiences tend to be exploratory rather than experimental. These children need to build a rich store of images, concepts, and vocabulary. The activities in the ESS and SCIS units (see Chapter 5), the Nuffield Materials (see reference 3, Chapter 9), the activities in Hone, and those in the many science activities books described at the end of this chapter and in Chapters 7 and 8 provide excellent building experiences. In addition younger children have not yet developed the conservation concepts and the formal logical operations that enable older children to handle experimentation with its variables and quantitative requirements.

From exploratory activities young children gain valuable familiarity with sensing and manipulating objects, and in turn develop a strong foundation, which will, in time, facilitate object manipulation with less concentration on the objects and more concentration on the outcomes of the manipulation. Handling magnets, making sounds, studying birds in comparison with other animals, finding weeds in the schoolyard, and classifying objects are only a few of the many firsthand exploratory experiences that will lead young children naturally into the experimentation.

Experimentation

The heart of the matter

The phenomenal growth of science as a social and economic force in modern society began in the seventeenth century with the invention of the experimental methodology we know today. In operational terms experimentation is the purposeful changing of conditions, under rigid controls, to determine the effect of these variations. Experiments test hypotheses, which may have originated from earlier experiments, from theoretical reasoning, and from intuitive insights. The power of science rises chiefly from this testing of hypotheses. The results of an experiment may permit an unequivocal confirmation or negation of the hypothesis. Classroom activities are experiments only if the child explores the *unknown*. Experiments are *not* verifications of textbook laws, although verification activities can be useful and stimulating.

Problems in studying biology

Experience indicates that the experimental approach in the biological and the earth sciences is difficult for fourth grade and fifth grade children. Plants and animals are usually too variable and complex for a truly scientific approach within the limits of the elementary classroom; the techniques and equipment required for valid and reliable results are too sophisticated. Experimentation with animals may require vivisection or other inhumane practices. Vast domains of biology can be appreciated only through observation of microscopic sections and enlargement of small organisms; the limitations of child perception, the need to interpret microscope images, and the general unavailability of *good* microscopes are obvious handicaps. The Dutch microscopist Anton van Leeuwenhoek saw a whole new world with his simple water-drop microscope, but he was a genius. We can hardly expect such results from younger children. (See, however, the class-tested unit "Small Things," published by the Elementary Science Study, which is briefly described in Chapter 9.) The earth sciences also suffer from a shortage of suitable experimental activities. Earth phenomena are often complicated and may be meaningless without analytical (mathematical) treatment. The earth sciences are still primarily observational because of their complexity, the vastness of earth matter, and the enormous spans of time and distance. Of course, there can be considerable experimentation in the biological and the earth sciences, but it is of a different order than in the physical sciences.

Experiments with living things

Children at all grade levels can experiment with germinating seeds. They can test the effect of altering the kinds of soil, the amount of water, the kinds of seeds, and the position of the seeds; they can also test the growth of plants in many ways. Although similar activities with animals are more difficult, many elementary classes have conducted embryological studies with fertilized chicken eggs, have studied the conditions under which fruit flies, ants, fish, and frogs grow, and have organized and maintained balanced aquaria.

Experiments with earth materials

In geology the expansive force of freezing water, the erosive strength of running water, the layering of sediments, and the erosion-retarding ability of plants, to name only a few manipulative activities, are practical for younger children in typical classrooms. Although astronomy and meteorology are almost nonexperimental, children can readily discover by experiment the physical concepts that form the foundation of these sciences. For example, they can easily discover gravitational interactions and the effect of relative humidity on the dew point.

Despite these exceptions firsthand experimentation in the elementary schools is most likely practicable in the realm of the physical sciences. Firsthand experiences in heat, sound, light, mechanics, and electricity lend themselves much more effectively to the experimental approach because of their relatively simple experimental demands.

Planning Experimental Activities

Simple experiments

Insight plus knowledge

It is almost platitudinous to say that the teacher should be thoroughly familiar with a variety of experiments appropriate for each field of science her class will investigate. She must be aware of the purposes of the experiments, their relevance, and their conceptual and experimental values. Aimless experimenting has no point, except perhaps that of interesting the class in a possible outcome. The experiment should provide a genuine question, a perplexity of some kind. Do frogs hop farther on a warm day? Is it really possible to find out what the temperature is from the chirping of crickets? Why does a heavy iron boat float on the water? What makes a rocket ship fly?

The best experiments are uncomplicated, affected by only one or two obvious variables, and are managed by easily controlled manipulations with ordinary apparatus. The teacher, as the guide, is responsible for seeing that the experiences are within the intellectual and manual abilities of the group. What at first may seem to be a problem amenable to simple experimentation may prove to be exceedingly complex and far beyond the reach of most children. For example, children may enjoy playing with a toy gyroscope and sampling some of its tricks, but only a physicist can understand beyond the most general terms the laws of the gyroscope. Maintaining a balanced aquarium, changing its environmental conditions, and observing the relationships of plants and animals in the aquarium are stimulating and profitable experiences, but scientific explanations for the changes observed are much more difficult to propose.

A not-so-simple experiment

Dissolving sugar in water and comparing the rate at which lump sugar, granulated sugar, and powdered sugar dissolve or the variation in the rate of dissolving as the temperature changes, is an experiment that is appealing, is easy to control, and yields clearly defined data. The effect of surface area on speed of solution appears to be direct and obvious, but is it? Are the fifth grade children who can perform the experiment easily aware that the surface areas of equal weights of lump and powdered sugar are unequal? Do they realize that powdered sugar particles have surfaces? This experiment, designed to provide an answer to the problem "Does changing the kind of sugar change the speed at which the sugar dissolves?" is only the first step toward a solution. Ultimately at any advanced level of explanation the electrical attraction of water molecules is an important consideration. Therefore the teacher must exercise careful watch so that the children do not become submerged in a deceiving experimental sea. Experiments are all the more valuable if they stimulate new questions, which the children may then investigate, either by follow-up experiments or by referring to other sources.

Planning   The key to a successful program of experimentation lies in planning—in the cooperative outlining of an experiment or a series of experiments and the possible hypotheses and in the evaluating of results. We repeat this warning again and again because of its urgency. Experiments from a textbook or trade book are often easy to perform, but the teacher must consider thoroughly their implications and assumptions.

Children must learn *how* to experiment. Some individuals may have an innate ability toward experimentation, but because there is both an art and a craft to planning and carrying out valid experiments, the teacher will discover that she will unavoidably overemphasize the experimental technique unless her children have been prepared properly. Chapters 1 and 4 describe the general techniques of inquiry—the nature of hypothesizing and testing hypotheses. Children must learn, or better, begin to learn, how to select a representative sample, how to choose the pertinent variables, how to control experiments so that only one factor at a time changes, and how to hold conditions constant. They must recognize that both implicit and explicit assumptions affect every phase of an experiment. They must also learn to master manipulative skills—for example, using a wirestripper for removing the insulation from wire, focusing a microscope, and heating a test tube without getting burned.

Safety

The teacher must also think of the safety of the children. Experiments that call for razor blades or flammable liquids are best omitted or left to older children. The common use of "tin cans" for constructing "telegraph" sets is hazardous because of the sharp edges of the metal surfaces. Experiments in which 110-volt electric current may be directly accessible must, of course, be omitted. Some types of commercially manufactured equipment are improperly grounded and, under certain conditions, absolutely unsafe.

Repetition

Experiments should be reproducible and should almost always be checked by either the same pupils or other pupils. Reproducibility is one way to evaluate the reliability of experimental work. In addition teachers and children soon discover that check experiments may not confirm their original experiments. This discovery puzzles children so that in turn they try to find out why their results are so different.

Measurement

An absolute essential   In the earliest years of science instruction children should become accustomed to look for some measurable qualities in the scientific phenomena they study. Measurement requires mathematical skills, which if not available to the children, must be taught when necessary. For example, in the sugar experiment previously described, equal weights in equal volumes of water at the same temperature are required; therefore skills in weighing, in measuring volumes and temperature, and in keeping records are essential. Children will probably be unable to devise a technique for determining how much sugar actually dissolves until it is all dissolved. However, they may be able to estimate qualitatively the rate of solution by inspection and by examination of the containers at regular time intervals until all the sugar has gone into solution.

Whenever possible, the teacher should promote the application of quantitative tools in experimentation. For example, second grade children can comprehend bar graphs. Older children may build on this foundation in working with conventional coordinate graphs. Children can understand relationships more easily from graphs than from tabulated data and algebraic equations; graphic analysis simplifies prediction of effects caused by varying experimental conditions, and minimizes one of the obstacles to quantitative thinking by children. As a case in point children can easily visualize the rate of growth of seedlings from bar graphs showing seedling height. The flattening of the growth curve as plants approach maturity and the rates of growth of different seedlings are obvious. Hence the children develop a better understanding of differences in plants and in their own measurements. However, extrapolation from a graph may prove to be difficult even in the fifth grade because many children have not had the necessary subexperience in graphing.[3]

Controls—too often ignored

Valid scientific experimentation requires controls; lack of suitable controls weakens many experiments. Looseness in selecting representative samples and overgeneralization because of improper sampling are often associated with lack of controls. There is little chance of discovering cause-and-effect relationships without the standard for comparison provided by the control. Consider, for example, the simple experiment in which the volume of a balloon changes as its temperature changes. In this experiment a similar balloon kept at room temperature serves as the control. If the experimenter assumes that the air in the balloon is unchanged by heating and cooling and if the control balloon is unchanged, he may conclude that the change in volume is correlated with the change in temperature. If he had used only one balloon, the experimenter's conclusion would be much less reasonable. However, because controls are often difficult to construct and maintain the experimenter might assume, *if* environmental conditions are constant, that comparable results would have been attained were a control feasible.

Assumptions

Consider also the reactions of ants to environmental changes. The responses of ants to different kinds of light, chemical stimuli, and temperature change are meaningful only if the experimenter assumes that the only change has been in the particular interaction tested and if, when the stimulus is removed, the ant colony returns to its previous state. Clearly, then, children should be aware of the premise that the *only* change that took place was the planned change and that the results come from *that* change.

Setting the stage

When children are unaccustomed to an inquiry approach, the teacher will find that she must prepare them. No matter what their grade level, children who have had no experience in planning or carrying out open-ended experiments will fail quickly. The whole-class approach to the analysis of problems is particularly valuable in providing children with experience in analyzing problems. The teacher can set the stage for a simple, thought-provoking demonstration — for example, turning a tumbler upside-down and plunging it into water or crushing a can by creating a vacuum within it. By judicious guidance, she can lead the class to propose the problem and a variety of hypotheses; to propose some ways of testing these hypotheses, no matter how crude; and to decide whether these hypotheses are valid. In the process she helps expose the assumptions, the illogical jumps, the overgeneralizations, and the lack of "controls," which are certain to arise. The teacher must act as a model for identification throughout. "Most important, by her willingness to pose questions to which she may not know the answer, she demonstrates to the child the fact that knowing the right answer may not be so important as being willing to find out."[4] The teacher, as model, determines the thought processes of the classroom. She may get what she asks for but only if she asks.

The teacher must feel confident that these procedures, although slower and more awkward than reading textbooks, will result in the kind of learning that comes only from direct experience. In the words of Piaget:

> We need pupils who are active, who learn early to find out by themselves, partly by their own spontaneous activity and partly through material we set up for them; who learn early to tell what is verifiable and what is simply the first idea to come to them.[5]

Therefore, if the teacher can gradually build some of the necessary skills by relatively simple demonstrations in which the entire group participates, small group work should reasonably follow. With younger children, small group study will require a longer period of whole-class participation.

Physical Science Experimentation

Ideas that can be studied experimentally abound. Many "experiments" in science textbooks are easily adapted to the kind of discovery experience of

A fascinating experiment

which we speak. *A Sourcebook of Elementary Science*[6] provides a sufficient number of uncomplicated science experiments for boys and girls at any grade level. Consider, also, the following experiment, the goal of which is better understanding of energy interaction.[7] The materials are inexpensive: two alcohol thermometers, cellophane tape, cardboard, and colored construction paper. By properly cutting and folding the paper, the teacher or children prepare several boxes of different colors. They then place a thermometer in each box sealing the bulb within the box. After having kept the boxes in the shade, the children expose the boxes to the sun and record the temperatures on a "Heat Absorption Chart." The temperature of each box will be different. (Metal cans painted different colors or bottles covered with various colors of cellophane or filled with liquids of different colors may also be used.)

Possible procedures

The teacher may use this experiment to introduce the study of heat or weather or to provide certain data during the study of either of these phenomena. She begins by asking the class whether white clothing or black clothing is more comfortable on a hot day or whether a concrete sidewalk or a tar sidewalk becomes hotter. The resulting discussion will probably end in a vote favoring white clothing and the tar sidewalk. Then the teacher suggests that the class think up as many ways of testing the questions as possible. She may bring out the prepared boxes, refer a committee to appropriate sources, or lead (follow?) the class in planning an original approach. After the discussion there should be a concise statement of what the class is trying to find out, a list of the suggested hypotheses, some tentative procedures, and a plan for recording data, accompanied by a collective willingness to suspend judgment at least until the results are in.

The teacher should not try to anticipate every disaster that might occur, such as improperly sealing the boxes or using inaccurate thermometers, but the teacher and children should discuss the possible difficulties in advance. The teacher should lead the children to see that the important difference between the boxes is color. They should find out whether heating for a shorter or a longer period than the fifteen minutes suggested makes a difference and how long the thermometers take to return to control temperatures. The teacher may provide an interesting variation by having the children compare the rate of melting for differently colored ice cubes or the rate of heating or cooling for differently colored gelatins. She may provide still another variation by having the children investigate the differences in the rate of ignition for differently colored papers by focusing the sun's rays on them through a lens.

These experiments are exciting. The challenge of predicting and testing the color that absorbs the greatest amount of heat will hold the children's interest. The experiment is controlled; it is semiquantitative; it is reproducible; and it is within the ability of intermediate grade children.

*Underlying
assumptions*
Naturally the meaning of the experiment depends on certain assumptions; for example, that the only difference between the black and the other kinds of construction paper is in the dye and that the absorption of light energy by the dye is the only change increasing or decreasing heat transfer. Conceivably extreme pressure may have been used to blacken the paper, which is so compressed that its heat conduction is more rapid. It is also possible that black dye heat conduction is more rapid or that black dye molecules absorb energy more rapidly from colliding air molecules.

Matter of limits
The teacher must set the limit of abstraction of explanations. For instance, she may ask, "Does our experiment explain *why* one color is a better absorber than another?" This question is at the upper limit of difficulty for younger intermediate grade children because explanation must be in terms of absorption and reflection of the various components of light. In addition the principle of differential absorption is involved. If black absorbs *all* light energy and if light energy is converted into heat energy, a black object must become hotter than a white object, which absorbs little or none of the light energy that falls on it. The reasons *why* a black object absorbs light cannot be pursued far because the explanation involves energy absorption by electrons and molecules, and this abstraction will not be meaningful to children below the age of twelve or thirteen.

The reader may reasonably question the value of such an experiment. After all, the information gained is trivial; surely everyone eventually learns that light-colored clothing is appropriate warm-weather garb. Any further practicality of the concepts for most people is minute. The worth of this experiment, however, lies in the way it exemplifies physical experimentation — the need to identify the problem and the assumptions, to propose and test hypotheses, to identify and limit variables, to measure and record data, and in time to assess the validity of the hypotheses. The experiment will lead to new questions and to new directions of thought; the more we learn, the more we find to learn.

Biological Experimentation

Experimentation with animals or plants is more difficult than with inanimate matter. Clear-cut changes do not always occur when desired because of the close intermeshing of many variables and the difficulty in keeping plants and animals alive in the classroom. Hence biological experimentation is rare in the schools, although practical inquiry experiments with living organisms are possible. Chapter 11 describes several inquiry experiments in detail.

*Experiment with
living things*

The following experiment with turtles, which are excellent experimental animals, illustrates the nature of biological experimentation and is appropriate for intermediate grade children in any classroom.[8]

Once the "turtlearium" is established in the classroom, the children will spontaneously ask questions, which should be recorded for future reference: How does the turtle swim? How does it walk? Does it swim all the time? Does it close its eyes under water? The answers to these inquiries can be found by careful observation. On the other hand the answers to questions concerning the effect of environmental or nutritional change—for example, What happens to the speed at which the turtle, a cold-blooded animal, moves as the temperature changes? Are turtles color-blind? Do they see or smell their food? How do they react to electric current?—can be found through experimentation.

*Answers by
observation and
experimentation*

The teacher will probably ask about temperature change and its effect on the turtle and with this stimulus she will encourage the class to make suggestions for testable hypotheses and suitable experimental procedures. Their suggestions for temperature control will probably include using a light bulb or an immersion heater, warming the water on a hot plate and then pouring it into the "turtlearium," and placing the "turtlearium" in the direct rays of the sun. If no one in the class mentions lowering the temperature, the teacher should make the suggestion: "We plan to raise the temperature. Is there something else we can do to the water temperature?" This hint will lead children to propose that ice cubes or ice water be added. The children can observe the experimental animals along with the proper controls, one or preferably more turtles at the ideal temperature. The class should select some measurable index of activity, such as the number of times the turtles in the experimental groups and the control groups surface for air within a prearranged time period. (How long should this interval be?) They should also carefully record other changes in activity. Exchanging control and experimental turtles and repeating the experiment enhance the validity and reliability of the experiment.

*A suggested
procedure*

Some variations

The teacher may work out a similar experiment for comparing the effect of a good diet in contrast to an inferior diet. The class may compare the health and rate of growth of turtles (weight? length? vigor?) fed on raw hamburger, lettuce, raw chopped fish, or chopped earthworms with that of turtles fed on commercial turtle food. This experiment is likely to run for months, and the usual hazard of biological experimentation, loss of animals, is present. If they obtain worthwhile results, the children may then come to appropriate conclusions about the importance of temperature and diet in the growth of their turtles.

Experimentation in the Earth Sciences

The earth sciences offer few experimental activities for elementary school children. Of course, the teacher can set up sand tables for the children to compare the different rates of erosion by water flowing at varying velocities. Children may also investigate the dew point of the atmosphere, but this investigation is not truly an experiment, for conditions cannot deliberately be changed. In general, elementary science must fall back on a series of chemical and physical experiments instead of "pure" earth science experiments. For young children the earth sciences are almost entirely observational and nonexperimental.

One appropriate experiment for intermediate grade and upper grade children is the study of the sorting of earth materials in water. Sedimentary rocks are ordinarily formed by deposition of river-transported materials as the river empties into a large body of water, decreasing its velocity, or as the river slope changes. In many areas school children will discover evidence of such deposition in a neighboring field or of a somewhat similar water-caused deposit on their windows. An appropriate first question is: Will a mixture of pebbles, sand, and gravel in water settle out if it is thoroughly shaken? This question invites a number of hypotheses, which may be tested by mixing test materials and permitting the mixture to settle or by pouring the mixture down an inclined trough and examining the resulting delta. Are the results the same? Are the particles that settle out most quickly in the jar the same as those that flow the shortest distance in the trough? Do the shaking time, the amount of sample and the amount of water, the kinds of earth materials (for example, mud as contrasted to gravel), and the slope of the trough have any bearing on the result? Obviously the answers to these questions have some relevance to problems of soil erosion and, of course, to those of rock formation.

Planning Experiments

It is impossible to set down a rigid sequence of directions for planning, carrying out, and evaluating experiments. Because so much depends on the kind of experiment, the maturity of the children, their previous contact with experimentation, the facilities of the classroom, and the teacher's confidence and skill in directing experimentation, an authoritative guide for firsthand experiences is worthless. The teacher will experience failures: failure to anticipate difficulties, to narrow what is attempted, to examine the alternatives, to pose workable hypotheses and procedures, to keep records, and to develop efficient groups. For obvious reasons the teacher should try to keep these failures at a minimum, particularly with younger children. Frequent failure is demoralizing to children and teacher alike.

The following list of general criteria will assist the teacher in planning experiments and in evaluating their success:

Guidelines, not prescriptions

I. *The Problem*

1. Can the question be answered by experimentation?
2. Is it clearly and specifically stated?
3. Are the children interested in it?
4. Which themes and schemes are involved?
5. Can the class understand the concepts?
6. Is the problem likely to branch out too widely or become too complex?
7. Is experimentation the *best* way to find the answer?
8. What assumptions do we bring to the problem?

II. *Hypotheses*

1. Are the hypotheses clearly stated?
2. Are they testable in class?

III. *The Experiment*

1. Can the experiment be performed with simple materials?
2. Is it better suited for small groups or for the entire class?
3. Is it safe?
4. Is it humane?
5. Are the variables controllable?
6. What measurements can the children make?
7. What is the best way of recording the data?

IV. *Evaluation*

1. Will the same results occur if the experiment is repeated?
2. Are the data complete enough to accept or deny the hypothesis?
3. Are the conclusions too general?
4. How may they be checked?
5. Did the children grow significantly in ability to work together? To plan? To evaluate their results?

6. If the experiment were to be repeated, what should be changed?

7. Is the experiment worth doing?

8. What new problems arose as a result of *this* investigation?

The Demonstration

Definition

A *demonstration* is a firsthand experience performed in front of the class by the teacher, by a child, or by a group of children. It may be a true experiment that gives previously unknown information to the class; it may be verificatory or explanatory. In view of the need for each child to become involved in directly handling concrete materials, the reader may ask whether a demonstration is truly a firsthand experience. No matter; for some purposes and in some situations there is no substitute for demonstration teaching, even though the child is not participating physically. For example, to furnish guided practice in observation, the teacher may demonstrate a traditional elementary experience, such as the "egg in the bottle," and then ask her children to tell exactly what they saw, step by step. A surprisingly large number of children, despite warnings to watch carefully, will miss much of the action. Few children, for example, will see the egg bounce up and down in the mouth of the bottle before it pops in. The teacher may relate exactly what she is doing, step by step, leaving explanations for later. Or she may say nothing and slowly work through the demonstration to help children develop observational skills.

Practice in observation

Reasons for demonstration

There are many other sound reasons for demonstration teaching. The teacher should demonstrate activities that require heat, particularly open flames. Primary level children should not handle burning candles, canned Sterno, or Bunsen burners. Despite the dangers many "experiments" in textbooks and manuals list these heat sources. The classic experience with the burning candle, which is inserted base down in a pan of water and covered with a tumbler, is a case in point.[9]

In general the teacher should do the work when the required manipulations are beyond the ability of the children or when a series of manipulations is required. Because of time limitations, as well as possible hazards and manipulative difficulties, the teacher may wish to lead the class herself.

Concrete to abstract, and back again

A question that comes from discussion or reading can often quickly be answered by demonstration. For example, children have difficulty picturing a vacuum. They understand the concept of a vacuum more readily if the teacher performs this demonstration. She prepares a can by boiling a little water in a sturdy, uncapped gallon or two gallon can, permitting some of the steam to escape and, after removing the can from the heat, capping it. If it is sturdy, the can will be crushed but not broken. The teacher should ask the class to listen when the stopper is opened. The children will hear a hiss as the can bulges out. This action is evidence for the existence of a vacuum. If the teacher opens a second can, after crushing, under water colored with ink or food dye, the water will rush in to fill (or almost fill) the can. The presence of colored water inside is evidence that the water was not the original water required to prepare the vacuum.

This manipulation is difficult for children, even though the explanation is not complicated. It gives the teacher a splendid opportunity to guide the thinking of the class by means of questions, hints, supplementary demonstrations, and special information. The demonstration with the inverted tumbler of water, described in Chapter 4, exemplifies this procedure.

Demonstrations are particularly suitable for arousing interest and stimulating in children the desire to investigate entirely new areas of study. The exciting Bernoulli demonstration requires only a Ping-Pong ball colored on one side and inserted in a large funnel. The class unanimously declares that blowing into the tube of the funnel will blow the ball right out. But the ball surprisingly stays in place; and the harder the teacher blows, the more firmly fixed the ball will be, even though it rotates faster. Indeed the teacher can easily turn the funnel so that she is blowing directly down the tube, with the ball unsupported by the funnel yet remaining suspended in air. This Bernoulli phenomenon has many variations, which the children will be anxious to try; and from these firsthand experiences, accompanied by hypothesizing, discussion, and explanation, the children will be in a position to verbalize a crude version of the Bernoulli principle. They will also want to try the experiment themselves to see what happens if they change it around and to follow up some of the questions that arose during the demonstration.

In addition demonstrations are of value in that they require a minimum of equipment (although if the teacher uses inexpensive and readily available materials, this point is less important). In the upper grades and with more complex phenomena demonstrations have proved to be exceedingly effective, although they are not the same as firsthand contact that individual or small group experimentation provides.

Avoid boredom

The dynamic teacher who has learned how to prepare and carry through demonstrations will present exciting demonstrations. By her enthusiasm and inspiration the teacher will foster interest in every area of science. On the other hand, if the demonstration is merely a reiteration of what children already know, if it is presented in a monotonous, hesitating way, or if children fail to see what is done or why each step is taken, the demonstration will fail and the potential for promoting growth in thinking, observing, inferring, and evaluating, as well as arousing interest, will be unrealized.

Some practical considerations in preparing demonstrations

General guidelines

1. The teacher should think through her reasons for each demonstration. She should test it before class use; if a group of children is responsible for the demonstration, the group should be well rehearsed.

2. The demonstration should be as simple as possible. The fewer the pieces of apparatus, the fewer the steps, and the shorter the period of waiting for results, the more successful the demonstration will be.

3. The demonstration should be clearly visible to all children in the room. The apparatus should be large; scales for reading such data as weights, movements, and volumes should be oversize. Nothing the teacher does should hinder student visibility.

4. As the demonstration proceeds, the teacher should ask questions to be sure that all the children can see what she is doing and that she is moving at an appropriate rate.

5. Demonstrating is an art. It requires skill, which comes only through practice. The teacher must project her own interest and excitement to make the demonstration provocative and dynamic.

6. If possible, the outcome of the demonstration should be unexpected and dramatic.

7. The demonstration is most valuable with a minimum of explanation and a maximum of stimulating questions. The "silent" demonstration is often effective if the children have had some experience in observing.

8. Whenever possible, children should carry out the demonstration.

9. The purpose of demonstrating is to help children learn certain aspects of science more effectively and economically. The teacher should continually keep the children's needs in mind. The teacher should avoid overattention to experimental minutiae, to the detriment of the important aspects of the demonstration.

10. Student understanding is essential. A child's question should be answered, if possible, by another child as the demonstration progresses; the teacher should also ask questions to help the children focus on the significant steps.

11. The demonstration is the creature of the demonstrator. There are no precise rules with which to operate. Imagination in devising or in selecting

suitable demonstrations is essential. The teacher should not feel that she must perform the demonstration exactly as it appears in the manual or book. She should feel free to substitute and improvise. Children frequently think of variations which, for their purposes, are as good as or better than traditional demonstrations.

12. The teacher should never assume that children "see" the same events the same way, even though they are all attentive. She should not assume that the children are all aware of the important things they were supposed to see. Analysis of the demonstration at its conclusion will reveal how much the children have missed and perhaps will lead to a second trial.

13. The teacher must be willing to run the risk of occasional failure in even the most carefully prepared experimental demonstration. Disaster sometimes provides an excellent opportunity to find out what went wrong so that a fiasco may be turned into at least a strategic withdrawal.[10]

14. The analysis following the demonstration should elicit from the class the reasons for each step. Why is a funnel used in the Bernoulli demonstration instead of a cylindrical tube? Why is the Ping-Pong ball colored on one side? Can another kind of ball be used? Will another kind of funnel work? Smaller? Larger? Why is the mouth of the funnel open? Does the ball rest directly on the funnel? How does the ball change position as the teacher blows harder?

Don't rush

The teacher and the children may think of many other questions to explain what happens and to elicit new problems. The Bernoulli demonstration and its follow-up are clearly not planned to be neatly dissected and laid away to rest in a half-hour period. The teacher can perform the demonstration in five minutes or less, explain what happened in another five minutes, and finish in not more than fifteen minutes. However, this kind of science teaching does not produce the attitudes and abilities we are seeking in elementary school children. If a demonstration, an experiment, a field trip, or a film is worth doing, it is worth doing well and worth taking all the time necessary to develop it fully.

"Fully," of course, must be interpreted by the teacher. The treatment outlined previously may tell children more than they want to know or should know about the Bernoulli principle; if so, the teacher will decide just how far to go. If the children appear to be losing interest, the teacher is foolish to wade on remorselessly. She would be far better to drop the activity, summarizing it, and then to move on to something more rewarding, perhaps eventually to return after this failure has been forgotten.

Again we remind the reader that demonstration does not replace student experimentation. But student experimentation need not be, indeed cannot be, the only "laboratory" technique. Demonstrations are useful if they rest on a sound pedagogy. Demonstrations may introduce scientific concepts, inspire interest, answer questions, verify interesting textbook activities, and stimulate reflective thinking. Modern science is concerned with inquiry. The demonstration experiment is one more pedagogical technique for building a sound, interesting kind of science learning.

The Field Trip

Definition

The third major category of direct experience with the world of science is the field trip. The *field trip* is an out-of-the-classroom experience, primarily to observe natural phenomena that cannot be brought into the classroom or that, because of their immediacy, are best studied in their natural setting. At the elementary school level one would not expect that explanations of physical concepts and experiments are pertinent functions of field trips. However, the field trip is an exceedingly valuable educational device for studying the earth sciences and living things.

It is perplexing that children, who spend so much time out-of-doors, are aware of so few of the environmental phenomena that almost shout to them to stop and look. Whether the children live in a crowded city or a small village matters little; with so much to perceive and investigate local resources are almost impossible to exhaust. Consider, for example, a unit in geology that includes a study of rocks and minerals. In the urban school the class may

The school as a world

begin with the rock compositions that make up the school's construction. Children may find in and near the school a slate blackboard, a man-made aggregate of cinder blocks and bricks, a flagstone or concrete walk, macadamized roads, granite curbstones, and marble steps. An unpaved school yard has a variety of rocks, some rounded and water-polished, others angular and cracked, all waiting to be handled, broken open, and examined with a magnifying glass and all with a history to be traced. An unpaved school yard also contains some perfect desert regions — hard-packed, sandy areas in which a few low, hardy plants struggle for survival and on which a variety of insects scurry busily to and fro. If the yard has a sloping area, evidences of erosion are usually clearly visible, accompanied by the characteristic alluvial fan composed of more or less well-sorted soil particles.

A field trip need not be a "nature walk." A "nature walk" is good exercise, but it is sometimes not good instruction. Neither does a field trip have to be a long trip, especially when there is so much to see in the immediate neigh-

Planning

borhood of the school. The field trip should be planned so that relatively little walking is necessary; the center or centers of interest should be close together. In a well-planned trip the students study thoroughly only *one* particular phenomenon—for example, a tree stump. The teacher might ask the following questions to stimulate an experience in observation and inference: What kind of tree was it? What killed it? If tools were used, what were they? In what direction did the tree fall? How old was the tree when it died? Does it have any animal inhabitants? What kinds of plants grow on it?

Teachers have always taken their children on formal field excursions, sometimes to great distances, to visit a zoo, a natural history museum, or a nature center. These experiences, if properly planned and followed up, are natural learning experiences and provide an incomparable learning environment. The informal neighborhood trip, however, is more likely to be productive simply because it does not involve long distances and because the teacher and class can return repeatedly, collectively, and individually to reexamine what they have seen.

The trees in front of the school offer a real challenge. What kinds are they? What are their shapes? How do they differ from one another? How tall are they? How thick are their trunks? What are their bark and leaves like? What kinds of animals live in them? When do their flowers and leaves appear? How rapidly do they grow? Are they flourishing? These are only a few of the questions that may guide the study of trees.

How often have children viewed the environment only through the thick lenses of a textbook, while outside the entire living world waits for them! This direct entry into the world of nature, just outside their windows, makes field trips so valuable for eager, active children.

The teacher should be thoroughly familiar with the chosen site, and if possible she should visit it several times so that she is cognizant of the seasonal and environmental changes. Because conditions are never exactly the same, the teacher should anticipate possible deviations and be prepared to adapt her procedures accordingly. The following precautions will assist teachers in planning for worthwhile results.

Planning field trips

Guidelines

1. The teacher should know exactly the special purpose of the trip. She should visit the site one or more times prior to the trip so that she will be familiar with its educational possibilities and can plan her course of action. She should estimate the time for each part of the trip. She may want to ask someone trained in the pertinent science to come along (for example, a science teacher, a member of the local garden or bird club, an amateur miner-

alogist). Most communities contain a surprising number of individuals who are anxious to help children learn science and will volunteer their time for this purpose.

2. The class should agree on some common-sense rules of behavior.

3. Children should understand the reason or reasons for the trip: *why* they are going out and what relevance the trip has to their in-class learning.

4. If the class is large, the trip leader should concentrate on a few clearly visible centers. Children should be encouraged to return to the site, especially if it is near the school, to investigate independently, providing they are old enough or are accompanied by an adult.

5. The teacher must continually look after the safety of her children. This is her *most* important task.

6. The teacher should try to take at least one parent along on each trip, particularly if the class is large and the visit is off the school grounds. If transportation is needed, the school principal will make the necessary arrangements, which must include parental and school permission.

7. On extended trips the teacher should arrange for toilet facilities, drinking water, and lunch.

Field trips *are* troublesome! They are often hard to arrange, and if trips are novelties, the accompanying holiday atmosphere interferes with serious learning. At the conclusion of the day the teacher may wonder whether the outcome was worth all the trouble.

The difficulties are invariably aggravated on longer trips for which transportation and lunch must be provided. The local visit, taking from fifteen minutes to an hour, is preferable to the longer trip. All schools have resources for firsthand exploration. Even so commonplace an experience as tracing through the school the path of the steam generated in the boilers or the electricity which enters from the outside utility line enlarges the experience of youngsters.

Projects

Projects are special individual or small group "researches" designed to enrich the scientific experience of individual children. Projects are particularly suitable for older boys and girls who can work independently or cooperatively on tasks outside of normal classwork and who are motivated by a challenge to do something for themselves. The incentive for projects should come from the child or the group; projects must not be teacher-assigned because they are then merely another kind of teacher-imposed task.

Types of projects

    The project may be as simple as an investigation into a class problem, with a short, oral report, either to the class or to the teacher. It may be an entry for a science fair, an experiment or demonstration in which the child is interested, or the construction of a model that will help explain or illustrate a class activity. Whatever the project is, the initiative must be the child's. The value of the project increases as the child delves more deeply in his research. The teacher acts as guide because of her special knowledge; she merely refers the child to the appropriate school and community resources.

    The teacher will also need to provide working space and time for children who come from homes in which investigation is not encouraged. Because of the need for space and because the child is unlikely to achieve success unless he is self-starting and self-charging, few projects will be under way at any one time.

    A project is a good way to provide extra, stimulating work for the science-centered child who can stay well ahead of the class in his formal science study and is ready for new opportunities. Of course the project must be so safe that the child working by himself is in no danger. It must be on a level at which success is probable. Even the most ambitious and hard-working child can undertake too much, with the strong probability that frustration will soon end the project.

Projects are only for some children

    The child who succeeds in putting together a terrarium that survives, who builds an exhibit of the simple machines, or who identifies the plants in his lawn demonstrates that he can surmount problems. He is more than a textbook reader or an able listener. His teacher also has an excellent opportunity to evaluate his tenacity, resourcefulness, imagination, and ability to synthesize knowledge in a nonclassroom context. For these reasons the wise teacher encourages some children to undertake projects.

    Unfortunately few children below the fifth grade level are sufficiently advanced to tackle projects successfully. Indeed in the sense in which projects are defined in this book few children in any grade ought to be invited or permitted to attempt extra projects. Few children are ready to work on their own, and the teacher is rarely in a position to give enough of her own time.

Summary

    Because children lack both direct interactions with natural phenomena and psychological mechanisms that would enable them to learn science by verbalistic and abstract instruction, elementary science should be experience-centered and provide frequent, direct contacts with the world of science. This contact should include experimentation, demonstration, field trips, and projects. In addition to building a stock of sensory impressions and relevant information, such experiences represent the same kind of investigation that has produced the knowledge and structure of science.

No simple method or type of organization assures success in teaching science by direct experience. Teachers succeed when they incorporate their understanding of how children learn into an inquiry approach, which helps these children to grow in their ability to hypothesize, to gather and evaluate data, to test their assumptions and hypotheses, and to come to reasonable conclusions. The outcome of this approach is a direct comprehension of nature, which comes from this rich exposure to firsthand experience.

For further study

1. Why are firsthand experiences for young children believed to be so important in learning science?

2. Can words alone depict scientific phenomena accurately and satisfactorily?

3. In what ways can planning help to overcome some of the limitations of equipment and facilities in elementary school classrooms?

4. Must experiments in science be restricted to problems whose answers are unknown to the child? What are the advantages of verification experiments?

5. What implications do the difficulties in biological and earth science experimentation have for firsthand learning of science in the classroom?

6. Is the statement "One learns to inquire by inquiring" justifiable?

7. What are some of the ways in which children may be grouped to expedite experimentation?

8. Do the authors contradict themselves when they say, "It is impossible to set down a rigid sequence of directions for planning . . . experiments," and yet list some criteria for planning experiments?

9. What are some approaches the teacher may use to teach children *how* to experiment? Does this question imply that there should be more attention to sequentially organized curricula?

10. From textbooks, trade books, and courses of study evaluate several firsthand experiences that pose potential safety hazards.

11. What are the implications of the new elementary science curricula for preparing children to make and interpret experimental measurements?

12. Must children always be successful in science experimentation? (See Barth's article cited in reference 10.)

Notes and references

1. Ausubel, D. P., and F. B. Robinson, *School Learning* (New York: Holt, Rinehart and Winston, 1969), pp. 420–21.

2. Bruner, J., ed., *Learning About Learning* (Washington, D.C.: United States Office of Education, 1966), p. 269.

3. *Science—A Process Approach, An Evaluation Model and Its Application,* 2nd Report (Washington, D.C.: American Association for the Advancement of Science, Commission on Science Education, 1968), p. 61.

4. Bruner, J., *op. cit.,* p. 17.

5. Piaget, J., in E. Duckworth, "Piaget Rediscovered," R. E. Ripple and V. N. Rockcastle, eds., *Piaget Rediscovered* (Ithaca, N.Y.: School of Education, Cornell University, 1964), p. 5.

6. Hone, E., et al., *A Sourcebook of Elementary Science* (New York: Harcourt Brace Jovanovich, 1971).

7. Adapted from "How Hot is Red?", *Nature and Science,* 2: 11–12, September 21, 1964.

8. Adapted from Fletcher, A., "How to Keep and Study Young Turtles," *Nature and Science,* 2: 6–7, January 18, 1965.

9. In this experience the candle is firmly attached to the pan, usually with hot wax. The candle is lit, the water poured in, and the tumbler is placed carefully over the candle; the water rises and partly fills the tumbler. The common explanation that the water rises as a replacement for the oxygen consumed by the burning candle is incorrect. See Glanz, J., "The Burning Candle Experiment," *The Science Teacher,* 30: 29, November 1963. Because it is complex and is best explained as a chemical combustion in which large quantities of water vapor and carbon dioxide are released, this experience is probably not meaningful for children in the intermediate grades.

10. For an illuminating discussion of learning through failure, see Barth, R. S., "Science: Learning through Failure," *The Elementary School Journal,* 66: 200–207, January 1966. See also the excellent sources of experiments for the elementary schools in the reference section of Chapter 11.

Tools of Learning: Books

Children who like to read find sheer delight in the world of children's books. Casual browsing in the elementary school library or in the children's room of the public library reveals a treasure trove of science resources, with something for every child, whether he reads for sheer enjoyment or is seeking information to complete an assignment. Because of this diversity and richness, however, teachers should be ready to evaluate science trade books critically to weed out the worthy books from the second-rate ones. Many books written for children unwittingly distort or misinterpret their subjects or are uninspired and dreary. This chapter presents criteria for judging the quality of science trade books. Unlike textbooks, trade books are not intended to make up the hard core of science instruction in a particular grade; they are supplemental, enriching, and inspirational, and are appropriate for more than one age group.

Choose children's science books carefully

Few textbooks for children can engender a spirit of excitement, anticipation, or enjoyment; many trade books do. In addition to the detailed information, special activities, and creative insights, rarely encountered in textbooks, trade books often stimulate children to learn more and to explore new horizons — in other words, to inquire.

Trade Books in the Classroom[1]

As a rule, the teacher should not *require* children to read informational books, for the charm and value of these books lie in the child's option to select a book and in his reaction to the book he selects. Rather, teachers should use these books in a seemingly casual way, turning to them herself as a matter of course, so that when her children need information, they will naturally look to books just as their teacher did. They will know they can find answers to their questions because their teacher has shown by example how books are used. In process-centered instruction the children have ample opportunity for and frequently are in urgent need of additional information because of unexpected, unplanned questions and investigations. Besides interpreting directions for experiments and experiences, the major focus for elementary school science centered on firsthand experience is in finding answers to the many questions that result from curiosity, from frustration because an experiment is not working, and from the need for more information to plan and evaluate an experiment or to carry out a field study.

Books are necessary for process science

Even if they must follow a rather inflexible and heavily structured program, such as one of the standard elementary science textbooks or the SAPA program, children will ask many questions about their reading, about the experiences, or about a television program that excited them. Usually the answers or the information they seek is not in their textbooks or in the teacher's manual.

When children ask her for answers, the teacher may well answer directly, depending on the context of the questions, but she should as soon as possible encourage questioning children to use the classroom library or the school library. She and the school librarian should make a consistent effort to guide the children in finding the right books and then in using these books to find

Teach use of source books

the information. Some children will need a great deal of help in locating suitable sources; others will be unable to use the table of contents or the index, and still others will be unable to read for meaning. Teachers should show the class *how* to search for information, particularly when the children are inexperienced readers and "researchers." Once the children have found the proper books, the teacher and class (or better, the teacher and group) should read each section together, discussing the important points and the best ways of using the information. Throughout these discussions the teacher should encourage the children to think about what information they need and how they can get it. The children should know that their teacher will always be ready to help them when they have problems finding information or understanding what they read. But they should also be encouraged to talk over these problems among themselves before they come to the teacher.

In teaching children how to use trade books the teacher will find that by reading selected portions of these books she can emphasize how useful that material can be in helping children learn science. Oral reading by the teacher will also open up new lines of interest and future investigation. The practice of sharing reasonably short selections from science books is particularly valuable for children who are not good readers.

Identification and classification questions demand good reference sources. Process-oriented instruction often calls for identification and classification of plants, animals, and many kinds of objects, not as ends in themselves, although many children are fascinated by identification tasks, but because these process skills are important for proper cognitive development. Learning the proper name, however, is *not* the goal, except in a rather limited sense, for a name is only the handle that opens the door for children to find out, for example, more about the Viceroy butterfly, the Copper Beech, or the piece of basalt rock they might be trying to identify.

In firsthand science experiences certain identifications are necessary. If a child asks his teacher to name the caterpillar or the flower he is holding, the teacher may answer in one of several ways. She may:

Books help in identification

1. Name the object. If she does not know the name, she will look it up and then tell the child.
2. Name the object but add one or two interesting facts and suggest that a book in the classroom library has some other interesting things to say about the object.
3. Suggest to the child that he find out for himself.
4. Ask the child how he can find out for himself.

The teacher's response will depend on the child's ability, his experience and capability in using references, his depth of interest, the availability of suitable books, and the difficulty in making the identification. The teacher should help the child succeed as often as possible by assisting him in using identification manuals, setting time aside to talk about the different kinds of manuals and explaining their use. She should point out the pitfalls, such as untrue colors, inaccurate drawings, and exaggerated sizes. Identification keys that are sometimes successful with upper elementary children are often difficult for younger children; therefore some excellent, inexpensive natural history manuals, whose color plates are so helpful, should be in every classroom.

Reading and doing belong together

As the class or group plans its attack on a problem, reference to direct experience or information books may help them in their planning. Indeed it may change their approach because they may find a more interesting experiment than the one they had decided to try for themselves. If they plan to keep animals in the classroom, the children will certainly want to read about the care of animals.

Reading is a vital part of elementary science instruction. Reading has always been important in traditional science teaching, which was a *reading* and not a *doing* science. In modern science teaching, however, children read because they *need* to read—they seek information! But in addition, if the classroom has an adequate supply of science trade books and periodicals for children to pick up and browse through as they choose, if the teacher frequently picks up and reads these books because they are particularly striking, if she frequently suggests to her children certain books she thinks they will find interesting, and if she is a model for them to follow, the chances are great that the children will read for enjoyment as well as for information.

Kinds of science books   Children's trade books may conveniently, although arbitrarily, be divided into six classes: direct experience, information, biography, fiction, periodicals, and encyclopedias and dictionaries.

Direct experience

Some good direct-experience books

Currently literally hundreds of books and pamphlets make available to children, in both primary and intermediate grades, the fascinating world of experimentation and observation. Some of these materials such as Nelson Beeler and Franklyn Branley's *Experiments with a Microscope,* Harry and Laura Sootin's *The Young Experimenter's Workbook,* and Millicent E. Selsam's *Play with Seeds* are extremely specialized and narrow in scope.[2] Such books are valuable because of their relevance to particular problems and the ease with which children can find appropriate activities for their science work. Unfortunately specialized books are not published as frequently as books with a few experiments or activities suggested in each of several different sciences or fields of science. Rose Wyler's *The First Book of Science Experiments* and Harry Milgrom's *Explorations in Science: A Book of Basic Experiments* are more or less typical of this latter group.[3] Milgrom's book, for example, gives carefully detailed descriptions and some theoretical background for twenty-seven major, plus some subsidiary, experiments in such diverse areas of the physical sciences as sound, electricity, magnetism, fluid phenomena, mechanics, and astronomy. Wyler's book, which ranges even farther afield, includes a series of experiments in atmospheric phenomena, weather, plants, electricity, magnetism, chemistry, and light.

A model inquiry book   A fascinating and extremely popular book in recent years is A. Harris Stone's *The Chemistry of a Lemon.*[4] With simple, everyday materials, the young experimenter moves through the realms of physics and chemistry as he seeks answers to such questions as: Do lemons float? What happens to a peeled lemon when it is placed in a strong salt solution? What does lemon juice do to a dirty copper penny? This book is a model for directed inquiry investigation. The reader must do his own experimenting because answers are not given.

Lawrence F. Lowery and Albert B. Carr's "I Wonder Why" series for beginning readers includes attractive and beguiling books that focus on physical qualities such as color and touch. Other volumes in this series, such as *Dark as a Shadow,* suggest many simple experiments with shadow formation.[5]

*Difficulties in using
direct-experience
books*

Books of direct experience are sometimes difficult to use in the classroom because they may be too general. To use them efficiently the teacher must know their general content so that she can suggest to her children the appropriate sources for their activities. In addition direct-experience source books are valuable in the classroom only to the extent that they supplement textbooks and other available resources. A book that merely duplicates activities, although in different words, is unlikely to be useful, and all too often general experiment books are imitative. Milgrom's and Stone's books are splendid examples of ingenuity in devising unusual and delightful experiments that are easy to perform according to simple directions. Books of direct experience have a long history, and the old standard experiments reappear continually with little or no variation. Rarely does the teacher find a different, provocative, accurate experiment book.

Such general collections of activities have a place, but because of their limitations that place is not usually the classroom. They are often designed to interest children in performing experiments at home. The teacher may capitalize on this interest, however, by encouraging children to describe what they did at home.

Many books in this category, such as Illa Podendorf's *The True Book of Weeds and Wild Flowers,* by which children can identify common neighborhood plants, Dorothy Sterling's *Creatures of the Night,* which describes what to look for on a night walk, and Anne Pistorius' *What Tree Is It?,* focus on observation rather than experimentation.[6] To a certain extent such books are informational and explanatory, but their function is primarily to motivate children to study their world by themselves and not merely to read about it. In other words children are encouraged to break away from the narrow boundaries of a book-centered environment and to cultivate their own senses.

Information

Seeking information

Information books comprise the largest single category of science books for children. Their purpose is to describe and explain environmental phenomena by presenting the appropriate facts, concepts, principles, and theories. Firsthand experiences are frequently provided for their illustrative and motivational power, but these experiences tend to be confirmatory, verifying what the book says rather than leading children to find out for themselves. As a result information books sometimes are indistinguishable from science textbooks. For this reason they may not be particularly attractive to children, unless they can satisfy a particular need. Children will turn to information books to find answers to questions when the answers are not in their texts.

Books for the classroom or school library must be chosen carefully because they vary so widely in quality, accuracy, and detail. Even the inclusion of a book in a generally acceptable series, such as the "All About" or "First Books" series, is no guarantee of quality.

The information in books for younger children is often so meager that children are unlikely to find the answers to their questions in books they can read easily. On the other hand, information books for the intermediate grades and upper grades are sometimes filled with unusual bits of information impossible to find in textbooks or even in the usual encyclopedia sources. For example, one astronomy book for children names the "Trojan planets," the small planetoids that move around the sun, both preceding and following Jupiter, at approximately its distance from the sun. Another lists more than one hundred nebulae included in Charles Messier's catalog of "celestial nuisances." Just about every field of science, great or small, is touched upon in one or more of these books, and because of this broad coverage, these books are valuable in elementary science instruction.

Teachers will profit from these books

Adults as well as children can extend their scientific knowledge immeasurably by selecting judiciously from these books. The classroom teacher should feel no more hesitation in referring to these books for additional information than in augmenting her own resources for firsthand science teaching by consulting the experiment and activity books previously described.

Biography

Science teachers have traditionally tried to transmit to children some of the spirit of science and an appreciation for the work of scientists through appropriate biographical reading. Although the teacher may have this purpose in mind, biographers are not so single-minded. If these books are to fulfill the teacher's purpose, children must want to read them. They may have their own reasons for wanting to learn about the man, or they may be so fascinated by the story that, once begun, the sheer momentum of the narrative carries the child along. Therefore to sustain interest biographers try to dramatize the scientist's story so that children will identify with him, will suffer and triumph with him, and will want to emulate him.

Avoid sentimental biographies

In some conventional, overimaginative biographies scientists (or inventors) are poverty-stricken, rejected by society, and unable to obtain a hearing for their great ideas. Their long-suffering wives alone remain faithful to their vision. Such literary embellishments for the purpose of "humanizing" great men are suspect if they detract from ideas, methods, and achievements. Many scientists and inventors have undeniably suffered from crushing poverty and have eventually triumphed over countless difficulties. Yet the importance of their perseverance is the intellectual legacy that follows; unfortunately many biographies never do explain why their heroes were important figures in the world of science.

Good scientific biographies for children are rare

Children look for a story line and are unlikely to be interested in isolated bits of information. In this area the utmost skill of the writer is essential; unfortunately most biographers fail at this task. Scientists are individuals. Many have lived in quiet desperation; others have led adventurous and exciting lives. The majority, however, adventured only in the realm of ideas. Only a writer of great ability and insight can transform the lives of men such as Albert Michelson and Albert Szent-Györgyi into accurate, provocative narratives. The classic biography, written for adults by a historian, is not suitable for children, who need a more intimate contact with the characters. Action, even if nothing more than invented dialogue, is sometimes essential. This biographical mode is acceptable provided the dialogue is plausible, it is acknowledged as fiction, and the story of the scientist's life explains his times and achievements.

Because of these restrictions the few good biographies of scientists contrast strikingly with the large number of biographies of soldiers, explorers, and politicians. Only a handful of books written for intermediate grade and upper grade children set in perspective the work of Isaac Newton, Michael Faraday, Albert Einstein, Glenn Seaborg, Linus Pauling, and Jonas Salk, men whose genius has immeasurably changed the intellectual foundations of the world. Perhaps their achievements are too difficult for any but the gifted writers to explain clearly to young children. In addition some of these men led lives lacking the military or political drama so familiar in the history taught in schools—history focused on men and deeds, not on intellectual pursuits.

One publishing company has recently inaugurated a series of biographies with the title of "The History of Science" series under the editorship of Derek J. de Solla Price, Professor of the History of Science at Yale University. The aim of this series of books for upper intermediate and junior high school children is to "describe a significant phase of work done by a noted researcher or theoretician in a particular field of science, giving a picture of the man himself and his method of work." The first four men selected for this series are Ernest Rutherford, a founder of modern atomic physics, Dimitri Mendeléyev, a chemist who proposed the first useful periodic table of the elements, Robert Boyle, a seventeenth century scientist who took all nature as his province, and Justus von Liebig, a chemist who made organic chemistry a science.[7] For younger children the "I Wonder Why" series offers a number of delightful biographies such as *Up, Up in a Balloon*, which describes the achievement of the Montgolfier brothers who pioneered balloon flight.[8]

In contrast to the emphasis in social studies on the great figures in history, elementary science texts and elementary science instruction rarely point out the contributions of individual scientists. For example, one contemporary fifth grade science text of more than 300 pages mentions only twelve scientists and inventors, and then primarily to identify certain principles, laws, or phenomena. Science is the creation of many thousands of men and women. Elementary science textbooks, however, treat science as if it were the inevitable product of a vast, automatic, human factory. As a result, because they do not conceive science as man-made, children are unlikely to want to know about the men and women who bring about the innovations in science.

Science is created by people

Fiction

The genre of fiction in science books is of ancient lineage. It is characterized as fiction because, despite a strong dependence on accepted scientific knowledge, the author's imagination reaches far beyond this formal limit. For example, writers frequently use fictional techniques in portraying animal life. The author describes an animal's birth and daily struggle for existence in intimate and sometimes harrowing detail. This close identification between the young reader and the animal creates a high level of excitement and interest. Unfortunately this storytelling technique is often coupled with undesirable anthropomorphic and teleological elements. The animal seems to think and act as if it were human, coping with its problems of survival as if it were capable of purposeful thought. The best of these books, such as Robert McClung's *Sphinx: The Story of a Caterpillar* and *Green Darner: The Story of a Dragonfly*, George Mendoza's *The Digger Wasp*, and Barbara Goodheart's *A Year on the Desert*, are free of such errors.[9] They succeed in combining the information children seek, with a strong incentive to continue to read.

A classic kind of science writing

To the extent that it is dependent on scientific ideas and relationships, a narrative belongs properly in the category of science books. On the other hand if the plot, dialogue, and "adventures" are overemphasized, the book is not primarily informational and is more appropriately labeled fantasy. The fundamental criterion is not how heavily the information is sugarcoated to make it easier to read, but rather how effectively the story enhances the book as a tool for scientific learning.

*Avoid the "all-
knowing" adult*
The reader should immediately be on his guard when he encounters in a book the antiquated device of the bright-eyed youngsters, usually a boy and a girl, with an all-knowing adult. Authors who use this technique lack confidence in their ability to interest children and in the inherent charm of their subject matter. They expect that interest will grow as their reader identifies with the children in the story. To stimulate the reader, authors sometimes invent a series of implausible adventures, which deceive no one, least of all the young readers. After all, children read science primarily for information; a strong plot with contrived dialogue and extraneous and unnecessary characters interferes with the search for answers.

This criticism is not intended to belittle books with literary rather than informative objectives. These books strive to tell a story, to develop characterization, to illumine the minds of children. Although they may have a scientific basis, such narratives are not science books and are best categorized as "science fiction." Many fine examples of this genre have been written for upper elementary youngsters and junior high school students. They are not, however, science trade books. Despite this somewhat arbitrary definition, science fiction offers an all but untapped potential for enriching instruction in the schools.

*Science fiction attracts
many children*
Many children will turn away from science fiction, but those children attracted to it are apt to be especially interested in science and in reading. Unfortunately few works of science fiction are intended for younger elementary school children, although many books in the related class of fantasy are available. Both fantasy and science fiction are imaginative—free of earthbound shackles. Science fiction is much more restrained because it must be scientifically plausible in conceivable physical and biological laws. Such books as Ellen MacGregor's *Miss Pickerell Goes to Mars* and Jay Williams and Raymond Abrashkin's *Danny Dunn and the Anti-Gravity Paint* are delightful examples of science fiction written for children.[10]

In a statement about the importance of science fiction Isaac Asimov estimates that fully half of the creative scientists he knows have read and enjoyed science fiction during their lives. Because this interest apparently begins in early adolescence and because "interest in science is stimulated by reading rather than the reverse," Asimov argues that by identifying children interested in science fiction we will simultaneously identify a group of potentially creative scientists.[11] Unfortunately science fiction has not always found literary favor in the eyes of English teachers, and conceivably many boys and girls are reluctant to pursue this reading interest because their teachers deride and consider it to be an illegitimate literary form akin to comic books and the newspaper "comics."

Encourage children to read science fiction

The portrait of the scientist in science fiction tends to be optimistic, favorable, and worthy of emulation. Science fiction frequently deals with the theme of a new world shaped by the application of trained intelligence. In this respect science fiction is a worthy vehicle for inculcating desirable scientific attitudes.

Periodicals

Invaluable in the elementary school

Two journals in particular contribute to improved teaching in elementary science. *Science and Children,*[12] published by the National Science Teachers Association, helps the teacher to keep abreast of scientific progress, suggests better ways of teaching science, and informs her of new instructional materials in the sciences. In its eight annual issues *Science and Children* publishes numerous articles of theoretical as well as practical importance in elementary science. The September 1971 issue, for example, packs into forty pages excellent suggestions for beginning teachers, for investigating the geology of the school yard, for experimenting with soap bubbles, for finding the fall constellations, and for introducing children to the study of ecology. In addition the magazine includes brief reviews of new books, films, and apparatus for both children and teachers.

An exciting children's magazine

Ranger Rick's Nature Magazine,[13] published monthly except for June and September by the National Wildlife Federation, concentrates on natural history. In forty-eight pages each issue includes a liberal variety of short articles, excellent color photographs, games, and nature poetry. The January 1970 issue, for example, contains articles on the Olympic Rain Forest in the state of Washington, a family of beavers, ice fishing, mythological monsters, spiders, turtles, and chickadees, among others. The magazine emphasizes the building of sound attitudes toward the natural world and good habits of conservation. Because of its cost few classrooms will be able to have their own copies. Issues should certainly be available in the school library. *Ranger Rick's Nature Magazine* is not written and edited primarily for school use. Although it has no teacher's edition and few activities that children can perform in school, the magazine is a splendid reference source on nature for both children and teachers.

Encyclopedias and dictionaries

The usefulness of encyclopedias in inquiry teaching is limited because editors cannot possibly anticipate all the information needs of children and teachers. Within the restrictions imposed by staff resources and available space, encyclopedias provide reasonably accurate and up-to-date summaries of information on many topics. Unlike encyclopedias for adults, children's encyclopedias are not intended to probe deeply into either the theoretical or the practical aspects of the phenomena discussed. For a complete treatment of any one topic, children often need to refer to more than one volume. For example, in the *Young People's Science Encyclopedia*,[14] which has twenty volumes including a special index and study guide, the heading "Frog" in the index gives twenty references to eleven different volumes.

Interesting browsing

The *Young People's Science Encyclopedia* is a desirable addition to the school library, although it is probably not an absolute necessity. A well-stocked library with up-to-date children's trade books can satisfy most, if not all, of the demands for science information. On the other hand, if these books are not available, this encyclopedia will help to fill the gap. One of its features is the more than 200 experiments and "Things to Do" scattered throughout the text. Despite the editorial acceptance of discovery learning many of these experiments are merely verifying activities, which are imperfectly outlined.

Other science encyclopedias for young people are not geared to elementary school children. They suffer from the unavoidable defect of encyclopedias in that children must turn to more than one volume to answer any one of their questions. They are useful as supplements, for enrichment and casual browsing, but the value of purchasing them for an elementary school classroom is questionable.

A classroom-tested dictionary

Compton's Dictionary of the Natural Sciences[15] is an illustrated, two-volume dictionary of biology and earth science, focusing mainly on individual species and classes of animals, plants, and earth science nomenclature. Definitions, which are about 200 words long, give the name, taxonomic relationships, habitat, description, and geographic range, together with a colored drawing. The impressive editorial board and consultants include many well-known science educators and specialists in the fields covered. The dictionary contains a number of illustrated charts, such as "Geologic Time Chart," "Classification of the Plant Kingdom," "Ocean Surface Currents," and "Table of Common Metallic Elements," as well as a detailed and helpful index–glossary. This dictionary is valuable as a reference for upper elementary science classes and should be on hand in each classroom for regular use.

A useful dictionary

The *Compton's Illustrated Science Dictionary*[16] is worthy of mention because of the few science dictionaries for children. Although most of the definitions appear to be worded for junior high school children, this dictionary is still useful in the elementary classroom. The incorporation of brief, accurate definitions into one volume increases its ease of handling and frequency of use. In its more than 600 pages the dictionary defines most words encountered in the study of elementary science. The center part of each page has diagrams and drawings, which elucidate some of the definitions on that page.

Sources of Information
for Choosing Science Books

Judging children's science books is difficult

Because of space limitations a detailed evaluation of individual children's trade books and mention of more than a few selected books would be impossible. In general the books mentioned are outstanding either because of their quality and content or because they have been extraordinarily popular. The criterion of popularity is often questionable; many copies may have been sold only because the binding and illustrations attract the adults who buy. Few adults can judge a child's reaction to a book or foresee the child's use of the book. Few books are popular with a majority of children who like to read. Many books are unread either because they are unattractive or poorly written or because children do not know about them. Other books, limited in scope, may be extremely valuable to a few boys or girls. For example, a book on the aerodynamics of model airplanes will be indispensable to a few boys yet of little interest to everyone else.

In addition books may be filled with errors, false assumptions, and dubious generalizations, which, although not apparent to children, limit their value appreciably. Few publications that evaluate children's science books rely on knowledgeable reviewers to point out errors and misinterpretations. As a result children's science books are often judged according to the attractiveness of story line and style.

It is impossible to keep up with the hundreds of new children's science books published each year. Books frequently go out of print or are superseded by better books, and within a year or two the reviews are out of date. A detailed set of criteria, which a teacher may use to evaluate children's books, will help her make decisions for her class and teaching situation. Excellent sources exist for preliminary screening of books; however, examination of the book itself, although often difficult, is the best means for screening.

Good evaluative sources

The most convenient evaluative source in libraries is the *Children's Catalog,* which is published every five years and kept up to date by annual supplements. The *Children's Catalog* lists any children's books with suggested grade levels, prices, publishers, and brief outlines of their content. However, the publisher often supplies these outlines. In most cases the listing also includes a short review from one of the children's book journals. The review tends to be brief, somewhat gentle, and uninformative, in part because it rarely mentions the author's qualifications. The review is generally not the type accorded books written for adults. The catalog also stars specially recommended books.

Several sources of science book reviews are cogent, informative, and critical. For example, Harry C. Stubbs' column "Views on Science Books," in the *Horn Book* is knowledgeable and pertinent. In about 1000 words in each of the six issues published each year, Stubbs reviews five or six books, which he generally approves, although he carefully points out errors and misinterpretations. Unfortunately the number of books Stubbs reviews is small in the course of a year.

Several additional sources review a smaller number of books; these reviews are of high quality because they are both uninhibited and knowledgeable. The December children's book review (principally of books for older children) in the *Scientific American* and the children's section of the *Library Journal* are excellent sources.

Science Books, a quarterly review published by the American Association for the Advancement of Science, is more inclusive. In half a dozen lines, more or less, it summarizes the desirable and undesirable characteristics of books for readers of all ages. This source, like the *Children's Catalog,* employs the Dewey decimal classification, which makes it more useful to libraries and facilitates comparison with other books of the same kind. Like *Natural History,* another source, it is brutally frank and therefore provides a critical element unusual in reviews of children's science books.

Appraisal is an excellent review journal, which treats only children's science books. Published by the Harvard Graduate School of Education, this quarterly offers a scientist's view and a librarian's opinion of each book.

Each issue of *Science and Children,* published monthly by the National Science Teachers Association for elementary school teachers, contains half a dozen brief reviews, which are generally limited to books approved by a special committee of science teachers.

Lay reviews may miss scientific errors

Many other sources of reviews are available, but few are written by individuals with scientific competence. Damaging errors or misconceptions are much less likely to be discovered. Only the scientifically literate reviewer is equipped to discover these inaccuracies and to point them out to the reader. Most reviewers are well aware of the dangers of animism, anthropomorphism, and teleology; but only a few, however, are likely to know that an author has accepted a particular theory uncritically or that the theory is discredited on the basis of new research. In many sciences rapid change is inevitable, and a book that describes only the dust cloud theory of the origin of the solar system or speaks of the atom as a miniature solar system is harmful.

Criteria for Evaluation

The following criteria will assist teachers in the selection of science trade books:

1. What are the author's qualifications?
2. Is the information new to children?
3. Are the concepts within the intellectual grasp of the children?
4. Is the book up to date?
5. Is the book accurate?
6. Does the book contain objectionable teleological or anthropomorphic ideas?
7. Is the book too sensational?
8. Are the activities safe?
9. Is the vocabulary suitable?
10. Is the style interesting?
11. Are the illustrations functional?
12. Are the illustrations accurate?
13. Is the binding sturdy?
14. How will the book be used in the classroom?

In general, criteria for selection of trade books for the classroom or school libraries are much like those for nonscience information books except that accuracy and recency are of the greatest importance. Teachers are well qualified to judge science books on all bases except accuracy and attention to contemporary research. Unless she can find a review in one of the sources previously mentioned, the teacher must rely on the qualifications of the author and the reputation of the publisher.

Author

Author's qualifications are crucial

Writers with impeccable qualifications have written bad books; authors with minimal qualifications have written good books. These reversals are probably somewhat uncommon. First questions about a new book are: Who is the author? Why did he write it? What special training does he have that qualifies him to write this book? Franklyn M. Branley, the author of many elementary science books, is an astronomer at the Hayden Planetarium of the American Museum of Natural History. The teacher can be confident that Branley's book *The Sun: Our Nearest Star,*[17] for primary grade children, will be well within the author's special area of competence and therefore scientifically accurate. On the other hand a physicist is not an authority in chemistry or biology. For example, a recent book in chemistry for intermediate level children, written by a well-known physicist, is filled with dubious and misleading statements. However, some writers without formal training in science have, through research and innate ability, written outstandingly good books for children. Irving and Ruth Adler, for example, have written over three dozen children's books on such diverse and specialized subjects as air, numbers, rivers, the earth's crust, the ears, and the eyes. Irving Adler, a mathematician, is an excellent writer whose books are well received by children as well as scientists. In addition Millicent E. Selsam has written many books on natural history and experimental biology. Her formal science qualifications are certainly less extensive than those of many other writers, but this limitation has not affected the value of these books for children.

Occasionally, and less often than is desirable, publishers include on the dust jacket or in the body of the book a brief author's biography, which gives the reader an opportunity to judge the writer's qualifications.

Publisher

The publisher's reputation

In addition to finding out what the qualifications of the author are, which is in itself an achievement of some magnitude, the teacher should consider the reputation of the publisher. No responsible publisher knowingly prints inferior books, although somehow such books do appear. In one recent study, of a total of 115 children's science books in the various fields of natural history, only seventy-five books were considered to be worthy of presentation to the *Natural History* panel of scientist–writers. This panel rejected thirty-one out of hand and reviewed forty-four in detail, some quite unfavorably. In the words of the panel:

Publishers . . . are not living up to their responsibilities. One solution of the problem would be to employ trained science editors, specialists in the art of expressing technical ideas in straightforward terms. A few publishers have already taken this step. Another step is to draw on the experience of scientific consultants, although experience has shown that, by itself, setting up panels or boards of experts may not be enough. Consultants must be given ample time to consider manuscripts and illustrations, and to discuss details with writers and artists. Equally important, they must be well paid for their time.

In the long run, more attention will also have to be paid to the problem of who is to do the writing. Relatively few scientists have the time and qualifications to present technical information simply and vividly; relatively few professional science writers have the background required for preparing accurate and balanced reports on progress in complex areas of research. An approach that has produced good results is the use of both specialists—a collaboration between scientist and science writer.[18]

If a scientist has been a consultant, the publisher will usually mention his name in the book, but the reader almost rarely knows the exact role of the consultant or the reception accorded his suggestions.

The millennium is not here. The established and successful publishers of children's science books must be given credit for good intentions and for attempting to ensure the quality of their books despite the castigation by the *Natural History* panel. Even so, the careful teacher should examine the critical reviews in appropriate sources before making any final judgments about purchase and use of science books.

Content

Imitative science books

Many books are fashioned after books already in print and are published apparently because of mounting public interest in some scientific or technological advance. The multiplicity of books dealing with space, with astronautics, with the planets, and currently with conservation, ecology, and pollution problems is a specific example of this unfortunate, although understandable, tendency. Some of these books are excellent; some are acceptable; but many are inferior. They show evidence of hasty publication to take advantage of the current interest in the topic. They also show a weakness in editorial supervision.

Many books range widely over an entire field of science and are incapable of providing answers to specific questions. These books are not suitable for inquiry teaching because they are too general, not necessarily because they are poor in quality. Although the inspirational or synthesizing book has an important place in science teaching, the teacher should recommend books that foster depth of classroom learning — in other words books that are directly informative. Such books contain a reasonably thorough treatment of some limited aspect of science — for example, the microscope, elephants, or the sun.

Exaggerated claims

Within the confines of fifty or a hundred pages an all-embracing treatment of a topic is inevitably diffuse and superficial. In particular the discerning reader is not impressed by arrogant, misleading titles. Books that are "all about" are not *all* about; the fact that many of the books in the "All About" series are of high quality does not diminish the absurdity of their titles. Titles chosen to be striking and arresting are likely to be exaggerated. Books that begin with "The Wonder of" or "The Amazing Story of" are typically misleading.

The teacher should look to books that encourage children to think for themselves, that ask questions and suggest direct ways for children to find answers to these questions. Desirable books explain how scientists study nature and clarify the forces that drive scientists on. These books will distinguish clearly between facts and hypotheses, between plausible and implausible hypotheses, between theory and practice, and between assumptions and experimental and observational data. Books that open new vistas, stretch the mind, and liberate the imagination are especially desirable. This invitation to inquiry is a particular strength of science fiction.

The best children's information books also open new vistas. A book whose subject is the stars may be nothing more than a collection of star characteristics. The inclusion of stellar evolution, which is known to few children but is of great significance in placing man in his universe, would enrich such a book significantly. Few fields of science are so mature that they harbor no unknowns or are without contradictory and confusing elements. Surely one function of children's books is to lead children to see how much more there is for them *and* for scientists to discover.

Organization and development

Is the information new to children? Is the book likely to stimulate new learning, lead to new facts, new ideas, and new understanding? Heavy duplication of textbooks or encyclopedia content is a sufficient reason for prompt discard. Does the book stress ideas rather than a relentless accumulation of individual facts? Does it develop the important scientific concepts, principles, and generalizations that give meaning to its subject matter? Important ideas are intrinsically interesting; only a writer guided by an antiquarian idea of child mentality would ignore the hows and whys. Children *are* interested in the many facts that so commonly fill children's books; they delight in the interesting but trivial fact that the diplodocus was probably the longest animal ever to walk the earth. But they should also learn how the diplodocus fits into its ecological niche, the adaptations by which the species managed to survive for many thousands of years, and the interplay of complex forces that led to its extinction. Concomitantly children should understand the role of the paleontologist in establishing the facts and assumptions that have led to the modern conception of organic evolution. A book that interweaves these threads of fact, assumption, principle, and theory is infinitely preferable to a collection of isolated facts.

Are the concepts within the intellectual grasp of the children who will read the book? If Jerome Bruner's contention that no concept is too difficult for children to grasp at some intellectually honest level is valid, then clarity and accuracy of conceptual statement become vital. This contention is yet

Avoid repetition of what children know

another argument for thoroughness. Building a concept from its first elements into a more sophisticated and abstract notion is not a task for the hasty and superficial writer. The need to show the limitations and uncertainties of scientific knowledge compound the difficulties; only an intuitive writer, who knows how much is just right, can accomplish such a task.

Books may be outmoded on publication

Is the book up-to-date? Enormous changes have occurred in many fields of science within the past decade. Much of what was taught as scientific gospel a few years ago has become obsolete. The tremendous strides in nuclear physics, biochemistry, data processing, and genetics are specific examples. Less dramatic revolutions have occurred in such fields as animal behavior and microbiology. The practical sciences of engineering, medicine, and astronautics have transformed dramatically. A book on rockets published ten years ago is now ancient. Certain classes of books, however, have hardly aged. Many books of experiments, of plant, animal, and star identification, and of natural history, despite publication a decade or two ago, are still useful and interesting, although their pace may be somewhat slower and their illustrations somewhat dated in comparison to contemporary works.

Accuracy is essential

Above all, science books must be accurate in their facts and in their interpretation of these facts. A grave deficiency of many science books is the unwitting inclusion of serious factual errors, either because of carelessness or the author's lack of awareness. For example, one chemistry book refers to H_2SO_4 as a chemical symbol rather than as a chemical formula; the same book also describes atoms as miniature solar systems, a common but incorrect mental model. Perhaps these "errors," committed unwittingly, are not serious, but they are troublesome misinterpretations and lead to doubts about the author's competence. Books often equate mammals with animals and refer to "insects and animals" or "animals and birds." Many astronomy books explain the orbits of satellites, moons, and planets as a result of the combined action of centrifugal and gravitational forces, even though "centrifugal force" does not exist. Even experts are capable of error. A reviewer often discovers incorrect statements and interpretations in texts and monographs written by scientists. However, because of the specialist's competence in his field, mistakes in books written for specialists are less harmful than in books intended for the general public.

In addition many books often convey implicitly (and sometimes explicitly) teleological, anthropomorphic, and magical ideas despite the scientific consensus that ideas of purpose do not govern animals, with the exception of man, or plants. Living forms other than man do not, consciously or unconsciously, plan in the human sense. To say that plants "like" dry, sandy soil or that some field birds are dull-colored for purposes of camouflage is an unnecessary extension of human motivation. To explain animal actions as "instinctive" is also questionable, and modern animal behavior studies reject the term.

Some children's books capitalize on sensational, morbid, or exciting headings; "Funeral of a Town," for example, is a heading in one book on volcanoes. Such books breathe magic, mystery, and wonder as they overdramatize science. The life of an ant colony is hardly "amazing!" and "mysterious!" Exciting and provocative, yes, but hardly amazing. A book with such titles as "The Mystery of the Chemical Cabinet" for a chapter on the discovery of photography and "The Magic Messengers" for one on the invention of the telephone is guilty of a literary misdemeanor.

Relevance

Social consequences of science and technology

Children should be aware of the social consequences of science and technology. So much of what man does to ease his life leads to unexpected consequences or to consequences which, even though foreseen, did not appear to be important at first. Books about discovery and invention should point to these effects. For example, chemistry books should describe the effects of DDT and other pesticides on bird life, balancing the good that pesticides do in increasing crop yields and decreasing insect-borne diseases with the harm that they do to animal life and to man himself. They should also tell about detergents whose high phosphate content increasingly pollutes streams and lakes, drastically changing the chemical balance of these waters and leading to horrifying disturbances to plants and animals. Conservation, in the best sense of the word, is too important to leave to adults; for this reason teachers and parents should direct children to such books as A. Harris Stone's *The Last Free Bird,* a poetic evocation of the tragedy facing bird life in a hostile, man-ravaged world.[19]

Few such books have appeared

The opportunity to introduce the social effects of science and technology into trade books is virtually unlimited. For example, a book might weigh the glamour and romance of man's conquest of space against the demands for medical research. Another book might contrast the obvious potential of computers with the forced mechanization of the customary way of life as individuals are forced to adapt to a routine suitable for computer treatment.

Authors can no longer sufficiently follow the canons of good writing for children in most categories of science books unless they also convey the social, biological, and technological consequences of scientific advances, which cause even more problems for the already crowded world. Scientists must be responsible for the actions of their science on society; they can no longer pursue their traditionally narrow conception of scientific truth. In the same way the teacher should judge children's science books by an additional criterion: the extent to which they lead to a balanced picture of science as a force for both good and evil.

Vocabulary

Proper vocabulary is necessary

Not only must the author set concepts in an explanatory framework, he must carefully select his vocabulary. Of course he will have to introduce many new words to avoid circumlocutions, approximations, and overlong explanations; but with their introduction he should define technical words, either formally or informally. The long or unusual word is not in itself discouraging, although the overuse of technical words for their own sake is. To write about dinosaurs without giving some of their names or to describe space travel without the words *light-year* or *galaxy* is incomprehensible. How can a writer explain the science of hearing without using the words *decibel, cochlea,* or *Eustachian tube?* Each science has its own jargon; one of the first tasks that confronts prospective scientists is that of mastering the language of their specialty, which will otherwise be incomprehensible.

"Writing down" is a major error

Some writers deliberately limit themselves to words they assume are within the grasp of their readers. But the difficulty authors encounter in writing compelling, vigorous prose with a restricted vocabulary may outweigh its advantages. Writing down to children is not an answer because children soon recognize this form of condescension. Writing for children is not merely a matter of translating an adult book into simplified language. Avoiding technical terms or forcing on the reader unrealistic analogies, such as the solar system atom model, is not the best means to explain complicated ideas. The author should choose words that are either familiar or capable of being converted into the desired mental imagery. Difficult ideas become meaningful as they are developed in context. The fusing of simpler, previously known ideas build new hierarchies of understanding.

Irrelevant and unimportant facts, interesting though they may be to the casual reader, make no contribution to the exposition of scientific concepts and principles. For this reason the best books for children tend to treat one, or at most a few, topics at length. With the possible exception of taxonomic and descriptive natural history, a framework of principles, relationships, and interpretation of facts will contribute to the longevity of the book. Facts rapidly become obsolete; principles are more resistant to change.

Writers should not dwell on the curious, the unusual, or the accumulation of facts to maintain children's interest, without building steadily to higher levels of thought. Children do search for facts, but isolated bits of information do not contribute educationally.

"Sugarcoating" is suspect

Children tend to disregard books embellished with sugarcoated information—that is, trite stories, stock characters, or the author's own responses. Dialogue has a tendency to get in the way of the story line without serving a useful function. Teachers should beware of writers who talk of "wonders," "marvels," and "mysteries." Children are suspect of the transparent device of storytelling to present information.[20] They are not interested in "good" or "bad" animals or in morals drawn from nature, and they tend to shun books in which information gushes forth from adults or precociously knowledgeable children.

Style

Even children's books written in a pedestrian style are useful if they help children find answers to their questions. As a result significant generalizations about styles of writing for children are difficult to make. Of course writers should avoid involved, highly technical language in favor of clear, direct, straightforward exposition. Through his expository style the author should lead the intended audience to easier reading and understanding; however, children's reading levels and backgrounds tend to vary and are often unpredictable. For example, a bright fourth grader may read profitably a book advertised for grades four through six; on the other hand a slow sixth grader may need strong motivation to read the same book. The gifted writer of children's books inspires children to want to learn more about science. Unfortunately not many writers meet these specifications, just as few writers of adult science literature are, in the best sense of the word, popularizers—that is, writers of vivid, clear, and accurate science for the layman.

Adults are not good judges

Humor is often desirable in the text of the book and in the illustrations, but humor is no substitute for insight. Humorous touches should not interfere with the narration. Short sentences with a minimum of digressions and definitions add vigor and increase the child's interest in the book. Figures of speech should come out of the child's experience. Many books appropriate for a child in a middle-class socioeconomic level school are meaningless for a disadvantaged child who has never wandered through a woodland, observed the sharpness of a dark night, or attempted a scientific experiment at home.

A brief overview at the start of each major section of a science book seems desirable from a psychological point of view, although there is little evidence that an introduction of this kind is actually helpful. Few children's books use this organizing device consistently.

Rachel Carson has proved that science books for children can be sensitive and poetic in feeling and language, but she is a splendid exception. Children's books should make their points directly and clearly, beginning with familiar experiences, to satisfy young readers.

Illustrations

Illustrations should be functional

Children's science books are often marred by mediocre illustrations. The function of illustrations in science books is not primarily aesthetic; rather they should supplement the text by visual explanation or description. More often than not, illustrations are garishly overcolored, almost as if to establish the book's *bona fides* in a color-mad world. Color is often essential, either to accentuate certain points or to enhance the fidelity of the illustration, but color for its own sake is useless.

Some illustrations are so encumbered with details and labels that they bewilder the reader; others are equally frustrating because they are unlabeled and enigmatic. Illustrations are valuable if they are intimately integrated with the text, both physically and conceptually. Nothing is more irritating than to be forced to search through a book for a relevant diagram. The young reader has difficulty visualizing the size of an object from stylized, unrealistic drawings, lacking the slightest hint of scale. Many illustrations are either scientifically inaccurate or directly contradictory of the text. Some illustrations are unsuitable at the age level for which the book is written, perhaps because they have been copied without change from books written for adults. An added dimension of reality is available with photographs, but photographs should be used only if accuracy of representation is essential; otherwise the versatility of the specially prepared drawing is preferable.

Inferior illustrations, which add little to the text, indicate a lack of editorial supervision. In books with this defect, the writing and art work have been artificially separated by the publishers, who keep their authors and artists apart.

Mechanical factors

What's inside is most important

True, a book should not be judged by its cover, but when they are browsing, looking for something interesting to read, children are often tempted by an attractive cover. Publishers are well aware that striking dust jackets and attractive bindings help to sell books. However, external charm is less important for books to supplement science instruction in the schools, because children go to these books for the information they contain. Books for use in schools must be sturdily bound and therefore will be more expensive than books for home use. Books for young children should be big enough to hold comfortably and should be printed in a type size sufficiently large and well spaced to make reading easy. Surprisingly many books run on endlessly without a break in the flow of narrative, even when the topic changes sharply.

Some authors have succeeded in extending the reading levels of their books by writing separate but concurrent texts. For example, opposite each page in his "What's Inside" series,[21] Herbert Zim places a diagram or illustration for younger children; on the next page he supplies additional information in smaller print for older readers, parents, and teachers. The *Young People's Science Encyclopedia* provides a descriptive introduction for third or fourth graders in its entries and an amplification in a smaller type size for children up to the ninth grade. This device is helpful in extending the range of an expensive encyclopedia, although it sacrifices depth of explanation for younger children.

Another mechanical factor to be considered is the presence of the appropriate bibliographical apparatus. A detailed table of contents should compensate for the omission of an index, although if the book is a potential reference source, a detailed index will be helpful. Even if the definition and pronunciation of new words are given when they are first encountered, a glossary and pronunciation guide are indispensable. Incorporation of references to guide the reader, in addition to the references on which the author relied, is also desirable. If books are intended to stimulate new ideas and new investigations, their authors should encourage children to pursue further learning. These references will benefit teachers and parents as well.

Bibliographical aids cannot compensate for errors of fact or for stylistic shortcomings. However, they will enable children and teachers to exploit the potential of books more fully. Because elementary school children are just beginning to use references and to search for information in school and public libraries, the inclusion of bibliographical aids is even more imperative.

Experiment Books

Many collections of science experiments are on the market. Some books are devoted entirely to experimentation and firsthand investigation; others include a number of activities in their narrative, to interest and intrigue children and to add a concrete-empirical referent. Although some experiment books are hastily compiled grab bags of standard experiments, many books present ingenious experiences that introduce children to learning representative of modern science education.

Two broad classes of experiment books exist. The first type describes every step minutely, prescribing apparatus and technique in paralyzing detail and explaining the implications of the experiment (although many books do not discuss these implications). These books, by far the most numerous, leave the child with only the task of verification. However, the teacher can adapt these "tell-all" experiment books by presenting the experiments as demonstrations without using their explanations.

"Tell-all" books don't tell all

To fulfill its role of home instructor for the child who is *not* a creative experimenter, the "tell-all" book must provide lists of easily constructed or readily available supplies and equipment; it must be well illustrated, lead easily to success, and give simple, accurate explanations. Unfortunately a book of this kind may lead children to think that they have learned everything important and that little remains for the future. This type book should, at the very least, provide additional suggestions for investigation, supported by appropriate references.

The imaginative child seeks new awareness

The second class of experiment books challenges the child, presents him with questions that will lead him to a new awareness of his world, and suggests the many ways to gain scientific knowledge. These books, by virtue of their design, are particularly well adapted to inquiry teaching in the classroom.

George Barr's "Research Ideas" series and A. Harris Stone's "Adventures for Future Scientists" series, for children of age ten or older, are splendid examples of this second class of experiment books.[22] The bulk of each book in these series contains problem experiments and questions that can be answered only by relatively unstructured experimentation. Several suggestions for gathering further information are appended to each section. These books are especially appropriate for inquiry teaching. Their freedom is in contrast to a well-known experiment book, which directs children to prepare hard water and compare its behavior with soft water that has soap added. The writer announces not only that the soft water will form no curd but that the hard water sample will have a curd at the surface.

Safety factors once again

Teachers should examine experiment books closely before recommending them. Children who follow the directions in some books, particularly those including chemical experiments, may actually be in serious danger. Some experiment books call for commercial muriatic acid, a hazardous acid for children's use. Other books require pieces of "tin can" metal for a telegraph sender, without warning their readers that the edges of these pieces are razor sharp, capable of inflicting severe cuts. The teacher should also be suspicious of experiments that require 110-volt current, sharp instruments, or fragile glassware, especially if the children must work at home without trained supervision.

Many "experiments" are meaningless

In addition to these potential hazards many experiments are valueless because they are either uncontrolled or poorly controlled. If experiments, not intended to cultivate in children either desirable attitudes or skill in scientific investigation, are included only to add a little frosting to an explanatory cake, the lack of controls may be an unimportant criticism. But when causal explanations are sought and when variables are changed, controlled experiments enormously enhance the potential for valid explanation and for securing meaningful data. Whenever an experiment is too complex to allow for proper controls, authors should clarify for their readers the assumptions and weaknesses of their experiments. However, few experiment books make such clarifications. The other criteria for effective experimentation, such as the need for adequate sampling and the insufficiency of one experimental trial, also apply to experiment books.

Too many answers too often

Still another weakness of experiment books is their tendency to label activities "how something happens" (for example, "how plants obtain water," or "how rockets work"). Titles such as these are misleading because they confuse direct experience with real explanations. For example, colored water rising through the xylem of a celery stalk is an observation; it does not show "how plants obtain water." If, through experimentation, the child learns that water passes by osmosis and diffusion through cell walls and rises by means of osmotic, capillary, and transpirational processes, only then will he know something about the "how" of water movement in the plant.

Indication for caution

Teachers who incorporate scientific theory in their explanations often fail to refer to its hypothetical and frequently questionable basis. For example, in discussions of magnetism or the age of the earth they rarely include the cautionary remarks "Many scientists believe . . ." or "A hypothesis many scientists accept is that . . ." On the other hand many experiments omit explanations. A well-known experiment book, which in selection and style is superior, merely ends with the experimental description, although some activities have a few practical examples appended. In one experiment, which does not even hint at the implications of controls, an ice cube sprinkled with salt melts more quickly than a control ice cube. The result is equated to the melting of ice on roads and sidewalks by sprinkling salt on the ice. But the child is given no explanation. Although they are necessary in many books of experiments, explanations are meaningless if they are not gradually and systematically developed in the appropriate context. For example, a book for intermediate grade children explains the magnetization of a needle in eight lines according to the Weber–Ewing theory of magnetism, which dates from 1891. There is no hint of modern magnetic theory.

Summary

Trade books are one of the most valuable and useful tools of elementary science instruction, especially in inquiry teaching, because the content of these books is relatively narrow, detailed, accurate, and interesting. The almost endless diversity and richness of trade books extend the child's learning horizons, whether he is in the first grade or the eighth grade. Children can never perform enough experiments and make enough observations to gather all the facts and ideas they need; they must turn to such sources as books for this knowledge. Unfortunately trade books vary widely in quality, and the teacher or school librarian should evaluate them carefully according to such criteria as accuracy, quality, and pertinence of illustrations, originality, attractiveness, and the author's qualifications. Sources such as the *Children's Catalog*, the *Horn Book, Natural History, Science Books,* and the *Library Journal* are most helpful in making these judgments.

Excellent science periodicals, such as *Ranger Rick's Nature Magazine,* are also published for children. These periodicals are provocative, accurate, and well written and should be on hand in every intermediate and upper elementary classroom.

The potential of trade books for improving science teaching in the elementary schools has barely been explored. The very fact that they are not textbooks and cannot be used as textbooks is a point in their favor. But most important they provide flexible, informative, and stimulating materials and lend additional strength to science teaching by inquiry.

For further study

1. Review two books in each of the first four classes of science trade books — direct experience, information, biography, and fiction — according to their potential for process instruction. For additional evaluative criteria, see Huck, C. S., and D. Y. Kuhn, *Children's Literature in the Elementary School* (New York: Holt, Rinehart and Winston, 1968), Chap. 9.

2. Choose one scheme from each area of science and list several appropriate trade books that will enrich the study of each area. What are the strengths and weaknesses of books for this particular purpose?

3. Contrast reviews of the same book in the *Horn Book, Library Journal, Natural History,* the *Children's Catalog,* and *Science Books.*

4. Describe some of the different ways to use children's periodicals in inquiry instruction.

5. Write a critique of an elementary science encyclopedia or dictionary, discussing its adequacy in helping you find out:

   (a) why the sky is blue,

   (b) why sidewalks crack,

   (c) why ocean liners float,

   (d) why some birds migrate and others are year-round residents.

6. Analyze the reading level of a trade book, using one of the reading level formulas. Is the reading level of the book compatible with the publisher's suggested level?

Notes and references

1. Some of the ideas in this section are based on the Nuffield Junior Science, *Teacher's Guide 1* (London: William Collins, 1967), Chap. 6.

2. Beeler, N. F., and F. M. Branley, *Experiments with a Microscope* (New York: Thomas Y. Crowell, 1957); Sootin, H., and L. Sootin, *The Young Experimenter's Workbook* (New York: W. W. Norton, 1965); Selsam, M. E., *Play with Seeds* (New York: William Morrow, 1957).

3. Wyler, R., *The First Book of Science Experiments* (New York: Franklin Watts, 1952); Milgrom, H., *Explorations in Science: A Book of Basic Experiments* (New York: E. P. Dutton, 1961).

4. Stone, A. H., *The Chemistry of a Lemon* (Englewood Cliffs, N.J.: Prentice-Hall, 1966).

5. Lowery, L. F., and A. B. Carr, *Sweet as a Rose* (New York: Holt, Rinehart and Winston, 1969), and *Soft as a Bunny* (New York: Holt, Rinehart and Winston, 1969); Lowery, L. F., *Dark as a Shadow* (New York: Holt, Rinehart and Winston, 1969).

6. Podendorf, I., *The True Book of Weeds and Wild Flowers* (Chicago: Children's Press, 1955); Sterling, D., *Creatures of the Night* (New York: Doubleday & Co., 1960); Pistorius, A., *What Tree Is It?* (Chicago: Follett, 1955).

7. Kelman, P., and A. H. Stone, *Mendeleyev: Prophet of Chemical Elements* (Englewood Cliffs, N.J.: Prentice-Hall, 1970), and *Ernest Rutherford: Architect of the Atom* (Englewood Cliffs, N.J.: Prentice-Hall, 1969); Kuslan, L. I., and A. H. Stone, *Liebig: the Master Chemist*

(Englewood Cliffs, N.J.: Prentice-Hall, 1969), and *Robert Boyle: The Great Experimenter* (Englewood Cliffs, N.J.: Prentice-Hall, 1970).

8. Lowery, L. F., *Up, Up in a Balloon* (New York: Holt, Rinehart and Winston, 1960).

9. McClung, R. M., *Sphinx: The Story of a Caterpillar* (New York: William Morrow, 1949), and *Green Darner: The Story of a Dragonfly* (New York: William Morrow, 1956); Mendoza, G., *The Digger Wasp* (New York: Dial Press, 1969); Goodheart, B., *A Year on the Desert* (Englewood Cliffs, N.J.: Prentice-Hall, 1969).

10. MacGregor, E., *Miss Pickerell Goes to Mars* (New York: McGraw-Hill Book Co., 1951); Williams, J., and R. Abrashkin, *Danny Dunn and the Anti-Gravity Paint* (New York: McGraw-Hill Book Co., 1956).

11. Asimov, I., "Science Fiction: Clue to Creativity," *Library Journal*, Children's Section, February 15, 1964, p. 916.

12. *Science and Children* (Washington, D.C.: National Science Teachers Association), $8.00 per year for eight issues.

13. *Ranger Rick's Nature Magazine* (Washington, D.C.: National Wildlife Federation), $6.00 per year for ten issues.

14. *Young People's Science Encyclopedia* (Chicago: National College of Education, 1970), twenty volumes including an index volume.

15. *Compton's Dictionary of the Natural Sciences* (Chicago: F. E. Compton Co., 1966), two volumes.

16. *Compton's Illustrated Science Dictionary* (Chicago: Children's Press, 1964).

17. Branley, F. M., *The Sun: Our Nearest Star* (New York: Thomas Y. Crowell, 1961).

18. "The Editors of *Natural History* Present a Survey of Children's Science Books in 1961," *Natural History*, December 1961.

19. Stone, A. H., *The Last Free Bird* (Englewood Cliffs, N.J.: Prentice-Hall, 1967).

20. Williams, A. M., *Children's Choices in Science Books* (New York: Bureau of Publications, Teachers College, Columbia University, 1939), p. 5.

21. Zim, H., *What's Inside of Animals?* (New York: William Morrow, 1953), *What's Inside of Plants?* (New York: William Morrow, 1952), and *What's Inside of Me?* (New York: William Morrow, 1952).

22. Barr, G., *Young Scientist Takes a Walk* (New York: McGraw-Hill Book Co., 1959), *Young Scientist Takes a Ride* (New York: McGraw-Hill Book Co., 1960), and *Young Scientist Looks at Skyscrapers* (New

York: McGraw-Hill Book Co., 1963); Stone, A. H., and B. M. Siegel, *Have a Ball* (Englewood Cliffs, N.J.: Prentice-Hall, 1969); Stone, A. H., and D. Ingmanson, *Drop by Drop* (Englewood Cliffs, N.J.: Prentice-Hall, 1969); Stone, A. H., and H. Spiegel, *The Winds of Weather* (Englewood Cliffs, N.J.: Prentice-Hall, 1969); Stone, A. H., *Science Project Puzzlers* (Englewood Cliffs, N.J.: Prentice-Hall, 1969). This series of inquiry books has more than a dozen titles, for intermediate and upper grade children.

Tools of Teaching:
Audiovisual Aids

abundance and variety of contemporary educational audiovisual teaching aids are probably the most striking differences between past and present science teaching. Where once the teacher was happy if the classroom held a chalkboard, a globe of the earth, and a map of the United States, today teachers have an abundance of teaching devices, ranging from rear-screen synchronized-sound slide projectors to television receivers. If material possessions mean superior teaching, modern instruction must be superlative. However, each new device introduced into the classroom for the worthy purpose of improving learning also adds new complications. This chapter considers critically the problems of audiovisual instruction and suggests evaluative criteria so that the teacher can make the best selection from the multitude of teaching materials available. In the context of this book audiovisual aids include filmstrips, slides, motion pictures, television, sound records, charts, posters, diagrams, flannel boards, and transparencies.

Audiovisual materials usually have more than one commercial purpose. They may serve motivational, inspirational, factual, reinforcing, questioning, summarizing, aesthetic, historical, probing purposes; or they may be intended to replace the classroom teacher, to substitute occasionally for the teacher, or to assist the teacher. No one audiovisual aid is appropriate for all purposes. A film helpful in one fifth grade may be completely useless, even detrimental, in another.

Audiovisual aids are vicarious means of instruction; that is, they introduce an additional level of abstraction to children, who are forced to associate an image on a screen or some other depiction of "reality" with a reality they have never known. Instead of reading about something, they are *seeing about something,* an important characteristic of audiovisual aids.

343

Function of Audiovisual Aids

Much science content is abstract and conceptualized, yet for psychological reasons teachers must make extensive use of concrete experiences. Children have not built up the internally verbalized structures that enable them to deal symbolically with reality and are therefore unable to use Piagetian formal logic in abstract thinking. Educators emphasize abstract thinking because of its obvious freedom and power for children. The case for concrete learning materials is not limited to young children, however, because such abstractions as the atom and force are meaningless to adults unless they have some conceptual framework based on physical experience with the world.

One of the most important reasons for using audiovisual materials in the elementary school instruction is to help the children to become familiar with content not directly at hand. Audiovisual aids are therefore a substitute for direct experience. The motion picture brings into the classroom experiences far from children's immediate experience. Filmstrips and slides have much the same power. For example, what does a child know about volcanoes if he has only been told of their destructiveness, has looked at the simplified diagrams of his textbook, or has inspected a photograph of an eruption? Although learning from diagrams and photographs in textbooks is more meaningful than learning from words alone, the motion picture can vividly show sequential changes in volcanic activity, bombs of volcanic matter hurled through the air, bubbling lava on the volcano floor, and molten lava oozing slowly down the mountainside. The textbook could not possibly match the capacity of the film to convey the power and the awesome beauty of a volcano.

The value of animation

Another value of audiovisual aids lies in the ability to create visually explanations of scientific phenomena. Animated film visualizations of molecular movement in gases, solids, and liquids is far superior to mechanical models of molecular movement. The ability to show motion when motion is necessary for understanding is a great strength of the motion picture film and of television.

The attitudes of intermediate grade children toward "science, scientists, and scientific careers" can be "favorably changed" if they watch films selected for this purpose. The most striking and longest lasting changes occur if the class and the teacher discuss the films and a list of guide questions at the end of the screening.[1]

Motivating factors

Some audiovisual aids may be strongly motivating; that is, the impact of their careful planning, direction, story line, photography, and content may spur children to learn more about what they have seen. Such positive results are not often attained in the classroom, possibly because films are often improperly used or because children have not been conditioned to respond actively. Young viewers have a tendency to settle back, relax, and shift quickly from high gear to neutral when the room is darkened. The nagging thought recurs that audiovisual aids produce "a passive person waiting for some sort of curtain to go up to arouse him."[2] Children expect to be entertained, not taught with audiovisual aids.

Audiovisual aids may also reinforce previous learning. For example, using an overhead projector, the teacher may reproduce from cellulose acetate transparencies questions for class review and discussion. As the teacher analyzes children's responses to the questions and situations projected, both teacher and children benefit from the evaluative strength of audiovisual aids. Audiovisual aids may also summarize, reinforce, and connect the threads of classroom discourse. The bulletin board often fulfills this role, as the children outline on it the important concepts and conceptual schemes with which they have dealt.

Previewing is essential

One precaution in using audiovisual aids is mandatory. Before use the teacher *must* identify to herself, and perhaps to the children, the reasons for bringing in each aid and then use it for these purposes. She may have to alter her plan of attack as a result of unforeseen circumstances, but unless each aid leads to at least *one* desirable outcome, its use is not worth the class's time.

Value for Process Teaching

Audiovisual aids expedite process teaching

In general, audiovisual aids are functional in process teaching. As Chapter 4 suggests, most classroom activities in inquiry teaching should be centered on direct, concrete-based investigations because from these experiences desirable concepts and conceptual relationships ordinarily grow. However, firsthand experience cannot provide the only path for learning; because of the nature of elementary schooling learning must also take advantage of vicarious experience. Experience by proxy is necessary as children mature, to ensure maximum growth in ability to function independently and efficiently.

Audiovisual aids help overcome verbalism

Therefore, even in inquiry teaching, films are especially valuable for explaining conceptual structures. For example, animated films that "show" electrons flowing will help children visualize the flow of electrons in a wire. The term *electron* is, of course, a scientific abstraction; no matter how glibly children speak of electrons, they probably do not think of electrons as anything more than electrically charged bits of matter too small to see; and likewise they probably do not conceive an electric current as anything more than a flow of these bits of matter through a "hollow" wire, much like water flowing through a pipe. Animations of electron movement in elementary films help the teacher to raise children's level of understanding provided she also points out that what they see is a *model* of electron flow. The proper time for a film of this kind is after a study of electric current in wires, when the children seek explanations for the differences in flow resulting from such variables as wire composition, diameter, potential difference of the dry cells, and resistance. Purely verbal explanations of electron flow, by either the teacher or the textbook, are verbalisms; animation is an effective antidote to symbolistic oratory.

Audiovisual aids are often good sources to obtain information for inquiry purposes. Of course this role does not rule them out for arousing student interest, proposing new directions of study, and reinforcing previous learning; inquiry does not mean the abandonment of drill, review, and testing. The use of teaching aids in evaluation is particularly valuable. As a case in point at the end of a unit on plant interrelationships, the teacher may show a filmstrip of some common lawn or woodland plant groups. Her questioning after the film will soon reveal how well children can apply their newly acquired knowledge in describing and interpreting what they saw in the filmstrip.

Some new films and filmstrips include experiments, observations, or field experiences that are not feasible for the classroom. These experiences should lead to new conceptual organizations, which are impossible to achieve without these experiences. Lack of equipment or of special facilities is no longer a valid excuse for studying from the textbook alone the winter adaptations of animals, the characteristics of reptiles, or the connection between air masses and weather changes.

When children are working alone or in small groups, audiovisual aids should be at hand so that children can use them as resources when needed. Children need help in selecting these resources, extracting pertinent information from them, and evaluating this information. Children should know what information is available in the room and in the school's media center or how to find out the necessary information. In addition, the teacher should discuss with children how teaching aids can help them. She should also draw attention to new materials, describing their uses.

Audiovisual aids enrich teaching

In short, audiovisual aids are valuable in process teaching for much the same reasons texts, trade books, and other educational resources are. They are reference sources for gathering the data to formulate or corroborate hypotheses. But, as we have implied, they are not limited to this role alone. The following critical analysis of the different kinds of audiovisual aids probes into their assets and deficiencies in some detail.

Motion Pictures

Films have traditionally been a dominant teaching aid. Most schools own at least one 16-millimeter projector, although many schools lack proper facilities for projection—a room that may be darkened, convenient electrical outlets, and a ready supply of carefully chosen films. These handicaps are more prevalent in large city schools than in suburban or rural schools, perhaps because many urban schools are hopelessly out of date. Modern projectors are simple to operate, relatively invulnerable to abuse by inexperienced operators, and powerful enough to overcome imperfectly darkened rooms.

Visual images are powerful

Any resource that increases the effectiveness of concept formation is desirable to avoid wasting time with meaningless words. Films are valuable in building many abstract, nonexperience-centered ideas of space, time, growth, and sequence. They are unsurpassed in depicting change and motion and in explaining through animation. Even with their two-dimensional approximation of reality, films are often successful in presenting otherwise inaccessible experience. We have already briefly described animations of processes difficult to visualize mentally. But consider, for example, the difficulty of creating, from either experiment or reading, a visual image of plant growth, which is magnificently portrayed by time-lapse photography. In minutes the plants germinate and mature. Children can thus observe the differential growth of each plant structure—for example, the circumnutatory movements of pea tendrils and the maturation of the flowers. Of course study of the growth of living plants and animals at firsthand is most desirable, but children have difficulty observing each stage as it occurs. For example, children may miss the joy and excitement of watching a Monarch butterfly emerge from its chrysalis unless they have a chance to see the various stages on film. Even the static succession of developmental steps that slides or filmstrips offer is preferable to a textbook drawing.

When study of movement is important

In studying the adaptations of birds to their environment, close examination of wing movements for taking off, flying, obtaining food, diving, slowing down, and landing is impractical without motion pictures. The revolution of the planets around the sun, the moon around the earth, and the motion of the solar system through space are beautifully visualized on film. Children have difficulty conceptualizing these complicated movements from reading and drawing alone because of their limited understanding of mechanical forces and their generally insufficient conceptual structure.

The introduction of experts into the classroom by means of the motion picture is still another source of assistance to the teacher. The expert, a man who knows his field intimately, may present important ideas and questions in a challenging and provocative fashion. He may perform a difficult demonstration, provide new data, and direct attention to significant events.

Films can also bring to children in the upper grades experiments and demonstrations ordinarily impractical in the classroom. The expert demonstrator on film, fortified by ample time and experience, can explain in a few minutes phenomena too difficult or too dependent on specialized equipment for most schools. For example, much that we know about atomic structure comes from the study of the radioactive decomposition of certain atoms. Children have heard of Geiger counters and alpha particles. As they study the atom in the upper elementary grades, they will meet these phrases in their reading. Suitable scientific equipment, designed to match these words with their scientific meanings, is not often available in schools. Films that illustrate Geiger counters and explain their operation, with or without far-reaching scientific implications, substitute for firsthand experience. Such films, carefully selected, are far better than an inferior classroom demonstration. Their educational value depends on their quality, the degree to which children are prepared to profit from them, and the skill with which the teacher relates facts and concepts to the problems.

Teacher narration versus film narration

The narration that accompanies commercially prepared films is often a bland, syrupy concoction, which in its headlong struggle to describe everything describes nothing. Films with disturbing narration may be excellent if the teacher turns off the sound and replaces it with her own commentary. Rarely does the sound track of a film add to the action; such occasions (for example, bird songs, study of sound itself) are obvious. The teacher may thus emphasize the most significant parts of the film; she may even rely on slow motion and frequently halt the film for discussion.

Films are sometimes used to teach the tactics of inquiry. Richard Suchman, formerly at the University of Illinois, has prepared a series of films, each of which silently demonstrates one scientific principle in the course of a few minutes.[3] After each film elementary school classes attempt to explain the principle by directing a series of questions to the teacher. The children narrow the scope of their inquiry, eliminating irrelevant ideas and conditions, and finally learn to focus on the relevant elements of the demonstration. Such a film is useful for this purpose because children can see precisely what happens without the distracting side effects of classroom experimentation. In every case, however, the teacher can carry out the demonstration in the classroom exactly as shown in the film.

Proper use of film

Films should be chosen carefully. The brief annotations of the thousands of films listed in the various catalogs do not usually provide enough informa-

Help from the director of audiovisual aids

tion. The teacher who uses motion pictures wisely seeks advice from the director of audiovisual aids in her school system; yet no matter how competent the director is, the teacher cannot delegate her responsibility because only *she* knows the children for whom the film is intended. She might consult a list of time-tested, popular films, to eliminate the obviously unsatisfactory ones. However, because film guides do not generally classify films according to their most suitable uses, teachers must preview the films and, no matter what the financial sacrifice to the school, refrain from using them unless they are exactly right. Although films cost several dollars a day to rent, the cost in wasted time, disappointment, and disillusionment is much too great to justify the showing of poor or inappropriate motion pictures. To allow time for prior screening, the film should be available least a day before the planned showing. The following criteria will assist teachers in assessing the strengths and weaknesses of motion pictures:

1. What can the film do that the teacher and class cannot do as well or better?
2. Does it waste time on extraneous ideas and activities?
3. Is its production competent? Is the image sharp and clear?
4. Is it up to date? Is it accurate? Are the consultants or advisors listed in the credits scientists?
5. Is the class prepared to see it? Will the children profit from it?
6. Is it likely to stimulate activity? Will it motivate the class to make use of the ideas in some constructive way?
7. Is a simpler audiovisual aid, a filmstrip for example, more likely to be useful?
8. Is the film worth the time and effort to use it properly?

Research on motion pictures has led to many important guidelines for their proper use. For example, children like to watch films, but this interest is no guarantee that they learn. Learning depends on the organization of the film and its use in the classroom. A sleek color film embellished with melodious musical accompaniment may result in diminished learning because color and music are distracting. Humor, despite its appeal, distracts. These irrelevancies divert attention from the important task at hand.

Some difficulties with motion pictures

Most films do not stress important ideas sufficiently. They move too rapidly for children, and their brief summaries are therefore meaningless. Two showings of a film are more productive than one; yet three showings are not *necessarily* better than two. From a psychological viewpoint the less able student as well as the academically superior child profits from repetition; however, the two film showings do not necessarily need to be carried out in exactly the same way. For example, if the teacher first presents the film with its recorded narration, she may rerun it in slow motion with her own commentary.

Learning from films is improved if the teacher directs the class to significant portions, by comments, by pretesting, or some other attention-focusing device. These techniques are especially valuable prior to the second showing because children will then have a frame of reference to judge the second viewing.[4]

Films should use many clear labels and pointers in identifying important structures or processes. Inclusion of questions also increases the effectiveness of films. However, the film should allow children enough time to read or listen to the questions and answer them at once. Questions at the end of each segment of the film are more effective than introductory questions, although the latter may direct attention or help motivate children. The teacher may also ask her own questions.

The teacher need not feel obligated to show the entire film; in some situations she might show only the important parts even if for only three or four minutes. She should not yield to children's demands to see the entire film. Motion pictures in elementary science are not entertainment; they are tools for learning, to accomplish specific purposes.

Film loops

A promising modern development for overcoming the problem of excessive length is the 8-millimeter film loop, which is a short, three- to five-minute, continuously running film. It deals with one major idea or process and because of its continuity and repeatability is an astonishingly useful device for special purposes. The number of film loops suitable for elementary science instruction is increasing rapidly because of their low cost, convenient manipulation, and inherent worth. The subject matter available includes experiments on air and other gases, seed germination, microscopic organisms such as paramecia and amoebae, molds, fertilization of frog eggs, the life cycle of the butterfly, the pendulum, and the undersea world to name only a few of the current film loops. The projector is astonishingly easy to use, and children have no difficulty in learning to use it effectively either by themselves or in groups.

Above all, when using motion pictures, the teacher should use every device at her command to force children to interact vigorously with the stream of words and images in the film. Unless she succeeds, the class will be entertained, but it will not learn.[5]

Problems in the use of films

Scheduling films

Few schools have film libraries with enough prints to provide meaningful choice. Ordinarily the school must book a film weeks or months in advance from a commercial film library. Because the film is available for only a day or two, the teacher might sometimes skip previewing. Scheduling far ahead is undesirable because it structures the curriculum around films. If, for example, the only free date for a film on beavers is March 22, then March 22 becomes the target day for a study of the ecological adaptations of beavers. This pre-scheduling is a perversion of curriculum planning because convenience takes precedence over rational ends. The teacher must show the film at an inconvenient time or else sacrifice its genuine values for a more readily available but less desirable substitute. The teacher may overcome these disadvantages by ordering films for a longer period. A film costing five dollars for one or two days may not cost more than ten dollars for the full school week. With this extended time the school may exploit the film. However, the added cost and the increased competition with other schools, which arise from scheduling a number of films for more than one day, add to the difficulties of ordering films.

Many schools have not yet made the use of films easy for teachers. It is not unusual to find rooms insufficiently darkened, projectors mechanically inadequate, operators untrained (although the newest projectors are almost self-operating), and an inordinate amount of time wasted in threading and rewinding the film. The dogma equating films with entertainment is responsible for the unpardonable practice of inviting into the classroom unprepared classes of children (and teachers) or of showing the film in the school auditorium to many more children than are ready to profit from it.

Television

Television is potentially superb

Throughout the nation children can watch science lessons on closed- or open-circuit television. Most metropolitan centers, many school systems, and indeed entire regions have improved the quality of educational television by means of carefully planned sequences of science programs. Televised science lessons may be strikingly similar to motion picture films, but because they are usually programmed televised lessons are a technique for bringing to the child a structured content of secondhand experience. The television teacher, a specialist in science education, is not always an experienced teacher of young children. At its best, however, televised science is superb in its use of every technological resource for effective teaching. For example, the action may move smoothly from a demonstration to explanation by animated cartoons or from a magnet board, with questions and summaries recorded, to a photographic enlargement of the phenomenon being discussed. The possibilities are limitless.

There is little reason to doubt the mesmeric quality of television because of the conditioning to television children bring from home. The excellence of television receivers in the schools is continually increasing; screen sizes are larger and the power and the number of broadcasting outlets are growing daily. Technically classroom television is more potent than ever before.

Television may structure content

The most pertinent objection to teaching elementary science by television is that television, like motion pictures, structures classroom content. Titles and lesson plans for the televised lessons are usually known in advance so that instruction may keep step. This rigidity is not necessarily disastrous as long as these lessons are taught by inquiry techniques to guide teachers who adapt them for their particular classes. Unfortunately this is not the usual teaching pattern. Science on television is generally a series of demonstrations by a manipulator who merely substitutes for a textbook. The teacher has neither opportunity nor reason for developing inquiry procedures nor does the television instructor have feedback so that he can profit from classroom experience. Television also suffers from most of the drawbacks of motion pictures; instead of the projector bulb burning out in the middle of the lesson, atmospheric conditions or a low-flying airplane may disrupt the image.

This kind of instruction may be preferable to the conventional presentation of science in elementary school classrooms throughout the country. If science is to be taught in conventional ways, if the major goal is learning facts and principles as judged by achievement on standardized tests, then educational television, like films, has a contribution to make because of its capacity for enriching instruction. However, because it ignores the goals of inquiry, such science teaching is sterile and will take an unusually discerning and skilled teacher to use these predigested capsules of science in educationally justifiable ways.

Although television science is not usually designed for discovery teaching, teachers who know the program content in advance may propose problems whose solutions rest on data from the television lessons. In this case television is another source of information, although not necessarily the best. In general, inquiry teaching is unlikely to benefit from televising elementary science. A textbook is not improved because it is reshaped and projected on a 21-inch television screen.

A process television series

The Eugene, Oregon public schools, however, have produced a series of inquiry television programs now available on kinescope.[6] Each series of programs, for grades one to three, is composed of fifteen-minute lessons, which reflect the content, style, and objectives of the new elementary science programs. The teacher's guide describes in detail behavioral objectives of each lesson, preparatory activities for the children such as measurements and observations to be made by the class during the telecast, sample questions for the television teacher to ask, and suggestions for post-telecast activities and evaluation. This series of television programs is one of the finest examples of the use of television to stimulate process science and to help the classroom teacher to achieve the best possible results.

Outcomes of research   Research studies on television teaching of science report somewhat contradictory results; the methods, content, and subjects of the studies are so different that there is no common basis for generalizing. One of the best studies concluded that a series of eight biweekly, twenty-minute science lessons conducted on inquiry principles with fifth grade children "significantly stimulated" their achievement in science, when combined with teacher follow-up such as discussion, experiments, and reading.[7] However, the results of research in televised science instruction are difficult to interpret. Television science taught by heuristic methods, which aim at creating in children an involvement and interaction with the science process, is almost nonexistent. Children do not seem to learn appreciably less science in terms of retention of facts and scientific principles, nor do they appear to learn more. Some evidence indicates that children from a higher socioeconomic level or of superior intelligence are *less* stimulated by televised science to form positive attitudes, to develop interest in finding out for themselves, and to make the desired shift from extrinsic to intrinsic motives.

Television has its advantages, of course. It brings to children a vicarious experience with the whole world. In a superficial sense it has been instrumental in raising children to greater sophistication. The reality of a rocket launching, the impact of a rocket probe on the moon, the excitement of an eclipse of the sun are events which, because of their immediacy and emotional content, are uniquely adapted for television. News programs and documentaries add to the educational value of television. With few exceptions, however, commercial television almost completely ignores elementary school children in its public service programming. Educational television has not yet accepted its proper responsibility in providing for these children the richness of experience it has promised.

Closed-circuit television in individual school systems frequently rises above the banality of talking at children. This improvement over the traditional model of elementary science instruction occurs when a gifted teacher is joined by an understanding director and producer in working closely with a relatively small group of classroom teachers. Such an arrangement can introduce and maintain the excitement and interest of firsthand exploration in science. But only large school systems have the necessary resources of staff, time, and money for closed-circuit television; and the larger the system the greater the demand for a carefully sequenced curriculum lockstep. Unfortunately the inquiry science teaching cannot begin and end in thirty-minute programmed bundles on Monday, Wednesday, and Friday; within a few days teachers who practice inquiry teaching will be hopelessly outdistanced by their television colleagues.

Filmstrips and Slides

Another promising medium

Elementary science instruction has yet to benefit from the full potential of filmstrips and slides. Filmstrips are inflexibly sequenced collections of visual materials. Although the teacher may omit individual frames, the order in which images appear is almost impossible to change without physically destroying the filmstrip. If the teacher changes the order by moving frames back and forth, the result is likely to be a bewildering series of kaleidoscopic images. However, with standard-sized slides the teacher can easily arrange frames, although the slides are troublesome to catalog, store, and handle.

Filmstrips and slides share many advantages of motion pictures and television and are probably better for most elementary science uses that generally do not require motion or animation. They are helpful in the phases of science that are difficult to illustrate with concrete examples in the classroom — for example, ecological relationships and industrial applications. The low cost of filmstrips — approximately eight to ten dollars for forty or fifty frames in color — encourages schools to build a filmstrip library and makes obtaining good filmstrips easier for teachers. A detailed syllabus or a recorded narration synchronized with each frame accompanies many newer filmstrips. These narrations may impede good teaching in the same way that motion-picture sound tracks can be obstructive: They may focus on matters of little concern to teacher and class; they may cover too much, move too fast, and confuse rather than clarify. The teacher's own commentary is usually much more suitable for most elementary classes.

Pertinent titles and questions in the body of the filmstrip help children attend to the proper points, prepare them for new ideas, and guide their review. As often as she desires, the teacher may stop the filmstrip to discuss a single frame in detail; or she may turn back to an earlier frame to contrast or reinforce learning.

Careful evaluation of filmstrips

There are literally hundreds of commercially available filmstrips, but because of their variance in quality teachers should evaluate them carefully. The excellent "Process of Science" series strives to cultivate such process skills as observation, measurement, and classification.[8] The "Measurement" filmstrip illustrates the unique procedure: In the course of the filmstrip the question "Which of the following objects are measurement tools?" precedes pictures of peanuts, a shoe, a pile of sand, a spring, and a big toe. The children decide which of these objects can be used for measurements and how they can be used.

Teachers should always preview filmstrips before use and refer to criteria such as the following in their evaluation:

1. Can the class obtain the information more easily from other sources, such as reading, classroom experimentation, field trips, discussion, or films?
2. Is the filmstrip likely to be helpful? Is it within the grasp of the class? Is it clear, both intellectually and photographically?
3. Is it burdened with extraneous material?
4. Will it be available when needed?
5. Is it interesting? Exciting?
6. Will it organize previous knowledge effectively? Does it provide challenging situations for children's learning?
7. Is it accurate? Who produced it?

The teacher must decide whether the time taken for showing the filmstrip will be well spent. Good teaching calls for "right" decisions. The teacher is everywhere confronted with competing pathways for attaining her (and the children's) goals. The master teacher, perhaps intuitively but more often because of a practiced critical judgment, chooses the technique that is right for her and the class. The probability of being right increases with an understanding of the techniques and their assets and liabilities. Therefore the teacher should not rely on someone else's appraisal of even so troublefree a teaching aid as a filmstrip.

The value of slides

A chief asset of slides, despite their infrequent use in the classroom, is that individuals in the community may have useful teaching collections on hand. The teacher who, in her travels, has taken color slides of the Grand Canyon or Yellowstone Park is fortunate. If she lacks this resource, the teacher can probably find one or more individuals locally who will lend their collections or will even show the slides themselves, with their own commentary. Although personally owned slides are probably better adapted for social science or geography instruction, teachers should not neglect the possibility of other people's slides for science instruction. Excellent sets of standard-sized, commercially prepared slides are available on a wide range of science topics, such as animals, plants, ecology, rocks, minerals, geological processes, and weather.

Transparencies

The transparency is one of the newer audiovisual aids. The teacher uses an overhead projector to reproduce these sheets of acetate film, on a screen. Transparencies are clearly visible even in a lighted room and are a major resource for classroom instruction. Commercial sets of transparencies are available for the upper elementary grades. Each of these prepared sheets costs several dollars or more. The more expensive transparencies include overlays, which are sheets folded over a base sheet to introduce new structures, concepts, explanations, or questions, in a predetermined sequence.

The many uses of transparencies

Transparencies are substitutes for writing and drawing on the chalkboard. As she projects the transparency, the teacher faces the class so that she may speak directly to the children as they look at the magnified image on the screen. The time-honored but undesirable technique of referring to a picture in the textbook, or to a picture or chart at the front of the room which most children cannot see, is therefore unnecessary.

Overhead projection is clearly destined to be an ever more important educational tool, even though few commercially produced transparencies on the market today are worth their price. Their potential for clarifying individual points, such as the relationship of body organs, through a series of overlays, as well as for reviewing and drill is almost unexplored. Many school systems now own the necessary apparatus for copying photographs and diagrams and

Teachers can make their own transparencies

for creating black and white or color transparencies. Teachers need not be tied to commercially prepared materials but are free to select from all available sources pertinent illustrations and diagrams, which within minutes become useful audiovisual aids. However, production of color transparencies and overlays is much more time-consuming than simple copying in black and white.

In general, overhead projection of transparencies is one more technique for supplying resource information to children. For the purpose of analyzing the relationships of structures or summarizing and identifying structural features or characteristics, the teacher should consider carefully the possibility of using transparencies.

The Chalkboard

We should not ignore the chalkboard among the multitude of audiovisual devices now available, if only because it *is* in every school room. Chalkboards have no moving parts to burn out or to break. The teacher can draw or write on it in letters so large that every child can read the ideas, concepts, and summaries presented to them. In the course of a lesson the teacher or the class secretary can create a visible record of the important points. Although it is not an important necessity in science teaching, the chalkboard is unsurpassed in its operational simplicity. Several small chalkboards in different parts of the room are useful for individual or group work because of their convenience.

Unfortunately drawings and writing can remain on the board for only a short time. Detailed drawings consume time and are all too quickly erased. The teacher should either reproduce important drawings or have the children copy them. Unfortunately manufacturers usually design chalkboards for the teacher; as a result children are often unable to reach the upper part of the board.

Flannel Board

The flannel board serves functions similar to those of the chalkboard. It is particularly useful for the "What We Learned about Air Pressure" kind of display; the teacher or children mount cutout letters, drawings, and diagrams. The flannel board is also useful in discussions of those phases of science that involve changes of position or relativity of position. For example, the teacher can move the figure of Mr. O, the outside observer invented by Robert Karplus, from position to position to illustrate how the observer's point of view changes with physical orientation (see Chapter 5).[9] In the study of planetary motions the teacher can readily illustrate the relative distances of the planets from the sun at perihelion and aphelion. Because it is a simple, sturdy device and because it provides one more aid for better learning, the flannel board should be available in every elementary classroom.

The Bulletin Board

The bulletin board tends to be a static, rather inflexible teaching tool. All too often its main function is to exhibit the "finished" work of the class to

*A means for motivating
and summarizing*
visitors. However, the bulletin board has many other, more appropriate func-tions.[10] It may help to generate or focus interest on some phase of instruction. For example, the teacher who plans to introduce gravitational forces in our solar system may set up a photographic display of the planets of the solar system from such sources as *Life* or *National Geographic;* this exhibit may have a caption, such as "What Keeps the Planets Moving?" or "Why Does the Earth Move around the Sun?"

As the class begins its study the teacher should periodically change the display to new subjects. Scale drawings of the moon moving around the earth might represent the earth–moon system. Labeled arrows can depict gravita-tional forces holding the moon in its relatively circular orbit around the earth. Questions draw attention to important concepts: "Why doesn't the moon fly off into space? How do man-made satellites resemble the moon? Why doesn't the moon fall to earth? How long does it take the moon to move all the way around the earth?"

Results of research problems are well adapted for bulletin board display. Each group of researchers should plan an effective exhibition, with the artistic children providing the leadership. The need to fit their discoveries and con-clusions into a minimum space with maximum narrative power will challenge each group.

The bulletin board is also useful for summarizing both long-term and short-term activities. Important concepts, principles, and laws recorded on the board serve to remind the children of what they have learned. These ideas provide a nucleus for review and synthesis in the culminating phases of class-room investigation.

The bulletin board can be helpful to the teacher who is concerned with discovery teaching, although it makes no unique contribution itself. Carefully designed bulletin board displays combine economy of content with clarity of meaning. The teacher should select drawings, photographs, and captions for the contribution each makes to the total effect. Colored string joining bright captions with vivid illustrations enhances visibility and relationships; however, excessive color may produce a garish, self-defeating jumble. Artistic excess must be subordinate to scientific accuracy. Plant drawings or cutouts are much more effective if in natural color. On the other hand colored circles purporting to represent gas molecules are meaningless because colored gas molecules are meaningless. Children may misconstrue "colored" molecules, even though they are colored to enhance visibility. In every case the teacher should endeavor to portray nature realistically; she should weigh carefully the comparative advantages and disadvantages of color on the bulletin board.

Records, Tapes, and Cassettes

Limited value for science teaching

At present phonograph records, tapes, and cassettes have little value in inquiry teaching, partly because few records and tapes have been prepared for elementary science. Some recordings of songs written especially for science purport to teach such assorted facts and concepts as magnetic interaction, the water cycle, and the simple machines. But the cost of such records is difficult to justify for a school. They may arouse interest in younger children, although this point is conjectural. The attempt to correlate science with music is a far-fetched extension of the Herbartian correlation of the elementary school subjects. Science songs are sugarcoated doses of facts and principles; if they have a function, it is to encourage the painless learning of information. Teachers may find some opportunity to introduce science songs in the summarizing activities she and her class plan. They *are* enjoyable and are harmless when so used. With this exception their place in elementary science instruction is questionable.

One major exception to the general unsuitability of records in elementary science teaching is in the investigation of sound phenomena — for example, the Doppler effect, musical overtones, and pitch–frequency relationships — which are not easy to produce in the classroom. Excellent recordings of animal sounds — insects, birds, mammals, and fish — will add still another dimension to the study of the living world. Probably only one set of these records is necessary in most schools. Also an interesting innovation is a two-record album entitled "Blacks in Science," which describes the life of such black scientists as Charles Drew and Norbert Rillieux.[11]

Science information recorded on records or tapes all too often exemplifies the product aspect of science. Commercially produced records tend to center on facts. They may be less effective than motion picture sound narration because they are not integrated with a visual image.

Especially useful for self-study

Teachers, however, are not confined to commercially prepared auditory aids. Many teachers tape classroom discussions and student reports, which, replayed at leisure, allow them to analyze what happened. In this way teachers can evaluate their own contributions — their actions and decisions — and the blind alleys that sometimes confront them; at the same time they are free to listen to and analyze each child's contribution. By replaying the tape in the classroom, the teacher can begin a cooperative analysis of the hypotheses generated by the class, their assumptions, conclusions, and general strategy in attacking problems (see Chapter 10). Richard Suchman has proved the effectiveness of such training for problem solving.[12]

Opaque Projection

Useful but limited

At one time scorned as a trivial gadget the opaque projector has established a legitimate role in instruction. The teacher can easily project a picture or diagram directly from a book or periodical. Without special equipment to transfer the picture onto a transparency, the opaque projector is often the only way to project an enlarged image. Few classrooms have an opaque projector on hand, ready at a moment's notice, however. Many teachers feel that requisitioning the projector, putting out the lights, and drawing the dark curtains are hardly worth the effort to show one or two illustrations. Teachers who rely on the opaque projector try to select stimulating illustrations that help to explain pertinent ideas and present important information most economically. The magnificent photographs of the surface of the moon and the detailed electron microscope photographs of cells, which have been published in many periodicals, are ideal for opaque projection.

Unfortunately because the classroom should be dark, note taking is difficult, and the customary teaching techniques for analyzing and summarizing the concepts and relationships must be postponed. The teacher should carefully weigh the relative advantages and disadvantages of opaque projection. The belief that the class will profit from opaque projection is sufficient, but if more convenient and simpler means will achieve the same ends, the teacher should leave the opaque projector for some other time and duty.

Models

Don't invest much money in models

A model is a more or less faithful copy of some physical structure. The function of most models is to allow close examination of structural detail and the functional relationship of parts. A three dimensional model helps children to translate a two-dimensional drawing or photograph into a reasonable approximation of a real object.[13]

Costs and values of commercial models vary widely. Although its cost may be prohibitively high, a model of a human torso is valuable because the relative sizes and spatial relationships of the body organs are clearly visible. A tellurian is helpful in simplifying the complex motions of the moon and earth around the sun, but its inevitable distortion of scale and velocity is likely to produce new misconceptions. The advantages of more or less realistic, three-dimensional physical replicas are real and numerous, but sturdy models are expensive. If they are too simplified or are intended to reduce cost or eliminate unwanted detail, then models are meaningless. Leaf models are often so generalized that their resemblance to actual leaves is minimal so that children may easily form incorrect ideas based on such models.

Why build models?

Inexpensive, plastic toy models, usually in kit form, are popular and sometimes instructive, but they are usually too small to be effective demonstration models. Plastic models of many common animals and plants are available at neighborhood stores. The assembling of kits is worthwhile if the activity helps children to understand the structure of the prototype, the relationship of its parts, and the method of its operation. The meager intellectual outcomes of model airplane construction well illustrates the difficulties in achieving conceptual growth by model building. Most boys can put together a reasonably well-built model, which bears a strong resemblance to its prototype. However, from this experience few boys learn how an airplane flies, how the rudder and elevators function, and why the airplane "defies" the law of gravity. Teachers must pursue the "why" and "how" instead of the "what" models.

Models should look like their prototypes

The model should operate and be as realistic as possible. Stimulating operation can lead to difficulties. For example, the construction of a plaster of paris volcano often culminates the study of earth changes. Decomposition of ammonium dichromate simulates eruption. In a semidarkened room, the action seems quite realistic. Lava belches forth; sparks flash from the crater, accompanied by clouds and an impressive hissing. But because real volcanoes are not charged with ammonium dichromate and because their lava is not green, the model may be deceptive and, from the standpoint of safety, somewhat hazardous.

In assessing models teachers should consider visibility and accuracy of detail. The following criteria will assist teachers in evaluating science models:

1. Are the important parts clearly visible?
2. If it is a working model, does it operate like the prototype? If operation is simulated, will you need to explain that the prototype operates in a different way?
3. Is the model faithful in scale and appearance to the prototype?
4. Is it durable?
5. Are transparencies, photographs, or charts effective substitutes?
6. If construction is necessary, will the physical act of fitting the pieces together promote learning?
7. If commercially produced, is the model worth the expense?

The Diorama

Dioramas are fun to make

The diorama is a two-dimensional painting on a large scale, or a three-dimensional composition that joins a painted background to objects and structures in some kind of natural relationship. A diorama of a river valley may be valuable in clarifying erosional processes. A diorama of the dinosaur life during the Cretaceous period may be an interesting way to summarize the study of prehistoric plant and animal life. Construction of a diorama involves numbers of children. Because it requires physical actions, the activity will be enjoyable; because its outcome is tangible, the outcome of the diorama is easily evaluated; and because it is dramatic and clearly shows how hard the children have labored, the activity makes for good public relations.

Construction by itself and for itself, however, serves no useful purpose in science. Yet if children grow in planning the diorama and working together and if they obtain the data they need in educationally sound ways, children will have taken a positive step in their education. Learning does not automatically take place with the physical activity of diorama construction. Despite extensive model building children can easily escape from a unit on erosion with no understanding of erosional forces or the time scale erosion normally takes.

Community Resources

Museums, planetaria, nature trails

All cities and many towns and villages have excellent resources open to elementary school children. For example, many cities have natural history, science, and technology museums, which are a rich source of well-conceived and cleverly executed audiovisual displays. Just a trip to see the prehistoric animal models, the visual presentations of industrial processes, and the clever models demonstrating scientific principles is well worthwhile. Museums frequently have seasonal nature "shows," special film programs, and planetarium presentations. Planetariums offer exciting astronomy programs on the constellations, the planets, the moon, the stars, and the changing seasons—all through the use of audiovisual media. In large city planetariums lectures are usually planned well in advance and are not adjusted to the age level of the visiting children; however, in smaller university and science-center planetariums lectures are usually adapted to the appropriate level if special arrangements are made beforehand.

Some schools have purchased or been given tracts of land nearby, which they have converted into nature and conservation areas with marked trails.

Both teachers and children maintain these areas. The interest in conservation and ecology, coupled with the federal open-spaces program, has spurred the conversion of land into natural history areas. In addition, city, state, and federal parks, wildlife preserves, private and public arboretums, Audubon centers, and natural history preserves, all open to children, are abundant.

Summary

Elementary school science is in an ideal position to capitalize on the flood of old and new audiovisual aids now on the market. The possibilities of enriching and broadening learning more efficiently and more economically than ever before are within the grasp of most elementary schools. Effective learning depends on many interactions with the physical and intellectual environment of the child. The school cannot possibly present all the direct experiences that ideally make for good science instruction. Audiovisual aids such as motion pictures, slides, filmstrips, television, opaque projection, and models can, if wisely used, provide many vicarious experiences that catalyze learning. Audiovisual aids are convenient and effective ways of motivating children to study fields of science of which they have no experience. They can help the teacher to organize her teaching so that she spends a minimum of time clarifying important ideas, drilling, reviewing, and summing up.

Before each audiovisual presentation, the teacher should question the value of the aid she plans to use. Will it do what she wants? Is a motion picture better than a filmstrip? Will a model so enhance learning that its cost is immaterial? Is there time to preview the film or filmstrip? Unless the answers to these questions are strongly positive, the teacher would be wiser to rely on such simple devices as bulletin boards, transparencies, and chalkboards. Time, the teacher's and the children's, is too precious to waste in superficial and trivial instruction.

The teacher should carefully consider such disadvantages as the conditioning of children to passive behavior, mechanical difficulties with apparatus, room scheduling, and room darkening. She *can* schedule a program of science instruction around a motion picture, but this kind of science instruction will not produce active, inquiry-centered children with the intellectual strength for coming to grips with modern science learning. Wisdom and judgment in selecting the right audiovisual aid comes with experience and practice. Audiovisual aids *are* aids. They will neither replace the teacher nor cause extraordinary growth in learning. They will, however, help the teacher to present, more efficiently and more dynamically, the entire world of science.

For further study

1. Do motion pictures encourage passive learning?

2. To what extent is the availability of audiovisual materials a determining factor in structuring science instruction in the elementary grades?

3. Write a critique of an elementary science program televised on an educational station.

4. Make a close study of science motion pictures and film loops for primary grade children and intermediate grade children in each of these categories: (a) physical science, (b) biology, (c) earth science. Repeat the analysis for filmstrips, science records, and a set of transparencies for overhead projection.

5. How can photocopying machines improve audiovisual instructional techniques?

6. What are some reasons for the relative failure of motion pictures in many classrooms?

7. When is showing a motion picture film only once educationally justifiable?

8. What are the implications of research studies concerning the major contribution of audiovisual aids to teaching, with minimal classroom teacher participation?

9. How can closed-circuit television strengthen elementary school science?

10. Is the lack of immediate feedback in television teaching a serious objection to its use? Explain.

11. Many educational psychologists believe that more and better learning results when more than one "sensory channel" is engaged in learning — that is, when image and sound are combined, or when several different but related images are used. Is this belief justified?

Notes and references

1. Allison, R., The Effect of Three Methods of Treating Motivational Films Upon the Attitudes of Fourth-, Fifth-, and Sixth-Grade Students Toward Science, Scientists, and Scientific Careers, unpublished doctoral dissertation, Pennsylvania State University, 1966.

2. Bruner, J. S., *The Process of Education* (Cambridge, Mass.: Harvard University Press, 1960), p. 72.

3. Suchman, J. R., *The Elementary School Training Program in Scientific Inquiry* (Urbana, Ill.: College of Education, University of Illinois, 1962), Chap. 4.

4. May, M. A., and A. A. Lumsdaine, *Learning from Films* (New Haven, Conn.: Yale University Press, 1958), p. 103.

5. See Walsh, W. J., "Are We Using or Abusing Educational Films in Our Junior High Science Classes?", in L. I. Kuslan and A. H. Stone, eds., *Readings on Teaching Children Science* (Belmont, Calif.: Wadsworth Publishing Co., 1969), pp. 197–202.

6. Great Plains National Instructional Television Library, University of Nebraska, Lincoln, Nebraska.

7. Skinner, R., An Experimental Study of the Effects of Different Combinations of Television Presentation . . . , unpublished doctoral dissertation, Kent State University, 1966. See also Galey, M., "The Development of Inquiry through the Use of Television," paper given at the forty-fourth annual meeting of the National Association for Research in Science Teaching, 1971, in *Abstracts of Presented Papers,* pp. 217–18.

8. "Process Science" filmstrip series (New York: Interaction Productions, 1968).

9. *Relativity of Position and Motion* (Berkeley, Calif.: Science Curriculum Improvement Study, University of California, 1964), p. 3.

10. For many interesting bulletin board suggestions see Vessel, M. F., and Wong, H. H., *Teaching Science through Holidays and Seasons* (Belmont, Calif.: Fearon Publishers, 1960).

11. "Blacks in Science" (Chicago, Ill.: Society for Visual Education).

12. Suchman, J. R., *op. cit.,* p. 52.

13. Cleminson, R. W., A Comparative Study of Three Fifth Grade Classrooms on Five Selected Piaget Type Tasks Dealing with Science Related Concepts, unpublished doctoral dissertation, University of Iowa, 1970, p. 105.

9

Tools of Teaching: Facilities and Equipment

elementary science based on experimentation requires a variety of equipment and supplies, most of which the teacher can make easily from materials at hand. But many teachers are not skilled at improvising substitutes for necessary apparatus, and they lack the interest in, the time, and the tools for improvising. A common complaint of the classroom teacher is that she is expected to teach science without proper science equipment.[1] Of course some teachers are either incapable of using or unwilling to use supplies and equipment already at hand.[2]

Teachers need science equipment

The term *facilities* refers to the physical aspects of the classroom—the storage space, electrical outlets, demonstration desk, dark shades, work surfaces, sinks, projection screen, and so forth. *Equipment*, or *apparatus*, means the more or less permanent materials for experimentation and demonstration, such as the ring stands, lenses, hot plates, and the aneroid barometer. *Supplies* are the materials used in the course of the year; they may be fragile objects that frequently need to be replaced—for example, chemicals, test tubes, balloons, iron filings.

Much homemade equipment is helpful

An ingenious teacher or child can perform most elementary experiments and demonstrations with improvised or substitute equipment. If, by constructing a piece of apparatus, the teacher helps children to understand fundamental principles better, the construction is clearly of value; but the teacher must carefully weigh this value against the demands of time. If she finds little of scientific value gained by construction, a commercially manufactured piece may be much better. For instance children can assemble a crude galvanometer, which will respond to an electric current. The operation of this homemade galvanometer is easier for children to understand than the operation of commercially manufactured instruments, because the working parts are open. However, the homemade galvanometer is too insensitive for comparative measurement of current flow. Children can also build a simple device to compare the rate of heat flow through different metals, but the elegance and simplicity of the conventional heat conductometer may counterbalance the values of the homemade apparatus. On the other hand the child who *builds* a small telescope learns far more about the science of light than the child who merely *uses* a telescope.

Many elementary science teachers advocate children's planning and constructing equipment. If they use only commercially manufactured apparatus, children may think that science is a special subject they can only study with special equipment. This attitude is directly contradictory to "science as a way of discovery which can be applied anywhere, at any time, with whatever materials happen to be available."[3] David Hawkins, an early pioneer in the new elementary science, has stressed these ideas:

> The central emphasis of most of the new science has been that children learn from nature, from selecting and carrying through their own investigations. Thus it is laboratory work and field work rather than the use of texts and lectures, that dominate this new development. Teacher's guides are often accompanied by kits of apparatus, specially constructed for particular uses. . . . Such equipment has proved its usefulness . . . many teachers have discovered that laboratory science in the classroom can be an exciting educational adventure.

> As schools tackle an ever-widening range of science topics, however, the collection of special kits does not really add up to a generally well-stocked, reasonably priced elementary school laboratory. As teachers and children are liberated from set lines of study, moreover, and develop the capacity to pursue investigations where interest and opportunity lead, it becomes imperative that the schools have a wide range of simple equipment and materials to meet planned lesson needs and for improvising new apparatus. . . . The design of apparatus is not the least of the scientist's skills. The ingenuity and manual skill which may be called forth from children in producing apparatus to meet their own particular needs are likewise an important part of science in the classroom. *The child who builds his own apparatus from familiar materials is more likely to relate his findings to the everyday happenings in the real world outside than one whose experience is limited to the "conjuring trick" atmosphere of the ready-made science kit.*[4]

Science kits may be restrictive

Hawkins points out that these prepared science kits are for the typical classroom situation in which the teacher schedules science for a fixed amount of time and has most children doing the same activity. Duplicate equipment is necessary in this case because children working on their own or in small groups will need a much greater variety of tools, equipment, and supplies.

To maintain an effective elementary science program, the classroom should have a basic store of equipment and supplies—running water, adequate counter, work, and storage space—designed to facilitate instruction.

Help for the teacher

Many good sources of equipment and supplies exist.[5] Most school systems expect each teacher to order and maintain science materials required for her classes. Many school systems employ science supervisors or consultants to assist teachers in planning and in ordering necessary items. They have a library of catalogs and time-tested lists of materials on hand. In addition the teacher can turn to innumerable publications for help in selecting equipment and supplies. Most elementary school science curriculum guides and syllabi include detailed equipment and supply lists. Teachers should feel free to call for help from their colleagues in local junior and senior high schools. Elementary school teachers often fear they will be intruding on high school teachers. On the contrary high school teachers are eager to help, but they in turn hesitate to force themselves into the elementary schools. Teachers who turn to the high schools will find that they are welcome and will receive prompt and effective assistance.

Lists of supplies and apparatus, important though they may be, are not the final answer to the problem of selecting materials. These lists are compiled for courses of study with emphases and purposes that are likely to be markedly different from the teacher's. However, wise planning over a period of a few years will stretch a limited budget for supplies and apparatus. Frequently a science supervisor will provide special items, such as a mercurial barometer, vacuum pump, or demonstration steam engine. Children often add such useful materials as their shell and insect collections brought from home.

The following general criteria for selecting scientific apparatus and supplies are useful:

Guidelines for selecting equipment and supplies

1. Is the apparatus or supply functional? Does it perform according to its specifications?

2. Is its expense justified by its potential uses?

3. Is it safe?

4. Is it durable, reliable, and uncomplicated? Will it work with a minimum of maintenance? Is repair likely to be expensive and time-wasting? Can it be repaired locally?

5. Will children who sit at the rear of the room be able to see the important details? Is it large enough so that children can manipulate it?

6. Are there less expensive substitutes?

7. Is it a "black box" instrument, whose internal operation is hidden from the class? Is it too advanced, too complex for the class?

8. Is it easy to store?

9. Are operating directions easy to follow?

10. Does it have potential for different kinds of learning experiences, or is it more limited? If it is not versatile, is it indispensable for its intended purpose?

The cost of a piece of scientific equipment is not always a sound guide to its value. Although low-cost equipment is often unsatisfactory, high-cost equipment does not guarantee high quality. A few companies in search of quick profits from shoddy merchandise have invaded the elementary science equipment market. Reputable supply houses guarantee their merchandise and do not mislead the unwary buyer with deceptive advertising.

Science Centers
and Science Corners

The center of action

Teachers who see children are interested in science often reserve a section of their room for the "science corner," where children congregate to investigate a provocative new exhibit, repeat a demonstration, or work out a science problem for themselves. Here the children keep class pets, grow plants, store equipment, and maintain the classroom collection of science trade books and periodicals. The science corner is a positive incentive for science study in many classrooms. Moving science facilities away from the center of the room has been criticized on the grounds that it minimizes the importance of science in the classroom.[6] This criticism is not justified as long as the majority of children regularly use the science corner as their laboratory.

The science corner *is* physically limited, however, because it accommodates only a few children at one time and has storage space for only a small variety and quantity of materials. The new elementary science programs tend to have a heavy demand for storage space because of the many different kinds of materials drawn on.[7] Because special resources facilitate the task of teaching science, a number of schools have either built or remodeled rooms just for elementary science instruction. This special science room has many uses: a place for teachers to take their classes for science lessons; a facility for groups of children to pursue their science interests; a storage area for all the science materials, carefully inventoried, in the entire school; a natural location for inservice science workshops and for inspection and evaluation of new pieces of equipment.

A compact area

In one school the science center includes an animal area located in a corner near the sink; facilities for aquaria; a plant-growing area in an improvised greenhouse heated by an electric light bulb; a U-shaped demonstration table with accessory shelves and drawers; a weather study area near the windows, equipped with appropriate charts and instruments; a reference area supplied with trade books, picture collections, and a resource file listing local field trips and consultants; and a storage area for science materials not stored elsewhere.[8]

A science room does present some problems, particularly in the primary grades: It may isolate science from the remainder of the curriculum; also, if a number of different classes use the room, scheduling will be necessary so that at times children may not be able to delve immediately into activities of interest. These problems are in addition to those of maintenance and inventory.

Central storage

Some schools operate a less elaborate center from which teachers draw whatever special equipment they need for regular classroom instruction. Teacher and pupil volunteers usually supervise the centers. These volunteers are responsible for checking equipment in and out, keeping an inventory, and maintaining the equipment in operating condition.[9] Continual maintenance is necessary; in many schools vigorous initial efforts have ended in disaster because no one on the staff took on the responsibility for cleaning and repairing.

Special Equipment

Extras for the wealthy school

Within the last few years many elementary schools have purchased large pieces of special equipment, such as portable science tables, microscopes, and planetariums. The portable table is a worthwhile accessory. With a work surface of about four and one-half feet by two and one-half feet, one commercially available table has a twelve-inch stainless steel sink, a water tank, a storage area, which holds a large variety of science equipment, as well as built-in electrical outlets. The exterior of the table is resistant to fire and chemical corrosion. The table itself, exclusive of apparatus, lists for approximately 300 dollars. It can be moved quickly and easily from room to room. Because its working surface and facilities promote experimentation, the table has great potential for science instruction. A number of companies manufacture similar tables and accessories; teachers should study carefully the advantages and disadvantages of equipment from competing companies because price is not always related to quality.

Many special pieces of equipment, such as the planetarium, are now advertised for elementary schools, although most models are far too expensive for the elementary school level. Yet for slightly more than one hundred dollars a school can purchase a small planetarium where ten children can view stars of the northern and southern hemispheres together with constellation names and a projected ecliptic line. Because its ceiling is domed, the planetarium does not distort the image as other inexpensive planetariums do. Naturally the quality of the image is not the best, but the children *do* see an approximation of the night skies.

Models of the earth–sun–moon relationship range in price from a few dollars to two hundred dollars. The more expensive motor-driven models simulate the seasons, the phases of the moon, and eclipses with artificial "sunlight," which falls perpendicularly on the "earth." These pieces of equipment are usually purchased for the entire school and requisitioned by teachers as needed.

Science Kits

Kits are often useful

Science kits are popular with elementary science teachers, even though teachers can order individual items from catalogs and save a great deal of money without lessening in any way the quality of the materials purchased. Busy classroom teachers and administrators do not always have the expertise and time to take advantage of these savings. Kits *are* convenient. Attractively packaged and extravagantly advertised, they seem to include everything needed for high-level performance.

Kits tend to be expensive

Many science kits cost more than the sum of the separate pieces because of their expensive packaging, which is occasionally carried to ridiculous extremes. They sometimes include individually wrapped paper cups, paper straws, and lengths of string. Teachers and administrators should reject kits with a large number of items that they can obtain locally—for instance candles, straws, paper cups, drinking glasses, and dry cells.

The management of kits

Many experiment manuals accompanying these kits obstruct or channel experimentation because they explicitly tell children what to do and how to do it. The materials and their containers are often too flimsy to stand up under daily use, especially if they are made of plastic. Some science kits that begin classroom life neatly organized soon become a shambles; neither the teacher nor the children can manage to return all the items properly so that in closing the case they can easily damage the contents. Few kits contain enough materials for more than a handful of children to use at a time. Several companies produce class-size kits for experiments in the various sciences, but to keep prices low these kits are of poor quality, and breakage is high. Replacement of some items in a kit is frequently expensive, particularly when the items are not standard pieces.

The price of a science kit depends on the method of packaging, the material of the case (wood, plastic, or cardboard) and of the equipment and supplies (plastic or metal), the kind of manual supplied, and the number of standard, mass-produced pieces included. For prices ranging from twenty-five dollars or more many companies sell standard science kits, which include such items as rubber stoppers, test tubes, hot plates, pulleys, spring balances, insect pins, magnets, iron filings, and ring stands. Specialized kits for nature study, embryology, plant growth, magnetism and electricity, water and its properties, heat, physiology, light, sound, air pressure, weather, and machines are also on the market. At least one commercially produced kit is available for every content area of elementary science.

Make your own kit

Many teachers make their own science kits, storing the materials in shoeboxes or in other containers of the right size, according to topics. These kits, augmented with specially purchased material, meet the teacher's and the class's science needs as well as the more expensive commercially prepared kits. Backed up by this basic equipment, the teacher draws on the supplementary resources of the central supply when necessary. The teacher should clearly label the shoebox kits so that when the kits are stacked, she can easily identify each. Also within each box the teacher should keep a list of all the items. An inexpensive multidrawer plastic storage cabinet will hold the small supplies such as wire, screws, tacks, straws, and string. Children are always thrilled with the opportunity to take on the responsibility for maintaining their homemade kits.

Safety

Teachers should always look after the safety of the children. Considering the potential hazards in scientific experimentation even with relatively harmless materials, that so few accidents occur in school rooms is a source of wonder. The teacher *must* warn children about all potential dangers; she must *never* take for granted that children are old enough to anticipate what can happen. Safety rules, which teacher and students cooperatively draw up, together with direct instruction in handling scientific materials are necessary in avoiding accidents.

Be careful!

Think of the hazards associated with household and schoolroom electrical supplies! Most commercially manufactured electrical equipment operates on 110-volt alternating current. Under normal operating conditions equipment approved by the Underwriter's Laboratory is safe. Sometimes, however, unsafe extension cords may stretch between an electrical outlet and the machine. The teacher should immediately replace a dry, cracked cord exposing bare wire and beware of connecting several cords simultaneously to one outlet because of the possibility of circuit overloads. She should also try to substitute an electric hot plate for alcohol lamps, candles, or Sterno, but a defective hot plate is just as unsafe. The danger of open flames from candles and alcohol lamps is well known; an alcohol lamp explosion is common, especially when a partly empty can of alcohol is near the flame. The mixture of alcohol vapor and air in the can is explosive! A qualified person should check a hot plate for defective wiring. Even an electrically safe hot plate should rest on a good heat insulator, such as a sheet of asbestos or an asbestos oven mat. Commercially purchased equipment is sometimes hazardous. For example, a chick-hatching incubator, devised for elementary school classes, has 110-volt electrical connections exposed. Children reaching into the incubator to handle eggs can easily brush against these contacts. Numerous suggestions for building heaters, incubators, and hot plates have appeared in science literature. But many such homemade devices embody shock hazards; someone who knows electricity should certify the safety of these devices before children use them. Reputable manufacturers take proper precautions. For example, a new incubator on the market is advertised as follows: "The heavy duty AC line cord has a grounded plug. The 75-watt light bulb . . . is completely shielded and can easily and safely be replaced. All electrical connections and equipment are completely insulated."[10]

Teachers are usually alert to the dangers associated with chemicals. For instance, ammonium dichromate, which is used to simulate volcanic eruptions, causes occasional skin rashes and leaves irritating fumes. The value of the ammonium dichromate volcano is insufficient to balance these risks, even though there is little chance of danger in a well ventilated classroom.

The teacher should also caution children never to mix chemicals from their home chemistry sets at random, never to taste chemical mixtures, and to wash their hands thoroughly after using chemicals.[11] They should never use potassium chlorate (particularly if it is mixed with manganese dioxide from old dry cells) or chemicals like it. Many books of chemical experiments for children include potentially hazardous experiments. The recent rash of explosions young adolescents have encountered in making rockets and bombs testifies to the need for sound safety practice.

*Avoid experiments
involving animals*

Handling classroom animals can also be dangerous. White rats, guinea pigs, rabbits, and other animals sometimes inflict painful bites. Of course no teacher should permit children to keep such dangerous animals as black widow spiders and poisonous snakes. Even small snapping turtles are dangerous, and children should learn to avoid them. Children should be aware of the responsibilities as well as the dangers in handling animals. They should treat animals humanely, feed them properly, give them water regularly, and keep their cages clean and locked. In general schools should avoid animal experimentation; it inflicts needless pain and serves *no* scientific purpose. Films and other audiovisual aids are much better sources of information on the purposes and outcomes of animal experimentation. The higher wild animals should not be confined for more than a few days. A special permit from the state is often required to keep these animals in captivity. Some states prohibit keeping specific kinds of animals, and the wise teacher should be aware of state statutes governing permissible materials for the classroom.

The potential dangers of scientific experimentation seem almost to forbid active science in the classroom. However, these dangers rarely occur because with sufficient experience children learn to avoid them and to handle scientific materials easily, carefully, and confidently.

The teacher must be at least one step ahead of her class at all times. She should ask herself: What activities are likely to lead to cuts? To bruises? To fires? To electric shock? To bites? To inhumane treatment of animals? To noxious odors? To burns?

Materials Brought by Children

Home resources

The teacher can depend on one excellent source of supply—the children's homes. In most communities an appeal to children will inundate the teacher with useful materials of all kinds, as in this school:

> After all the children had visited the [nature] center, plans were made to begin collecting supplementary materials which would enhance the science program but for which monies were not available. A suggested list of such materials went home with the children. The response was tremendous and the center was not quite ready for the deluge of materials that this request brought forth. The yield from this collection phase ran the gamut from live turtles to a stuffed great horned owl; from candles to old electric appliances; and such

treasures as a bottle of volcanic ashes from Hawaii, to a worn, but prized, chipmunk skin.[12]

The teacher can rely on the home for bottles, thread, hard-boiled eggs, special science toys and science sets. This source supplements, but does not replace, the standard classroom materials. In teaching the biological and earth sciences in particular teachers will often ask children to bring in different rocks or collect small animals or plants. Collecting live materials provides opportunities for practicing such sound conservation habits as picking only common and abundant plants, which the law does not prohibit.

The teacher never knows exactly what children *will* bring in; children sometimes forget, and parents may object to furnishing materials the school should supply. Nevertheless the resources of every community for obtaining simple science materials are vast, and the teacher should not abandon a promising investigation because the necessary equipment is not immediately at hand.

Tools and Hardware

Each classroom should have a basic set of tools. The most useful tools for children are hammers, saws (crosscut, hack, and jig), a bit brace and bits, a hand drill, an assortment of screws and nails, and glues for wood, metal, and paper. Each child will probably not use all these tools—some children may not use any—but those children who do use them should receive proper instruction.

Equipment for the New Elementary Science Programs

New curricula need new types of equipment

A teacher using one of the new science curricula will find that the accompanying teacher's guide gives helpful suggestions for selecting the most practical equipment. In addition specially designed kits of equipment are commercially available for these programs. These kits may include only materials difficult to obtain or in some cases they may contain virtually all the equipment on the equipment list. Usually the teacher needs to order specially designed pieces from a designated supplier.

The rationale that led these programs to design certain equipment is clear:

If science in the elementary school is to be based on the experience a child can gain with his own hands and eyes, then laboratory equipment is of prime importance. Characteristically, equipment should be designed so that it is safe, easy for each child to handle at his own desk, adaptable, sturdy, reasonably accurate, easy to store and maintain, and inexpensive enough for elementary schools to buy in quantity. Ideally, teachers and students should not be supplied only with the neat kit, the package that works, the thoroughly tested output of the developers. As scores of elementary teachers know, a great deal of equipment can be improvised out of rubber bands, toothpicks, tin cans, soda straws, and other readily available materials. Indeed, this creative process is frequently encouraged in our units, and much of our equipment is of this casual nature. But this is not enough. Obviously, carefully designed equipment is needed also, and no teacher should be expected to elaborate such devices from scratch, to ensure their technical accuracy, nor take the time to produce them for each child. For both technical and economic reasons, therefore, some apparatus should be developed by specialists and made available in classroom quantities.[13]

These supplies available everywhere

Let us examine the kinds of equipment required for some of these curricula. For example, consider the lesson on "Observing the Weather" in *Science—A Process Approach.*[14] This lesson, written for the early primary grades, is the second exercise that makes use of the thermometer to help children observe and interpret weather phenomena. The teacher's guide suggests the following items: a Celsius thermometer for each child; three large cans of water, each at a different temperature; a five-day temperature chart; a weather chart; lengths of red and white ribbon (for making temperature charts themselves).

Many of these require special kits

In "Observing Color and Color Changes in Plants," a number of chemical materials are necessary: red cabbage or blackberries, red begonia or coleus leaves, beets, ammonia or baking soda, vinegar, litmus paper, 1000-milliliter beakers (or one-quart Pyrex pots), an old handkerchief, four pint-sized, heatproof containers, sodium thiosulfate (photographer's hypo), a hot plate, tincture of iodine, medicine droppers, teaspoons, small jars or paint cans, and tongs.[15] Most of this material is in the special kit, which the school can purchase from the publisher of the program.

When an activity is experimental—that is, when the teacher or class must change conditions—the list of requirements tends to be longer. The teacher can save a substantial amount of time if she has the accessory kits on hand. However, many items are already on hand either in the school or at home.

Even in the experiences for older children the SAPA course is not overly dependent on specialized equipment or supplies. For example, the list of suggested materials for "Analysis of Mixtures," which is intended for fourth–fifth graders, is well within the reach of elementary classrooms: baking soda, talcum powder, iodine, vinegar, funnels, baking powder, sugar, sand, salt, plastic sandwich bags, mineral oil, marbles, magnets, and food coloring. However, petri dishes, 25-millimeter graduated cylinders, iron filings, 50-milliliter containers, Congo red, and bromothymol blue indicator solution are also suggested.[16] These are available in the "Color and Color Changes in Plants" kit, but they are also on hand in many schools or through the elementary science supervisor.

For "Growth of Mold on Bread," an exercise on increasing understanding of variables and control of variables, the following items are necessary: at least two petri dishes for each child, a hand lens for each, mold cultures (each easily prepared in advance by teacher or science helpers), varieties of bread, plastic sandwich bags, plastic squeeze bottles, rulers, incubator (can be improvised), refrigerator, heat lamp, and aluminum foil.[17]

Elementary Science Study was the first major elementary science project to prepare kits for classroom use, in keeping with their philosophy. More than fifty units and accompanying kits are now commercially available. "Small Things," a unit for middle grades and upper grades, is a series of investigations involving onion cells, differential stains, human epithelial cells, plant cells, pond water organisms, structures of nonliving things, and yeast cell growth. These investigations are extraordinarily well presented. They guide children without being so heavily structured that they suppress both pupil and teacher initiative, interest and freedom.

The "Small Things" kit contains materials sufficient for six children to work individually: simple but practical microscopes with a basic magnification of sixty;[18] hand lenses; tweezers; eyedroppers; balances constructed out of soda straws, wood bases, screws, and pins. The teacher's kit provides additional supplies for thirty children: several hundred microscope slides and plastic cover slips; lens paper; methyl cellulose solution; methylene blue stain; Lugol's iodine stain; eosin *Y* stain; toothpicks; one pound of calcium chloride;[19] grass seed. The teacher can obtain locally such supplies as scissors, masking tape, facial tissue, bottles, onions, rubbing alcohol, potatoes, and lettuce; but she *must* order some items from biological supply houses, for example, amoeba and euglena cultures.

Supplementary materials, such as the film "Paramecium, Euglena, and Amoeba," exist specially for this unit. This fifteen-minute motion picture "emphasizes the various questions about protozoa with which the children have been concerned." Several 8-millimeter film loops, each taking no more than a few minutes, show some of the common protozoans found in pond water.

The Elementary Science Study kit for "Gases and Airs" is quite different from the "Small Things" kit. For six students the "Gases and Airs" kit includes newly designed racks and trays, plastic tubes, a syringe pump, and a variety of other items. The teacher's kit duplicates these pieces and adds a larger syringe pump, rubber sheeting, mung beans, pyrogallol, and sodium hydroxide. The teacher must obtain such supplies as vinegar and birthday candles locally.

Film loops are good but costly

The "Gases and Airs" unit, in which children work in pairs, is twenty-five to thirty lessons long. The teacher can add supplementary experiments or shorten the unit to as few as sixteen lessons. In addition she can purchase a number of film loops to add demonstrations not provided for in the kit or to give children an opportunity to look more closely at experiments they have already done. These film loops are excellent in orienting teachers to experimental techniques. On the assumption that a class has thirty children, five kits, which contain enough materials for all students, will cost about one hundred dollars, with an additional fifty dollars for the teacher's kit. With the film loops, work sheets, and replacements, the total for each room is approximately three hundred dollars; about 45 percent of the teacher's kit and about 70 percent of the student's kit is reusable.[20]

For thirty students, six student kits for "Small Things" will cost approximately 150 dollars, with an additional thirty dollars for the teacher's kit. If the teacher rents the film "Paramecium, Euglena, and Amoeba" and purchases only a few of the eight available film loops, the cost per room will be about 250 dollars. The teacher's kit is not reusable, although about 70 percent of the student's kit is reusable.

The more unconventional the experiments are, the less compatible the equipment they require are with the usual elementary science equipment. At first glance the cost of adopting the Elementary Science Study units appears to be much higher than that of traditional elementary science instruction. There have been estimates that the introduction of a new elementary science program costs roughly three times as much as the introduction of a textbook-based traditional curriculum and costs perhaps five to six times as much to continue the new program.[21] Some units cost as little as twenty dollars, not including supplementary and audiovisual aids, whereas other units cost more than two hundred dollars. Cost comparison is misleading, however, not only because elementary schools do not need to purchase sets of textbooks but because they do not often buy apparatus and supplies for individual experimentation.

The activities in *A Sourcebook for Elementary Science,*[22] in *Science Experiences with Ten-Cent Store Equipment,*[23] and in the elementary science textbooks are almost always based on conventional apparatus and improvised and child-supplied equipment. For instance the third grade edition of a well-known textbook series suggests that these materials be on hand for the unit on air: balloons, paper fans, bicycle pump, aquarium, glasses, jars, yardstick, aneroid barometer, handkerchief, soil, sponge, dishes, and thermometer. The chapter on energy in a fifth grade text lists these items: string, weight, vacuum bottle, jars, thermometer, empty milk cartons, wooden board, spring balance, ruler, sand, coffee can lids, marbles, white cloth, plastic bags, nails, pulleys, and yardstick.

Traditional kinds of equipment

Once the basic supplies and equipment are available, the teacher can present numerous science experiences with little need for supplementary materials beyond those the children can supply. When the teacher introduces new problems or different ways of investigating old problems, however, conventional materials are not completely satisfactory. For this reason the Elementary Science Study, like other projects sponsored by the National Science Foundation, has licensed commercial production of its unique apparatus.

Planning

The teacher can simplify her task of deciding what equipment and supplies are necessary for the year's work by adopting a preplanned curriculum—either a conventional textbook or one of the new programs. With a loosely structured curriculum the teacher must anticipate equipment needs and be willing to take certain risks. Partly for this reason structured programs appeal to experienced teachers and to those teachers who, for one reason or another, are unwilling to chance a day-to-day pursuit of the goals of science education.

Some Recommended References

Many sources of information exist for purchasing, ordering, storing, and using scientific equipment and apparatus wisely. The following guides are particularly recommended:

1. *Purchase Guide for Programs in Science and Mathematics,* Council of Chief State School Officers (Boston: Ginn and Co., 1965). This book,

although somewhat out of date, is available in every superintendent's and science supervisor's office, and in the offices of many principals. It provides detailed lists of equipment according to field—for example, biology, chemistry, elementary science (basic, standard, and advanced). The book describes each item and its uses in detail and includes a section on elementary school facilities (pp. 335–38) and a section on laboratory safety. It also lists sources of audiovisual aids and provides an annotated bibliography of science books (many on the elementary level) in the various fields.

2. Hone, E., et al., *A Sourcebook for Elementary Science* (New York: Harcourt Brace Jovanovich, 1971). This source of many simple science activities contains an excellent section (pp. 423–30) on adapting the elementary classroom to science, and it includes many suggestions for handling materials safely and for storing chemicals and other substances.

3. Piltz, A., *Science Equipment and Materials for Elementary Schools* (Washington, D.C.: U.S. Department of Health, Education and Welfare, Office of Education, 1961), OE–29029, Bulletin No. 28. This source is available from the U.S. Superintendent of Documents. It offers wise and time-tested suggestions for using equipment, storing it, and evaluating it.

4. *Safety thru Elementary Science* (Washington, D.C.: National Commission on Safety Education and the National Science Teachers Association, 1949). This pamphlet, although out of print, is available in many college and university libraries. It is the most complete discussion of safety education through science and in science activities published to date.

5. "Science Equipment in the Elementary School," *Cornell Science Leaflet*, 56 (2): December 1962. This pamphlet offers excellent suggestions for handling practical science materials, purchasing inexpensive substitutes, and preparing a place to work.

6. Stone, A. H., et al., *Experiences for Teaching Children Science* (Belmont, Calif.: Wadsworth Publishing Company, 1971), pp. 116–18.

7. *Teacher's Guide 1*, Nuffield Junior Science (London: William Collins, 1967). See especially Chapter 5, "Problems in Classroom Organization."

8. Heldman, L. J., "Planning a Science Facility," *Science and Children*, 4: 17–19, 1967.

Summary

Lack of equipment, facilities, and supplies is a traditional handicap to progressive science teaching in the elementary schools. Busy teachers have little time to improvise equipment or supervise the construction of makeshift equipment. Therefore, although the useful materials from the home and the ten-cent store are important, the school has a real need for many special pieces of science equipment, which are both durable and effective. The classroom should have adequate working space, augmented by sinks, electrical outlets, and storage space. Even with good supplies and work facilities a special science room or science center can be helpful to teachers; from here they may requisition the less frequently used or more expensive pieces of apparatus.

Local science supervisors can offer teachers assistance in planning science instruction and in ordering and requisitioning science equipment. Unfortunately most school systems lack science supervisors; teachers in these towns should turn to science teachers in the junior or senior high schools, most of whom are willing to help. Most elementary science textbook series provide detailed lists of required and supplementary pieces. The new elementary science programs have also made available special kits, which include the basic items for their activities. These kits are somewhat expensive and quite different from the traditional kits and items of equipment usually suggested; however, expense is not really a meaningful comparison because in the new programs the cost is for individual pupil experimentation whereas in traditional instruction it is for demonstrating to the whole class. The important issue is philosophical and psychological: To what extent are schools willing to accept the goals of science education by giving each child direct experience with the materials of science? These new materials are exciting and practical.

Whenever they observe, handle, manipulate, and build, children will encounter hazards to their personal safety. Safety rules cooperatively formulated and strictly enforced will help to avoid serious accidents. Dangers exist whenever children use 110-volt electricity, handle chemicals, or keep animals in the room. Nevertheless children who are properly instructed and approach experimentation cautiously and attentively can easily avoid such dangers. An important behavioral objective of elementary science instruction is the incorporation of sound safety practices into the child's daily living.

For further study

1. To what extent is the teaching of textbook-centered science legitimate because of inadequate supplies and equipment?
2. As a cooperative project, make an analytical study of the elementary science facilities and equipment in the school where you do your practice teaching. Is the school equipped for modern science education?

3. Ask an elementary science supervisor what she thinks the most important problems of elementary science teaching are. How does she rate facilities and equipment in comparison to curriculum organization, teacher preparation and interest, and community attitudes?

4. Compile a list of equipment required for teaching one lesson series in a new science curriculum. Estimate its cost if everything were to be purchased from a scientific supply house. Which items can easily and inexpensively be improvised?

5. Select whatever mode of science teaching you find most interesting, and apply the criteria for selecting scientific apparatus and equipment to the purchase of the following items for a second grade class and then a fifth grade class:

   (a) aneroid barometer

   (b) anatomical model of the human torso

   (c) electrolysis apparatus

   (d) radiometer

   (e) aquarium, twenty-gallon tank

   (f) commercial mineral and rock collection

6. Write a critique of a commercially prepared new science kit.

7. Study the safety hazards children may encounter in the experimental portions of any one of the new elementary science curricula.

8. "Manufacture" a shoebox science kit, which contains enough material for several children to experiment individually on one unit. How expensive is the kit? How durable is it likely to be?

9. Compare the cost of materials for an entire year of a conventional textbook program in science with the cost of a new program. What reasons can you propose for the difference?

10. How valid is this statement: "Every effort should be made to make use of simple equipment so that the attention does not become focused on the equipment rather than on scientific facts, ideas, and principles"? Under what circumstances is the statement oversimplified?

Notes and references

1. Alford, G., "An Analysis of Science Interests of Selected Children and an Identification of Problems Encountered by the Teachers of These Children in Science Instruction," as reported in *Research in the Teaching of Science* (Washington, D.C.: U.S. Department of Health, Education

and Welfare, Office of Education, 1965), OE–29000–61, Bulletin No. 10, p. 9.

2. Victor, E., "Why Are Our Elementary School Teachers Reluctant to Teach Science?", *Science Education,* 46: 185, March 1962.

3. *Teacher's Guide 1,* Nuffield Junior Science (London: William Collins, 1967), p. 34.

4. Hawkins, D., as cited in *ESS Newsletter,* No. 14: 3, March 1968. Italics not in original.

5. See list in A. H. Stone et al., *Experiences for Teaching Children Science* (Belmont, Calif.: Wadsworth Publishing Co., 1971), pp. 116–17.

6. Piltz, A., *Science Equipment and Materials for Elementary Schools* (Washington, D.C.: U.S. Department of Health, Education and Welfare, Office of Education, 1961), OE–29029, Bulletin No. 28, p. 7.

7. For excellent storage suggestions, see *Teacher's Guide 1, op. cit.,* pp. 158–60.

8. Nelson, N. L., "Beginning a Science Center," *Science and Children,* 2: 16–18, March 1965.

9. Plotnick, M., "Electricity via a Science Resource Center," *Science and Children,* 2: 5–6, March 1965.

10. *Kimtec Educational Catalog,* 1969–70, p. 4.

11. "Chemistry Sets," *Consumer Reports,* 30: 548–51, November 1965.

12. Nelson, N. L., *op. cit.,* p. 17.

13. *Introduction to the Elementary Science Study* (Boston: Houghton Mifflin, 1965), p. 13.

14. *Science—A Process Approach* (New York: Xerox Education Group, 1967), Part B–G, Observing 10.

15. *Ibid.,* Part B–O, Observing 12.

16. *Ibid.,* Part E–L, Interpreting Data 2.

17. *Ibid.,* Part E–P, Controlling Variables 3. For details on a homemade incubator, see A. H. Stone et al., *op. cit.,* p. 118.

18. See Lockard, J. D., "Shedding Light on the Lens," *Science and Children,* 6: 27–32, May 1969.

19. *1969–1970 Science Materials Catalog,* Webster Division, McGraw-Hill Book Co., p. 44.

20. *1969–1970 Science Materials Catalog, op. cit.,* p. 24.

21. Butts, D. P., "The Price of Change," *Science and Children,* 6: 7–8, April 1969.

22. Hone, E. B., et al., *Teaching Elementary Science: A Sourcebook for*

Elementary Science (New York: Harcourt Brace Jovanovich, 1971).

23. Lynde, C. J., *Science Experiences with Ten-Cent Store Equipment* (Princeton, N.J.: D. Van Nostrand Co., 1950).

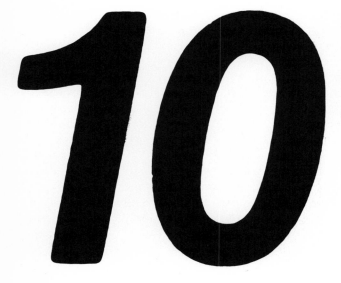

Evaluation in Elementary Science

Evaluation for Direction
The Art of Testing
Interpretation of Science Tests

ffective science teaching at the elementary level requires that teachers recognize children as learners who have had, and continue to have, many different experiences. To these experiences children bring various ways of perceiving, sensing, and reacting; and from these experiences they take away different combinations of meanings, attitudes, and concepts. Teachers should also get to know the children as individuals. Each teacher should find out to the best of her ability what each child is like, what he can and cannot do, and what factors contribute to his successes and failures. She should resign herself to helping the child attain the goals of science teaching, which she, and to an ever-increasing extent, her class accept as important. She should evaluate, therefore, on a broadly based spectrum of growth in conceptual learning, process skills, and attitudes.

This chapter has three sections, each of which presents concepts and techniques that will help teachers to evaluate meaningfully children's growth in science and their own growth in teaching science. The first section, *Evaluation for Direction,* describes in detail the purposes of evaluation of science in the schools and explains ways to apply evaluational techniques to process-centered science instruction. The second section, *The Art of Testing,* analyzes many different tests used in science classrooms. The third section, *Interpretation of Science Tests,* reports on ways of judging the reliability and validity of tests and on the uses of special kinds of tests, including programmed materials. This section also includes a self-evaluation checklist for teachers.

Evaluation for Direction

Overview

To make wise decisions about children teachers must rely on effective techniques of evaluation. One such technique is observation: The teacher can gain valuable knowledge about a child as the child participates in the everyday class activities, as he asks and answers questions, as he thinks up hypotheses, as he works with others, as he reads and experiments. Pauline Sears summarizes the meaning of evaluation well:

> A teacher's evaluative activities go far beyond marking papers; they include attention to many experiences of success and failure, of expanded or restricted autonomy, of immediate and long-term goal-setting, of recognition of individual progress and of attitudinal responses to divergent behavior. These evaluative behaviors have the characteristics of positive and negative reinforcers, and, as such, are motivationally relevant to learning.[1]

In place of the unrelated cross sections of behavior that emerge from measurement the teacher should try to assess the child's growth in terms of the important aspects of science. The intent of evaluation is to learn what each child is like, not to find out how he differs from his fellows.

Functions of Evaluation

Decision making

The necessity for evaluation

Evaluation in elementary science teaching is necessary for many reasons. Teaching, as an art form, calls for making decisions. For instance, the teacher must decide whether the class is ready for an experimental sequence on electricity, whether sufficient resources are available, and whether electricity is a better subject for study at this time than insect life. She must decide whether the class is ready to participate freely and effectively in planning and whether the children are sufficiently skilled in cooperative work to make small-group study worthwhile. Even the permissive, or authoritarian, atmosphere of her classroom is the result of decisions she may or may not have consciously formulated.

Wise decisions should take into consideration such factors as these: What are the children like? What do they know? How well do they read? How well do they work together? What are they interested in? Which children are creative? Which are rote learners? and, specifically, What knowledge of electricity and electromagnetic phenomena have these children mastered? If the children do not know that a current flowing through a wire generates a magnetic field around the wire and if they have had no firsthand experience with magnets, the study of electromagnetism must begin with simple magnets. The teacher might decide to use the more knowledgeable children as group leaders in planning small-group investigations.

The wisdom of the teacher's decisions depends on her knowledge of the children. If she knows that they have been successful in analyzing simple problems, the teacher and class can begin with a greater probability of success. No teacher, if she values her self-image, will jump into free, unstructured inquiry instruction unless she is confident that her class is well prepared. She *What the teacher must find out* should also be aware of the inner forces that affect the children individually and collectively so that she can try to form or to reform attitudes and appreciations she believes are important. The teacher can easily assess subject matter knowledge and judge whether children are adequately informed; her most difficult task is determining whether children are growing in the process and developing appreciational–attitudinal aspects of the sciences.

Feedback

An important, yet so often rejected, function of evaluation is providing sufficient feedback to each child so that he may assess his own progress. Children are often unaware of their own deficiencies. They may admit to "not being good in science" or to disliking science, but this vague, imprecise judgment is neither a stimulus to remedial action nor an instructional guide. According to modern learning theory immediate feedback enables the learner to change his responses more quickly and more effectively. In her evaluation the teacher should give the child information about his development. The customary testing at the end of the marking period to measure "total" learning is harmful because its interpretation comes too late to help the child in his day-by-day learning.

Feedback is essential True, some children are satisfied with minimal achievement, and feedback is unlikely to motivate them. Other children modify their responses to conform to what they know the teacher wants; they adjust not because of the intrinsic value of doing things differently but because they seek the reward of academic virtue. The teacher's written and oral testing reveals her real goals. No matter how much time the teacher gives to the noninformational aims of science instruction, the children will soon know that she seeks recall of facts if that is what her tests stress. This kind of evaluation reveals what the teacher thinks are the real goals of science instruction.

In short if she is to make wise decisions about classroom teaching and if she is to match content and process for individual children, the teacher must not settle for a few scattered bits of information. The complexity of science learning and the number of more or less discrete skills, abilities, concepts, and principles encompassed in the learning process make a mockery of decision making that ignores continual sampling of these aspects of learning.

Administration

In addition to its value in decision making evaluation has an administrative function. Parents wish to know the progress their children are making in science, yet report cards rarely provide more than a letter grade or a percentage mark. Parents may be satisfied if these marks are high, even though *The "whole" child* otherwise they have little positive information. How often are parents informed about their child's success in interpreting scientific phenomena, his scientific likes and dislikes, the books he reads about scientific phenomena or scientists?

In the traditional school, children are either promoted or retained in each grade. Promotion, which is not automatic, must be based on evaluative evidence. In addition evaluative records are often essential to plan remedial instruction or special classes of gifted children.

The function of evaluation is to consider each child as a total organism, not merely as a bundle of a few isolated strengths or weaknesses. As Lee Cronbach remarks, "An ideal evaluation would include measures of all the types of proficiency that might reasonably be desired in the area in question."[2] A child is a complex of countless submerged strengths and weaknesses, fleetingly visible here and there. The usual objective test is scored as a totality or at best is sliced into a few subscores, which are difficult to interpret. The student who scores high on a reasoning test may have done little reasoning if previously he had encountered similar problems. He may have been tested only on simple recall, not reasoning. However, if each item on the test has some specific purpose, such as measuring ability to select relevant from ir-relevant data or to recognize hidden assumptions, assessment of these individual elements of behavior and of learning becomes feasible.

The success of instruments and techniques for evaluation depends on a complicated interplay of child–teacher–school relationships. For example, children who show severe anxiety are less likely to achieve well in timed tests; children of moderate or low anxiety are much more likely to do well. Certainly no one expects to find in the authoritarian classroom much evidence of progress toward autonomy in science learning and toward strengthening the higher aspects of cognitive and affective behavior.

Cooperative planning—
key to evaluation

Students must also know what the teacher expects of them. One of the values of teacher–pupil planning lies in the joint acceptance of planned goals that are genuinely cooperative so that children know what they are to do and have some idea of how to do it. Cooperative planning may help to reduce the undesirable anxiety of some children particularly in taking the paper-and-pencil tests, which children traditionally regard as the real basis for the marks on the report cards they bring home.

The Evaluator

Although it does have a place in the elementary schools, the standardized test is inferior to informal classroom evaluation for most purposes. The teacher is responsible for selecting and remaking the curriculum with her children. She is also the evaluator, because she is the *only* person who knows each child as an individual and as a member of the class group. If the curriculum grows out of teacher–pupil interaction, outside tests that stress facts and recall are unlikely to be valid for this class, whatever the statistical reliability of these tests. No nationally available tests have demonstrated validity in measuring growth in process skills, although the SAPA "Competency Measure" and "Science Process Instrument" seem valuable for schools that have adopted the SAPA program (see the second section of this chapter). In teacher–pupil planning the teacher and class know what they are trying to do and what success they have attained. The teacher is in a position to know whether a particular child is an intuitive thinker, whether he can relate cause and effect, whether he is rigid in his behavior, and whether he is cooperative with other children. Standardized tests in elementary science provide interesting information, but they presuppose a standardized, homogenized curriculum contrary to the spirit of American education.

Informal Evaluation

These labyrinthine evaluative processes are apt to frighten the prospective teacher. How can she possibly look at the "whole" child, keep track of him as an individual, and at the same time carry on the daily academic, social, and physical business of the classroom? Actually the elementary teacher does not practice such intensive evaluation. Surely the lack of this continuous evaluation is not because teachers are shortsighted or content to give lip service. Most teachers accept the need for progressive evaluation. Why then is the evaluative outlook so bleak? Why does the classroom teacher have difficulty seeing that Johnny cannot separate the pertinent variables to plan an experiment and that Jane never understands the need to verify the hypotheses she proposes? One reason for difficulty in evaluation is that evaluative instruments are crude. In a sense they are like neatly classified science books, which a librarian categorizes as physical, biological, and earth science without noting that one book is a chemistry of amino acids, a second is on the structure of viruses, and a third describes the mineral components of granites. Admittedly evaluative tools are neither powerful nor sensitive instruments, and few have improved significantly in recent years.

A second reason is that only within the last two decades has important progress been made in the theory of evaluation, and this new evaluative sophistication has not yet been incorporated into the action structure of practicing teachers—certainly the case in elementary science evaluation, which has lagged behind secondary and collegiate assessment. Traditionally teachers have not considered science as important to the curriculum as arithmetic or reading, so in general they are not in a position to apply what is now known in science evaluation. The "whole-child" concept has been trimmed down to academic achievement, measured by tests of recall, and to interest, intelligence, and social adjustment. The fine structure of the cognitive and affective processes has just begun to come into view, much as the fine structure of the atomic nucleus has just begun to make sense to nuclear physicists. In contrast to the hundreds of millions of dollars spent in the search for nuclear knowledge, the progress in child learning is heartening, considering the almost total lack of support for evaluation.

A third reason is that a formal, thorough program of evaluation is inordinately time-consuming. The teacher who attempts to record the multiple varieties of learning achievement for each child, assuming that the proper evaluative tools are at hand, is a clerk, not a teacher. So minor a task as correcting a short written quiz once or twice a week is exhausting, especially if the teacher must record and report the strengths and weaknesses of each child. Too often, records which must be maintained at the expense of other worthwhile activities gather dust. Keeping records is time-consuming; interpretation takes even more time. In actual practice "troublesome" students, those children who for emotional, intellectual, or social reasons disturb the others, preempt the time that the teacher might otherwise use for detailed record keeping. Parents are familiar with the soothing phrases, the easily recognized and all too often meaningless testimony, of an uninformative report card. These words, which are not deliberately made obscure, emerge from the many stresses to which the teacher is exposed in a formal, time-harassed evaluation.

The evidence is everywhere

Evaluation is obviously necessary, and many different kinds of evaluative knowledge about each child are desirable. But how is such knowledge obtained in the classroom? In a subject such as elementary science, which is often not a formally scheduled subject, the teacher must rely on the accumulated evidence of her senses, resorting to written records of each child's progress only if exciting and vital classroom science is unimperiled. Evidence of pupil growth will come from hard listening and hard looking at everything that children do and do not do in class. This informal observation is almost devoid of record keeping. The professional teacher can sense the general strengths and weaknesses of her class. As she gains experience in process, she will focus on important evidence and develop impressions based on expressed and stored decisions as to whether Johnny has proposed a wildly irrelevant scientific hypothesis or whether he has learned to exclude meaningless aspects of motion pictures.

These remarks are not intended to deny the importance of written tests and records. Written tests provide information the teacher cannot gather by skilled observation. Tests also provide data to corroborate or deny the validity of the teacher's observation of child learning. These functions of written tests, and their appropriate techniques, are described in this chapter in some detail.

Statistical interpretation is relatively unimportant in elementary science teaching. Of course the teacher should be able to distinguish between good and bad hypothesizing and between relevant and irrelevant application of principles. To the degree that the validity of his assessment of behavior is important, the experienced teacher is sufficiently knowledgeable to make quick decisions and to refine them so that they are both reliable and meaningful. The information that a child consistently fails to connect three dry cells in series is significant to the teacher; the information that 65.3 percent of all children of that age can succeed in this task is not. The pertinent question is: Can each child carry out the necessary steps to complete the activity successfully? If not, why not? How should the child revise his strategy and tactics to increase the chances for success?

In informal evaluation the teacher does not award grades, nor does she make comparisons between children. There is time later on, in the formal science of the junior and senior high schools, for this kind of measurement and for the narrowing of assessment to paper-and-pencil testing.

Techniques of Evaluation

The evaluative domains

For convenience, let us divide classroom learning and behavior into the cognitive, affective, and psychomotor domains. The cognitive domain encompasses the intellectual skills and the process elements of knowledge. The affective domain includes the emotional and attitudinal components, which so decisively spur on or retard cognitive learning. The psychomotor domain is restricted to the physical and manipulative skills, which are of minimal importance in elementary science.

The lengthy catalog of evaluative behavior in the appendix is a guide to the actions that reflect cognitive and affective learning. Even the most gifted teacher, with every resource of the educational establishment available to her, will not find evidence for each behavior. Rather she should select and emphasize only the most important forms of behavior that affect her and her class.

There are numerous evaluative techniques for gathering behavioral evidence. No matter which technique the teacher uses, her evaluation must be continuous and cumulative. She must seek detailed knowledge of behavioral change; yet dramatic behavioral changes rarely occur.

Gathering evidence

Gathering this knowledge can be an exciting, revealing, challenging search. The wise observer is a skilled listener who allows little to go by without mental memos. She is alert during the classroom discussions, sharing periods, experiments, and demonstrations, as well as during the children's free time. She looks for signs of stasis or regression as well as signs of progress to new, more desirable patterns. Identifying active and inactive children as individuals and as group members is a necessary part of the teacher's task. These questions will help the teacher in this search:

Questions for the teacher

Does the child participate in different activities? What is the nature of this participation? Is he a doer, a leader? Does he take part in discussions but never in sharing period? Does he shun science, participating instead in social studies or arithmetic? Is the child just a listener—perhaps an active listener, but never more than that? How efficiently does the child begin his work? Does he move ahead without wasting time? Is he a self-starter? No teacher expects children to be self-regulating in *all* elementary school endeavors. In what respects is the child an independent learner? Must he be directed at every step? Does he spring ahead at the beginning of each new enterprise but fall back soon?

What is the quality of the child's observations? Quality of observations refers to the accuracy and inclusiveness with which the child sees and hears. How much does the child miss? Does he see unusual configurations, images, or relationships which others fail to see? Is he quick to see what is there? In watching demonstrations and experiments, does he carefully follow the successive steps and record the results?

Are the child's explanations factual, without teleology, anthropomorphism, or animism? Does he make statements such as these: "The viceroy and monarch butterflies are alike so that the viceroy may escape birds that would otherwise eat him." *Are his explanations phrased in causal terms,* in which dependent and independent variables are included in some theoretical context? On a less abstract level can the child think thus: If this is true, then that must also be true. Does he state the relevant conditions of a phenomenon or event?

Are the child's statements clearly worded, or are they vague and diffuse, offering no clear indication as to whether he understands what has happened and why it has happened? If his answers are vague, is this vagueness the result of an inability to express himself? Is it because he does not identify specific individual events or because he has not established the conditions under which the event takes place? Can he separate the totality of the experience into its parts?

Are the child's questions precise and unambiguous? Does he phrase them so that their meaning is clear? Do his questions imply a certain direction to the answers? Does he try to sort out objects and functions, the conditions under which they exist, the systems into which they are grouped, and the sequence of events? Does he ask questions about problems that interest him? Does he ask questions that seek the reasons for a procedure or search for ways of eliminating discrepancies between expectation and occurrence? Or are his questions frivolous, cunningly contrived to waste time and divert the teacher and the class from their course of action?

Are the child's reasons or hypotheses logical, or are they mere guesses? Are his guesses profitable? Is he naturally intuitive, capable of moving to the heart of the problem through insight? The cognitive styles of children vary greatly, and some bright children ignore logical analysis and jump to premature conclusions. Is this such a child?

Does the child limit his comments and questions to relevant points, to items and incidents that should reasonably be included, or are his comments and questions precisely worded yet irrelevant? Has he missed important ideas?

Is he verbose, straying quickly from the topic? Does he oversimplify, seeking single causes of complex phenomena, or neglecting to maintain experimental controls?

Is the child aware of the assumptions that affect every phase of his daily thinking? Does he accept the importance of isolating and analyzing the assumptions on which the quality of his scientific thinking must depend?

Does the child hypothesize? Are his hypotheses pertinent, even though they may not be correct? Are they reasonable? Once he formulates a hypothesis, can the child think of ways to test it, to evaluate its worth? This skill, if it is skill, is not a philosopher's stone that will magically make the learner a scientist. The long history of science testifies that the formation and testing of hypotheses has always been the standard separating the creative scientist from the noncreative scientist, the producer of science from the user of science. The evaluation of hypothesizing is a strikingly complex, almost unexplored aspect of science education. For this reason the teacher's evaluation of the child's struggle to form and test hypotheses must be charitable and generous.

How well does the child interpret data and find meaningful relationships, assuming that they exist? Is he aware of the boundaries of the problem and the limitations of his techniques and apparatus? Has he sufficient skill in computation and in graphing to interpret data?

Can the child tease the plausible inferences out of these data? For example, if moist iron nails consistently rust more quickly than dry iron nails, does he conclude that rusting will probably slow down or cease if iron nails, and presumably other iron objects of the same composition, are dried?

Can the child predict certain inevitable consequences of laws, principles, and conclusions? For example, knowing the laws of vibrating strings, can he explain how the pitch of a violin string changes as its length is changed? Knowing that many plants selectively absorb and concentrate minerals from the soil, can he foresee how the distribution of plants may indicate the presence of certain minerals? No teacher expects the intuitive leap the great scientist makes as he moves far beyond the limits of his information. Children are just beginning to gain a foothold on science. What *is* important is the child's *progress* in these aspects of science learning. Has he begun to make predictions? Are they justified according to the logic of the situation, even though they may eventually turn out to be wrong? In the absence of teaching, which boldly and consistently seeks to strengthen these abilities, little positive growth is likely to occur.

What is the child interested in? What is he *really* interested in? Does he consistently pursue these interests? Does he vacillate, jumping from superficial interest to superficial interest? Is his interest so strong that he turns to reference sources for more information? Does he participate in out-of-school activities in which science interests are likely to be fulfilled? Does he concentrate on activities in which his strengths nurture his interests?

Can he read for comprehension, locate source material, take notes, and summarize? Each of these phrases is a deceptively innocent condensation of a multitude of lesser, but no less important, subskills, understandings, interests, techniques, and psychomotor aptitudes. In a textbook such as this prescription of appropriate diagnostic and remedial techniques for these reading skills, despite their relevance both for learning and liking science, is impossible.

Is the child's physical coordination good, or is he clumsy and awkward in manipulating apparatus and performing experiments? Is he accident prone? Are his disastrous manipulations caused by not thinking through the possible outcomes of his course of action or by impulsiveness and haste? Carelessness may mean only that he made three unnecessary errors in arithmetic, which he easily rationalizes away with the comforting thought that he still knows how to do the problems. In science, however, carelessness or impulsiveness may destroy an experiment on which many children have labored. The group which keeps careful records can identify the child who forgets to water germinating seeds or inaccurately records the period of the pendulum. Carelessness is a way of life with some children, and remedial action is difficult under normal classroom conditions.

Is the child sufficiently aware of his successes and failures, his weaknesses and strengths, to reinforce success and to attend to difficulties? Does he seek feedback so as to minimize future errors? In many children the urge to reorganize behavior in order to eliminate mistakes is weak, perhaps because being wrong and engaging in undesirable behavior is unimportant to them. Teachers must demonstrate to children the power of appropriate behavioral changes in improving science thinking. Teachers should point out how helpful feedback is to the class and to the individual child, presenting specific examples to show how errors are convertible into future strengths. One condition for successfully reorganizing behavior is immediate recognition of errors. Immediacy is one of the strengths of programmed instruction. The learner becomes aware almost instantly of his mistakes and successes and therefore pushes himself through the series of steps in the program to bring about "correct" learning. At present, however, there is no way to program this kind of error correction with the higher kinds of learning, such as hypothesizing, inferring, recognizing hidden assumptions, separating variables, and coming to reasonable conclusions. Unfortunately few tested techniques exist for creating feedback other than that of programmed learning.

Can the child follow directions? A common complaint, both in and out of school, is that a child is either unable or unwilling to do as he is directed, even when directions are simple and clear-cut. However, the directions may not be as clear as the teacher imagines them to be. The child may have reading and comprehension difficulties; or he may simply be impatient, assuming that the task is so simple he can figure it out in the course of the activity. Even in inquiry, which avoids lengthy directions, rules, procedures, and approaches are necessary for increasing success. The child who disregards these rules interferes with classwork and adds to its difficulty both for himself and for others. If the underlying causes of disregard are psychological or social, to expect much improvement in the classroom may be unreasonable.

Does the child work cooperatively? Process teaching relies on small-group investigations in which each member of the group contributes his talent and insight. Children must come to realize that group success depends on the positive contributions of each working member. A cooperative child willingly accepts the rules for classroom investigation, which come out of joint teacher–student discussion. Occasionally a child is more effective by himself—thinking and performing more efficiently alone than in a group. Nevertheless he should have some experience with other children because of the refinement of ideas and the valuable criticism that arise from group work. Does he talk about his ideas and his work with the other children? The child who shrinks from the give-and-take of discussion, either in a small group or in class, is missing out on an effective social tool for better thinking and learning.

The tape recorder

The tape recorder is a valuable mechanical aid for evaluation—both for self-evaluation by children and teacher and for evaluation of children by the teacher. Children quickly accept the tape recorder if the teacher presents it as a tool to help them learn science rather than an electronic spy. Novelty is a recognized stimulus to learning—the excitement engendered by tape recording is in itself a sound reason for its evaluative use.

Talk and "retalk"

Replaying the tape or tape cassette after a discussion in the classroom is a revelation to children, who are not aware of how the teacher has focused their discussion on a particular theme. As they listen, the children begin to realize the misconceptions, erroneous information, and unwarranted statements they have hurled at one another and at the teacher. The tape replay also indicates whether a few children have monopolized the discussion.

The teacher can stop the tape at any time to ask if children choose to revise their statements, to point out dubious assertions and illogical thinking, or to call for criticism of what was said. The tape recorder provides more-or-less immediate feedback; the repetition, although not the important reason for taping, is also valuable. With this instrument the teacher may, at leisure, assess the children's progress and plan necessary remedial action. She can analyze the contributions of each child and the pertinent information recorded. However, this evaluation by the teacher is somewhat less important than the cooperative study of the tapes by the teacher and children.

Observation

Record keeping takes time

Specialists in evaluation have suggested a number of valuable techniques. Unfortunately most of these techniques involve record keeping or other paper work, which is time-consuming and laborious to prepare and use. Even if time were available, the teacher must decide whether some bit of behavior is an example of inferring, assuming, or questioning. How can a busy teacher find the time in the midst of an active science lesson to keep an active record of the cognitive and affective behavior for even one child? Instead she can decide quickly that behavior X is an example of good or bad scientific thought and file this as a mental record. Such indepth behavior analysis is achieved most easily through tape replayings either with class participation or after school.

Surprisingly enough, the English primary schools which American educators looked to as models of informal, progressive, "learning-is-joy" education, place great emphasis on evaluation and record keeping, even in classes of thirty to fifty children. The informal approach of these English schools makes "heavier and not lighter demands upon the skill of the teacher," and particularly so in evaluation and record keeping to:

> . . . ensure that over a period, say of a term, there is a proper balance between subjects and appropriate progress within subjects. Part of this record will consist of the child's own work. If each child has a folder in which all his written work in whatever subject is kept, it will be possible to see quite rapidly whether both these requirements are being met. The teacher will also maintain his own records and these two together will constitute a much more informative and useful account of work done than the old type of teacher record which was simply a statement of lessons given and set.[3]

In preparing these records the teachers in these English schools often seek information about such aspects of child behavior as the following in preparing these records:

*Evidence from the
English schools*

1. Areas in which a child shows a keen or sustained interest, has done especially good work, or has particularly good background knowledge, and/or grasp of scientific ideas.

2. Original thought or inventiveness in devising explanations and in testing them; skill in devising ways of solving a problem.

3. Keen observation often giving rise to pertinent questions.

4. Skill in devising and constructing apparatus necessary for experiments.

5. Ability to evaluate evidence critically, including experimental evidence.

6. Knowledge of sources of information and skill in using them.

7. Changes in attitudes.[4]

Whenever possible, teachers supply evidence for these judgments in the form of samples of each child's writing, drawings, diagrams, and other pertinent work products.

To ease the burden of record keeping and evaluating, English science educators have developed an interesting and informative record-keeping *flow diagram*. These diagrams, which teachers use primarily to keep track of the progress of the class, show how the classwork develops from the children's centers of interest and how it relates to their other interests. By expanding these diagrams, the teacher can include such information as the initials of the children who participated in each activity as well as brief comments on successes and failures. Figure 1, a linear flow diagram, shows how the classwork developed in a three-week period. Figure 2, a "radiating" flow diagram, conveys a sense of exploration in different fields to a greater extent than the linear flow diagram, although it does not indicate the time taken for the classwork.

*An eye-opener for
the teacher*

Team teaching in the elementary schools may make the task of record keeping somewhat easier because the team usually includes a teacher's aide who is the recorder. At present anecdotal records, interviews, and intensive observation of individuals are as impractical as they are desirable in filling in the picture, which the teacher must otherwise paint with rough, informal strokes. For problem children detailed records and the widest possible range of information will be necessary. The teacher will always "interview" children, which is precisely what she does as she stops to chat with a child to see how he is getting on and to question him on his problems. However, if he believes that whatever he says will be held against him, the child is likely to give stereotyped answers or to withdraw into silence.

Week no. 1	Week no. 2	Week no. 3
Children given different types of "soil"		
builder's sand	used 1 container to measure sample of each type of soil	heating each type
"I think builder's sand will be the heaviest or it would crumble"	weighed each sample recorded results	weighing before and after
peat	weighed 2 oz of each type of soil noticed contrast in volume	
potting compost		
sea-side sand		
	weighed dry sand added 1 tablespoon water	*"how much water will the sand hold?"*
"I think wet sand would be heavier than dry sand"	weighed again did this with each type of soil	added so much water, couldn't get all sand back; tried heating it
clay	free modeling a. figures b. forts c. pottery	decided to try baking models in gas oven; cracked—decided oven too hot
Vermiculite	looked at under microscope and painted	decided to try painting one particle rather than the mass
gravel		
discussion on appearance:		
children quickly noticed difference in weight	*"does the water stay in the soil or go straight through?"*	
	water poured through each type of soil	*"I wonder which would be best for sowing seeds in?"*
	Vermiculite retained most water sea-side sand least	beans sown in 1. sea-side sand 2. potting compost 3. Vermiculite

Figure 1. *Part of a linear flow diagram showing the early stages in the work of a class of children aged seven.*[5]

Special observational tools are best left to specialists in the schools, who have the required time and skills. The classroom teacher, on the other hand, is in the best position to gain a valid insight into her children's progress from informal observation of their everyday business.

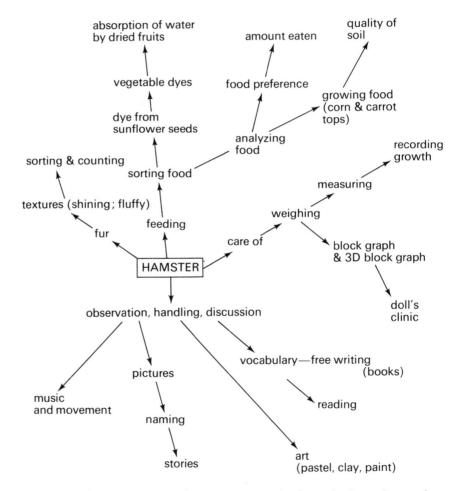

Figure 2. A teacher's flow diagram record of work done by a class of children aged five, in the autumn term.[6]

Summary

Evaluation is a significant science teaching function. The teacher strives to learn what each child is like, how well he is progressing, what cognitive and affective difficulties he is encountering so that she can help him to achieve his full learning potential.

Modern programs of elementary science are process centered. They focus on the higher cognitive and affective components of behavior, which are difficult to measure by conventional assessment. Evaluative instruments in elementary science are still too crude to make such fine discriminations as a child's failure to propose hypotheses because he cannot do if–then thinking or because he cannot give the sustained attention necessary for discovering that some aspect of the natural environment seems to be completely out of phase. For this reason teachers of elementary science must rely on continuous, informal observation of actual pupil behavior as it occurs in experimenting, discussing, planning, observing, hypothesizing, inferring, and concluding.

For further study

1. Explain the dichotomy between evaluation for educationally valid purposes and for determining grades.

2. What flaws do you find in the authors' arguments supporting informal evaluation—for example, in the statement that statistical interpretation is unimportant in elementary science teaching?

3. Can the ungraded school eliminate the major problems of formal, long-term evaluation? Explain.

4. Arrange a discussion of a scientific problem in class and tape-record the session. Play the recording to the group and constructively analyze the outcomes, the interactions between leader and students, and the participation of each group member.

5. How would you proceed if you noticed that some children in class are not successful at hypothesizing or perhaps never try? That some children never seem to know what their weaknesses are? That some children rarely follow directions? That many children do not word their questions clearly?

Notes and references

1. Sears, P. S., and E. R. Hilgard, "The Teacher's Role in the Motivation of the Learner," in E. R. Hilgard, ed., *Theories of Learning and Instruc-*

tion, Chap. 8, Sixty-third Yearbook of the National Society for the Study of Education, Part 1 (Chicago: University of Chicago Press), 1964, p. 199.

2. Cronbach, L. J., "Course Improvement through Evaluation," *Teachers College Record,* 64: 680, May 1963.

3. Blackie, J., *Inside the Primary School* (London: Her Majesty's Stationery Office, 1967), p. 48.

4. *Teacher's Guide 1,* Nuffield Junior Science (London: William Collins, 1967), pp. 190–91.

5. *Ibid.,* p. 190.

6. *Ibid.,* p. 189.

The Art of Testing

Overview

Testing is one aspect—a major aspect to be sure—of evaluation. As valuable as skilled observation is, teachers who avoid written or oral science tests will inevitably miss certain information they should have about the science learning of the children. Teacher-made tests tend to stress factual knowledge and probe for command of the lower cognitive behaviors (see appendix). Standardized tests prepared by experts are more likely to include questions that seek higher levels of cognitive behavior, but with few exceptions these tests do not meet the needs of primary grade teachers. Whatever testing means they use, teachers should remember that they are the authorities when making judgments about children. Because they observe the actions, successes, and failures of the children in the everyday classroom situation, teachers are best qualified to interpret the children's test scores. Hence tests serve merely as diagnostic instruments of conceptual and process growth in science and not as a means for assigning grades. Although testing in elementary science is important, test results provide less information than the evidence teachers continually gather from informal observation.

Testing

What do marks mean?

Testing is the process of using evaluative devices to obtain quantitative measures of ability or knowledge. However, *nothing* is more meaningless than a single raw score! Let us assume, for example, that a child receives a mark of 75 percent on a paper-and-pencil test on magnetism. This figure does not mean that the child knows three quarters of what the teacher thinks is significant; it does mean that on this particular sampling of test items, this child answered three quarters of the items "correctly." Depending on the child, this outcome may be either excellent or inferior. Whether the test is teacher-made or standardized, the teacher alone is in the position to make a valid judgment. A child's ranking in the thirtieth percentile on a national examination means little, because comparison of norms is the most trivial aspect of test interpretation. The questions on the examination may be irrelevant; they may be too difficult, too easy, or even invalid because they do not test what they are supposed to test.

Specialists *can* devise tests that examine how the child thinks, how he infers, reasons, analyzes, and concludes. In addition tests may also motivate children susceptible to such motivation. On the other hand children who are poor readers or writers, overanxious, or indifferent are likely to be penalized. A valid paper-and-pencil test of experimental ability is almost impossible to construct because actual experimentation is far different from talking about it. Paper-and-pencil tests are at present limited to certain aspects of affective and cognitive learning. And unfortunately tests of affective behavior generally lack validity and reliability.

Informal paper-and-pencil testing

Criticism of conventional paper-and-pencil testing in science is almost cruelly gratuitous because the shortcomings are so obvious. Teachers often construct or adapt such informal tests for their classes without analyzing the items and weeding out inferior ones. The most serious criticism of informal paper-and-pencil testing is that teachers take too little time to prepare enough fair, unambiguous, and clear questions to allow for a convincing judgment.

Testing errors

All too often the important goal of the test is to find out how much each child can recall. Whether it is short-answer, fill-in, matching, true–false, or multiple-choice, the test tends to emphasize questions conveniently answered from memory: "Name the planets in order from the sun. A piece of iron that attracts one end of a piece of iron, and repels the other end is called a _____. All insects have _____ legs." Concentration on recall is understandable for two reasons: Knowledge of factual material has always been the controlling aim of elementary science instruction, and most classroom teachers cannot create valid test items for measuring the higher cognitive skills. Nevertheless to make recall of knowledge the sole goal of informal (or formal) testing is to make a mockery of evaluation.

Children lose time trying to understand poorly written directions and perhaps never clear up these confusions. In addition many test items are so poorly written and ambiguous that children are unable to decipher the teacher's intent. On the other hand some answers are obvious because the questions include leading words or inadvertent clues. Children are aware that a long statement is likely to be correct and that questions with "always" or "usually" are likely to be incorrect.

The teacher must write specific questions to learn how well children can infer, recognize assumptions, sort out variables, and keep factors constant. Elementary science tests frequently have questions that are irrelevant for the behavior the teacher seeks. These tests rarely include enough items written about one ability or item of knowledge to diagnose strengths and weaknesses — that is, to serve as diagnostic instruments. Any one test has only one or two questions for each concept. For example, a test on "why objects float" includes only one question on density. The teacher can hardly conclude from this one question that the child either does or does not understand density. Simple errors of reading or interpretation may be responsible for an incorrect answer yet such a test provides no way of learning the reason for failure.

Tests should be diagnostic

Although the interpretation of tests is time-consuming, the teacher should tell the child *why* he is wrong. Has he made the error because he does not know that density depends on both volume and weight? Because he does not understand the difference between density and volume? Because he does not know that the density of water is 62.4 pounds per cubic foot? Because he cannot visualize what pounds per cubic foot means? Because he does not realize that as long as the volume of an object remains the same, despite changes in form, its density is constant?

Skill and content fields, such as reading and arithmetic, have made great progress with diagnostic tests, which provide feedback to the child and to the teacher. But diagnostic tests are almost unknown in elementary science.

Picture tests

By and large, paper-and-pencil science testing is not useful in the primary grades because children cannot interpret questions that probe the higher cognitive processes. Hence written science tests should be infrequent, perhaps given more to familiarize children with test-taking procedures and to prepare them for testing in the upper grades than to act as evaluative instruments.

Picture tests may be helpful

An intriguing and promising variation of paper-and-pencil testing for younger children is the picture test, which minimizes reading and verbal skills. Pictures — either the teacher's own drawings or illustrations she has clipped from a periodical — avoid the ambiguities and confusions of written matter. The picture test is desirable, however, only if the questions are effective in assessing modes of thinking.

Note the following examples of picture test items:[1]

1. Directions: Mark an X across the picture that shows a complete circuit.

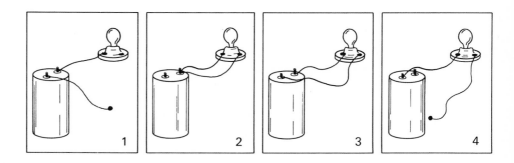

2. Directions: Here is a picture of a tree with names of some of its parts printed on it. Use these names to complete the statements about the tree.

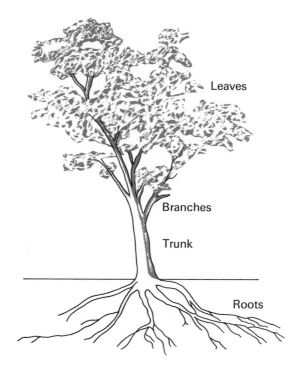

(1) The food for the tree is made in the _____.
(2) The tree is held in the ground by the _____.
(3) Water is taken into the tree through the _____.
(4) The sap is carried to the branches through the _____.
(5) The food for the tree is stored in the _____.

3. Directions: Look carefully at this picture of a sailboat being moved by the wind. There are two statements about the boat listed below. Mark an X across the word which makes each statement true.

(1) This boat will move because the wind is pushing the _____.

                    sail   water   air

(2) This boat will move toward _____.

                 A   B   C

4. Directions: Put an X (color in) the drawing that you think best answers the question. In which jar will the candle go out first?[2]

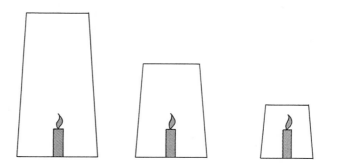

    These questions have been used with some success in grades ranging from first to third. Whether the teacher should read the directions and answer choices to the class depends on how well the class reads. These questions do not probe deeply into the kinds of learning children exhibit.

The first item is a paper-and-pencil laboratory exercise. The task is to apply the information that in a complete circuit, which includes a bulb and dry cell, one wire runs from the positive pole of the dry cell to the bulb and a second wire runs from the negative pole of the dry cell to the bulb. Some children will recall what they have already studied either in the textbook or in direct manipulation of electric circuits. Other children, however, will analyze each picture to identify the elements and their relationships and answer the question by applying the principle or whatever variation of it they have formulated. A number of the cognitive behaviors previously described are presumably involved in giving a thoughtful answer.

The second item is almost entirely recall, although the correlation of graphically represented structures with function raises the level of thought. The third item requires analysis of the picture elements so as to relate the bellying sail to wind direction and to separate the irrelevant directions *B* and *C*, from the logically necessary direction *A*. Only children who have had sailboat experience will be prepared to answer the question from memory alone.

A

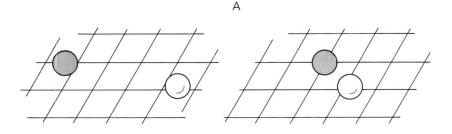

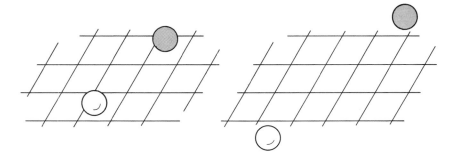

The fourth question is recall if children have performed a similar experiment. Even if the experiment illustrated is new, children have one chance in three of guessing correctly, and they will probably choose the first jar because bigger and longer seem to fit together.

Another example of a picture test is adapted from *Interaction and Systems,* an experimental primary grade textbook published by the Science Curriculum Improvement Study.[3] These pictures are used with children who have had much direct experience in identifying objects, interactions, and systems:

> Here are picture stories of two experiments. The black croquet ball and the white croquet ball are the objects in the experiments.
>
> Did the objects interact in experiment A? _____
> Did the objects interact in experiment B? _____

The teacher can change the last question to multiple-choice form so that children can mark the correct choice or choices as she reads the question to them.

B

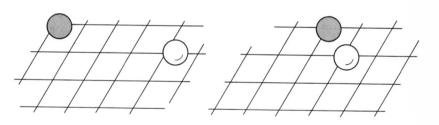

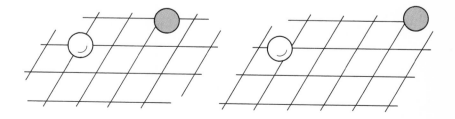

The following examples have been used with some success in grades ranging from first to third:

1. Directions: Mark an X on the jar of water which shows what happens to the water level in the first glass when the toy soldier is put into it.

2. Directions: This seesaw is longer on one end than on the other. Let us say that you sit where the boy is sitting in the picture. Where should another boy who weighs as much as you do have to sit so that the seesaw balances? Mark the place with an X.

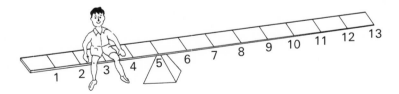

Both examples are open to the criticism that the child's answer may simply be recall. At most, the items demand an ability to apply certain principles of science to situations that may not be very different from the contexts in which the child first learned these principles. The seesaw question may be new because the seesaw arms are not of equal length, and the child must be aware of the effect of the extra length on the right-hand side.

Picture tests are good choices for paper-and-pencil testing despite the difficulty of writing questions for younger children. All too often picture tests test knowledge of nomenclature and rarely assess the higher cognitive behaviors. However, such tests are not *limited* to testing recall.

Overhead projection

Using a transparency and overhead projector to reproduce the test with its directions and supplementary information, the teacher is better able to direct her children; in addition the children can quickly correct their own papers when discussing their answers in class.

Essay and restricted-answer tests

Essay tests are potentially one of the most promising ways to appraise the quality of children's thinking. Such examinations can reveal how well children analyze problem situations, assess hypotheses, and derive inferences and generalizations from carefully selected data. Unfortunately children have not mastered the writing skills and the analytical abilities necessary for essay testing.

Planning essay questions

Despite this severe limitation children in the intermediate grades should begin as soon as possible to write essay responses not only because writing improves with guided practice but because children will be better prepared for the writing tasks of the higher grades. Writing answers to essay questions is an acquired art. Teachers should phrase questions so precisely that children need not wander far afield in search of fuzzy words to answer fuzzy questions. Frequently the teacher can easily rewrite poor essay questions as objective test items; for example, "List the names of the planets in order from the earth and identify each as larger than, smaller than, or about the same size as the earth," and "When the sun shines on the north pole, what is the season in the northern part of the world?" are not designed for reflective thinking and are better incorporated into fill-in, true–false, or multiple-choice items. On the other hand, "What is gravity?" and "What effect do the changing seasons have on our way of life?" are extremely diffuse questions: The first has no answer, and the second needs a good deal of time to answer. These questions are sharper worded thus: "What things happen in nature that lead us to believe in gravitational force?" and "What effect does the change from fall to winter have on your use of electricity at home?"

Special values of essay questions

The teacher can adapt properly written essay examinations to assess a youngster's ability to analyze a new, perhaps more complex, situation than he has previously encountered. Through the essay the teacher can follow the child's unique quality of thought, the way he puts ideas together, as well as his ability to think logically and respond intuitively. These aspects of the essay test fall into the evaluation subcategory 5.10 (see appendix), "Production of a unique communication." Objective testing has not yet demonstrated that it can come to grips with this kind of synthesis of multiple abilities and ideas.

Despite the obvious value of teacher-prepared scoring guides for marking essay papers, the teacher must always guard against rigidity in her expectation, which leaves no room for unexpected ideas and bright insights. If she uses a scoring guide, the teacher should award points for originality as well as for relevance of facts, logical inference, and sound conclusions. The teacher should accept the essay test as a device by which children can escape from the conformity of stereotyped and memorized answers.

Children are more likely to accept restricted-answer essay tests because such tests reduce the inevitable frustrations that children encounter in organizing thought patterns at length and in coping with the sheer mechanics of writing. Questions in restricted-answer essay tests set specific tasks; children may answer such questions in a few lines or paragraphs. However, restricted answer questions should not be so worded that memory will carry the child through.

Objective testing

In striking contrast with answers to essay examinations, which permit some element of freedom, answers to objective examinations are either "right" or "wrong." Teacher judgment is by no means diminished, however, because the teacher must decide which precise bits of information and skills to test and how to phrase the questions to fit her objectives and curricular stresses.

Objective test marks — meaning?

The form of the objective test she chooses — completion (which is not necessarily objective), multiple-choice, matching, or true–false — is a subjective judgment. In addition at the close of the examination the teacher must decide what the scores mean. Is the arithmetic mean to be the starting point? If the mean is high, does the child who is right on three quarters of the items fail? Decisions like these are difficult to justify for a class and for the individual children in the class. Instead of a mark to be recorded beside each name, the teacher should squeeze from the child's test all the information it can supply on the progress or lack of progress and use this information as feedback for relearning.

Good objective-test items that probe the higher cognitive behaviors are difficult to write. Completion tests, which usually attempt to minimize student guessing, inevitably require some teacher judgment in evaluating the correctness of the answers. An exceptionally well-informed or creative child may come up with a completely unexpected answer. Objective tests almost always imply that *one* and *only* one answer is correct, which is a constricting and un-realistic expectation. True–false items are often ambiguous because they are only relatively true or false and are susceptible to informed guessing. Because of these restrictions true–false questions are almost always narrowly limited to factual items and in general are inappropriate for science teaching by inquiry.

Multiple-choice tests are more versatile, in that they provide samples of the higher cognitive and affective behaviors. Consider, for example, the following experiment:[4]

Directions: The experiment described below is followed by questions with four choices for each. Only one answer is correct in each question. Place the letter of the correct answer after each question.

Two healthy geranium plants are kept in a dark closet for 24 hours before the start of the experiment. Plant *A* is then watered and placed in sunlight. Plant *B* receives the same amount of water but is left in the dark closet. After 24 hours a leaf from each plant is tested for starch with [iodine]. The leaf from Plant *A* showed a much better test for starch than the leaf from Plant *B*.

1. This experiment is designed to find out: _____ 1.
   (a) if plants need water in making starch.
   (b) if plants need sunlight in making starch.
   (c) if plants in sunlight have greener leaves.
   (d) if plants need air in making starch.

2. The control in the experiment is: _____ 2.
   (a) the watered plant left in the sunlight.
   (b) the watered plant left in the closet.
   (c) the dry plant left in the sunlight.
   (d) the dry plant left in the closet.

3. The results of the experiment show: _____ 3.
   (a) that plants need warmth to make starch.
   (b) that plants need air to make starch.
   (c) that plants need sunlight to make starch.
   (d) that plants need darkness to make starch.

This exercise is written for fifth grade and sixth grade children who have tested plants for starch, one of the products of photosynthesis. The questions sample several of the lower cognitive skills. In addition the exercise calls for application (3.00) in the cognitive hierarchy (see appendix), analysis of relationships (4.20), and evaluation (6.00). The questions test children on knowledge of criteria and methodology in controlled experiments (1.24–1.25), ability to interpret data (2.20), and synthesis in drawing conclusions (5.00).

Best-answer questions require that children make judgments, although they may still rely on recall for the proper answer. To write a five-item question with only one indisputably correct choice is a taxing intellectual task. To write the other four choices — the so-called distractors — so that they are reasonable is no easier. As a result test items are often a series of true–false questions disguised as a multiple-choice test. For want of a sufficient number of distractors, teachers sometimes include the choice "none of these." Unless the teacher occasionally words questions so that "none of these" is right, children quickly learn to disregard this choice and thus increase the probability of their guessing correctly.

Avoid disguised
true–false

At the intermediate grade level four choices should be the maximum number in each multiple-choice question because most children cannot handle five alternatives simultaneously. Multiple-choice tests are more or less impractical in the primary grades because of time and reading limitations, although with practice second graders and third graders can manage three-choice items.

In general teacher-constructed objective tests in the intermediate grades are not valid instruments for evaluating the higher cognitive behaviors, which are so important in science, because the questions and choices are complex and because most classroom teachers cannot devise appropriate questions.

Matching tests

Matching tests are restricted to lower-level learning, such as knowledge of terminology, facts, conventions, and principles. Although they are not easy to construct, such tests can include much specific information. Unless she seeks the miscellany, which is the strength of matching items, the teacher should disregard matching tests because they add nothing to the proven virtues of fill-in and multiple-choice testing.

Standardized objective tests

A number of commercially published standardized tests are now on the market. These tests have been given to thousands of children at several grade levels, and from this mass testing age-group norms are available for comparison with national norms. The better tests supply test reliability, standard error of measurement, some information on the standardizing group, and a test manual for diagnostic purposes. The items are carefully constructed, and those of little value have been eliminated along with typographical errors and confusing wording.

These tests assume, however, that all children have been exposed to the same science learning, an assumption that ignores individual differences. A low score on a standardized test does not necessarily mean little science learning; it may mean only that the child has not been exposed to *this* kind of science or that the child is not an experienced test taker.

Standardized tests are not always valid

Standardized tests are of little value in assessing the outcomes of science teaching not committed to recalling facts and principles—that is, science teaching concerned with the observational, interpretive, and analytical aspects of science learning. There is no reason for accepting the claims that these standardized tests yield information commensurate with the cost and the time required to administer them.

Of the more than half a dozen nationally circulated tests that include either a separate science test or a science section, few have been designed for modern elementary science instruction. The most surprising aspect of current evaluation is the relative inactivity of the new elementary science curriculum projects in developing formal testing materials. Only the well-financed and well-staffed organizations, such as the American Association for the Advancement of Science, the Science Curriculum Improvement Study, and the Elementary Science Study, have the resources to develop and test their materials. By contrast the secondary school science groups, which created revolutionary new biology, chemistry, and physics programs, began immediately to design new tests because the available ones were incompatible with the philosophy and procedures of their programs.

Sequential Tests of Educational Progress

STEP science content

The best known of the nationally available science tests are the Sequential Tests of Educational Progress (STEP). These tests, published by the Educational Testing Service, are written on four levels. Level 1 is for college freshmen and sophomores, level 2 for senior high school students, level 3 for junior high school students, and level 4 for children in the fourth, fifth, and sixth grades. Each test is available in A and B versions. The level 3 and level 4 tests are composed of fifty items, taking a total of forty minutes. The content is distributed thus: biology 50 percent of the test items, chemistry 10 percent, physics 24 percent, astronomy 4 percent, geology 4 percent, and meteorology 8 percent.[5]

STEP objectives

The tests are designed to measure "a student's knowledge and understanding of fundamental concepts and processes of science." The items in the cognitive categories are organized thus: knowledge 26 percent of all items, comprehension 20 percent, application 46 percent, and higher abilities 8 percent.[6]

Content for the tests was selected from a list of "important," arbitrarily chosen "concepts and principles." The emphasis on the lower levels of the cognitive hierarchies is obvious.

Most questions in the tests are unrelated, but several are grouped into subsets, which follow brief descriptions of home-related situations that can be explained by a certain principle. These subsets are made up of three or four questions. Only one answer of the four choices supplied for each question is correct.

The teacher has some flexibility in the test level she chooses to use. For example, she may use the level 3 test, which is designed for the seventh, eighth, and ninth grades, in above-average sixth grades. Unfortunately the two forms of level 4 are the lowest level of tests.

The helpful manual   A detailed manual accompanies the STEP tests and helps the teacher interpret results; it provides percentile bands (in contrast to percentile ranks), norms, lists of schools from which the norms were constructed, and validity and reliability estimates. The tests are valuable for both feedback and diagnostic purposes, but like any other tests dependent on the quality of the questions, the generally high level of the STEP tests suffers somewhat from a few questionable items. Consider, for example, items 17–24 in the level 4B test of the 1957 series, which are not included in the 1969 version:[7]

> The Brown family wanted to plant a spring flower and vegetable garden. Mr. Brown said the first flowers to grow and bloom would be the crocuses, jonquils, and tulips.

> 17. Their crocuses and tulips will bloom before their zinnias and marigolds partly because the crocuses and tulips
>   (a) are watered more often
>   (b) get more sunlight
>   (c) are planted deeper in the earth
>   (d) grow from food stored in bulbs

> 18. Sue Brown found some dandelions growing in the garden. The dandelion seeds were most likely
>   (e) washed in by the rain
>   (f) carried by the wind
>   (g) dropped by a bird
>   (h) planted with seeds from a seed package

> 19. Sue wanted to test some of her father's fertilizer to see if it would really make plants grow better. She thought of three different experiments.

1

Soil and
fertilizer

Experiment 1. Add fertilizer to one flowerpot of soil. Plant three bean seeds. Watch them grow while giving them each the same care.

2

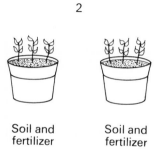

Soil and   Soil and
fertilizer   fertilizer

Experiment 2. Get two flowerpots. Add fertilizer to the soil of both pots. Plant three bean seeds in each pot. Watch them grow while giving them each the same care.

3

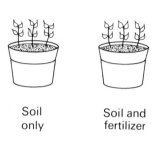

Soil   Soil and
only   fertilizer

Experiment 3. Get two flowerpots. Add fertilizer to one flowerpot. Plant three bean seeds in each. Watch them grow while giving them the same care.

Which experiment would show if this fertilizer was good for the plants?
(a) Experiment 1
(b) Experiment 2
(c) Experiment 3
(d) None of the experiments above will tell her anything about the fertilizer.

20. Sue read on the back of the package of lettuce seeds, "Thin the plants to stand 4 to 6 inches apart in the row." What is the best reason for doing this?
(e) To give each plant enough room, air, sunlight, and water
(f) To get more plants into a garden
(g) To make the garden pretty
(h) To grow many kinds of plants

21. In the fall of the year, John still had many large tomatoes on his plants. He read the weather forecast in his newspaper.

Weather Forecast

Clear and colder tonight and tomorrow.
Low of 28 degrees expected tonight.

Why should John gather in all his tomatoes?
(a) Frost was expected that night.
(b) There would be no more warm summer days.
(c) The tomatoes were all as large as they could grow.
(d) Plants need cloudy nights when the temperature is low.

22. John counted the tomatoes picked from his garden each week. He kept this record:

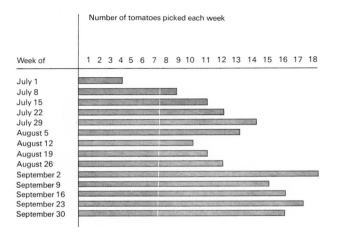

During which week did John pick the most tomatoes?
(e) July 22
(f) August 5
(g) September 2
(h) September 23

23. A pair of robins built a nest in a tree near the window of Sue's bedroom. She watched them every day. Sue saw the eggs one day when the birds were away, but most of the time a robin sat in the nest. One day broken eggs were found on the ground, and the empty nest was not used again by the mother and father robin. Sue knows that the eggs were broken by
(a) the mother robin
(b) a strong rainstorm
(c) the father robin
(d) an enemy of the robins

24. Sue saw a new bird come to their garden. In a book she found its picture and a circle graph to show what the bird eats in summer.

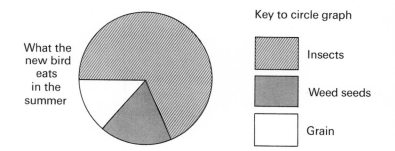

From this graph, she was able to tell that this bird was
(e) helpful and ate mostly insects
(f) helpful and ate grain
(g) helpful and ate mostly weed seeds
(h) harmful and ate mostly grain

Response *d*, the suggested answer for question 17, is identified as a test of ability to suggest hypotheses. Choice of *d* may indicate ability to hypothesize, but the question is just as likely to be answered correctly from memory. Children may exclude alternatives *a* and *b* because they know that the amount of water and sunlight falling on plants growing under the same conditions will be the same. They may also know that sunlight is ineffective in "germinating" seeds and bulbs. Therefore response *d* does not really test how well children can propose hypotheses. However, the cumulative effect of the thirty-five items, which presumably test hypothesizing, may allow for some valid conclusions to be drawn.

Question 18 is also subject to prior school or home knowledge. On the other hand question 19, which requires selection of a feasible procedure, is less likely to be responsive to memory. Question 20 does reveal the child's awareness of controlled experimentation as a source of data. Interestingly only a quarter of the fourth grade normative group correctly answered questions 17 and 18, and only one-third selected the "correct" answer for question 19. Only about a third of the group correctly answered question 23, which was designed to test ability to draw conclusions. The "correct" choice, *d,* is illogical in view of the given data. Children may reject items *a* and *c* on the grounds of "parental instinct"; they may reject *b* because, although not specifically stated, Sue did not see the rainstorm. Item *d* is therefore the "best" answer, but it is not logically best. To answer correctly, the child must believe that the father and mother robin would not destroy the eggs they had tended and that only an "enemy" could have broken the eggs.

This analysis shows the difficulties involved in making up a paper-and-pencil test that successfully evaluates complex cognitive behaviors. Of course we do not intend to diminish in any way the obvious value of the STEP tests. If the conditions and qualifications of each question were spelled out in detail and if the choices were more precise, the questions would be too difficult for children to read. However, in a deeper sense the tests fail as a diagnostic instrument: the teacher cannot determine whether the child misses the hypothesis because he does not know what to look for, because he fails to examine the hypotheses objectively, or because he does not know how to test the plausibility of the hypotheses and how they are related to scientific principles. The child may rely on faulty memory for facts or principles.

With the best intentions . . .

Even if they do supply some information on the child's ability to recognize appropriate assumptions, these tests give no hint of his power to formulate hypotheses, to define problems, to select procedures, to draw conclusions, to evaluate critically, and to reason quantitatively in a practical situation. To the extent that "knowing about" is transferable to "knowing how," these STEP tests are valid; unfortunately the degree to which these two aspects of knowledge and behavior are correlated is one of the imponderables that confront science educators.

The 1969 version of the STEP tests in science for the elementary schools rely less on assessing the higher cognitive behaviors and stress to a much greater extent knowledge, comprehension, and application of science facts and principles. The tests are based on a traditional elementary science textbook approach to instruction because of the many facts and principles included. Children in the new programs are likely to be penalized if they take the STEP tests. None of the questions is designed to reveal affective behavior.

The Nelson–Mason Test of Science Comprehension

The Nelson–Mason test is another excellent attempt to devise a test that does not merely convey children's knowledge of facts and principles. It was devised primarily by highly skilled professionals, in a particular teaching context, for developing critical thinking skills in a framework of selected content. Its organization is similar to that of the STEP test: a series of situations to be interpreted, science principles to be applied, hypotheses to be tested, and conclusions to be drawn.

> In working through the test items to the situations, the pupils become involved in making distinctions between what is given and what must yet be learned by making further observations, between facts and assumptions, between problems and hypotheses, and between inductive generalizations . . . and deductions from such assumptions or generalizations.[8]

The test, composed of sixty items, was "standardized" for children in the fourth, fifth, and sixth grades. Fourth graders should answer "correctly" approximately twenty-four items, fifth graders twenty-nine items, and sixth graders thirty-four items. A high ceiling was deliberately established on the premise that an unchallenging test deprives the best students of the opportunity to convey their knowledge and abilities. The test was judged difficult for most fourth and fifth graders, even though the questions were apparently not too difficult for most children to read with meaning.

Three of the eight test situations are biological, three are physical, and two are drawn from the earth sciences. The test authors did not itemize the individual thinking skills each question attempts to elicit, although they have included questions in most of the cognitive categories.

The following "situation" shows how content and interpretation are interrelated. The example is based on the scientific principle that most substances expand when heated. Ten objective questions were written to test the child's ability to recognize observations, assumptions, and deductions arising from this principle.[9]

Numbers 36 through 45 refer to the following situation:

One hot July morning the center span of a low steel bridge across a river was swung open to allow a long string of barges to pass through. While the bridge was open the temperature rose many degrees. When the bridge tender tried to close the bridge again, the center span would not fit. It was too long!

Problems:

1. What had happened to the bridge to prevent it from closing?
2. What could be done to get the bridge closed?

Numbers 36 through 45 are statements that have some bearing on the solution of these two problems. Classify each one into one of these three groups:

1. Something that could be seen (observation)
2. Something taken for granted that has to do with scientific theory (assumption)
3. Something that can be figured out from scientific theory (deduction)

36. The center span of the bridge had increased in length.   (1)

37. The center span was composed of rapidly moving molecules.   (2)

38. An increase in temperature causes an increase in speed of movement of molecules.   (2)

39. When the molecules of which a steel structure is composed move faster, the steel structure becomes slightly larger.   (2)

40. If the steel bridge span was made of moving molecules, then increased speed of movement due to increased temperature caused the bridge span to become longer.   (3)

41. Molecules move faster when the temperature goes up; molecules will slow down when the temperature goes down.   (2)

42. If a hot piece of steel is cooled, its molecules should slow down, and the piece of steel should shrink in size.   (3)

43. After the fire department had squirted cold water on the bridge span for about 15 minutes, the bridge swung shut without any difficulty.   (1)

44. Cooling the bridge span caused it to become shorter.   (1)

45. Cooling the bridge span caused the molecules in it to move more slowly.
                                                                              (2)

To answer these items correctly, children must know the meaning of such terms as *swing bridge, center span,* and *bridge tender.* Items 36, 43, and 44 are described as statements; they are not logically equivalent. Item 36 is described as a part of the situation, whereas item 43 is an additional fact. Item 44 is not an observation in the same sense because it is a cause-and-effect inference, and a case can be made for defining it as an assumption. The fact that the bridge became shorter after cooling is not proof that these two events are causally related. This judgment is justified only if other variables have no effect and if the bridge shortens only when it is cooled. Item 44 is meaningful only if children know or assume that metals decrease in length when cooled, other conditions remaining constant.

The child is supposed to classify items 37, 38, 39, 41, and 45 as assumptions. These items are *all* either fundamental postulates of kinetic molecular theory or applications of these postulates to this particular bridge. Items 40 and 42 are listed as deductions—that is, as predictions derived from kinetic molecular theory. Items 37, 39, and 45 may, with equal justice, be included as deductions because they are predictions applied to a specific problem.

Difficulty in specifying kinds of behavior

The difficulty in assigning statements to specific kinds of behavior is no reflection on the Nelson–Mason test, which is a praiseworthy attempt to evaluate elusive and imprecise behavior. This test does reflect that arbitrary judgments must be made in test construction. The test constructors can undoubtedly make a convincing case for the particular categories they have chosen. The value of limiting the number of choices to three for this particular question is debatable, because the probability of guessing correctly is increased, but undoubtedly good reasons do exist for this limitation. Some other questions supply two or, in some cases, four alternatives; most provide three. This test has feedback and diagnostic value although the limitation to three choices precludes fine discriminations. Discussion of test answers with children will provide feedback.

The Concept Prerequisite and Development Test

A test for younger children

This paper-and-pencil test was devised by H. Jess Brown, at Utah State University, for children in kindergarten through third grade. It is not a test of scientific process skills but rather an instrument for diagnosing the readiness of children to profit from concept-centered instruction. The author chose four "abilities" he believes are essential to the formation of concepts. He formulated ten questions to assess each of these abilities and included ten additional questions on concept application. The test is composed of five subtests:

Detection of Differences, Detection of Similarities, Logical Memory, Attention [to tasks], and Concept Formation.[10]

The questions in the first four categories are similar to those in many intelligence and reading tests. Children select an item in a set of drawings, which differs from or is like a key drawing; in the "Logical Memory" subtest they must recall oral directions; in the "Attention" subtest they must also rely on memory. The questions are open to the criticism that the "Attention" and "Logical Memory" tasks are quite similar and that the validity of the tasks as measures of the child's capacities is impossible to estimate on theoretical grounds.

Six of the ten questions on concept formation are based on scientific principles such as heat conduction, gravitational force, and musical pitch. The teacher is directed to explain briefly the particular principle, with appropriate demonstrations, before the children answer the question. The following extract is typical of the technique:[11]

Question #44: Teacher: "Here is a drawing of another experiment. (Copper is a good conductor and wood is a poor conductor. So let's take a round wooden bowl and a square copper pan of the same thickness and put hot water in them, the same amount and temperature in each container, and hold one in each hand.) Draw a big X through the hand which would be the warmest."

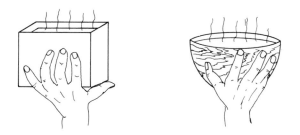

Question #45: Teacher: "Now I'll talk about gravity. The laws of gravity indicate that every object has a gravitational attraction for every other object. The strength of this attraction depends upon two things, (1) the size or mass of the objects or things and (2) the distance between them or how far apart they are. The heavier the objects are the more attraction they have for each other, and the nearer they are to each other the more they attract each other. When two things are large like the earth or the moon this attraction is very great, but when two things are small like you and I the attraction between us is so small it is difficult to measure. When one thing is very big like the earth and one is very small like you or a ball the attraction is still quite large if the objects are close to each other.

The earth attracts me quite strongly. I can jump up away from the earth a foot or two [demonstrate] but the earth quickly and forcefully pulls me back down against it. You can throw a ball into the air away from the earth but it is quickly pulled back against the earth. Now I hope you have the idea that every object has a gravitational attraction for every other object; the large heavy objects attract strongly, the small light objects attract very weakly. I am attracted to you and you to me but the attraction is so very small we can only measure it with difficulty, but it is still *there* whether we feel it or measure it or not.

The other aspect of gravity, the distance factor, is interesting too. An object such as a ball is very much attracted to the earth when the earth is close to it. But if you put the ball out into space, away from the earth a great distance, the attraction of the earth for the ball and the ball for the earth may not be strong enough to ever bring the earth and the ball together again.

So you see gravitational attraction is greatest when objects are *heavy* and when they are *close together.*

Now we'll have some questions to see how well you understand the gravitational attraction idea.

Below, beside the picture of a hat, are some sets of balls which are much the same except the larger ones are *heavier* than the smaller ones. Their centers are all the same distance apart. Which pairs of balls attracts each other with the greatest gravitational force? Draw an X between the two which attract each other the most, then turn to the next page.''

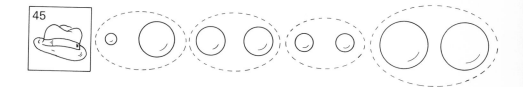

Some reservations

The ideas presented in this test are difficult for children who have not had concrete experience with them. Children better at remembering, attending, *and* forming concepts are more likely to answer correctly, although little evidence indicates that such is the case. The test may merely reflect the ability of children to learn a new vocabulary without understanding the underlying scientific principles. In addition the test may contain certain methodological flaws. For example, the value of the drawing in question 44 is questionable. This heat transfer demonstration is only valid if the two containers have the same shape, although for all practical purposes the wooden bowl will be cooler than the copper pan. Children encounter difficulties enough in picking out and controlling variables without confusing them with a partly uncontrolled demonstration. However, the teacher could use this drawing to assess the child's ability to judge how well the experiment has been controlled. Furthermore the subject matter of the first four subtests is not scientific, and therefore the test may be less relevant to scientific concepts and to the child's general ability to learn scientific principles than if its content included tasks more closely related to the sciences.

Reliability and validity   Because the pertinent data are not yet available, we cannot judge the effectiveness of this test for children who have experience in inquiry. Norms exist for approximately 1200 first grade children in several western states. In addition to a calculated reliability of 0.78 "content validity was established through careful examination of the goals of nine recognized elementary curriculum projects and authorities."[12] The author states that he intended to harmonize this test with the "major curriculum developments in elementary science" in which these goals are recognized.[13] The stated correlation between the first four subtests with subtest 5, "Concept Formation," is 0.34. This correlation, although indicative of some relationship, is not highly predictive.

In general this test is a praiseworthy attempt to assess cognitive skills, and it should be valuable to the elementary school teacher who seeks deeper insights into the intellectual capacities of her children.

Competency Measures for
Science—A Process Approach

Performance testing   The Commission on Science Education of the American Association for the Advancement of Science has prepared appraisal and competency measures for all the exercises of *Science—A Process Approach* (see Chapter 5 for an analysis of this curriculum). Because the objectives in each exercise are behavioral or performance objectives, the Commission has written the appraisal and the competency measures to assess the child's mastery of these behaviors. The intent of these measures is not to find out how much subject matter the children know or how efficiently they use laboratory materials but rather whether their behavior has actually changed desirably. For example, the Commission proposes the following behavioral objectives, which accompany the appropriate exercises in Part A for lower primary grade classes:

At the end of this exercise, when a child is shown a collection of specimens (or of pictures) of well-known objects, he should be able to:

Performance objectives

1. CONSTRUCT a classification of the objects according to variations in a single characteristic which has been specified by someone else.
2. CONSTRUCT a classification of the objects according to variations in a single characteristic which he has chosen.
3. DESCRIBE to others the characteristic he chose for his method of classification.
4. IDENTIFY and NAME words which are used in the construction of a classification system which is based on a single characteristic.[14]

Children collect and study different kinds of leaves, nuts, seashells, fruits, and vegetables in the course of this exercise. The appraisal requires that they pick out red objects and certain other colors and shapes in the room. Children also classify several objects, which they have not previously handled, according to color, size, shape, and texture. They propose as many different ways as they can to classify the objects and explain each classification.

A measure for small groups

The competency measure, which is administered most conveniently to individuals or small groups, comprises five tasks:

1. To group a number of different pieces of paper according to size.
2. To classify a number of geometric shapes.
3. To explain the basis for these classifications.
4. To arrange seven balls into four groups based on size.
5. To explain their reasons for these groupings.

In comparison the exercises on classifying in Part C for intermediate grade classes are more advanced. The Commission proposes the following behavioral objectives:

At the end of this exercise the child should be able to:

1. IDENTIFY a substance as being a solid, a liquid, or a gas.
2. DEMONSTRATE whether a substance is a solid, a liquid or gas by using the following physical characteristics: it has a shape of its own; it has a top surface that can be felt or seen; and it takes the shape of the container.
3. STATE that some substances can exist in more than one of the three states: solid, liquid, and gas.[15]

Before this exercise the children have presumably learned to use a spring balance for weighing objects, to distinguish between observations and explanations of those observations, and to classify organisms and objects that appear to be similar.

The appraisal requires children to classify common substances — wood, syrup, ice cream, an inflated plastic bag — as solid, liquid, or gas and to explain why they made these classifications.

The competency measure includes four tasks:

1. To classify raw egg white and to give the reason for this classification.
2. To classify raw egg white after it has been heated and to give the reason for this classification.
3. To classify the contents of a plastic bag, which is divided into two parts by means of a rubber band, and to give reasons for the classification. (The lower part contains a citric acid solution and the upper part contains baking soda.)
4. To classify the substances in the bag *after* the rubber band is removed and the baking soda mixed with the citric acid and to give reasons for the classification.

The increase in sophistication of process skills between these two classification exercises is noteworthy. Appraisals and competency measures of the process skills on which *Science — A Process Approach* is based become progressively more demanding.

More is expected of older children

In "The Suffocating Candle" for upper intermediate grade classes children make predictions based on a series of observations and revise these predictions with new evidence.[16] This exercise involves experiments with candles burning under glass jars; from graphs of experimental data children predict the approximate number of minutes similar candles will burn under larger glass jars and then test these predictions by experimentation. In the appraisal exercise children divided into groups predict from their previous data the burning time of a candle under a tall, narrow jar, explaining how they might test their predictions both from their data and by experiment. Children then repeat the experiment at least once, report an average of "burning times," and compare the average with their predictions.

The competency measure tests children's ability to apply their mastery of process skills in a different experimental situation. In this exercise they have three tasks:

1. To predict from the experimentally determined rate of melting of four and eight ice cubes how long two and six ice cubes would take to melt.
2. To predict from a graph of the melting time of ice cubes how long three ice cubes would take to melt.
3. To decide, on the basis of additional information that two ice cubes in a jar half full of water melt in ten minutes, whether to revise their prediction on how long three cubes would take to melt.

Appraisal and competency— promising techniques

These appraisal and competency measures are a promising addition to the evaluative tools of the elementary school teacher: They are scientifically accurate, are based on psychological and educational theory, and allow for gradual growth of cognitive skills. Because children learn science by guided experimentation and observation, these tests of experimentation and observation are an important pioneering effort in the evaluation of the goals of science education. Many of these evaluative exercises are also useful with programs other than the AAAS curriculum but only to the extent that children have had some kind of process instruction.

These measures do have one disadvantage. To obtain reliable results the teacher should test children individually or in small groups because she can observe and record behavior more carefully. Yet because of the length of many exercises the teacher has little time for such evaluation. However, she might revise the answer sheets so that older children may test themselves, thus minimizing testing time while giving the children immediate feedback. This procedure is particularly advantageous when children can accept evaluation without feeling threatened by it.

These measures have not been standardized

These measures are not standardized tests; reliabilities, validities, and norms are unavailable. But the lack of this information is an advantage: Teachers should not compare the performance of their classes with other classes. Rather the teacher now has at her command a powerful tool for learning how well children have mastered the perceptual and cognitive skills at the core of modern science.

Some Special Tests

Sophisticated cognitive questions

Many researchers and teachers have written sets of cognitively structured science questions. However, few have written questions suitable for testing the higher cognitive levels. Consider, for example, these sample questions used in a study of children in grades two to six to learn "the relative levels of understanding of selected concepts from within the conceptual scheme — force":[17]

Knowledge

1. The mass of an object is the
   a. volume of the object
   b. amount of matter in the object
   c. speed of the object
   d. acceleration of the object
2. For every action there is
   a. a reaction in the same direction
   b. an equal and opposite reaction
   c. a greater reaction in the same direction
   d. an opposite and smaller reaction

Comprehension

A drawing presents this situation: truck X carries four cars, cars C and D are on the first level and cars A and B are on the second level. Cars A and B are identical; C and D are identical. C and D each have greater masses than A or B. The mass of truck X is greater than the mass of the individual cars.

1. The amount of matter in
   a. car A is greater than in car B
   b. car B is greater than in car C
   c. car C is greater than in car D
   d. truck X is greater than in car A
2. If the engine of the truck exerts a constant unbalanced force, the truck and load will
   a. stay at rest
   b. have a constant acceleration
   c. move at constant speed
   d. have a greater amount of matter

Application

A drawing presents this situation: a table on which there is electromagnet A which attracts a steel ball. As the ball rolls toward the electromagnet, it falls through a hole in the table and lands on the floor.

1. In the situation above, the ball is caused to move by
   a. one kind of force with one origin
   b. two kinds of forces with two origins
   c. three kinds of forces with three origins
   d. four kinds of forces with four origins
2. The force causing the ball to move from the table to the floor is
   a. magnetic
   b. gravitational
   c. electric
   d. magnitude

A useful technique

These questions seem quite difficult for primary and intermediate grade children, but they were written for a specific teaching situation with heavy emphasis on force concepts. No attempt to assess growth in process skills, in either the highest cognitive behaviors or affective behavior, is evident.

The literature of psychological testing provides many interesting tests. The "definitions" in the following example are designed to diagnose the different types of conceptual explanations a junior high school child might propose.[18] The child's answers indicate whether he uses *structure concepts* ("factual" explanations), *process concepts* (cause-and-effect explanations), or *quality concepts* ("value-oriented" characteristics). The child selects one of the three explanations he thinks best defines the concept:

1. Melting

a. _____ Melting is too much heat. A solid melts. Iron melts to make steel. (structure concepts)

b. _____ Melting is when a solid is changing into a liquid like when a piece of ice is set out of the refrigerator it will melt into water. Butter turns into a liquid when it is heated by the sun. (process concepts)

c. _____ Melting reminds me of ice and snow melting in the spring. Then I know that nice weather will soon be here and I can play outside. Melting makes me think of ice cream and popsicles and things that I like. (quality concepts)

2. Element

a. _____ An element is matter. It has weight and it occupies space. It is a chemical like iron. Elements are kinds of atoms. Molecules contain atoms. (structure concepts)

b. _____ Elements combine to form compounds like hydrogen and oxygen burn to form water. (process concepts)

c. _____ Elements are pretty and are found in many colors. Copper is an element and is greenish when in water. Elements are dangerous, too. For example, mercury is an element which is dangerous and can make you sick. (quality concepts)

Fourth and fifth graders actually gave these explanations of *melting* and *element*. Children who think "structurally" tend to respond to the first statement, "process"-oriented children to the second, and "quality"-oriented children to the third.

An interest inventory

Pencil-and-paper evaluative devices in science for the affective domain are scarce. One interesting attempt is the Informal Interest Inventory,[19] which asks children to respond to things they like or dislike. The inventory has nineteen statements on reading, including stories about animals, stories that explain how things work, stories about great scientists, stories about history, and poetry. It also has thirteen items on television programming, including mystery programs, programs about outer space, science programs, news broadcasts, and programs about the stars, the moon, and the planets. The category of "Things I Like to Do" has twenty items, including play baseball, make things, experiment with chemistry sets, go swimming, make electric toys, and make model airplanes. The general categories cover "Things I'd Like to Own," "School Subjects That I Like," "Things That I Should Like to Do in High School," and "Things I'd Like to Do When I Grow Up."

Another inventory has 150 uncategorized items such as the following:

Have you ever

An experience inventory

1. Tried to find out what makes magnets work?
2. Noticed that land and water plants are different?
3. Thought what the center of the earth would be like?
4. Made a telegraph or electromagnet?
5. Watched printing on a balloon spread out as the balloon is blown up?
6. Observed an eclipse of the sun?
7. Watched the liquid in a thermometer rise as it is heated?[20]

Several of these questions were claimed to discriminate significantly between high achievers and low achievers on the STEP science tests. About a third of the total number of questions seemed to be characteristic of high-ability children. The questions unfortunately display all the usual deficiencies of inventory questions: They mean different things to children of different environments and home experiences. They prompt children to ask themselves what the teacher wants them to say and to try to please the teacher by their responses.

Do children reject science?

The Allison modification of the Allen Attitude Scale seeks to find out how children react to science. The scale includes ninety-five multiple-choice statements. Children from grades four to six judge these statements according to whether they agree, disagree, or are neutral. The following statements are typical:

1. Science is not understood enough by most people.
2. Scientists are shy, lonely people.
3. A great research scientist gives little thought to how the things he discovers can be used in daily life.
4. Many of the findings in science go against the laws of God.
5. Americans place greater value on the everyday uses made of scientific discoveries than on the discoveries themselves.[21]

These "attitudes" are expressed attitudes and may not necessarily reflect real attitudes. Behavior on paper is not the same as actual behavior in the classroom, which is likely to be even more different in noncontrolled environments.

A new approach

In the past few years the semantic differential scale has aroused considerable interest as a method for gathering data to compare the feelings of a group of children before and after a given experience. This scale is reasonably reliable in providing affective data on how children are responding to class activities. Many elementary teachers have successfully used the following scale:

Doing experiments[22]

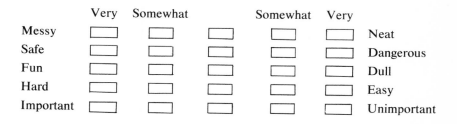

The Unique Test

Unless the teacher purposefully and thoroughly covers a broad range of science content and takes time to develop inquiry and critical thinking skills, children are not likely to score high on any test. Teacher–pupil interaction in planning and working through a program of science is so important that only the teacher, despite technical deficiencies in her science knowledge, knows what the children can or cannot do. In this sense the permissive classroom *is* unique.

Summary

Paper-and-pencil tests, which have conventionally been the major means for assessing student learning, are deficient in several important aspects. Valid and reliable teacher-made tests are difficult to construct for assessing intellectual skills and experimental ability. The primary grades have achieved some progress with "picture" tests, although the structure of these tests must be on a relatively primitive level of thinking. For intermediate and upper grades, essay and restricted-answer tests are useful provided the teacher is aware of their limitations. Objective tests, although convenient, are limited by the child's ability to answer questions on the basis of recall; however, with careful use these tests may convey samples of cognitive and affective behaviors.

Standardized tests are carefully constructed and provide much information about the class but little diagnostic help. Whether these children know more or less (as judged by the test) than three thousand other fourth graders scattered throughout twenty school systems in the nation is *absolutely* unimportant. The usual standardized test is a one-way procrustean bed; it is always longer than the unfortunate child, who is stretched to fit it.

Written tests are also open to criticism because the child can answer by recall of facts many questions that presumably probe reasoning abilities. Some of the best science tests, such as the STEP and the Nelson–Mason tests, try to minimize factual knowledge by presenting a series of related problems or by presenting problems for the child to solve by applying a scientific principle and some intellectual skills. The fact that both of these carefully constructed tests have some faults emphasizes the difficulty of constructing tests to get at knowledge beyond facts alone.

Tests help teachers to project a better picture of the child's cognitive skills and his deficiencies in science learning. The more diagnostic the test, the more useful it is in the classroom. Examination scores mean little in themselves. Interpretation of scores is never a simple matter, and for many children scores on any test will be meaningless even in comparison to national norms.

For further study

1. Analyze the validity of the questions on a standardized elementary science test.

2. Devise picture test questions for young children to test concepts of heat, light, sound, erosion, growing things, and satellites.

3. A teacher gives a standardized test prior to a year-long science course. At the end of the course she administers the same test. If the two test scores show no significant differences, what conclusions would you draw concerning the teaching and learning processes?

4. Analyze an elementary science test according to the categories of the cognitive and affective domains (see appendix).

5. Write a series of test questions to assess the higher cognitive behaviors of children at the fourth grade or fifth grade level.

Notes and references

1. Tannenbaum, H., N. Stillman, and A. Piltz, *Evaluation in Elementary School Science* (Washington, D.C.: U.S. Department of Health, Education and Welfare, Office of Education, 1964), OE–29057, Bulletin No. 757, pp. 44–46.

2. Blanc, S. S., "Sample Test Questions," San Diego State College, 1969; see also Blanc, S. S., "Testing for the Process Skills," *Addresses and Reports,* National Science Teachers Association Seventeenth Annual Convention (Washington, D.C.: National Science Teachers Association, 1969), p. 55.

3. *Interaction and Systems* (Berkeley, Calif.: Science Curriculum Improvement Study, University of California, 1963), pp. 44–45.

4. Blanc, S. S., "Sample Test Questions," *op. cit.*

5. Based on data in *SCAT–STEP Series II, Teacher's Handbook,* preliminary edition (Princeton, N.J.: Educational Testing Service, 1969), p. 32.

6. *Ibid.*

7. *Sequential Tests of Educational Progress, Science, Form B* (Princeton, N.J.: Cooperative Test Division, Educational Testing Service, 1957), p. 7.

8. Nelson, C., and J. Mason, "A Test of Science Comprehension for Upper Elementary Grades," *Science Education*, 47: 319–22, October 1963.

9. *Ibid.*, p. 329.

10. *Concept Prerequisite and Development Test, Form A, Manual for Administering, Scoring, and Interpreting Scores* (Logan: Utah State University, 1965), p. 7.

11. *Concept Prerequisite and Development Test* (Logan: Utah State University, 1965), p. 10.

12. *Concept Prerequisite and Development Test, Form A, Manual for Administering, Scoring, and Interpreting Scores, op. cit.*, pp. 11–12.

13. *Ibid.*, p. 1.

14. *Science—A Process Approach*, Part A–D, Classifying 1 (New York: Xerox Education Group, 1967).

15. *Science—A Process Approach*, Part C–M, Classifying 7, *ibid.*

16. *Science—A Process Approach*, Part D–M, Predicting 4, *ibid.*

17. Helgeson, S. L., An Investigation into the Relationship Between Concepts of Force Attained and Maturity as Indicated by Grade Levels, unpublished doctoral dissertation, University of Wisconsin, 1967, pp. 167–96.

18. Scriven, E. G., "An Analysis of the Types of Concepts Used by Fourth Through Ninth Graders to Explain Meaning," *Journal of Educational Research*, 62: 153–56, December 1968; also, private communication from Scriven describing tests in detail. Scriven found that children with lower IQs tend to use "quality" concepts much more than do other children. Most science instruction, however, is concerned with "structure" and "process" explanations.

19. Partin, M. S., An Investigation of the Effectiveness of the AAAS Process Method Upon the Achievement and Interest in Science for Selected Fourth Grade Students, unpublished doctoral dissertation, University of Southern Mississippi, 1967, pp. 102–8.

20. Wahla, J. C., The Relationship Between Sixth-Grade Science Background Experiences and Science Achievement in Selected Urban Elementary Schools, unpublished doctoral dissertation, University of Michigan, 1967, p. 84.

21. Allison, R. W., The Effect of Three Methods of Treating Motivational Films Upon the Attitudes of Fourth-, Fifth-, and Sixth-Grade Students Toward Science, Scientists, and Scientific Careers, unpublished doctoral dissertation, Pennsylvania State University, 1966, pp. 156–61.

22. Geis, F., New York University.

Interpretation of Science Tests

Overview

Teacher-prepared tests and standardized tests have merit according to classroom goals and conditions. All tests should meet the criteria of validity, reliability, and sampling if they are to furnish data for teachers to make informed judgments. Programmed instruction, an important technique in some classrooms, facilitates evaluation because children must periodically work through tests to see if they have achieved desired behavioral objectives before they can go on to the next learning task.

Validity

How do we recognize validity?

Most objective examination items used in the schools include only knowledge of facts and principles and therefore fall into the lower cognitive levels of learning. They tend to be hastily constructed from isolated and unrelated snippets of recall. Although they indignantly deny the charge that they are interested only in recall, in practice teachers seek recall as the major outcome. The teacher should ask herself, "What do I need to know about each child's ability to infer? To see relationships? To make use of the knowledge of science which he has?

Above all, tests should be *valid;* that is, they should measure what they are *intended* to measure. This statement is indeed easy to make, yet according to the stated goals of elementary science instruction many tests do not fulfill this criterion. Does the test give the teacher the information she is seeking? Of course, if she is only looking for a verbatim definition of *electron* or *insect* or a list of all the ways living things resemble one another, she can easily attain this kind of validity. Even if the test gives insight into the reasoning processes of children, such knowledge may be spurious:

One may . . . describe a biological environment and ask for predictions regarding the effect of a certain intervention. Students who have never dealt with ecological data will succeed or fail according to their general ability to reason with complex events; those who have studied ecological biology will be more likely to succeed, reasoning from specific principles, and those who have lived in such an ecology or read about it may answer successfully on the basis of memory.[1]

Only the classroom teacher, who has worked for months with her children, is in a *position* to know on what basis the children have succeeded, even though she may not actually know which of these alternatives fits each member of the class.

Grouping items into situational sequences as in the Nelson–Mason tests is often proposed as a feasible technique for reducing the emphasis on recall. Evaluators are hopeful that the child's ability to follow a chain of reasoning, to interpret a problem, to recognize hypotheses, to assess data, to deduce a course of action or a proposal from principles, to select reasonable alternative courses of action, and to propose appropriate solutions will be easier to test in this way. The difficulty in designing these tests and the inordinate amount of time required to formulate items and to reject worthless, confusing, and invalid items are an ever-present burden.

Because good tests are so difficult to write, we do not expect most classroom teachers to construct valid paper-and-pencil examinations of the higher cognitive abilities. However, we do expect teachers to strive constantly and consistently to observe children's behavior in the classroom. Their observations may be invalid, unreliable, and retrogressive, but they are still a more reasonable base for assessing the teaching of elementary science than is conventional paper-and-pencil testing.

Reliability

If test is not valid, reliability is meaningless

Reliability, a magic word in the lexicon of the test maker, is the consistency of test results within the same population or within a representative sample taken from that population, if the test were given again. Unlike validity, reliability is relatively easy to measure. An unreliable test is probably invalid, but the converse is not necessarily true. If the test does not measure what it is designed to measure and if the test is not known to be invalid, consistency is meaningless. If "ability to propose hypotheses," for example, is *defined* as success on a test purporting to test this ability, a completely arbitrary validity is introduced comparable to the facetious definition of intelligence as something measured by an intelligence test. Such validity is based on the arbitrary assumption that the test maker's *acceptance* creates validity.

Sampling

Can we generalize from this test?

Comprehensive tests should include a variety of situations, ideas, facts, and principles. Certainly we should not infer that a child cannot select pertinent hypotheses because he has failed to answer correctly *one* examination question which presumably demands this skill. Critical thinking is much too complex and intuitive to be sampled by a few questions, no matter how carefully constructed. Some teachers have developed minitests, purposely limited to a few kinds of intellectual behavior (sometimes only one); they administer these tests frequently to sample growth or lack of growth in these behaviors.

Each test item should measure a specific ability or item of information for diagnostic feedback. In the course of time the children should encounter enough single-skill or function questions so that the teacher can form a composite judgment based on several tests and dozens of test items. However, conventional tests, despite rigorous pretesting and analysis, tend to be diagnostically weak. No *comprehensive* diagnostic science test is available, but if one were in print, it would be too difficult for elementary school children. This is a strong argument for giving many short, specially constructed tests rather than one or two comprehensive tests.

Item analysis

Test makers frequently turn to the technique of item analysis to improve their tests. Item analysis is time-consuming but frequently rewarding. Testers assume that the best students and the worst students (selected from the group taking the test, according to prior performance, or from the test results themselves) will perform differently on each test item. The best students select the "correct" answers, those the test maker himself selects. The poorer students select the "correct" answers least often. Therefore test items that poor students answer correctly more often than good students are worthless, and items that only good students answer correctly have "high discriminating capacity." Questions that few students, and those that most students, answer correctly are also worthless, although test makers often include some difficult questions to give the best students an opportunity to display their ability.

In a sense item analysis is illogical because it depends on circular reasoning. In practice it is a useful device for detecting some, although not all, inferior questions, provided the teacher is well acquainted with the strengths and weaknesses of her children. Such a teacher, however, may not need this kind of paper-and-pencil testing, for she is already aware of the children's abilities. Furthermore the purpose of testing in the elementary school is not to compare groups of children but rather to find out as much as possible about each child. Hence tests should be diagnostic rather than comparative; they should indicate areas for reteaching, not serve as a baseline for marking children.

Before-and-After Testing

Are children making progress?

One of the strengths of standardized testing is the availability of reliable alternate forms that are statistically equivalent: Children who score at the fiftieth percentile on one form will be close to the fiftieth percentile on the other form. If they accept the validity of each form for their classrooms and if they accept a high mark on these tests as a measure of successful learning, teachers can assess learning progress by giving one form of the test at the beginning of the school year or learning experience and the second form at the end of the year or experience. If maturation, outside and concomitant learning, and practice in test taking are ignored, the growth shown by the second test is presumably the result of instruction. The outcome of such testing, however, is often dismaying, even after a full year of concentrated instruction. As Fletcher Watson once remarked, "We must wonder how it is that after a year of instruction, the gains are so meager. Certainly such results must be discouraging to teachers."[2]

Standardized tests are inadequate evaluative instruments for discriminating between what children have or have not actually learned and what they can or cannot do. A year of living experiences often exerts a much greater effect on a science test score than a year of instruction; that is, fifth grade children, even without additional science instruction, do better on a test than fourth grade children. Although we should expect this result, it is nonetheless startling.

Some doubts about written tests

These doubts about the validity of written tests are intended to induce a healthy attitude of skepticism toward the claims of science testers and tests. The creation of practicable elementary science tests that are also good diagnostic instruments may be an unattainable ideal. Real learning comes in such fine increments that it slips through the coarse mesh of cognitive testing. After all, the vast body of research in methodology and curriculum shows that the comparative differences in learning, as these evaluative instruments measured, are insignificant. They may be *statistically* significant, but they are educationally unimportant.

Final Tests

Final examinations in elementary science have little to offer. They *may*, of course, provide extrinsic motivation because they affect final marks. They may also stimulate students to review the year's work; although this review, without previous learning, may be nothing more than a quickly forgotten cram. Yet final examinations mark the *end* of learning, not the beginning; they leave no opportunity for the teacher to guide the child, to provide feedback and stimulate relearning. Therefore final tests do not meet the criteria for wise evaluation in science.

Programmed Instruction[3]

Another source of evidence

The disparity between the implied freedom of process-centered instruction and the minutely detailed structure of programmed instruction weakens the value of conventionally written programs as the center of progressive elementary science instruction. However, programmed instruction can help in evaluation of pupils' failures and success. The teacher can observe children's behavior and note their modes of response to written questions; she can see that because of frequent errors a child is moving slowly, through the program's error–correction cycles. Programs stressing the various cognitive and affective abilities could supply even more valuable information, but few seem to be coming to the market. Nevertheless, because of continual sampling, conventional programs do improve assessment of the child's learning of facts and concepts as well as facilitate individual marking and grading. William D. Hedges, who has carried out the best-planned research studies of elementary school science programming, emphasizes this point:

> Teachers become more keenly aware of individual differences. For example, they become sensitive to the fact that the fast student who is on unit seven but who typically gets about 75 percent of the material on tests correct is not necessarily a more able student than the lad who is on unit four, but who is making well over 90 percent on his tests. How to grade at report time is, of course, a local problem. Some teachers have worked this out by dividing students into four quartiles on the basis of the speed or rate they work through the materials and then within these quartiles grade students with the usual A, B system. The card goes home to the parent saying that Susy May is in the top group in terms of speed, but her comprehension is low and perhaps she should slow down.[4]

Children evaluate

In addition to using programmed materials as an evaluative device, the teacher can periodically give written or oral tests. As soon as he finishes a section, the child measures himself against a subtest; on completion of the final subtest he takes the final test. The fact that children take the test only when they think they are ready and receive immediate feedback may well be the most important aspects of programmed instruction. Unfortunately programmed instruction depends on specification in detail of behavioral objectives, and all too often poorly written behavioral objectives means poorly written programs.

Evaluation of the Classroom Science Program

This chapter has presented a detailed rationale for the evaluation of children's learning in science together with a number of evaluative techniques and devices. Obviously both the rate of children's progress and the quality of their learning are desirable criteria for teaching success. But we should certainly add to these criteria the teacher's satisfaction, the children's interest and joy, the spontaneous and unexpected twists in the daily activities that were instructional bonuses. The teacher should certainly think hard about the difficulties the children encounter and the reasons for their setbacks, adding to this analysis an objective assessment of her own teaching, which calls for introspective imagination and ruthless self-criticism. The teacher should regularly examine her goals and methods, the variety and quality of firsthand experiences she and her children provide, and the value of the vicarious tools of teaching they use. The following checklist suggests evidence teachers should look for in judging their own teaching:[5]

I. In my teaching is there opportunity or provision for children to:

	None	Some	Much
A means for teacher evaluation (a) Raise questions and problems of importance or interest to them?	____	____	____
(b) Study these questions and problems?	____	____	____
(c) Help plan "things to do" in studying science problems?	____	____	____
(d) State clearly the problems on which they are working?	____	____	____

	None	Some	Much
(e) Make hypotheses to be tested?	___	___	___
(f) Gather accurate data (information) in a variety of ways:			
Through reading on the subject?	___	___	___
Through taking field trips?	___	___	___
Through watching demonstrations?	___	___	___
Through doing experiments?	___	___	___
Through talking to resource persons?	___	___	___
(g) Analyze the data (information) to see how it relates to the problem?	___	___	___
(h) Think about the applications of their science learnings to everyday living?	___	___	___
(i) Think about science relationships and processes instead of merely naming things and learning isolated facts?	___	___	___
(j) Bring science materials of different kinds to school for observation and study?	___	___	___
(k) Engage in individual science interests?	___	___	___

II. In my teaching do I periodically and systematically check on the children's growth in:

	None	Some	Much
(a) Ability to locate and define problems right around them?	___	___	___
(b) Acquiring information on the problem being studied?	___	___	___
(c) Ability to observe more accurately?	___	___	___
(d) Ability to make reports on or record their observations?	___	___	___
(e) Ability to solve problems?	___	___	___
(f) Ability to think critically?	___	___	___
(g) Ability to explain natural phenomena?	___	___	___
(h) Ability to distinguish between facts and fancies?	___	___	___
(i) Suspending judgment until evidence is collected?	___	___	___
(j) Being open-minded, or willing to change belief?	___	___	___
(k) Cooperating with others?	___	___	___

These checklists and suggestions help the teacher to analyze honestly and searchingly her daily classroom procedures. We might easily criticize them as representing a superficial and simplistic approach to a complicated network of cognitive, attitudinal, and methodological competence. Nevertheless a useful self-evaluative instrument must be short, general, and suggestive; not only does the teacher have little time to fill in a longer, more detailed evaluative scheme, but such a comprehensive scheme will inevitably become artificial and restrictive. The case for self-evaluation is strengthened by evidence that some teachers aware of modern science teaching objectives are unaware that they have not attained these objectives.[6]

Many teachers have not mastered the skills and knowledge required for modern elementary science programs, although nearly all these programs have sought to "teacher-proof" their curricula. Unfortunately unless she sticks to the specific prescriptions and detailed instructions of the program, the teacher will have difficulty handling questions and coping with new interests and suggestions. She must not panic! She too can learn!

The teacher should recognize strengths and weaknesses in the cognitive and affective behavior of children in the sciences. She should also be aware of her strengths and weaknesses. Institutions that prepare elementary teachers have not often provided opportunities for teachers to develop these insights and skills. Indeed a teacher can hardly be sensitive to a child's need and growth if she has never critically analyzed her own competence.[7]

Summary

Teachers should carefully consider the criteria of validity, reliability, and sampling for their own tests and those they take from other sources. Commercially prepared science tests usually furnish these data to test users. Programmed instruction in science holds some evaluative potential because the teacher can continuously monitor the children's progress and because the tests children take when they are ready provide quick self-diagnosis.

Teachers must also evaluate their own teaching and intellectual processes to improve their teaching. Tools for the purpose are perhaps even cruder than those for pupil assessment, but no other kind of evaluation is more promising for improving elementary school instruction.

For further study

1. To what extent are evaluations valid when based on the three domains of classroom learning and behavior (cognitive, affective, and psychomotor)?

Is this classification of classroom learning and behavior a valid organization of pupil behavior? (See appendix.)

2. For the affective and cognitive domains prepare at least two evaluation instruments—one for a primary level, one for an intermediate level—written in behavioral terms.

3. Construct a checklist that a teacher may use informally to evaluate a child's interests and aptitudes in science.

4. Observe and report on a science lesson in an elementary school and record the interactions according to the Flanders Interaction Analysis or one of the other analysis schemes.

5. Evaluate the adequacy of an elementary science program as a diagnostic self-teaching device for children.

6. Discuss how to determine the validity and reliability of an intermediate level objective examination; of a primary level objective examination read aloud by the teacher.

Notes and references

1. Cronbach, L. J., "Course Improvement through Evaluation," *Teachers College Record*, 64: 681, May 1963.

2. Watson, F., "Research on Teaching Science," in N. L. Gage, ed., *Handbook of Research on Teaching* (Chicago: Rand McNally, 1963), p. 1052.

3. For a witty and penetrating analysis of "The Mythology of Educational Innovation" to counterbalance some of the statements in this section, see Oettinger, A. G., and S. Marks, *Run, Computer, Run* (New York: Collier Books, 1971), Chaps. 3 and 4.

4. Hedges, W. D., "Teaching Science by Programing," *Science and Children*, 2: 23, October 1964.

5. Blackwood, P., "Teacher's Checklist in Elementary Science," in H. E. Tannenbaum et al., *Evaluation in Elementary School Science* (Washington, D.C.: Department of Health, Education and Welfare, Office of Education, 1964), OE–29057, Bulletin No. 757, pp. 56–57. See also *Evidences of a Good Science Program* (Washington, D.C.: U.S. Department of Health, Education and Welfare, Office of Education, 1963), OE–29051.

6. Richardson, E. C., "Proposals for Improvement of Science Teaching in New Jersey Elementary Schools," *Science Education*, 47: 302, April 1963.

7. Sharefkin, B. D., "The Relationship Between Elementary School Student Teachers' Science Abilities and Their Self Appraisals," *Science Education*, 47: 342–47, October 1963.

11

Experiencing Process Thinking

as preparation for process thinking this chapter presents practical experiences for use in a college elementary science laboratory; the experiments are not intended primarily for elementary school children, although children in the upper intermediate groups have tested them successfully. We have described the first experiment in detail and followed it with a shorter, partially structured problem, which you should complete as a practical exercise. This experiment is preparatory to a third group of problems, which you might explore in the laboratory.

We do not intend to prescribe experimental procedures; it is desirable to approach these problems by different routes, and if you obtain contradictory results, so much the better! The discovery of differences is a necessary part of intellectual searching. You should propose hypotheses and experiments to solve these problems. Reference to the criteria for planning experiments (see Chapter 6) will help you to evaluate "model" experiments and devise your own experiments. Intellectual analysis of scientific problems, by itself, is not enough to give the insight, understanding, and confidence necessary for the laboratory study of process instruction. Therefore you should take time to outline your plans in detail and work out the experimental consequences of these ideas, recording your successes and failures for later discussion and analysis.

Teach process after experiencing process

The Rusty-Nail Problem[1]

The following experiment is illustrative of one approach to a laboratory problem. In one form or other it has been tested in many intermediate grade and upper grade classes as well as in science-curriculum materials classes at the college level. Specific suggestions will help you understand how the "elements" of scientific thinking may be applied in defining a problem, analyzing cause-and-effect relationships, providing controls, recognizing and evaluating assumptions, formulating and validating hypotheses, collecting and interpreting data, and explaining related phenomena.

A sample process experience

The key idea of this problem is that some materials are better conductors of electricity than others. Let us assume that in your class, which is studying electricity, a child has asked why the wires connected to the dry cells are made of copper. Will other kinds of wires work as well? This question is a starting point for an experimental study of conductivity.

Limiting the problem

Because it is impossible to test every kind of wire, the experiment must be limited to easily obtained materials, such as common nails. Nails, of course, are not usually used in electrical circuits for reasons which become obvious as the activity continues; neither are they "wires" in the customary sense. Different diameters and lengths of copper, aluminum, and iron wire are clearly more suitable choices, but testing them may require equipment not ordinarily available in the classroom. Therefore inquiry into the conductivity of common nails serves both as an example of simple research and as an introduction to some of the important concepts of electrical conductivity. It also involves some "dubious" assumptions.

Formulating the problem

The question "Do all nails conduct electricity equally well?" is a clear, reasonably specific statement of the problem. Because the problem is simple, the experiment should provide uncomplicated answers. By limiting the problem to testing *conductivity* in nails, you decrease the number of variables and minimize certain manipulative difficulties. In addition the problem is well within the intellectual grasp of intermediate grade children and requires neither expensive apparatus nor impossible feats of manipulation.

Proposing hypotheses

Having formulated an initial statement of the problem, you should then propose one or more tentative hypotheses that will not only answer the question but permit an evaluation of this answer from the experimental data. You should state these hypotheses so that the class can accept or reject them on the basis of the information from the experiment. This requirement is easy to state, but it is not always so easy to fulfill. Let us consider two hypotheses: (1) *All* common nails conduct electricity equally well, regardless of kind, size, or condition. (2) Nails do not conduct electricity. The hypothesis that nails do not conduct electricity is perhaps the first one to investigate because it is easily tested. If the representative nails do not conduct electricity, we have immediately solved the problem. This result is informative and directive because it prevents our wasting further time. It is also typical of many research projects, which, although they yield negative results, are still valuable in that they tell us what does *not* work.

Let us assume that this negative hypothesis is incorrect and that we must return to the first hypothesis. The obvious technique is to try to force an electric current through the nails and then to measure the amount of current that passes through each. The experimental apparatus for testing both hypotheses is presumably the same. The electrical source, the connections, and the system for measuring current strength are all important. These elements should introduce no new variables. They should be easy to manipulate, safe, reliable, and inexpensive. Figure 1 indicates a circuit setup.

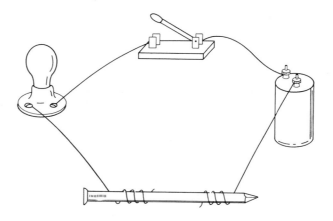

Figure 1

Source of current

The source of electricity must be powerful enough to pass a measurable current through each nail. A 110-volt alternating current (ordinary house current) is much too dangerous for elementary school experimentation. Dry cells are an excellent substitute, and a number six (1½-volt) dry cell is suitable. A quantity of these cells should be on hand to provide for increasing the current flow during the course of the experiment.

Electrical connections

The connection from the nail to the dry cell depends on two important factors. First some kind of conductor must bridge the gap between the dry cell and the nail; second this conductor must be connected to the nail. Because the function of the conductor is to permit the flow of electricity to the nail, we can use insulated copper bell wire, which is inexpensive and a good conductor of electricity. The insulation on the wire will materially lessen the possibility of a short circuit in the apparatus. Actually the choice of electrical conductor is not critical as long as enough current for the purpose of the experiment flows through the conductor and the current does not change as a result of heating or any other process within the conductor itself. For example, a wire that is too narrow may cause overheating, which will reduce the current flow and complicate the experiment. The choice of bell wire for the experiment illustrates the application of previous knowledge to specific problems. We can easily test the value of bell wire by substituting a length of bell wire for the nail. This procedure also gives us a standard for comparing the conduction of the nails with the conduction of the copper bell wire.

Besides connecting the wire to the dry cell, we must connect it to the nail without damaging the nail. Alligator clips provide effective contact, but they have relatively sharp jaws and may mar the surface of the nail. Therefore we merely wrap the bare ends of wire tightly around the ends of the nail, even though the relatively poor contact may reduce the current flow. A length of friction or vinyl electrician's tape wrapped around each connection helps to improve the contact. Here again we assume that the experimental method does not significantly alter the conductivity of the nail. Throughout the course of this problem we should be aware of a number of implicit or explicit assumptions, even though within the framework of this experiment we cannot test their effect. The validity of the results are, in large measure, dependent on recognition of these assumptions.

An assumption

Measurement of current strength

Some device for measuring the strength of the current that passes through the nail is necessary because the strength of the current is an index of the ability of the nail to conduct electricity. The ammeter, which is used to measure current strength, gives accurate and reproducible results. But because this piece of equipment is expensive and easily damaged, the ammeter probably will not be available in elementary schools. A flashlight bulb also serves as a practical, although less accurate, indicator of current. The bulb shines brightly if enough current flows and does not shine if the current flow is too low. Assuming that brightness is directly related to current strength, we can judge the strength of the current by the brightness of the bulb. For example, if the bulb is brighter with nail two than with nail four, then we assume that nail two passes more current than does nail four.

More assumptions

At this point we accept several other assumptions: the bulb will light if the current is strong enough; the strength of the dry cell does not change with use (for example, does not become weaker); changes in brightness of the bulb are the result of differences in conductivity of the test nails. If the dry cell is not constant, the results will be misleading because the measurements will reflect changes in the strength of the current source as well as in the kinds of nails. Another assumption is that the direction of current flow in the circuit is immaterial. We can test this assumption by reversing the connections to the terminals of the dry cell.

Testing experimental variables

Experimenters are especially interested in finding out what happens when they test the experimental variables. In this experiment we examine the conductivity of different kinds of nails. We should have an assortment of nails—shiny, dull, rusty, headless, thin, thick, short, long; steel, copper, brass, aluminum, and so forth—all of which are available in hardware stores. We should also keep a systematic record of the different nails and their effect on bulb brightness to organize and interpret the data. Figure 2 shows one kind of chart used for this purpose.

Degree of Conductivity of Nails as Shown by Estimation of Relative Brightness

Description of Nail	Very Bright	Medium Bright	Low Brightness	No Light
Shiny 2″ nail	✔			
Shiny 3″ nail	✔			
Shiny 5″ nail	✔			
Rusty 2″ nail				✔
Rusty 3″ nail				✔
Rusty 5″ nail			✔	
Shiny headless 2″ nail	✔			
Rusty headless 2″ nail				✔

Figure 2

Examination of these data indicates possible significant relationships. The condition of the surface of the nails appears to affect the amount of current the nails carry. These data are incomplete in the sense that the nails are alike in only one respect—the experimental variable. Yet this experiment does not require such a sophisticated analysis, so the simple method is suitable. A clear presentation of data helps you to understand and interpret the results and is therefore indispensible.

Rejecting hypotheses

Should we reject the original hypotheses? We must, of course, discard the hypothesis that common nails do not conduct electricity because of contradictory data. We must also discard the hypothesis that all kinds of common nails conduct electricity equally well because of the refuting evidence. We have now solved the originally proposed problem but in a rather unsatisfactory way because we have left unexplained the obvious differences in conductivity. Therefore we must propose an alternative hypothesis based on these experimental observations to account for these differences. Does rust on the nails

Recording data

affect the conductivity? From the chart we note that the rusty five-inch nail shows some conductivity. Is this effect a result of its greater length or of its coating of rust? How can we test these possibilities? One way is to compare two rusty nails that are alike in every way but length. We can test the possibility that the copper wire connected to the nail has worn away enough rust so that some flow of current takes place by changing the way the nail is connected into the circuit.

In much the same way we can also test other factors, such as the diameter of the nails and their chemical composition (aluminum, soft steel, or iron). Obviously we can extend the experiment far beyond the bounds of the original question.

One of the most important reasons for experimentation is to provide test data from which to derive conclusions and predictions. Once he has proposed predictions about electrical conductivity, the experimenter may begin another cycle of experimentation whereby he transforms predictions into hypotheses. For example, if he has not tested aluminum nails in the original experiment, the experimenter can plan an experiment for this purpose and can make predictions about the conductivity of the nails. He may find that aluminum nails, whatever their length, do not carry electricity. However, he would be more likely to suppose that aluminum nails are good conductors of electricity. Certainly if he has eliminated length as a significant variable in the earlier experiment, then this factor is unlikely to be important in the conductivity of aluminum nails. The experimenter can easily think of an experiment to test this hypothesis. Eventually he will propose, test, and either accept or reject a number of hypotheses. He will probably reject the majority.

Accepting a hypothesis   The accepted hypotheses are as valid as the experiments on which they are based. To the extent that the nails tested are representative and the experimental design has eliminated extraneous variables, answers to the questions originally proposed have some degree of validity. However, overextension of the generalizations that emerge from such limited experiments as the rusty-nail experiment would be most unwise.

Process Skills and the Rusty-Nail Experiment

Using process skills   The solution of the rusty-nail experimental problem calls for the application of a number of process skills. For example, the experiment started with a problem: Will other kinds of wires work as well as copper wires? Because we did not use wires that would seem to be the logical test materials (is the reason a valid one?), we substituted another metallic material. We often encounter substitutions of this kind in scientific studies provided the two situations are still analogous. Having chosen nails, we restated the problem in the form of a question that could be answered as precisely as possible. (This step is called *delimiting* the problem.) We proposed several testable hypotheses, with the limitations of our electrical circuit. We evaluated each of the components in the experimental apparatus to find out whether the component would affect the experiment in an undesirable way. We then studied and evaluated the underlying assumptions insofar as possible and recorded the experimental data on a simple chart so that we could compare the conductivity of each nail in a qualitative way. From the data we tested the hypotheses and either accepted or rejected them. We then made new predictions that led to further experimentation.

A Problem in Heat Loss[2]

Importance of a conceptual scheme   Science instruction at the elementary level aims at providing children with a sufficient variety of experiences and analyses of these experiences so that the children begin to perceive the existence of a conceptual framework in science and to make sense of scientific facts, principles, and theories. Theories of heat and their applications are striking examples of the value of conceptual schemes. Modern heat theory is a powerful tool for interpreting the endless variety of heat phenomena. Of course, a teacher may plunge her children into a textbook unit on heat, but such an approach to the physics of heat is almost certain to be a waste of time if children lack the concrete experience to extract meaning from the textbook.

We have selected as a topic for investigation the ability of different materials to conduct or retard the flow of heat, and we ask, "Are all materials equally good heat conductors?" Adopting the conductor–insulator terminology

Proposing hypotheses used in heat transfer studies, we can propose at least two hypotheses: (1) there is little or no difference in the insulating ability of materials; (2) some insulators are much better than others. Most students eliminate the first hypothesis on the basis of previous knowledge. At any rate testing the second hypothesis will confirm or deny the validity of the first hypothesis. To test the second hypothesis we must select appropriate materials. In addition we must devise some reliable and controllable way to measure the rate at which these materials conduct heat. Because good insulators transfer heat slowly, a substance at a high temperature should cool slowly if we cover it with a good insulator and

Testing the hypotheses heat quickly if we cover it with a poor insulator. We must also be able to measure the amount of heat retained or lost during a specified time period so that we can make comparisons between the different insulators.

Because temperature is an indicator of heat content, the temperature of a heat source surrounded by the test insulators, taken at regular intervals, should reflect the rate of heat loss through the insulators. The quicker the temperature drops, the less effective the insulator. The assumption that temperature is a direct measure of heat content is valid only in certain cases.

In this experiment we use an instrument called a calorimeter, which holds a known weight of hot or cold water whose temperature change depends on the rate at which the water loses or gains heat. Figure 3 illustrates this apparatus.

We fill the larger outer container with the insulating test material. The types of materials are limitless—water, air, iron filings, ground cork, sand, styrofoam, fiberglass wool, wood shavings, and so forth. The size of the particles of insulating material may affect the ability of the material to retard

Experimental details the flow of heat. Pebbles, for example, may make an excellent insulator; but if they fit so loosely that large air spaces are present, we may be testing the insulating ability of air rather than pebbles. Therefore we should be sure to fill the outer container with as much of the test material as possible, excluding anything else to the best of our ability. Some test materials—styrofoam, for example—may contain a considerable amount of air, and the results may be a composite of the insulating capacity of air and of the test material.

The small container, which is embedded in the test insulator, is the high temperature source. We should conduct the experiment with at least two pieces of apparatus, one of which serves as a control. We pour hot water into the inner container *C* and cover the container immediately with a cardboard

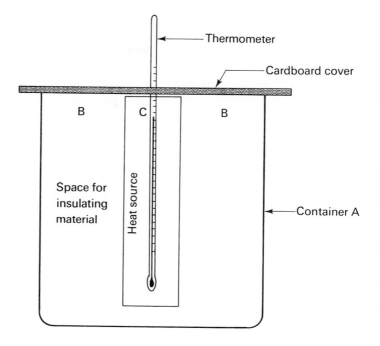

Figure 3

through which we have inserted a thermometer. To judge the relative efficiency of each material in retaining heat, we compare the rate of temperature decrease for each. If the rate of decrease is approximately the same for all the insulators, we have verified our first hypothesis. If the rate of decrease is consistently different from material to material, our second hypothesis is probably correct.

Refining the experiment

We must still refine the experiment, however, to reach a justifiable conclusion. At the beginning of each trial (how many trials for each material?) the inner container must hold the same quantity of heat. Equal quantities of water in the same kind of containers (does the shape of the inner vessel affect the rate of conduction?) at the same initial temperature satisfies this condition. Water boils at approximately 212 degrees Fahrenheit. Although atmospheric pressure affects the boiling point, pressure variation should be negligible provided we carry out the experiment in a reasonably short time. The temperature of boiling water is relatively constant; therefore, if we use equal volumes of water, the quantity of heat should be constant. A large container of boiling water stored close at hand is an excellent source of constant temperature water.

Suppose, however, that we use a standard measuring cup to transfer the boiling water to the test container. If the cup is initially at room temperature, its temperature will rise as it is filled with boiling water. If the measuring cup is still warm when the second trial begins, the hot water in container *C* will be at a higher temperature than it was in the first trial. Why? One way to minimize this difference is to begin the experiment with two or more measuring cups. The temperature drop of the water should then be relatively constant in each. As a substitute for the cup we can use a long-handled ladle immersed in boiling water and therefore at a temperature of 212 degrees Fahrenheit. If we return the ladle to the boiling water for a few minutes after each filling of the calorimeter, the ladle will remain at the desired temperature. There are other ways to eliminate these heat transfer losses, but no matter which method we use we should try to maintain equal starting temperatures.

We can conveniently tabulate, in chart form, the temperature readings taken at equal time intervals. Figure 4 is an example. The time intervals are five minutes; the temperatures for each insulator are indicated on the appropriate line.

Recording the data

Insulating material	Temperature at 5-minute intervals					
Water	96	91	86	81	77	72
Air						
Cork	96	93	90	87	83	80
Sand						
Fiberglass wool						
Iron filings						
Wood shavings						

Figure 4

Should we reject the first hypothesis? The insulators differ significantly in their ability to conduct heat, but we must decide whether these differences could be caused by chance or random errors. Assuming, however, that all the

Accepting a hypothesis variables except the test insulators are kept reasonably constant, we are persuaded on the basis of the consistent differences to accept the second hypothesis.

This experiment is appropriate for several reasons. The materials are simple, inexpensive, and safe. The experiment is fairly easy to control and duplicate, although it necessitates the cautious use of boiling water.

Process Skills and the Heat Loss Experiment

As in the rusty-nail experiment, we examined the assumptions and the dependent and independent variables in turn, estimated their effects, and summarized the data on a simple chart. However, in this more quantitative experiment we used a controlled procedure of measurement to obtain the data for testing the two hypotheses. Using such a procedure we could better identify the causative factor and obtain a more valid answer to the problem. We also adapted techniques and made decisions more often because of the elaborate apparatus and dissimilar test materials.

Applying process skills In both experiments we based our inferences on measurements. In the rusty-nail experiment we inferred that when the bulb is bright, a strong electric current is flowing through the circuit, and we therefore assumed that the test nail is a good conductor. In the heat loss experiment we inferred that cork is a good insulator as compared to air because the temperature drop in equal time periods is less with cork than with air. If we were to repeat the experiment a number of times, and if the same results were obtained, we would feel reasonably secure in accepting the hypothesis that some insulators are better than others (at least within the limits of the experiment itself and the general set of conditions under which it is run). We could, if we chose, even rank them in some kind of order from best to worst with some confidence, but again with the realization that this generalization is limited to these materials under these conditions.

A Partially Structured Investigation

The analysis of the following experiment is purposely sketchy so that you may plan and carry out the experiment, thinking up some of your own hypotheses, assumptions, and conclusions.

Electromagnets[3]

Magnetic phenomena are often difficult for children to understand. This point should not surprise us because acceptable scientific explanations developed slowly from many years of struggle with the chaos of natural phenomena. On the other hand children easily observe the physical effects of magnetism. The first level of understanding comes from informal play with magnets. Children soon realize that not many magnetic materials exist and that interactive effects identify these materials. With increasing conceptual maturity children accept the existence of some invisible force, which fills the space between the magnet and the object it attracts. Magnetic field interaction is a concept, a theoretical proposition defined by the physical evidence of attraction and by the effort required to separate the magnet and the magnetic object. Magnetic force is so intriguing and of such scientific importance that it can serve as a conceptual center for many experiments in elementary science.

An important conceptual scheme

The relationship between an electrical current and the magnetic field it generates can also add to the educational potential of magnetism. The common doorbell is an example of electromagnetic interaction. The current flowing through a coil of wire in the doorbell generates a magnetic field, which in turn interacts with a metal "hammer" that rings the bell. The energy of electrons in motion transforms into mechanical energy.

In the following experiment we can investigate several of these electromagnetic relationships. Let us assume that an electromagnet is made from a coil of wire wound around an iron core. Several questions about this simple apparatus should come to mind. Must the core be iron? Can other metals be substituted without affecting the strength of the magnet? Will more turns of wire affect the strength of the electromagnet? The setup shown in Figure 5 is helpful in studying these possibilities.

The metal bars differ only in composition. What effect will changing the bar have on the strength of an electromagnetic field? We can test our hypotheses by passing an electric current through the wire coiled around each bar.

Some assumptions

Several assumptions underlie this experiment. For example, current flow must be constant. In Figure 5 the source of current is a dry cell. Dry cells, however, run down with use. Despite this limitation they are almost mandatory for elementary school experimentation because they are safe and convenient. As with the rusty-nail experiment, a decrease in current flow from a weak dry cell leads to unexpected results. What are some of the other assumptions?

Testing the hypotheses

To gather enough "quantitative" data to test our hypotheses we must include some way of making quantitative measurements. Figure 6 illustrates a technique for measuring the relative strength of each electromagnet. This

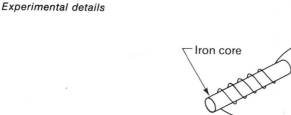

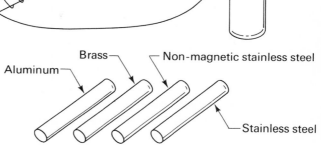

Iron core

Aluminum
Brass
Non-magnetic stainless steel
Stainless steel

Figure 5

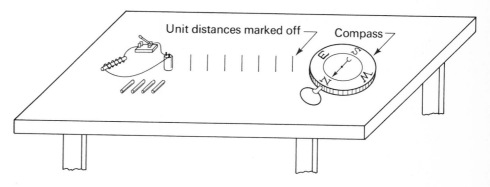

Unit distances marked off
Compass

Figure 6

A suggested procedure

arrangement is easy to set up; yet because it is quite sensitive, certain precautions are necessary to obtain reliable results. For example, the arrangement should be exactly the same in each trial. The orientation of the electromagnet should also be the same each time. We move the compass slowly toward the electromagnet until the needle barely quivers when we turn on the current. Thus we assume that the greater the distance of the compass from the electromagnet when the needle quivers, the greater the strength of the magnet.

Effects of the variables

There are other ways to measure magnetic strength, which provide an instructive exercise in experimental ingenuity.

With this apparatus we can also test other variables governing the strength of electromagnets. For example, what will happen if we increase the number of turns of wire around the core? Will the strength of the magnetic field change measurably if we wind these coils tightly? Loosely? If the wire is uninsulated? What will happen if we increase the current flow by connecting two or more dry cells in a series. Does the diameter of the wire, the kind of wire, or the type of insulation change the strength of the electromagnet?

You should perform this experiment yourself as a practical exercise. State the problem clearly, list the hypotheses and assumptions, organize the data, and show their pertinence for accepting or rejecting your hypotheses. As a final step be sure your acceptable hypotheses lead to a prediction or explanation of related magnetic phenomena.

Suggestions for Investigation

Try your own experimental search

Each of the following physical science topics leads to at least one fascinating inquiry. Based on the information in the discussion you should state the problem, propose one or more hypotheses, and think up an experiment to test these hypotheses. To plan your experiment as efficiently and carefully as possible you may find you will need to refer to the suggested reference sources for additional information. Do not be disappointed if the results are confusing or if the experiment fails to work as you expect; rethink your design and expected outcome. Investigators frequently encounter failure in scientific research. Only in the dry routine of verification experiences is success guaranteed.

Heat conductivity[4]

Young children soon learn not to touch hot metallic objects without taking precautions. At home the housewife usually handles a hot pot with a cloth potholder, but she knows that in a short time even the potholder will become unbearably hot. Some potholders take a longer time to heat up than do others. Compare the insulating efficiency of different kinds of potholders. Define the assumptions and variables in this experiment and plan the necessary controls within the limits of convenient experimentation.

Suppose you are given the task of finding out whether copper, aluminum, or iron pots cool off most rapidly. How will you phrase the problem? What hypotheses will guide your experimentation? What assumptions do you recognize? What variables should you control? How will you record the data? When you come to some conclusion as to the relative efficiencies of the different kinds of heat conductors, verify your results from a table of heat conductivity in a standard physics textbook.

Air pressure[5]

We frequently misinterpret physical phenomena that depend on atmospheric pressure. For example, consider the experiment, described in Chapter 4, in which a glass tumbler filled with water is covered with a card, and the entire system of tumbler, water, and card is inverted. A reasonable expectation is that the water will pour out of the glass; however, reason is not *always* a sound guide in experimentation. The water remains in the glass, held in by a more or less tightly adhering card. If the glass is half filled with water and the experiment repeated, the same thing happens. Surely in the latter case the pressure of the air trapped in the glass is equal to the pressure of the air outside the glass. The total force pushing the card down must be equal to the sum of the air pressure inside the glass and the water pressure; this total is obviously greater than the external air pressure, which is presumably holding the card in place. What holds the card on?

Investigation of these forces is an interesting, although somewhat damp, experiment. Try odd-shaped glass containers, polyethylene and styrene jars, liquids other than water, and a variety of covers in your research. You may not come to a valid conclusion about the different forces that hold the card in place, but you will profit from this experience because of the opportunity to try out your skills in inquiry.

Wetting agents[6]

The rather surprising characteristics of liquid surfaces provide many opportunities for simple laboratory experimentation. Students are often astonished when the teacher "miraculously" floats a razor blade or a needle in a container of water. The object "floats," they learn, because the surface tension of water is sufficiently high to hold a dense metal object on a "skin" of water. Actually, floating is not a proper description because a floating object displaces its own weight of water. In the case of the razor blade or the needle close examination of the downward bulge in the water surface dispels the notion that the object has displaced enough water to float.

If a surface tension "skin" is responsible, decreasing the surface tension should make floating the razor blade more difficult. Wetting agents, such as detergents, decrease surface tension forces in water. Based on this information, plan an experiment to change the surface tension of water systematically and draw reliable conclusions about the effect of wetting agents from the data.

Kinetic energy[7]

Objects of different mass, falling from the same height above the ground, strike the ground with the same velocity but with different kinetic energies. It is difficult to measure the velocity of falling objects because of experimental complications, but it is relatively easy to measure the kinetic energy of falling objects and to compare these measured kinetic energies with predictions from theory.

The track in Figure 7 is a seven-foot piece of wooden cove molding, available at any lumber yard. A thoroughly moistened piece of molding, left to dry as illustrated, will hold this shape for a number of days. By rolling marbles down the track, you can obtain the quantitative data necessary to calculate the kinetic energy of each marble. How can you use this apparatus to measure the kinetic energy of falling (rolling) balls?

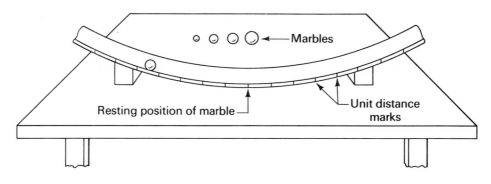

Figure 7

The Biological Sciences

Students are often misled by the ease with which they seem to learn biological principles and concepts. Their familiarity with individual organisms and with the biological systems of which these organisms are a part lulls them into the belief that biology is the least difficult science. The emphasis on biology in so many elementary science curricula is in part a result of this seeming simplicity. This attitude on the part of children and adults is not in accord with the comprehensive theoretical structure of scientific biology.

Biology is a complex of sciences

The experimental activities in this section are organized into a rather loose conceptual framework. None of the experiments suggested in this chapter is complete unless the data and conclusions are shown to be natural consequences of one or more of the themes and schemes of the sciences. If the framework of themes and schemes is functional, you should be able to fit into it each bit of information and each biological idea.

For the purposes of this chapter we have divided the subject matter of the biological sciences into the general classes of animal behavior, animal structure, plant behavior, plant structure, and interrelationships. The fifth class is important because behavior and structure become meaningful through knowledge of biological interrelationships. By the term *interrelationships* we mean the mutual effects of living organisms on their environment. Ecology is another name for this interaction of the physical and biological environment.

A plant is more than the sum of its cell-tissue and vessel arrangement, growth behavior, mode of germination, and adaptations for survival. It is also an inhabitant of an environment in which the underlying rock strata, the soil, the weather, and the native plants and animals have shaped its life course. We must somehow blend the individual disciplines, which collectively we call *biology,* into a unity, which is the organism habitat. Without the habitat we cannot know the individual; without the individual the habitat is barren.

In performing the investigations of this section you should fit the information you gather into an ecological framework. This task is not easy because ecology is still a relatively uncharted domain. Perhaps the nearest approximation is to match the facts and concepts you discover with the relevant ecological schemes and the arbitrary framework of the aforementioned classes.

Seed germination[8]

Questions about the sprouting of seeds

Let us turn to an investigation of the plant seed and its germination and subsequent growth. There are numerous questions we might consider about seed germination. Does the orientation of the seed matter? What parts of the seed are necessary for germination? What environmental factors inhibit or accelerate germination? Are there significant differences in the rates of germination of different seeds?

These are only a few of the questions we might study using simple experimental procedures. Consider, for example, the question about position of the seed. If the seed is placed upside down in an environment in which normal growth is possible, will its germination and growth be similar to that of a seed planted right-side up? For this question to have any meaning we must define *up* and *down;* preliminary tests of seed germination should provide enough information for an empirical definition.

From the standpoint of experimentation we can easily answer the second question. Each of the many different kinds of seeds has a covering of some kind, an embryo plant, and stored food. Therefore in each seed we can remove various structures and parts of structures. In the lima bean, which is botanically a seed, there are the cotyledons ("seed leaves"), which store the food for the embryo, the testa, which is the external covering of the seed, and the embryo plant.

Are the cotyledons necessary for germination, or do they serve some other function? What will happen if we remove one of the cotyledons? If we remove the right cotyledon of a lima bean, will the seed germinate differently than if we had removed the left cotyledon? What will happen if we remove the seed coat?

Students usually suggest that water, light, and soil are essential for germination. The teacher can easily devise experiments for testing these environmental variables. She can also expand these experiments to consider the effects of chemicals, such as salt, sugar, and fertilizers, added to the water. Is air necessary? Will a seed germinate in boiled water, which removes dissolved air? We can propose an almost endless number of hypotheses about seed germination, which are testable in the laboratory without expensive or complex apparatus. Of course we must control each experiment, examining only one variable and discerning some relationship between cause and effect. How many seeds of each kind make up a reliable sample so that the results are not attributable to such factors as defective seed or genetic variations?

Once germination has begun, many other variables affect plant growth. How much light must the plant receive? Is there a minimum amount of light necessary for growth? Are there differences in the rate of growth with different kinds of light or with different intensities? Figure 8 illustrates an experiment for testing the effect of light direction on plant growth.

The box in which the plant is growing gets the light only from the hole in the side. If we assume that the limited air circulation within the box does not affect temperature and if other factors are constant, the growth is presumably the result of the intensity *and* the direction of the light illuminating the plant. To justify our conclusion we should properly control the experiment, using another box identical in every way except for the direction from which the light comes. Of course, if we have good reason to believe that the only im-

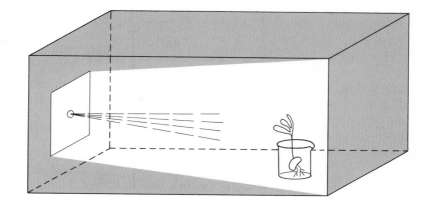

Figure 8

portant variable is the direction of light, then we may dispense with the control. This apparatus is also useful for comparing different species of plants.

The results of these experiments are interesting and informative. Yet, more important, these experiments lead to growth in experience and skill in planning and carrying through real investigations. From a pedagogical point of view the scientific facts and concepts that emerge from experimentation with seeds are important in understanding certain biological schemes and therefore in comprehending the structure of science. But practice in the kind of thinking and doing involved in simple scientific experimentation is of much greater significance than the knowledge gained.

A hypothesis to test

To enlarge on the role of the laboratory in inquiry teaching let us restate one of the original questions: Will lima beans from which entire structures or parts of structures are removed germinate as well as normal lima beans? We choose as our hypothesis this statement: Seeds that have physically been changed by removing some component part will germinate as well as unchanged seeds. In this sense we interpret the phrase *as well as* to mean as quickly, in approximately equal numbers, and with the same vigor. We may remove one or both cotyledons, the testa, the embryo, or smaller segments of these structures. The samples should be representative and as nearly alike as possible. Random sampling will help to ensure homogeneity provided a sufficiently large quantity of lima beans is available and selection is truly random. By inspection we can match the lima beans at least in outward appearance.

A controlled experiment

We plant experimental and control seeds under similar conditions, keeping continuous record of the length of time for each seed to germinate as well as the height and the rate of growth of the hypocotyl or the roots (whichever is more convenient). According to our hypothesis we might expect that if un-mutilated seeds germinate in approximately three days, the experimental seeds would take about the same time. If the altered seeds do not germinate in this time, the hypothesis is incorrect provided *as well as* means as quickly. On the other hand the conclusion that these seeds cannot germinate at all because of their physical condition is unjustified. The seeds may take as much as ten days to sprout. Perhaps only a few will germinate in three days, a few more in five days, and none after that. Even if many of these altered seeds fail to germinate, as is likely, injury to the seed is not necessarily the real cause. We may have chosen defective seeds, or the growth conditions may be sufficiently different to prevent sprouting. Repetition of the experiment with an increase in the sample size will increase confidence in the validity of the results, but we should expand conclusions beyond the experimental bounds. Even if it is valid for the lima beans, the hypothesis may not be valid for other kinds of seeds.

Although rather imprecise, this experiment is valuable because of its simplicity: It is not complicated by chemical tests. The apparatus is simple and unsophisticated. Measurement of growth rate is fairly easy, although precision is surely not great. Semiquantitative, or even qualitative, growth differences are probably sufficient to test the different hypotheses.

Assumptions

We have not discussed in detail most of the underlying assumptions in this experiment. They relate to the energy of light absorbed in photosynthesis, the various media in which the seeds germinate, sampling procedures, temperature effects, and adequacy of controls.

Many desirable and practical explorations of plant behavior do not easily yield quantitative data. Questions about the path of water conduction through stems or roots, leaf transpiration (evaporation through leaves), rate of leaf wilting, water loss in plants, swelling of seeds due to water absorption, excretion of carbon dioxide by plants, absorption of oxygen by seeds, and production of starch in plant leaves are problems better treated qualitatively than quantitatively.[9]

An additional problem

Let us consider this question: In what direction does absorbed water in plant stems move? Figure 9 illustrates an experimental arrangement for investigating this problem.

The hazards of experimentation with living organisms are well illustrated here. If the stem is a celery stalk (which, botanically speaking, is a petiole — a segment that supports the leaf — and is not a stem), the intake and movement of water is slow unless the stalk is fresh. The experiment may fail without your knowing why. The reason for failure may be that a decreased rate of water absorption resulted because the celery was not fresh, or it may be that a much more complicated chain of events is involved. If we prescribe in minute detail

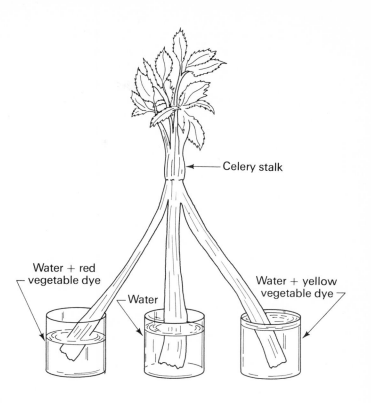

Figure 9

the route to experimental success, we will deprive you of the challenge and value of experimentation. On the other hand, from a practical viewpoint, teachers and students should not have to rediscover all knowledge, important and unimportant, on which the success of these experiments rests. Therefore we have suggested fresh celery in this experiment and have illustrated one kind of experimental apparatus for the purpose. Many other kinds of plant stems and roots are testable in the same way.

Partially Structured Investigations

An exercise in comparative anatomy[10]

Everyone knows that various species of fish in an aquarium differ in many ways. On the basis of gross characteristics—length at maturity, color markings, location and shape of fins, and overall physical form—we can distinguish

*An exercise in
observation*

the angelfish from the goldfish. By close study we can easily add more subtle differences—the way scales overlap, the number of rows of scales, the shape and appearance of scales, the position of the eyes, and the relative size of the mouth—to the external and internal structures and behavioral characteristics. Is the air bladder of comparable size in different species? Are their swimming motions comparable? Are they bottom feeders?

Additional questions come to mind: Is there any relationship between the number of appendages of fish and that of dogs? Does the fish have more or fewer appendages? Are these appendages alike in any way other than in function? Knowledge of these (and other) characteristic differences is necessary to differentiate systematically between fish and dogs. We speak of differences, but there are also similarities we should consider.

Louis Agassiz, a Swiss-born zoologist, was probably the best-known scientist in the United States during the nineteenth century. He always started his students on their graduate careers with exercises on comparative anatomy. Nathaniel Shaler, who became dean of the scientific school at Harvard College, has left an amusing description of his struggles with Agassiz's discovery-teaching procedures:

Is there a moral here?

> When I sat me down before my tin pan, Agassiz brought me a small fish, placing it before me with the rather stern requirement that I should study it, but should on no account talk to any one concerning it, nor read anything relating to fishes, until I had his permission so to do. To my inquiry, "What shall I do?" he said in effect: "Find out what you can without damaging the specimen; when I think that you have done the work I will question you." In the course of an hour I thought I had compassed that fish; it was rather an unsavory object, giving forth the stench of old alcohol, then loathsome to me, though in time I came to like it. Many of the scales were loosened so that they fell off. It appeared to me to be a case for a summary report, which I was anxious to make and get on to the next stage of the business. But Agassiz, though always within call, concerned himself no further with me that day, nor the next, nor for a week. At first, this neglect was distressing; but I saw that it was a game, for he was, as I discerned rather than saw, covertly watching me. So I set my wits to work upon the thing, and in the course of a hundred hours or so thought I had done much—a hundred times as much as seemed possible at the start. I got interested in finding out how the scales went in series, their shape, the form and placement of the teeth, etc. Finally, I felt full of the subject, and probably expressed it in my bearing; as for words about it then, there were none from my master except his cheery "Good morning." At length, on the seventh day, came the question, "Well?" and my disgorge of learning to him as he sat on the edge of my table puffing his cigar. At the end

of the hour's telling, he swung off and away saying: "That is not right." Here I began to think that, after all, perhaps the rules for scanning Latin verse were not the worst infliction in the world. Moreover, it was clear that he was playing a game with me to find if I were capable of doing hard, continuous work without the support of a teacher, and this stimulated me to labor. I went at the task anew, discarded my first notes, and in another week of ten hours a day labor I had results which astonished myself and satisfied him. Still there was no trace of praise in words or manner. He signified that it would do by placing before me about a half a peck of bones, telling me to see what I could make of them, with no further directions to guide me. I soon found that they were the skeletons of half a dozen fishes of different species; the jaws told me so much at a first inspection. The task evidently was to fit the separate bones together in their proper order. Two months or more went to this task with no other help than an occasional looking over my grouping with the stereotyped remark: "That is not right." Finally, the task was done, and I was again set upon alcoholic specimens—this time a remarkable lot of specimens representing, perhaps, twenty species of the side-swimmers or Pleuronectidae.

I shall never forget the sense of power in dealing with things which I felt in beginning the more extended work on a group of animals. I had learned the art of comparing objects, which is the basis of the naturalist's work. At this stage I was allowed to read, and to discuss my work with others about me. I did both eagerly, and acquired a considerable knowledge of the literature of ichthyology, becoming especially interested in the system of classification, then most imperfect. I tried to follow Agassiz's scheme of division into the order of ctenoids and ganoids, with the result that I found one of my species of side-swimmers had cycloid scales on one side and ctenoid on the other. This not only shocked my sense of the value of classification in a way that permitted of no full recovery of my original respect for the process, but for a time shook my confidence in my master's knowledge. At the same time I had a malicious pleasure in exhibiting my "find" to him, expecting to repay in part the humiliation which he had evidently tried to inflict on my conceit. To my question as to how the nondescript should be classified he said: "My boy, there are now two of us who know that."[11]

New investigations   Comparative studies of animals do not have to come from postmortem dissections, which demand manipulative skill. For example, consider a study of the different kinds of fish scales—form, size, shape, and arrangement. The comparative approach, so typical of the methods of nineteenth century zoology, is as useful for certain students (not all college students fall under its spell!) today as it was a hundred years ago for scientists. The possibilities of extending comparative investigation are almost endless. For example, there are obvious differences between the hair of dogs and that of rabbits as well as enormous variations in the hair of different breeds of dogs. Is beagle hair uniform in shape and color? Is there one preferred direction of growth? Is this direction the same on other beagles? From other characteristic features can you identify a strand of beagle hair? If you prepare an identification key for dog hair, can you positively identify a dog on the evidence of the hair alone? In a somewhat romantic and farfetched analogy think of yourself as a detective who must identify a few animal hairs to solve a crime. (How do you know they are not human hairs?)

The suggestions for investigation in this section do not satisfy the criteria for scientific experimentation. They are studies in comparative anatomy, and the data come from close observation. Although they are descriptive, the activities are of no less value. The student can test ideas concerning cause-and-effect relationships by experimentation, but the ideas must first come from knowledge of the world and then from close observation and comparison. Differences *and* similarities exist throughout life, and the possibilities for firsthand investigation of variation and uniformity are boundless. The afore-mentioned lines of inquiry are suggestions. Some are rather difficult because organisms are necessary. All the methods require time, effort, and thought; but each is a genuine, if minor, problem, which will increase knowledge and process skill.

The relationship of structure and function is frequently obscure; often the organism has no special organ or structure, which would be an apparent advantage. Attributing differences in the arrangement of fish scales or in the orientation of animal hair to functional differences may be presumptuous, but each organism *has* "solved" its environmental problems and is adapted for its particular mode of life. Specifically, however, the results obtained in the comparative studies suggested here often seem unrelated to the problems animals face in adapting to their environment.

Fly behavior-reaction to heat and light[12]

A study in behavior

Where do the houseflies that buzz around the porch on a warm winter day come from? Winter is not the usual season for fly breeding; and unless the warm spell is prolonged, breeding has doubtlessly not occurred. Still, the buzzing fly is no figment of the imagination. Are houseflies, which live through winter temperatures in a more or less dormant state, activated by the sun's warmth?

Testing the effects of temperature and light on insect reactions is an interesting experiment. Apparatus such as that in Figure 10 is useful for this purpose. (The drawing is purposely incomplete.)

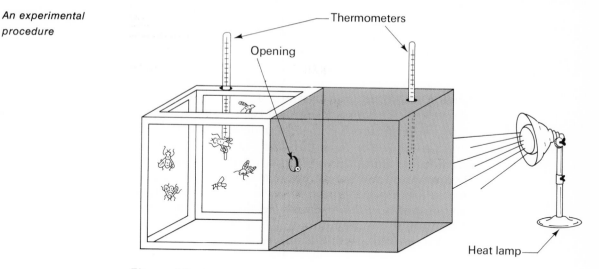

Figure 10

Do flies "prefer" darkness to light? A high to a low temperature? High temperature and darkness to high temperature and light? What other questions can you test with this or your own apparatus? Can you plan a series of experiments that will likely produce valid and reliable results? How would you verify your results? What are the assumptions underlying your experiment? Do the facts and conclusions suggest an answer to the original question about the emergence of houseflies in winter?

Chicken feed[13]

A medium-rare prime steak, a baked Idaho potato, tossed salad, and home-made apple pie—these words evoke certain delightful connotations. Yet the thought of this dinner ground up into an indistinguishable paste is most unpleasant. Nutritionally little difference exists between the individual foods and the combined paste, although taste, odor, and color preferences clearly influence the appetites of human beings. Household pets share some of these human preferences in addition to exhibiting their own idiosyncrasies. No one would give his dog a carrot in place of a steak bone.

Let us assume that we do not know the foods a bird such as a chicken prefers. How might we find out? Are chickens omnivorous? Is beak shape any indicator of food habits? We know that commercially grown fowl usually feed on grain. Are all grains equally appetizing? Does the color of the grain make any difference? What might happen if we gave chicks feed dyed with a harmless vegetable coloring? We can easily conduct similar research at an outdoor feeding station during the winter season.

What variables should we recognize in this food preference study? How should we collect and classify the data? Will the same program be equally convenient for both chickens and back yard birds? What kind of feeding container is best? How will changes in design affect the results? Suppose red-dyed grain in the feeder disappears quickly. Can we assume that birds prefer red? Could other animals possibly have interfered? Squirrels are excellent climbers; perhaps they, and not the birds, ate the feed. Pitfalls abound in animal experimentation, especially in improperly controlled experiments. For example, the attractiveness of the grain may depend far more on the availability of natural food than on the color or palatability of the grain.

Some assumptions

You should carefully study your techniques to pick out the assumptions on which to base your conclusions. Rather than commit yourself to a particular procedure or hypothesis, you should feel free to change your experimental design if necessary. Whatever the results their worth is directly proportional to the care taken to eliminate extraneous variables and the recognition of influences that cannot be excluded. Of course, you do not need to know that chicks prefer one kind of grain to another. Growth in imagination and ingenuity, practice in sound investigative habits and skills, and interaction of the intellect with the stubborn facts of nature give added meaning and value to an education in science.

A microcosm[14]

Is this "relevant"?

Green plants remove vast amounts of carbon dioxide from the atmosphere every day, returning in its place approximately the same volume of oxygen. (Plants, also use oxygen and give off carbon dioxide.) On the other hand animals respire oxygen and excrete carbon dioxide in roughly the same amounts. Hence the relative percentage of each component in the atmosphere remains nearly constant (except for the effect of man's industrial growth).

We can duplicate this equilibrium by sealing one or two small animals and a sufficient number of green plants in a container. This environment is sometimes called a microcosm. Figure 11 illustrates this simple experiment with life forms.

Once the system is well established, with healthy inhabitants, we can study the dynamics of "natural" systems. What experimentally testable questions come to mind? Must the data be qualitative? If not, how may they be quanti-

A challenge

Stopper

5-gallon bottle

Gravel

Figure 11

Questions about the microcosm

fied? You should propose at least one hypothesis about the interrelationships of the plants and animals in your microcosm and then clearly specify your observations, data, difficulties, assumptions, and controls. How long is the experiment to run? To what extent is the outcome of the experiment dependent on laboratory conditions? Affected by the container? By the water supply? By the seal, which separates the system from the room?

What new questions coming from this experiment are worth investigating? What modifications can you suggest to improve the study of this natural system in the laboratory?

The Earth Sciences

The earth sciences tend to be observational

The earth sciences are a rather dissimilar collection of nonbiological, nonchemicophysical disciplines, christened with this embracing name in the hope that it will lead to a unified, coherent discipline. The individual sciences that make up the earth sciences are distinct disciplines: astronomy, geology, meteorology, and oceanography. If there is a unifying structure, it comes from the principles of physics and chemistry that explain the different phenomena of the earth—its interior, surface, evolution, and place in space. These sciences in their collective status as the earth sciences are still primarily descriptive, although vast strides have been made toward establishing a firm theoretical framework. Experimentation in the earth sciences is generally more difficult to carry out than it is in the physical sciences, because it is limited to manipulating physical and chemical phenomena according to certain theoretical models of the mass phenomena of the earth sciences. For example, to study the process of cloud formation it is desirable to form clouds at will under appropriate experimental conditions; but clouds are not yet responsive to man's commands, and therefore laboratory experimentation is understandably difficult. B. J. Mason, professor of cloud physics at the University of London, remarks:

> There are serious difficulties in attempting to simulate cloud formation in the laboratory largely because it is impossible to scale down all the physical quantities in the correct proportions and because of the disturbing influences of the walls of the containing apparatus. Nevertheless, some valuable clues on the manner of cloud formation and evolution may be obtained from model experiments even though they cannot reproduce the natural conditions in all respects.[15]

Similar situations exist with earthquakes, volcanic eruptions, and ocean currents. Thus some of the earth science activities proposed in this book are not experiments at all. The following descriptive investigations tend to be less precise and of lesser pertinence to the larger world than those described previously. They are more illustrative, more dependent on observation, more time-consuming and less controlled. The variables and their effects are more difficult to control and to relate to hypotheses; the earth sciences do not often propose definitive experiments to test hypotheses.

Temperature—summer and winter[16]

A perplexing statement

The fact that in summer, when temperatures are high, the earth is several million miles farther from the sun than it is in winter often perplexes children in the northern hemisphere. This idea seems so contrary to common sense that children often refuse to accept it. They have not had sufficient experience to link the angle of the earth's axis with the plane of the ecliptic and to associate seasonal changes with heat absorption. The qualifying phrase *northern hemisphere* was inserted in the first sentence of this paragraph. Is this qualification necessary? What are the prevailing temperatures in the southern hemisphere during the northern summer? During the winter? Why should these temperatures differ from temperatures in the northern hemisphere? Do temperatures depend on the length of the day?

Questions about the "motion" of the sun

To investigate these questions we need to answer some others. What are the relative lengths of daylight and night during the summer and winter in each hemisphere? At the equator? Does the sun rise from the same point on the eastern horizon each morning? Does it set over the same point on the western horizon each evening? The answers to these questions are based on the apparent motion of the sun and on the orientation of the earth in space. The explanations are scientific because they are derived from a general theory, a number of independent, verifiable facts, and one or more assumptions.

Facts about the motion of the sun

We can answer the questions with observational data. Noting the location at which the sun rises and sets during the year, we soon become aware that the point of rising and setting changes. If in spring the sun rises each day farther and farther to the north, the path of the sun through the sky will change accordingly, rising higher in the sky. We then observe that the exact clock time at which the sun reaches its zenith is usually not noon and that this zenith position differs from day to day. Therefore, because the sun is farther north in May than it is in November, the angle at which the rays of the sun strike the earth should be correspondingly different. The shadow a fixed object casts should change length and direction if we observe it periodically at the same clock time each day the sun shines.

Comparison of the length, area, and direction of this shadow for several months indicates the apparent movement of the sun and the distribution of the light that strikes the earth. Figure 12 illustrates a simple apparatus for gathering the data.

A simple piece of apparatus

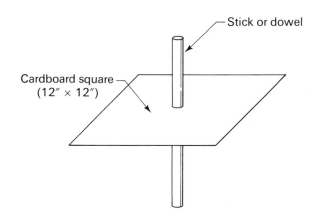

Cardboard square
(12″ × 12″)

Stick or dowel

Figure 12

If we hold a card one foot square up to the sun so that the dowel does not cast a shadow on the card, the card should be perpendicular to the sun's rays. (Your eyes should be properly shielded before you look directly at the sun at any time.) The size of the shadow cast by the card on the ground depends on the area of the card, the time of day, and the angle at which the sun's rays hit the earth. As the sun moves through the sky, the size of the shadow changes, provided the relationship of the card to the sun and the distance of the card from the ground remain constant. If the shadow is smaller during the summer months than it is during the winter months, the angle of the sun's rays has presumably changed. If we assume that the column of light falling on the card is constant, the area of the summer shadow, which is equivalent in area to the light blocked by the card, must represent a greater concentration of light than does the large winter shadow. If the heat striking the ground is proportional to the area of shadow cast by the card (and therefore of light), the dilution of light over a greater area in winter should lead to a decreased amount of heat per unit area of light-heat striking the ground. Assuming that the difference of approximately three million miles in the earth–sun distance is insignificant compared to the effect of a change in the angle at which the sun's rays strike the earth, we can now propose a tentative hypothesis to explain why summer is hotter than winter in the northern hemisphere. We can reasonably suppose that the light-heat striking the earth at the northern hemisphere is more concentrated, and as a result the ground is heated more effectively. The difference in earth–sun distance in the course of a year is approximately three percent. Can we justifiably neglect this variable in explaining summer and winter temperatures?

More assumptions

We might vary this experiment to determine the actual change of the sun's position during the year. For example, on September 21 at latitude forty-one degrees north the sun is at a noon altitude from the horizon of approximately forty-nine degrees. What will the altitude of the sun be on December 10? We can modify the apparatus of the preceding experiment by pushing a four-foot dowel (this length is not critical) through the card so that only a few inches of the dowel protrude through the top of the card. Now, when this card–dowel is oriented to the sun so that the dowel above the card casts no shadow and the other end of the dowel touches the ground, we can easily measure the angle between the ground and the dowel. This angle is the altitude of the sun.

Complicating factors

We should keep in mind the effect of arbitrary time changes, such as daylight saving time, on the time of observation, and the effect of apparent seasonal change in the velocity of the sun as it moves through the sky. For example, in mid-February, clock time is more than fourteen minutes ahead of the sun, whereas in early November, clock time is more than sixteen minutes behind the sun. Are these time differences significant? What measurement errors are unavoidable if we use the preceding procedures? What limits should we take into account in expressing these errors? What other assumptions are pertinent?

Deposition of sediments[17]

Sedimentation is an important process of rock formation. In the course of the process eroded and weathered rock materials are transported, usually by running water. In time the rock debris is squeezed and compressed into sedimentary rocks. This process of transportation and deposition, studied in miniature, is analogous, within broad limits, to the natural course of sedimentary rock formation.

A problem of running water

The investigation in this section correlates the distribution of rock materials in flowing water with the size of the individual rock particles. Their size will probably have something to do with the distance the stream of water carries these particles. By testing different kinds of particles under controlled conditions, we should be able to estimate the relative distances these particles are carried and to determine at least qualitatively the effect of size on the distance carried.

A suggested procedure

We will need at least half a dozen samples of different-sized rock materials, ranging from pebbles of about three sixteenths of an inch in diameter to fine sand or silt, each size stored in a separate container. The particles of approximately the same size may differ in density or shape so that in no case will these individual samples be identical.

Figure 13 illustrates a suggested experimental setup for this investigation. No unusual or expensive apparatus is necessary. The trough is narrower at the top than at the bottom. The distance the water flowing at the top carries the particles depends on the particles themselves, the slope of the trough, and the velocity and volume of the water. Because the slope, velocity, and volume are constant, the distance should depend only on the particles. Each sample drops into the stream through the funnel and flows to the plastic sheet at the base.

Questions to answer

We might first attempt to answer the question, Does the current carry particles of different sizes and compositions equal distances? One hypothesis is that the current will carry small particles farther than it will carry large particles. A second hypothesis is that as we increase the velocity of the water, the current will carry all particles farther. To this proposition we may add the subhypothesis that a larger flow of water at the same velocity will cause the particles to move farther. We can also compare the effect of a small volume of

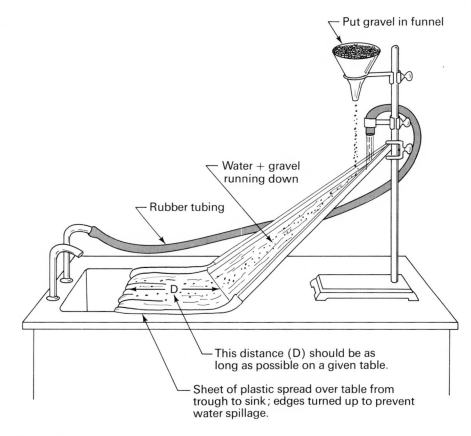

— Put gravel in funnel

Water + gravel
running down

— Rubber tubing

D

— This distance (D) should be as
long as possible on a given table.

— Sheet of plastic spread over table from
trough to sink; edges turned up to prevent
water spillage.

Figure 13

water moving at a high speed, with the effect of a large volume flowing at a lower speed.

If this experiment is to be predictive, the results should be pertinent to field problems; that is, natural rock-carrying processes should also depend on such factors as velocity, total flow, particle size, and slope. A field trip to investigate such natural processes is of great interest and value following or preceding such an experiment.

As previously suggested the assumption that each sample is homogeneous may be necessary; but this assumption is questionable so that you may have to test the average size or density of the samples experimentally. Suitable procedures are left for you to work out. Yet another assumption is that in the course of each experimental run the water velocity is constant. You can test this assumption by comparing, at predetermined intervals, the number of seconds required to fill a jar of known volume.

Rate of settling of soils in water[18]

A simpler experiment with running water

The investigation in this section is a variation of the preceding experiment. The major difference is that the running water variable is eliminated and the experimental technique is simpler. If we shake a number of different soil samples—sand, gravel, loam, silt, clay, for example—in water and allow the particles to settle, the rate of settling of the various soil components and the final composition of the soil layers are noticeably different. These differences should lead to a tentative hypothesis about the relationship between the settling rates of these soils and their composition. We will need to use jars of different sizes filled with different volumes of water to obtain verifiable results within a reasonable time.

The conclusions should be helpful in understanding the formation of sedimentary rocks. Appropriate field trips, films, or slides will be useful in pointing up these applications. Of course this miniature "duplication" of natural processes involves numerous implicit and explicit assumptions you will need to analyze so that you can properly limit your conclusions to the data gathered.

Mineral taxonomy[19]

A process-centered experience

Mineral collecting is a fascinating science hobby. Few children, or adults for that matter, who chance upon an unusual rock or mineral can refrain from taking it home. Identifying minerals provides a good opportunity for investigating taxonomy, a basic process important to each science in its early years and still actively useful in many of the sciences. Besides the psychological and developmental benefits, discussed in Chapter 2, classification facilitates the process of communication between scientists. Each classified object (there are more than a million different species of insects alone) has a precise and internationally accepted name, which in turn endows the object with rich meaning because of the many facts now known about it. Nomenclature *is* important. For example, to the mineralogist the name *calcite* conveys the information that the mineral is $CaCO_3$, with a specific gravity of 2.7, a hardness low enough to be scratched by a brass pin, a generally white or yellowish appearance, a hexagonal structure, and a cleavage of rhombic-shaped fragments.

Mineral characteristics

On the basis of the following characteristics the beginner can write out a scheme for classifying many minerals: color, luster, hardness, streak, cleavage, fracture, specific gravity, and magnetic properties. The main point of such classification is not to teach the beginner how to identify unknown minerals but rather to give him some experience with an important process skill, which has significant implications for improving children's cognitive operational skills. Hence using labeled samples of "typical" minerals, you can write your own taxonomy from direct handling and observation. If you have not selected the specimens carefully, you will find that you cannot distinguish many of the identifying marks of the minerals. The following minerals make excellent specimens: halite, quartz, olivine, mica (both muscovite and biotite), ortho-clase, albite, calcite, galena, pyrite, gypsum, magnetite, sulfur, corundum, azurite, fluorite, graphite, coal, garnet, hematite, talc, and siderite.

Although the previously selected physical characteristics are often used for identifying these and many other minerals, mineralogists must sometimes resort to chemical and other types of analysis, particularly if the minerals are in minute quantities or intermixed in some complex way. For the purposes of this experiment, however, you need only prepare a reliable taxonomic scheme based on the aforementioned physical properties.

For further study

1. Write a critique of the rusty-nail experiment, the heat-loss problem, and the other investigations, pointing out unrecognized assumptions, possible methodological and other errors, faulty reasoning, and so forth.

2. Work out in detail one of the partially structured experiments in this chapter.

3. Adapt one of the experiments for an intermediate grade elementary class-room.

4. Classify each of the experiments in this chapter according to its under-lying conceptual scheme.

5. Plan experiments based on the following conceptual schemes:

    (a) Each kind of plant and animal has a maximum average size.

    (b) A magnet always has at least two poles, surrounded by a force field.

    (c) The carbon dioxide produced by both plants and animals in respira-tion is used by plants in the process of photosynthesis.

    (d) Liquids are only slightly compressible.

6. After completing one of the partially structured experiments, list the process skills involved and explain how you used them to solve the problem.

Notes and references

1. *Cornell Science Leaflet,* 60(4): 3–22, May 1967; *Teacher's Guide for Batteries and Bulbs,* Elementary Science Study (Manchester, Mo.: Webster Division, McGraw-Hill Book Co.), 1967; See also reference 3.

2. Gardner, R., "The Heat to Melt Ice," *Nature and Science,* 4: 15–16, January 30, 1967; Stone, A. H., and D. Ingmanson, *Drop by Drop* (Englewood Cliffs, N.J.: Prentice-Hall, 1969), pp. 32–33; Barr, G., *More Research Ideas for Young Scientists* (New York: Whittlesey House, 1961), pp. 81–84; *Cornell Science Leaflet,* 61(2): 17–26, 1968; *Cornell Science Leaflet,* 61(1): 18–19, 1967; Swartz, C. E., *Measure and Find Out* (Glenview, Ill.: Scott, Foresman and Co., 1969), pp. 101–21; *The Teacher's Guide for a Conservation of Energy Sequence,* COPES (New York: New York University Center for Field Research and School Services, 1967), pp. 153–81; "Temperature and Thermometers," Measuring 11, Part C, *Science—A Process Approach* (New York: American Association for the Advancement of Science/Xerox Education Group, 1967).

3. *Cornell Science Leaflet,* 55: 3–7, April 1962; *The Teacher's Guide for a Conservation of Energy Sequence,* COPES, *op. cit.,* pp. 60–75, 1967; "Inferring Connection Patterns in Electric Circuits," Inferring 7, and "Conductors and Non-Conductors," Formulating Hypotheses 2, Part E, and "Electric Circuits and Their Parts," Defining Operationally 1, Part E, and "Magnetic Poles," Observing 16, Part D, *Science—A Process Approach* (New York: American Association for the Advancement of Science/Xerox Education Group, 1968); Barr, G., *Research Ideas for Young Scientists* (New York: Whittlesey House, 1958), pp. 15–16; Barr, G., *More Research Ideas for Young Scientists* (New York: Whittlesey House, 1961), pp. 47–50; Milgrom, H., *Explorations in Science* (New York: E. P. Dutton & Co., 1961), pp. 113–15.

4. Hone, E. B., et al., *A Source Book for Elementary Science* (New York: Harcourt Brace Jovanovich, 1971), pp. 302–4. See also reference 2.

5. *Teacher's Guide for Gases and Airs,* Elementary Science Study (Manchester, Mo.: Webster Division, McGraw-Hill Book Co., 1967); Hone, E. B., *op. cit.,* pp. 135–36.

6. *Cornell Science Leaflet,* 61(1): 5, 1967; Barr, G., *More Research Ideas for Young Scientists, op. cit.,* p. 85; Lynde, C. J., *Science Experiences With Home Equipment* (Princeton, N.J.: D. Van Nostrand Co., 1949), pp. 91–112.

7. Stone, A. H., and B. M. Siegel, *Have a Ball* (Englewood Cliffs, N.J.: Prentice-Hall, 1969), pp. 38–39; *The Teacher's Guide for a Conservation of Energy Sequence,* COPES, *op. cit.,* pp. 267–96.

8. Barr, G., *Research Ideas for Young Scientists, op. cit.,* pp. 97–99; "Observing Growth From Seeds," Observing 17, Part D, *Science—A Process Approach, op. cit.;* Klein, R., "How Does Light Bend Plants?", *Nature and Science,* 3: 10–12, January 10, 1966; *Cornell Science Leaflet,* 55(3): 30, April 1962.

9. Stone, A. H., and I. Leskowitz, *Plants Are Like That* (Englewood Cliffs, N.J.: Prentice-Hall, 1968), pp. 10–17; Klein, D., "Moving Water Into Cells," *Nature and Science,* 4: 10–11, January 30, 1967; Stone, A. H., and D. Ingmanson, *op. cit.,* pp. 58–59; "Loss of Water From Plants," Inferring 6, Part D, *Science—A Process Approach, op. cit.;* "Upward Movement of Liquids in Materials," Controlling Variables 2, Part E, *Science—A Process Approach, op. cit.;* "Loss of Moisture From Potatoes," Controlling Variables 4, Part E, *Science—A Process Approach, op. cit.* See also reference 8.

10. Cooper, E. K., *Science in Your Own Backyard* (New York: Harcourt Brace Jovanovich, 1958), pp. 141–47; "Observing Animal Motion," Observing 14, Part C, *Science—A Process Approach, op. cit.;* "Observing Animal Responses to Stimuli," Observing 15, *ibid.;* Miller, D., and G. Blaydes, *Methods and Materials for Teaching the Biological Sciences* (New York: McGraw-Hill Book Co., 1962), pp. 15–19; *Teacher's Guide 2,* Nuffield Junior Science (London: William Collins, 1967), pp. 202–5; Moore, W., *Here Is Your Hobby: Science Equipment* (New York: G. P. Putnam's Sons, 1962), pp. 53–54.

11. Shaler, N. S., *The Autobiography of Nathaniel Southgate Shaler* (Boston: Houghton Mifflin, 1907), pp. 97–99.

12. Moore, W., *op. cit.,* pp. 40–41; Kalmus, H., *101 Simple Experiments With Insects* (Garden City, N.Y.: Doubleday & Co., 1960), *passim; Cornell Science Leaflet,* 55(3): 29–31, April 1962; Cooper, E. K., *op. cit.,* Chap. 13; Barr, G., *Research Ideas for Young Scientists, op. cit.,* pp. 83–94; *Teacher's Guide for Animal Activity,* Elementary Science Study, *op. cit.,* 1967; *Teacher's Guide for Behavior of Mealworms,* Elementary Science Study, *op. cit.,* 1967.

13. Cooper, E. K., *op. cit.,* pp. 138–41; *Teacher's Guide 1,* Nuffield Junior Science (London: William Collins, 1967), pp. 79–92; *Teacher's Guide 2,* Nuffield Junior Science, *ibid.,* pp. 178–80.

14. See reference 10.

15. Mason, B. J., *Clouds, Rain, and Rainmaking* (Cambridge: Cambridge University Press, 1962), pp. 12–13.

16. Milgrom, H., *op. cit.,* pp. 44–49; *Teacher's Guide for Light and Shadow,* Elementary Science Study, *op. cit.,* 1967; "Using a Sundial to Describe Shadow Changes," Communicating 9, Part C, *Science—A Process Ap-*

proach, op. cit.; Barr, G., *More Research Ideas for Young Scientists, op. cit.,* pp. 37–41; Stone, A. H., and H. Spiegel, *Winds of Weather* (Englewood Cliffs, N.J.: Prentice-Hall, 1969), pp. 16–17.

17. *Cornell Science Leaflet,* 61(1): 23–25, 1967: Stone, A. H., and H. Spiegel, *op. cit.,* pp. 56–57; Stone, A. H., and D. Ingmanson, *Rocks and Rills, op. cit.,* pp. 40–48; Cooper, E. K., *op. cit.,* Chap. 4, pp. 53–57; Swartz, C. E., *op. cit.,* pp. 4–35.

18. See references 17 and 19.

19. *Teacher's Guide for Rocks and Charts,* Elementary Science Study, *op. cit.,* 1967; "Classifying Minerals," Classifying 11, Part E, *Science—A Process Approach, op. cit.;* Jensen, D., *My Hobby Is Collecting Rocks and Minerals* (Chicago: Children's Press, 1958), *passim.*

12 Planning for Teaching

lthough time-consuming, planning has traditionally been an important task of the classroom teacher. Once she had decided on the long- and short-range objectives of the science unit—provided she had this freedom and was not confined to a prescribed curriculum guide or textbook—the teacher struggled to describe in detail the tactics and strategies she planned to use. This resource unit included methods, motivational devices, books, articles, science experiences, local and school resources, films, evaluative and culminating activities; in short the teacher compiled a complete advance catalog of *all* eventualities, which she then divided into more conveniently handled subunits. Finally she worked out the lessons for each day and adjusted these lessons to provide feedback based on the successes and failures of the preceding day. Such exhaustive planning has helped teachers in the past and has received the approval of supervisors and principals. If she developed the resource unit properly, the teacher was forced to think carefully about what *she* was to do. If the teacher were absent because of illness, her substitute would surely welcome the daily lesson plan.

Shortcuts in planning

In all probability, however, after their college elementary education courses, rarely do teachers take the time to work out teaching resource units in this detail. Instead they turn for planning help to a curriculum guide or to the teacher's manual for the required elementary science textbook. Many cities and states have published curriculum guides that outline in detail an entire science sequence for kindergarten through grade twelve and provide a wealth of tested advice to help teachers plan excellent, although traditional, science instruction. In point of fact, however, teachers seem to depend on the science textbook manual even more than on the curriculum guide. Many elementary science textbook series combine the teacher's manual with the textbook and lead the teacher, page by page, to perhaps the best of the particular book for the ideal classroom whose children are from middle-class homes, who read well, who are easily motivated, and who are more inclined to let the teacher set the pace than to help set it themselves.

Unfortunately the science textbook is not always an infallible guide to accurate, classroom tested techniques.[1] Kenneth Ricker argues against such a teaching strategy:

> The teacher is supposed to know and show. The child is supposed to sit and get. Frankly, even if one supported this philosophy and tried to follow the directions given in [this] manual, I dare say the lesson would be a dismal failure.[2]

After evaluating a number of first grade elementary science textbooks with respect to their suggested activities, Ricker concludes:

> 1. Many writers do not have the slightest notion as to what six-year-old children are like. For example, walk into a class of six-year-olds. Drop a pin and ask them to describe the sound. In the last class I tried this not one of the 37 first graders described the sound caused by the pin as a soft sound. [This description is found in one science manual.] Many children did say, however, "It was a quiet sound." I consider this a very logical description for these children.
> 2. Many writers do not have any idea of how children learn, the kinds of experiences that they might have had, or the kinds of experiences that they should have. For example, how can a child acquire a concept of a high-pitch sound by looking at a picture of a canary, or a low-pitch sound by looking at a picture of a frog?
> 3. The writers only dream about instructional procedures. For example, put your fingers on a vibrating string and then announce that the sound must be loud and have a high pitch.[3]

Planning guides are sometimes misleading

Teacher's manuals usually provide simplified explanations of the science content of units as well as the most important concepts and principles. The manuals include recommended books, pamphlets, motion pictures, and film-strips for both teachers and children. They list in detail necessary supplies and equipment so that teachers may prepare for the many experiences described in the textbook. Numerous suggestions, including specific questions, help teachers introduce the unit. Following these questions are detailed procedures for capitalizing on them. Also included are children's answers as well as questions children might propose. Each daily lesson furnishes additional enriching experiences together with some activities for advanced or highly motivated children. Finally the manual suggests activities to summarize and culminate the lesson.

Most curriculum planning is heavily directed

This prefabricated planning is the mode in commercially available curriculum materials. Even teacher's guides for the new elementary science programs tend to channel teaching into a few well-charted paths. However, the new science education programs lean heavily on process and concrete experience, whereas textbooks rely on content, and recitation for learning—activity contrasted with passivity. Teachers are still regarded as well-meaning individuals who must be directed in every minute detail lest they blunder. The science curriculum materials of the 1970s are little different from the science teacher's guides of the 1890s in that the new materials are equally guilty of depreciating the competence of elementary school teachers. We have observed that as they learn more about how children think and act, inexperienced teachers become better at improvising, at quickly shifting mental gears, and at thinking ahead as they are working with their children. They tend to dispense with detailed written planning, whether their own or someone else's. Evidence also indicates that detailed planning "makes the teacher's thinking rigid and puts him on a track that is nearly derail-proof."[4] The typical planning model described previously may actually decrease the teacher's sensitivity to unexpected suggestions, to new ideas and interests, to individual differences. As a result she may miss opportunities to extend and elevate the responses of her children. Once she establishes the goals for her daily work, the teacher may move relentlessly to achieve them, no matter how her children respond.

Overplanning may decrease sensitivity

Some planning is essential

On the other hand planning *is* necessary to avoid utter chaos, but the teacher should organize the plans to increase her sensitivity to the children's actions and thoughts. The beginning teacher *should* spend a great deal of time in the traditional planning described, but she should not adhere in every detail to what she so laboriously drew up. The aim of such planning should be to build a repertoire of knowledge, skill, questions, strategies, and tactics from which she can draw. In a few years the purposeful teacher will develop the "tacit" skill and knowledge that comes from the integration of many different formative experiences. Yet experience itself does not lead to this wisdom; rather the teacher should consciously question, examine, evaluate, and probe. Ten years of bad experience leads to no more growth than five years of bad experience. The teacher should profit from past successes and failures; she should consider her past accomplishments and future objectives as open-ended exercises that will lead to new explorations. Perhaps her original objectives were not so important after all.

Mental planning

Before too long, planning should become a mental rather than a written exercise, although the teacher may have to note details in her plan book, on index cards, on the chalkboard, and on the bulletin board. The teacher and class should know what books, supplies, experiments, speakers, films, field trips, and other experiences are available to them. Meticulously detailed, day-by-day planning, however, seems to be a fruitless exercise, not only because it is too directive but also because it takes so much time that the teacher, who is responsible for social studies, language arts, arithmetic as well as science, will have to relinquish to the other, "more important" subjects. If the time saved is available for science, the teacher can use it better in reading children's reports, listening to discussion tapes, previewing films, and searching for new resources.

Individualizing Instruction

If contemporary understanding of child development and educational philosophy is a proper guide, schools must provide for children (and learners in general) as individuals *and* as members of a complex series of groups. All too often, despite earnest desires and strenuous efforts, learning seems to become institutionalized and group centered. As a result many experimental schools have proposed that instruction be individualized. To achieve this end they have suggested such remedies as smaller classes, informal schools, open spaces schools, team teaching, computer-assisted and programmed instruction.

From group to individual

Instruction in these schools ranges from highly directive—leaving no option to learners except that of working fast or slow—to almost complete freedom, but the schools all claim to "individualize instruction." From a psychological point of view individualized instruction should be effective as long as it satisfies these conditions, which serve as an operational definition:

1. There are levels of sophistication in the content to be taught which are adjusted to the learning style of the child.
2. The child can move ahead at a rate which is comfortable for him.
3. The child can begin when he wants to and can stop when he chooses.
4. The child can start at whatever level he is ready for.
5. The child will be forced to master a relatively small number of specific skills, abilities, and techniques in the unit.
6. The child will have a rich selection of learning and teaching material from which to select.[5]

Leave room for individuality

The teaching material should allow for the child's mistakes, aptitudes, cognitive skills and style, attention span, creative and imaginative ability, interests, and rigidity–flexibility. The child should agree that what he is doing is important, and he should be *willing* to do it. Do such experimental programs as Individually Prescribed Instruction (IPI), currently undergoing trials in many school districts, meet the goals of modern elementary science education? Perhaps . . . But more important, in the guise of research projects such programs provide much information on how "mass production to narrow specifications with rigid quality control" can help to improve "one of the ingredients of the educational mix":

> The result—the ultimate irony—is that IPI forces students into a passive, almost docile, role under the name of individualization. Because the material is presented in programmed instruction form, the student not only cannot specify his own goals, he cannot reach them in his own way; he is limited to the program with its preordained answers. He cannot "internalize" or apply what he has learned, for he cannot reconstruct in his own words or actions or construct his own applications and examples. The rigidity of the structure, moreover, implies that there is only one right answer and only one route to it; but what students (and teachers) may need to learn most is that some questions have more than one answer—and that others may have no answer at all.[6]

Another perceptive critic comments that "as far as the teacher is concerned, she is dispensing medicine supplied by others, with a crude thermometer as her main official guide . . . the student's independence in filling out their prescription is the independence of file clerks."[7] Planning is meaningless for teachers who are the functionaries in these schools. What then is the teacher to do? Most teachers are in schools with rather traditional orientation. Even if the school facilities are new, the teacher is probably not concerned with unorthodox educational practice at this time. She neither practices team teaching procedures nor presides over computer-assisted instruction. How then does she work with children as individuals, in groups, and with the whole class in pursuit of the one inclusive elementary science objective, *cultivation of the inquiring mind*. First of all she *must* believe that each child can and will learn and that the entire class, as well as she, will *enjoy* science. She must look ahead to deep involvement with the children; to sharing their joys, frustrations, interests; to extending those interests and creating new ones. She must take on the responsibility (shared with the children as fully as possible) of creating an environment that will stimulate interest in science. Jerome Bruner's dictum "When fully developed, is it [science content] worth an adult's knowing, and whether having known it as a child makes a person a better adult" should be rephrased as follows: Is science content worth the child's knowing? Will it make a difference to him if he knows it? If he can do it? If he succeeds with it?

The teacher's role

The teacher also knows that she and the children may begin with some science activity but that the activity may extend into the social studies, language, or art. Many, if not most, children can usually work in more than one subject field simultaneously. For example, a group of six- to seven-year-old children in one primary school were startled one fall day as they came into their classroom and viewed a complete sunflower plant. They became so deeply interested that they spent several weeks in individual and group study, including making life-sized paintings of the plant, making models of it and other plants, and painting sunflower designs on their book covers.[8] Elementary school children do not bind themselves within traditional science categories unless they are forced to do so. They are interested in erosion as a phenomenon, but they are also interested in the valley where erosion occurs, in its rocks and minerals, its plants and animals, its historical development, and in the people who live and work there. *Schools, not children, divide learning into arbitrary categories, disciplines, narrow specialties.* Drawing, painting, sculpture, drama, writing, oral reports, social studies, and arithmetic all play important parts in science instruction.[9]

Science must be related to life

Preparation

Preparing for the first day, the first week, or the first year is easier if the teacher turns to the science textbook as her primary source of techniques, questions, resources, and evaluation. But, even if she must, against her own judgment, teach from the textbook, the teacher may still tap the creativity and spontaneity of the children in cooperatively planning and critically analyzing experiences. She should grasp every opportunity to question, to lead, to follow, to inspire, to suggest, and often just to get out of the way! The teacher's manual provides a reasonably safe, tested introduction to science for inexperienced teachers who want to try but need extensive help. Science may well turn out to be exciting after all because concrete, open science teaching stimulates children. The beginning teacher should also go beyond the textbook and try out her own ideas. She should not feel anxious or insecure because she does not know the answer to a problem and must confess to her superiors that she does not know. They will forgive her, but she (together with the children) had better find out! The teacher who has prepared by reading and by planning a resource unit in some detail, who has a reasonably good grasp of the content, and who has tested the experiments can look forward to an adventure.

Some suggestions

The new science programs are even more useful for the beginning teacher because they arm her with classroom-tested materials and suggestions from

Help from the new science programs

the experiences of numerous classroom teachers over a period of years in schools throughout the nation. These programs are also more demanding for the teacher because she must foster a classroom atmosphere in which process-centered instruction is a natural development. Therefore in addition to having command of the science content of new program units the teacher should function effectively in a behavioral mode for which college science and education courses rarely prepare most teachers.

A model for planning and teaching

The following summary offers suggestions for planning and working out a unit on rocks from ESS, a less directive program.[10] The long period of classroom testing characteristic of Elementary Science Study is evident in this unit. The summary is written informally, so informally in fact that it does not mention objectives for either children or teacher. The suggestions are just suggestions; the series of steps sketched offers no prescriptions.

For exploration and motivation

1. A few days before starting the unit, the teacher places some rocks (purchased from the publisher but also available from many other sources) around the room so that the children may handle and study the specimens and then tell one another what they have "discovered": "I found a little one that's heavier than a big one. One of them is chalk — it writes on the blackboard. One of them gets all over your fingers."

2. On the day she "formally" initiates the unit, the teacher takes out three to five rocks so that the class is not overwhelmed by the total number (twenty-one) they will study. Some of the rocks are minerals, not rocks, but children nearly always call these mineral specimens rocks. The children touch, compare, and discuss the rocks by themselves for a few minutes. The teacher gives each child, or a pair of children, a set of rocks. Even though the rock sets described have worked well in many classrooms, the teacher should "feel free to introduce [the rocks] in other groupings if [she chooses] to — more rocks, fewer rocks, rocks which are easier or harder to tell apart." This flexibility suggests the degree of freedom in the Elementary Science Study program.

3. The teacher refers to the rocks in the first group (four are suggested) only as *A, B, C,* and *D.* She asks the children to look for similarities and differences.

Games for observational skill improvement

4. To help children who have had little experience with natural objects the teacher may introduce one or more games. For example, a child, elected by the class, describes one of the rocks, one clue at a time, and the class tries to name the rock. The "leader" may say, "It is black . . . it sometimes has sharp edges. [What is it?]" The fewer clues he is forced to give, the higher the game score.

Gathering data

5. One of the functional activities suggested for sharpening observational classificatory skills is a game of discovery through clues. For example,

in "Chart-Making," the teacher lists the names of rocks together with their color, but she provides no other clues to their identity:

feldspar	white
biotite	black
talc	white
obsidian	black

Because these clues are too few for identification, the class must discover additional clues. If they say that one of the rocks is layered, the children have identified biotite, and most of them will make this identification. However, some children may realize that they have also identified the obsidian. To help the children think through this clue-discovering procedure, the teacher may suggest another game in which she is a student, and her goal is to deduce from such clues as eye and hair color certain secret names the children have given themselves.[11]

6. If one of the children already knows some of the rocks, he may act as a "consultant" to give advice on the clues.

Some analytical tools

7. As she adds new groups of rocks—anthracite, slate, and shale, for example—the teacher may introduce additional ways to find clues. One means is the streak test. A streak plate, or unglazed piece of porcelain, acquires colored streaks that characterize many minerals rubbed on the plate. Slate and shale are difficult for many children to separate by appearance alone, but they can perceive the difference in streaks much more easily.

8. When the teacher introduces the fourth group of rocks, the children begin to draw their own charts instead of using the teacher's chart. The unit suggests many enriching activities. For example, each child draws up a chart with as many columns of clues as he needs for rock identification. The children then exchange charts so that each child can see whether his chart is descriptive enough for his neighbor to use for identification.

9. The fifth group of rock experiences includes the vinegar test to distinguish kaolinite, which children invariably call *chalk*, from their familiarity with the writing tool. They, together with the teacher, think of many questions about this unit, such as "What if you use water instead of vinegar?" and "What if you use colored chalk?"

A summarizing activity

10. One of the suggested experiences is a master chart, which each child composes with the fewest possible columns of clues for identifying all the rocks.

*A helpful
teacher's guide*

In addition to this rather permissive and flexible plan the teacher's guide includes a "background" section, which adds much useful information about classifying and identifying rocks together with helpful ideas for guiding children in understanding and extending these techniques. The treatment of density, color, hardness, appearance, shape, and other rock characteristics is particularly appropriate because the discussion describes the problems children in many schools have had with rock characteristics.

Using either a new science program or a teacher's manual–textbook as her guide, the teacher can focus the attention of a few children on some science-related object or event: a pet animal, a rock specimen, an exhibit in the science corner (created for the purpose), a striking demonstration (see Chapter 4). She might call on the advice of the science supervisor or a high school teacher for suggestions. The children will surely provide questions, which the teacher can use to initiate individual and group study. She might record the questions conspicuously on the chalkboard or on large sheets of paper tacked on the bulletin board.

Starting a science unit

Primary schools in England, which encourage this approach, are well known for science lessons that regularly result from miscellaneous materials children and teachers collect. Even though exciting and worthwhile science activities can spring up spontaneously, planning is essential; but the teacher must be willing to abandon her plans, at least temporarily, to "seize the flying thought." As a rule, in classrooms where science is alive, the teacher has planned the situation so that children take the initiative. At the point when cooperative plannning begins, all kinds of resource materials—books, articles, films, filmstrips, commercially prepared and homemade equipment, and tools— are helpful in extending and individualizing learning.

Housekeeping: A Planning Priority[12]

You must plan for safety

Safety is perhaps the only regulation the teacher *must* impose, although children usually accept safety rules they have cooperatively drawn up through discussion. Open flames, chemicals, acid, equipment requiring 110-volt electrical current, and sharp tools are potential hazards. Safety rules should be linked with procedures for expeditiously taking out and replacing science materials and other paraphernalia of science instruction and for working individually and in groups.

Time for Planning

The teacher who accepts the philosophy of process-centered science instruction (which has many elements in common with contemporary thought on elementary education) is free of anxieties about "covering" the textbook and completing the prescribed science outline. She takes as much time as necessary for the task at hand. Giving two or three hours to science for several consecutive days or even weeks does not reduce the time available for formal instruction in the other subjects, for these subjects will also be taught in blocks of time in much the same way. If she extends the time for science, the teacher also draws in other subjects; conversely she cannot ignore science in the study of social studies and language arts. Science will not be a center of interest every week. Far better to enjoy a few units in depth than to cover a specified number of pages each day!

This flexibility in scheduling is not always open to the elementary teacher. The school system, the principal, or her own philosophical adherence to the curriculum guide may dictate her classroom schedule so that she must jam her science instruction into three forty-minute blocks, Monday, Wednesday, and Friday afternoons. Activity-centered science cannot flourish when it must be shut off at 2:05 P.M. and wait for two days to be resumed at 1:25 P.M. Such rigid scheduling creates a hardship for teachers and their classes in schools that have adopted one of the new science programs, such as *Science — A Process Approach.* These schools must move from Exercise 1 in the first grade to the final exercise for the sixth grade because children in the upper grades must be able to use many process skills to succeed with their science tasks. Throughout the series the development of process skills occurs in an "intricately sequenced pattern," and "it appears that only a very experienced and self-confident teacher would assert his or her own ideas or improvisation into the curriculum."[13] At least twenty-five to forty minutes each day are necessary for this particular program. Most other elementary science programs are less structured and need not be scheduled in the same way.[14]

Planning for Motivation

The discussion of motivation in Chapter 2 and the related instructional dimensions of motivation stress the impetus that comes with an arresting, dissonant, introductory demonstration or exhibit, with an unexpected or intriguing question, as well as with an unplanned incident. The science table can display, at one time or another, a collection of artificial light sources, such as candles, light bulbs, flashlights, and an alcohol lamp; various mirrors and lenses; different kinds of springs; nails; pulleys and levers; an empty aquarium along with a few books on tropical fish. The teacher should encourage the children to touch, pull, and poke even though there may be some breakage

*Questioning is an
invaluable technique*

and perhaps an occasional loss. Usually the children will ask questions. At the start perhaps only one or two children will show interest, but even these few children indicate the beginning of inquiry. The teacher should not wait for the children to develop interest on their own. She should ask questions about the displays, about a story in the newspaper the day before or in the *National Geographic*. The teacher may draw on a repertoire of questions: Did you look at the demonstration today? What does the demonstration show? Can you think of another way to do the demonstration? What would happen if we were to try this . . . ? Can you think of a reason why we could not get the demonstration to work? She may stimulate them to think *what would happen if:* There were no iron in the world? Magnets had three poles? Water froze at 50 degrees Fahrenheit? You heat a magnet? You plant an orange pit? You put a celery stalk in colored water? Rocks were soft? You strike a piece of flint rock with a piece of steel? The center of the earth were hollow? Iron rusted only when it was dry? The earth were turned upside down in space? A grasshopper and a cricket were matched in a jumping race?

*But routine questions
are tedious*

The teacher's questions and her follow-up are probably the most important science instructional tools: What children *do* in class is largely decided by what questions the teacher asks and how she asks them.[15] Although the aphorism that "no one can ask a completely significant question for anyone else" is valid, teachers need not wait for children to ask questions. Successful teachers have long since discovered that children respond strongly to intriguing questions they can find answers to themselves, with thoughtful and affectionate guidance.

Questions are classified in many different ways. The following six types of questions, related to the cognitive domain described in the appendix, are the most useful for science instruction. Teachers who emphasize process-centered techniques and do not rely on the textbook and curriculum guide tend to use more questions on higher levels of this hierarchy than do more traditionally oriented teachers.[16]

1. A *recognition* question presents the pupil with cues that require only the selection of the correct option from two or more choices.

   Examples: "Is it easier to walk or slide on a scooter?" "Is the wood or the cotton warmer?" "Is the bean hollow or solid?"

2. The *recall* question asks the pupil to state one or more simple facts, drawing from his past experience. In this case there are no choices given.

   Examples: "How many turns does the moon make before it goes all the way around the earth?" "What are two minerals in their natural state?"

*Avoid recognition
questions*

3. The *demonstration of skill* question requires the application or use of knowledge in the performance of a skill, as in arithmetic, reading or science.

Examples: "What does that sentence mean?" (reading for comprehension) "How many fourths should we borrow from six?" (basic arithmetic processes) "What is your estimate for books on the shelf?" (measurement skill in science)

4. The *comprehension* question requires the pupil to produce evidence that he understands a point.

Examples: "Can you see an example of an abrasive in this room?" "What are the cells of the root like?" "Can you explain what a heart valve is?"

*Try higher level
questions*

   In the following two categories, it is assumed that the student has never been confronted with the question before; consequently he cannot answer the question merely by recalling something he has previously learned.

5. The *analysis* question requires the pupil to explain the relationship between elements in a totality in a situation he has not faced before. It involves the analysis of a complex phenomenon.

Examples: "Why did the lighted candle go out when we placed it in the closed container?" "What is different about these containers and the four containers we used before?" "Why did the first chick out show less strength?"

6. The *synthesis* question calls upon the student to combine or reorganize specifics so as to develop a new structure or generalization.

Examples: "What would have happened if the experiment had been organized in this other way?" "How could you find out which of these two sets of jars have the most liquid in them?"[17]

   The teacher should avoid giving answers to her own or the class's questions. Instead she should redirect the questions: Why, do you think, is the aquarium so dirty? Why did the light bulb burn out? Could we get a static electric shock another way? The teacher should rarely say, "That's not right!" or "This is the way you're supposed to do it." She should ask questions that *Questions should lead* will lead children to think about important but neglected points: Do you think *to higher levels* one dry cell is enough? How can we connect another dry cell into the circuit? Do you think the box is light tight? How can we block off the light? These questions are sequential. The first is a recognition question, which brings a new thought to the child's attention. The second is a synthesis question, which provides a challenge, a stimulus to test the answer for the first question. A rather simple, directive question is followed by a question that extends the answer of the first question to a higher intellectual level.[18] This technique is particularly noteworthy, for all too often a long series of questions may remain at the same conceptual level.

Some Procedural Suggestions for Planning

The beginning teacher should not expect young children to function at high cognitive levels; older children cannot do so without experience and encouragement in analytical and creative science. The teacher should start with simple activities, even in the upper grades, looking to growth in observational skill first. Deriving some inferences from these observations, she should perhaps take on much of the initiative and direction for the activities and discussions with the class; and in so doing, she will encourage children to participate, to take over more responsibility, to want to do things on their own. Above all, the teacher should be flexible. If one approach does not work, she should try something else. For example, the teacher might tape record some of the class sessions so that she and the class can talk about what they did and what resulted. The flowsheet technique (see Chapter 10) helps children to see where they are going and where they have been. As she moves around the room, the teacher should ask individual children and groups to talk about their problems, to write brief reports, to make drawings and models of what they are studying. She should plan some sort of summarizing activities to tie together the different activities. If she is sufficiently experienced, the teacher might work with five or six different science groups at the same time; she should recognize that each group will be working at different stages and will need different kinds of support. Instruction in the informal classroom is somewhat more complicated because not all groups will be working on science at the same time.

Planning in the New Schools

During the past several decades many suggestions for reorganizing the schools to meet the changing needs of society and the perennial needs of children have filled the pages of the educational and public journals. One such proposal is team teaching, "an organization in which two or more teachers are responsible for more than fifty percent of the instruction that a given group of pupils will receive during the course of a school day."[19] The group may be composed of children at the same grade level or at a combined primary–intermediate level. The team selects the children for each group and brings them together for films, lectures, demonstrations or splits them into smaller groups for special purposes. The teachers often specialize, one taking responsibility for science and mathematics because of interest and preparation. In theory a high degree of flexibility is available, but to make full use of this potential the teachers must work closely together as a team for planning, teaching, and evaluating. Sometimes team teaching turns out to be nothing more than the traditional departmentalization that has been part of the elementary school scene for years. Teachers trade classrooms so that teacher *A,* who is competent in science, takes teacher *B*'s children, while teacher *B* takes over the social studies with teacher *A*'s class. With full teaming one team member (or more) is responsible for planning and teaching a traditional subject. Throughout the week children have experience in each subject field, led by trained, selected resource teachers.[20]

Despite its potential the team approach has certain problems we should not minimize. The leaders and the other members of the team may not work effectively with one another because of personality differences, incompatible philosophies, or even oversensitivity in group evaluating sessions. They may not be sufficiently versed in their subject field to function effectively as science specialists. Teams sometimes spend too much time in planning and talking so that they become overdirected and waste time on trivia.

Science and team teaching

Team teaching cannot function effectively in traditional elementary schools because of their need for large classes. However, "open-space" schools are particularly suited for such teaching. These schools are often ungraded, or at least have no formal grade designations, although they usually separate primary children from those at the intermediate level. In theory, science teaching in these schools should be more effective than in traditional schools: The science teacher is a specialist; science is more easily integrated with the total curriculum because teachers know what the other members of their team are doing; the new schools have elaborate media and instruction centers; groups range from small (one or two children) to large and thus allow for individual interests, needs, and abilities. Children gain experience in working as individuals, in small and large groups in every aspect of instruction so that they are prepared for process-centered, concrete-based science instruction. These are the claims; the reality is as yet unknown.[21] Many schools that have announced *they* are in the forefront of educational advance may have changed only in their designation:

Most schools purporting to use team teaching do not distinguish either the role or the salary and status of the various team members. As often as not, in fact, "team teaching" is simply a new label for old-fashioned departmentalization. . . . What they *call* nongrading is nothing more than the conventional homogeneous grouping of students by ability *within* the same grade; the vertical grade organization is left unchanged, along with the curriculum, teaching methods, and everything else.[22]

In addition to the traditional elementary school many large towns and small cities also have a middle school. The grade organization of such schools may take several forms, but most are for grades four through eight. The middle school may be completely conventional in every respect, just as the upper grades of the traditional elementary school. Each teacher may be a generalist, responsible for all or nearly all of the instruction in the various subjects. However, the middle school is more likely to be departmentalized so that the science teacher teaches only science (perhaps with a class or two of mathematics). Because the teacher is a specialist, the public anticipates that she will be more *Science specialists* productive than the elementary school generalist. But in our experience we *may not be the answer* have noticed that science specialists tend to concentrate on content, on stuffing the learner with science facts and principles. Although they articulate the ultimate goals of science instruction, many science teachers ignore these goals in actual practice. Despite these somewhat pessimistic observations new school organizers have high hopes:

By working in multidisciplinary teams, no one teacher will be forced to attempt such diverse and psychologically incompatible tasks as are demanded in the self-contained classroom. Under the latter arrangement, teaching deteriorates into a series of perfunctory ritualistic passes at each task. One person cannot possibly cope with the conflicting role demands currently expected of teachers and realize other than the dubious effectiveness that characterizes traditional classroom teaching.[23]

Summary

Planning that depends on the science textbook, teacher's manuals, and some of the new elementary science programs tends to be rigid and teacher centered. However, teachers who rely on what is essentially a preplanned curriculum are not necessarily ineffective teachers. Many of these "authorized" sources are classroom tested and excellent guides on their own terms.

They may indeed stress science process and firsthand experience and may lead the inexperienced teacher to remarkably good teaching. But these curricula lack the freedom to explore, to adapt to individual differences, to stretch children's minds creatively and imaginatively. Teachers must know about children and their learning abilities as well as their own teaching abilities.

The informal science class, so widespread in England and now in a few American schools, is strenuous and frustrating.[24] But it is also exciting and much of the time absolutely enjoyable for both teacher and children. Some teachers cannot accept the informal setting for entirely legitimate reasons. Many others, whose philosophical convictions are in sympathy with the informal school (which is not by any means an unplanned school), cannot practice this form of schooling.

There are intermediate courses of action between prescriptive planning and teacher domination on the one hand and complete, anarchical, chaotic freedom on the other. These courses are based on a planned, although informally organized, series of experiences, developed by the children and the teacher and to a great extent probably instigated by the teacher. The plans remain loose so that the teacher may deviate from a science lesson when necessary to meet children's needs and capacities.

The test of all educational proposals is what happens in the classroom. An open, sensitive plan rigidly enforced by an insensitive teacher is less likely to be successful than a complete, undeviating, straightforward plan taught by a competent traditional teacher.

New school organizations offer some promise that science teaching can be accomplished more effectively than in the self-contained classroom. Whether this hope will come to pass is for the next decade to discover.

For further study

1. Compare the planning responsibilities of a teacher who uses an elementary science textbook with the responsibilities of one who uses a new science program.

2. Write a resource unit for one of the following areas: biology, earth science, physical science. Focus on a particular grade level. Show how you might integrate the unit with other subjects.

3. How would the unit you devise in question 2 differ for an ungraded school?

4. Select one of the units from *Science—A Process Approach* and rewrite it for a more informally organized classroom.

5. Plan an exhibit for a science table to use as an introduction to a science unit.

6. Analyze critically the planning suggestions in two units of any of the new science programs.

7. To what extent do performance objectives formalize science instruction? Give examples.

8. Select a particularly trivial bit of science content (ability of the mineral magnetite to conduct an electric current, for example) to build a center of interest for a day's science activity. What resources can you find for the purpose? How will you use them? What kinds of questions will you anticipate from the children? What kinds of questions will you ask? Are there any films, filmstrips, dramatic demonstrations or experiments you can use?

9. Analyze the questions on page 497 according to the question hierarchy on page 497. Do the same for the questions in 8 above. Rewrite your questions and those in the textbook to raise their cognitive level.

10. In an informal science curriculum some (most?) major science principles may not be discussed during the school year. Is this omission bad?

Notes and references

1. See Chap. 3, pp. 158–62.

2. Ricker, K. S., "Using Formative Evaluation in Developing Instructional Units," occasional paper no. 6, Research and Development Center in Educational Stimulation (Athens, Ga.: University of Georgia, 1969), p. 5.

3. *Ibid.,* p. 6.

4. Zahorik, J. A., "The Effect of Planning on Teaching," *The Elementary School Journal,* 70: 149, December 1970.

5. Adapted from Mitzel, H. E., "The Impending Instruction Revolution," *Phi Delta Kappan,* 51: 434–39, April. 1970.

6. Silberman, C. E., *Crisis in the Classroom* (New York: Random House, 1970), p. 201.

7. Oettinger, A. G., and S. Marks, *Run, Computer, Run* (New York: Collier Books, 1971), p. 145.

8. *Teacher's Guide 1,* Nuffield Junior Science (London: William Collins, 1967), pp. 66–68.

9. See Burrows, A. T., *Teaching Children in the Middle Grades* (Boston: D. C. Heath, 1952), pp. 115–28 for an excellent description of cooperative planning from beginning to end on a geology unit in which integration of other subjects plays an important part.

10. *Teacher's Guide for Rocks and Charts,* Elementary Science Study (Manchester, Mo.: Webster Division, McGraw-Hill Book Co., 1967).

11. *Ibid.,* pp. 17–18.

12. See Chap. 9, pp. 373–75 and *passim.*

13. *Program Report, Elementary Science Information Unit, Science—A Process Approach* (Berkeley, Calif.: Educational Products Information Exchange Institute, 1970), p. 9.

14. See Chap. 5, *passim.*

15. Fish, A., and B. Goldmark, "Inquiry Method: Three Interpretations," *The Science Teacher,* 33: 13, February 1966.

16. Moon, T. C., "A Study of Behavior Patterns in Primary Grade Classrooms During Science Activities," paper given at the Annual Convention of the National Association for Research in Science Teaching, 1970.

17. Wilson, J. H., "The 'New' Science Teachers Are Asking More and Better Questions," *Journal of Research in Science Teaching,* 6(1): 51–52, 1969.

18. Miller, E. L., *An Instructional Guide for Clinical Site Training of Student Teachers in Science Education* (Pittsburgh, Pa.: University of Pittsburgh, 1970), mimeographed, p. 29.

19. Fishler, A., "The Use of Team Teaching in the Elementary School," in L. I. Kuslan and A. H. Stone, eds., *Readings on Teaching Children Science* (Belmont, Calif.: Wadsworth Publishing Co., 1969), p. 217.

20. See Shoresman, P. B., "Teaming Up for Science Instruction," in *Readings on Teaching Children Science, ibid.,* pp. 223–27.

21. Fen Rhodes' recent study of team teaching in the elementary school, although not connected with science, provides some evidence that team teaching is less effective in skill subjects than non-team teaching, even though team teachers have more positive attitudes about their tasks than the non-team teachers. There seems to be little difference in the attitudes of the children in Rhodes' study. Rhodes, F., "Team Teaching Compared with Traditional Instruction in Grades Kindergarten Through Six," *Journal of Educational Psychology,* 62: 110–16, April 1971.

22. Silberman, C. E., *op. cit.,* p. 168.

23. Crawford, D. G., and R. G. Ragsdale, "Individualized Quasi Instructional Systems for the 70's," *Interchange,* 1(4): 75, 1970.

24. For an excellent description of an outstanding "progressive" school of the late 1920s, see Slavson, R. S., and R. K. Speer, *Science in the New Education* (Englewood Cliffs, N.J.: Prentice-Hall, 1934), Chaps. 13 and 14. The philosophy and practices are still far from being implemented by the great majority of schools in this country.

For additional assistance in planning, the following books are most helpful:

Brearly, M., et al., *The Teaching of Young Children* (New York: Schocken Books, 1970), Chap. 2.

Commentary for Teachers for Science — A Process Approach (New York: Xerox Education Group, 1970).

Kuslan, L. I., and A. H. Stone, eds., *Readings on Teaching Children Science, op. cit.,* particularly:

> Hawkins, D., "Messing About in Science"
>
> Katz, P. J., "Science for the Educable Retardate"
>
> Malkin, S., "The Culturally Deprived Child and Science"
>
> Fish, A. S., and T. F. Saunders, "Inquiry in the Elementary School Science Curriculum"
>
> Lansdown, B., "Orbiting a Science Program"
>
> Busch, P. S., "An Urban Field Guide to Elementary Science"

SCIS Elementary Science Source Book (Berkeley, Calif.: University of California, 1968), Chap. 7, and Part 4, pp. 96–125.

Teacher's Guide 1, Nuffield Junior Science, *op. cit.* Chaps. 3 and 5.

The Teacher's Guide for a Conservation of Energy Sequence, COPES (New York: New York University, 1967), *passim.*

Teacher's guides for the various Elementary Science Study units, of which there are approximately sixty published by the Webster Division of the McGraw-Hill Book Company.

Appendix

The Domains of Science Evaluation

For the purposes of this book, evaluation of classroom learning and behavior is more or less arbitrarily divided into three domains:

1. The *cognitive* domain of knowledge and intellectual skills.
2. The *affective* domain of emotional and attitudinal behavior.
3. The *psychomotor* domain of physical and manipulative skills.[1]

The cognitive domain

The cognitive domain, or some part of it, is the usual focus of science evaluation because it is concerned with knowledge of subject matter and with the intellectual skills that contribute to mastery of subject matter. These aspects of learning have traditionally been accented in science instruction. Despite many years of serious study of the cognitive domain, which is spread over the broad spectrum from simple recall of isolated facts to synthesis of new ideas, evaluators have not yet agreed on how to assess competence in the higher cognitive processes. The publication in 1956 of the first volume of *The Taxonomy of Educational Objectives* marks a turning point in this struggle to delineate and to make meaningful what has been fragmentary and submerged—although we must add that many educators do not agree with this judgment. We believe, however, that intellectual skills can now be arranged into a hierarchy with some confidence of consensus as to placement and identification. Once these skills or abilities are known, teachers should be able to recognize behavior representative of these skills. With this criterion for "behavior" in mind the actual behavior of children, which the teacher observes or infers, becomes the raw material of evaluation.

Lee J. Cronbach describes two types of behavior that also provide evidence of higher cognitive learning (see Chapter 2 for a more extensive treatment). One type, "applicational transfer," is an immediate application of new skills and knowledge to related problems.[2] For instance, a child who understands that rock and soil carried by water is usually "sorted" as water velocity decreases should be in a better position to explain why conglomerate rocks are composed of unsorted particles. That a child is unable to make this or any other specific application does not prove that he has failed to understand the generalization. After all, much that is now self-evident in the light of scientific advance was not so clear to great scientists in the past. Only when a child consistently fails to apply principles and processes in situations that do not appear to be conceptually difficult should the teacher study the child's pattern of thinking closely.

The second kind of transfer behavior, "gains in aptitude," requires a much longer time period for growth.[3] This behavior is the child's working frame of reference for looking at problems he encounters. In another sense it is mastery, at some level of competence, of the process-components of science. The student grows in confidence and in the mental agility required to tackle more or less complex problems and ideas, to define problems so they are feasible, to sense whether his hypotheses are testable, and to approach and carry through an investigation in as accurate, controllable, and unbiased a fashion as possible.

This list is an outline of the major levels in the cognitive domain according to Benjamin Bloom. We shall consider each level in some detail in subsequent sections.

Levels of the cognitive domain[4]

1.00   Knowledge
    1.10   Knowledge of specifics
        1.11   Knowledge of terminology
        1.12   Knowledge of specific facts and sources of information
    1.20   Knowledge of ways and means of dealing with specifics
        1.21   Knowledge of conventions
        1.22   Knowledge of trends and sequences
        1.23   Knowledge of classifications and categories
        1.24–1.25   Knowledge of criteria and methodology
    1.30   Knowledge of universals and abstractions in a field
        1.31   Knowledge of principles and generalizations
        1.32   Knowledge of theories and structures

2.00 Comprehension

    2.10 Translation

    2.20 Interpretation

    2.30 Extrapolation

3.00 Application

4.00 Analysis

    4.10 Analysis of elements

    4.20 Analysis of relationships

    4.30 Analysis of organizational principles

5.00 Synthesis

    5.10 Production of a unique communication

    5.20 Production of a plan or proposed set of operations

    5.30 Derivation of a set of abstract relations

6.00 Evaluation

    6.10 Judgments in terms of internal evidence

    6.20 Judgments in terms of external criteria

1.00 *Knowledge* is learning the child has acquired when he remembers appropriate facts, concepts, principles, structures, and phenomena. The child's knowledge is dependent on his memory even though each item he recalls may be somewhat restructured. Higher categories of the cognitive domain include judgments, relationships, and reorganization of remembered knowledge. This "knowledge" behavior is conveniently divided into several subbehaviors in a logical, although not necessarily psychological, order of complexity.

    1.10 *Knowledge of specifics* — recall of individual and unrelated items of information — is the simplest category of cognition. The following skills belong to this category:

    1.11 *Knowledge of terminology* includes familiarity with verbal and nonverbal symbols and an ability to associate symbols with their referents. Science students should become familiar with scientific vocabulary because of its conceptual power and frequent occurrence in scientific writing. For example, *magnetic field, test tube,* and *animal* are as unavoidable as they are necessary. The child who knows the meaning of the word *animal,* who includes insects and excludes trees from this category, has mastered more than an important term. He has learned an important scientific principle. Of course, familiarity with scientific terms does not mean that children will use them with the precision of mature scientists.

1.12 *Knowledge of specific facts and sources of information* — the distance of the sun from the earth, the names of the planets, the number of legs on a mature insect — is the kind of knowledge strived for in the past. This category also includes knowledge of ideas and principles learned as facts. Children should know as many facts as possible but never at the expense of meaning and relationships.

Teachers do not often test children on knowledge of where to look for facts, concepts, explanations, and principles. Children should know that such authors as Herbert Zim and Harry Sootin are reliable and authoritative and that their books are well worth looking into for specific information.

1.20 *Knowledge of ways and means of dealing with specifics* covers ways children organize, assess, and use facts, ideas, and information. Children who are at this psychological behavioral level recognize that science is an organized body of facts and ideas and that scientists usually test hypotheses against experimental and observational evidence — although they may not necessarily be able to use these procedures themselves. This category of knowledge, which is somewhat more abstract than category **1.10,** is divided into five subareas:

1.21 *Knowledge of conventions* is cognizance of the accepted and customary ways of manipulating ideas, facts, and events. Every scientific discipline includes some traditional but arbitrary usages. For example, astronomers may speak of the sun as moving through the sky, even though this phrase is not correct; chemists may symbolize the hydrogen ion as H^+, even though each hydrogen ion in water is associated with an indeterminate number of water molecules; elementary teachers often describe force in terms of effort and push or pull, despite the limitations of these words.

This subcategory also includes ability to work with others in the classroom, knowledge of the proper form to follow in writing reports, and mastery of the units of measurement.

1.22 *Knowledge of trends and sequences* includes understanding of the relationship of physical and conceptual events in time. This category is on a higher intellectual plane than the previous kinds of knowledge. Achievement demands knowledge of events and of their changes; thus some element of causal thinking is perhaps necessary, even though formal causal thinking, as such, is on a higher level of abstraction.

The child who is aware of the succession of the seasons, of the sequence of mountain building and mountain erosion, and of the water cycle evinces knowledge of trends and sequences, although he is not necessarily able to predict future events from these trends. Well-founded prediction requires that the child add the cautionary injunction that the future is predictable *if* the trend continues and other factors remain constant. The child who makes *this* kind of prediction is operating on a level far above simple knowledge of trends and sequences.

1.23 *Knowledge of classifications and categories* is important in science. Classification simplifies the task of the scientist and the learner. For example, the division of flowering plants into families with related structural and evolutional characteristics enables the botanist to recognize an aster, for example, because of its flower structure. Many botanists can quickly identify plants they have never seen before on the basis of general characteristics. Even more important, they know almost immediately what the plants are not! To cite another example, the word *metal* immediately reminds the chemist of the chemical and physical properties of metals and suggests methods of handling and analyzing. Of course an individual can learn and remember only a fraction of all the scientific classificatory schemes; in fact we would hardly expect him to master all the schemes for any one science.

Although children should try to apply this kind of knowledge to new problems, achievement in this category requires only recognition of relevant classes and recall of the criteria for selecting members of the class.

1.24–1.25 *Knowledge of criteria and methodology* includes awareness of standards for assessing actions, facts, processes, evaluations, and opinions. It includes judgments of the factors that make for experimental adequacy: elimination of irrelevant factors, good sampling, and sufficient repetition, accurate and logical recording of data, and limitation of generalizations. It also includes judging the cogency, precision, and objectivity of published sources as well as the reputation of the publisher and author.

Statements of criteria have meaning only in evaluation, which requires a much higher level of cognitive skills. In fact all the previous subcategories of cognition are meaningless in and of themselves. They are significant only in the proper contexts and, in themselves, do not meet Jerome Bruner's claim that the criterion for any subject taught in the schools should be "whether, when fully developed, it is worth an adult's knowing, and whether having known it as a child makes a person a better adult. If the answer is negative or ambiguous, then the material is cluttering the curriculum."[5]

1.30 *Knowledge of universals and abstractions in a field* has always been an important goal of science instruction. Such knowledge is more than awareness of both the structure of science and the way that structure is organized. As used in this book, knowledge of the universals and abstractions in a field implies insight into the meaning and importance of the great ideas of the sciences.

1.31 *Knowledge of principles and generalizations* is exemplified by ability to recall important laws and principles as *preliminary* to application. For example, recall of the law of gravitation is not at the same level on the hierarchy as application of this law in explaining events and phenomena. Principles and generalizations are derived from many different events and from the cumulative experience of centuries. They are descriptions, not explanations, and because they are abstract they have a general power. (See Chapters 1 and 2.)

1.32 *Knowledge of theories and structures* includes recall of theories that unify the principles and generalizations. The learner familiar with the theory of evolution or with kinetic molecular theory can state the important ideas, assumptions, and principles of the theory. Certain theories, which have been more or less generally accepted, characterize each discipline. Some of these theories are more soundly based than others. The theoretical structure of the physical sciences, with the exception of astronomy, is better interrelated and more easily derived from fundamental laws, assumptions, and observation than the structures of the biological and the earth sciences.

2.00 *Comprehension* includes intellectual skills and abilities, such as strategies and general techniques for studying and learning. Comprehension, although higher than recall, is on a lower level of complexity than is application or evaluation. To comprehend is to show insight into meaning and intent.

This category may conveniently be divided into three components: translation, interpretation, and extrapolation.

2.10 *Translation* involves rewording a statement into an equivalent statement, using one's own words. In so doing the learner must be acquainted with the facts in the statement, the ways of dealing with these facts, and the pertinent principles and abstractions involved. Even in scientific translation, the intent behind the words, not their literal meaning, must come through. For example, a nonchemist may, with the help of a dictionary, be able to translate a paper on chemistry from Russian into English, but he will miss delicate shadings and technical nuances because he does not *think* as a chemist. This meaning behind words is even more obvious in translations of poetry, as many translators have learned to their and the reader's sorrow.

Mathematics is an indispensable language for scientists. It simplifies the scientist's task of extracting information out of his data and improves his ability to make predictions. Because it is a language, most science students must translate mathematics into their own language. For example, they may represent columns of data in the form of a graph whose characteristic curve suggests previously hidden relationships.

2.20 *Interpretation* is perhaps the highest form of comprehension because not only must the interpreter select the ideas that give life to an event, a phenomenon, or a statement but he must also grasp the meaning and the relationships and limitations of these ideas. In addition the interpreter must suppress his biases, lest interpretation become misinterpretation. He must reorganize the elements and select the significant ones according to some criteria. He must deduce certain conditions or possibilities, even though they are not explicitly stated in the data.

For instance, he may interpret man's ability to live for weeks in a satellite hundreds of miles above the surface of the earth to mean that the chances of his colliding with a meteor or of his suffering from radiation at that altitude are slight. Or from the generation of heat and light as a candle burns, he may deduce that the products of combustion possess less energy than the original candle.

2.30 *Extrapolation* is similar to interpretation in that it involves inference, although the inferences are more tenuous and less probable. The learner extends interpretation well beyond the formal bounds of his data, keeping in mind limitations and possible errors. He predicts, implies, and thinks of possible consequences from a few events, statements of events, or facts to another, more hypothetical realm.

Predicting the effect of increased salt concentration in an aquarium from the effects of previous increments of salt is an extrapolation, as is predicting that the surface of the moon is weakly radioactive on the basis of preliminary data about the physical structure of its surface. Extending the known laws of physical and chemical change to the production, transmission, and interaction of nerve impulses in the brain is also an act of extrapolation.

3.00 *Application* is at least one level higher than recall and comprehension because the student must test what he has learned under new and somewhat different conditions. For example, the student comprehends the principle that the volume of gas decreases as its pressure increases (temperature remaining constant) if he correctly predicts the effect of pressure on the volume of gases. Of course, he may arrive at correct answers by "plugging into" a formula; but if he explains why weather balloons expand in volume as they rise, without having previously heard this explanation, the student has applied his knowledge of the gas laws.

A child quickly learns that photosynthesis in green plants occurs in the presence of sunlight. If he comprehends this principle and knows that sunlight is a mixture of violet, indigo, blue, green, yellow, orange, and red light, the child should be able to predict qualitatively what will happen to the food-making process in green plants exposed to red rather than white light.

To indicate his comprehension the student must demonstrate his ability to use a clearly specified abstraction for a particular purpose. To show application, on the other hand, the student need not know that the abstraction is pertinent because the test situation differs from practice situations. In the first case only recall of the original situation is necessary. In the second case, recall plus an additional imaginative leap is necessary.

In evaluation a learner is not at an operational level unless he can apply what he has learned, qualitatively or quantitatively. His success may be indicated by his ability to explain, predict, or perhaps even recognize that what he has learned is irrelevant to the problem or application sought. It is difficult to sense from a child's attempts at application why he is or is not successful. Knowledge of the skills that give direction and strength to this kind of cognitive behavior is not yet sufficient to serve as a guide. Partly for this reason much evaluation is confined to the lesser categories of understanding. Gagné's hierarchical problem-solving strategy, described in Chapter 2, is of considerable interest, but whether, even on psychological grounds, his analysis will be successful in most scientific problems is questionable.

4.00 *Analysis* is the separation of a problem or event into its logical elements, and the description of the relationships, equivalences, hierarchies, and subsets of these elements. This category includes distinguishing between facts, separating principles from hypotheses, pointing out conclusions and the steps to these conclusions, identifying implicit and explicit assumptions, and recognizing underlying themes. A child who comprehends the meaning of a statement may be unable to select the important parts and to recognize the direction in which the argument moves. On the other hand adequate analysis of a statement is not the same as judging its pertinence, accuracy, and validity. In a sense logical analysis is mechanical, even though it calls for many high-level skills, because it does not require the kind of insight vital for judgment.

4.10 *Analysis of elements* involves description of the distinguishing aspects of hypotheses, arguments, and conclusions, which are usually clearly identified in a textbook. In an experimental problem, however, there may be no hypotheses or conclusions to analyze until the class has examined the experimental procedures and the collected data. This subcategory includes what Richard Suchman calls "the analysis of causality," wherein children learn to analyze problems by identifying the kinds of objects they observe, by grouping these objects into systems, and by relating the various states and forms in which the objects and systems coexist to the sequences of events the children witnessed during their experiments.[6]

Children may treat events as isolated facts; however, if they are to understand the isolated events, they must realize that the aspects which give the events meaning must also give meaning to other events. That is, they must be able to explain each event on the basis of knowledge derived from other sources. Hence analysis is the process of identifying all the information in the problem to connect and eventually explain the information by associating it with familiar ideas.

In studying magnetic interactions, children should be aware of the shapes, sizes, weights, and colors of the magnets and the objects attracted. They should identify the magnet–object attraction system, the temperature, the distance between magnet and object, and the attraction of magnet for object and object for magnet, including sequences of movement. They should also identify the magnet as the source of the magnetic field, and the object as a preferred pathway for the magnetic field. This simple example indicates the complexity of analysis of elements.

4.20 *Analysis of relationships* clarifies the associations of the elements. Have the proper data been collected to test the hypothesis? Is the conclusion such that acceptance or rejection of the hypothesis is necessary? Are the data, conclusions, and arguments of sufficient strength? Which elements are too trivial to be included? Is the analysis consistent, harmonious, and supportive of the argument? What parts of the data and conclusions are irrelevant? Does the conclusion follow logically from the chain of reasoning? Does the writer contradict himself? Is contradictory evidence known to the reader?

In the pendulum experiment of Chapter 4, does the learner know why the length of the pendulum is a significant variable? The learner must relate the length of the pendulum, its period, and the gravitational acceleration of falling objects, which are the important factors, and disregard the mass of the pendulum bob, the material of the bob, and the arc of swing (within limits). As they analyze relationships, children blend the various independent variables into a fuzzy whole; lacking proper practice, they have not yet learned to think "if this thing happens, then that thing must happen next." If they know the relation of the flow of an electric current in a wire to the voltage, children should be able to infer that current must increase as voltage increases, provided the resistance in the circuit is unchanged. Children who show this level of scientific maturity have analyzed correctly the relationship of three important variables.

4.30 *Analysis of organizational principles* is probably not applicable to elementary experimentation, although the separation of the phases of an experiment into defining the problem, hypothesizing, gathering data, and coming to a conclusion may be an example of such analysis. Children who have learned how to read for information have also learned to analyze the table of contents. Is the book a methodical survey of a particular field, or is it merely a potpourri? Is the book unified by an underlying theme?

Children may similarly analyze the formal organizational structures of chapters, reports, projects, and even motion pictures may be similarly analyzed. For example, an organizing principle of Chapter 3, "Elementary Science: Goals and Curricula," is the generality and power of related and abstract ideas that collectively comprise the structure of science. In assessing a motion picture, the teacher may ask for a statement of purpose and of the function of each section. She may point out the special techniques for making various points and then discuss with the class the film producer's point of view.

Prospective teachers should consider the organizational principles of the various elementary science textbook series. Is the framework of the series the "big ideas" of science? Does the author periodically review and enlarge these "big ideas"? On what basis does he choose the ideas? What is the author's rationale for the ideas he presents at each grade level? How are the ideas interrelated? The answer to these questions will emerge from an analysis of the operational principles of these books.

5.00 *Synthesis,* one of the highest forms of behavior in the hierarchy of learning, may be equated with creativity because it involves the rearrangement of old ideas and the incorporation of old or new ideas into a novel structure. This kind of creation, which in hindsight often appears to be a relatively simple combination of obvious forms, is usually difficult to effect. The classical grumble of physicist James Clerk Maxwell, when he learned of the invention of the telephone, is an example of how even men of unparalleled creativity may be blind to what hindsight tells them is obvious. Maxwell said, "When at last this little instrument appeared, consisting, as it does, of parts, every one of which is familiar to us, and capable of being put together by an amateur, the disappointment arising from its humble appearance was only partially relieved on finding that it was really able to talk."[7]

Several categories previously described require some synthesis; for example, in application the child must combine elements in new ways, but he knows that the elements are related. In true synthesis the child discovers unsuspected relationships and uses.

No one expects an elementary school child to make truly novel syntheses in science, although he is capable of synthesis in the arts and literature. Perhaps he best approaches synthesis in elementary science by planning an experimental approach to a problem and proposing a scientific explanation.

5.10 *Production of a unique communication* includes written or oral reports of unusual experiences, with impressions. For example, a child may report on erosional phenomena he has observed and explain or relate the phenomena to what he already knows. This sharing of unusual experiences leads to renewed interest and study and to the production of new plans of operation by the children.

5.20 *Production of a plan or proposed set of operations* is inherent in inquiry teaching. Although individual children can sometimes propose plans of operation, such plans are more often the product of small-group or whole-class action, with guidance by the teacher. The teacher may judge a plan by its operational success, although obviously she cannot test all plans in the elementary school. She may gather evidence of growth in inquiry learning by proposing a hypothesis to the children and noting the different procedures they advance to test it. The class may design an apparatus for performing a particular operation, such as weighing objects too small to give a reliable reading on the classroom balance. Practical plans are a sign of high-level cognitive strength and creative effort. Because of the high probability that many different sets of intellectual operations will be necessary, children can make unique contributions in this cognitive category.

5.30 *Derivation of a set of abstract relations* is derived from observation. The creation of taxonomic keys to classify rocks or plants is a low-level example of this kind of behavior. By finding similarities and differences, children can invent convenient and logical sorting procedures. With the teacher's encouragement and close ministry, children can derive the kinetic molecular theory, or a simplified model of it, from observations of gaseous diffusion, pressure–volume changes in gases, evaporation, solubility, and change in state of solids.

This subcategory also includes the formulation and modification of hypotheses that explain and predict phenomena or events, and the possibility of looking at experience in more than one way or the realization that more than one explanation or theory may exist. At some early point in the growth of the new science fields there may be either no theoretical explanations or numerous hypotheses of various degrees of credibility. The question of the origin of the moon is not conclusively settled, nor is there a broadly based theoretical structure to account for the multitude of particles encountered in nuclear physics. Children should realize that explanations tend to be accepted in science because they are more "elegant" or simpler than other explanations or because they are the best at hand even though they are not completely correct.

6.00 *Evaluation* involves judging in terms of accepted criteria. Judgments are necessary in many of the categories previously described; the difference is that in evaluation the notion of value is introduced. Thus evaluation is closely tied to the affective domain. Although evaluation is the "highest" category in the cognitive domain, it is not necessarily the noblest kind of behavior or the ultimate intellectual act. After all, individuals always make judgments, even in so minor an intellectual act as recalling a particular fact. However, there is a vast difference between *opinion,* which is quickly formed on inadequate evidence or unconsciously accepted without serious question, and *judgment,* which is more deliberate and searching.

6.10 *Judgments in terms of internal evidence* rely on expressions of logical consistency, the existence of factual errors, the quality of thought, the range of data and of generalizations. Have the errors or possible errors in judging been reported? Will the same results be obtained if the experiment were to be repeated? Do hidden assumptions invalidate the conclusion? Is the conclusion logically correct?

6.20 *Judgments in terms of external criteria* make up the basic evaluational structure in science. For instance, are the experimental results compatible with present theory? Is the work that of a person with an established reputation? Is it adequately sampled and controlled? Is the theory or hypothesis advanced more inclusive or simpler than others? Is it better integrated with other theories? Does it explain more effectively? Has the experimenter examined alternative courses of action? Has he tested every conceivable hypothesis that could invalidate his results, or has he been content to "prove" his hypothesis? Does the hypothesis lead to new knowledge? In James Conant's phrase, is it fruitful? To what extent does the author's bias intrude? Does he take into account the pertinent work in his field?

Instilling in children the desire to make scientific judgments and providing frequent opportunities for judging is an essential part of the "new" elementary science programs. There is good evidence that children's skills in judging their work and that of their peers can be strengthened. In turn, teachers must learn to judge their own successes and failures as well as those of their students.

The subcategories of the cognitive domain shade indistinguishably into one another, overlapping to such an extent that categorizing a specific behavior as evidence of translation, interpolation, knowledge of conventions or of criteria is often more an act of faith than a scientific statement.

The affective domain

Objectives in science education are often vaguely phrased: "To appreciate the role of science in the progress of mankind"; "To develop a scientific attitude in dealing with problems of everyday life." These objectives and the behavior they imply are not included in the understanding and knowledge levels of the cognitive domain, even though they affect cognitive thinking. "Willingness to receive," as an example of affective behavior, will expedite learning at every age level, even though learning can occur without it.

The affective domain is the class of behavior dominated by attitudes, emotions, and appreciations. These subjective and inner aspects are vital for learning but are not often evaluated in science teaching. Many scientists and science educators maintain that desirable affective behavior will somehow emerge from science content. They believe that the student who struggles through a well-organized course in physics with one or two hours in the laboratory each week becomes an exemplar of science methodology and everything "good" in science. Because this notion is utter nonsense, the inquiry philosophy permeates many new programs in science education.

In the affective domain, agreement on the meaning of key words is rare; therefore at this point let us define and explain some of these terms as used in this book. *Attitude* is a willingness either to approach or to avoid environmental interactions; *appreciation* is a measure of satisfaction in interacting. We should also mention *pleasure* and *joy, unhappiness* and *avoidance,* which affect formal learning. Motivation is an important function of science instruction. Children should want to know more about their world, should enjoy working with scientific equipment, should like to read science books, and, by looking forward to a scientific problem, should enjoy the reward of autonomous learning.

Teachers want children to establish desirable attitudes, appreciations, and interests. They believe that the task of learning will be easier for both children and teachers and that learners can create within themselves the operational machinery and self-control to drive them on. One measure of effective instruction is the extent to which the children shift from external to internal motivation.

In a sense this process is circular and logically suspect, almost as if one could raise himself by his bootstraps. First the teacher should interest children in learning science! Interest leads to success. From success the children develop even more interest. But this growth does not stem from *exposure* to science materials. The teacher should consciously seek to arouse in children the *desire* to learn, and she should realize that she must serve as a model of the behavior she wishes to inculcate.

Evaluation in the affective domain is a formidable task because of ineffective evaluative instruments. The teacher's informal observation and judgment are the only substantial sources of growth data in this domain. The following outline and discussion of the stages of the affective domain, together with the accompanying suggestions for observation of behavior, is a tentative guide for the evaluation of affective behavior:

Levels of the affective domain[8]

1.0 Receiving (attending)

   1.1 Awareness

   1.2 Willingness to receive

   1.3 Selected attention

2.0 Responding

   2.1 Acquiescence in responding

   2.2 Willingness to respond

   2.3 Satisfaction in response

3.0 Valuing

   3.1 Acceptance of a value

   3.2–3.3 Preference for a value, commitment to a value

4.0 Organization

   4.1 Conceptualization of a value

   4.2 Organization of a value system

5.0 Characterization by a value or value complex

   5.1 Generalized set

   5.2 Characterization

1.0 *Receiving* (*attending*) is divided into three subcategories, which are given in ascending order.

   1.1 *Awareness,* the lowest level of the affective domain, is the act of giving attention to some occurrence or phenomenon, even if the occurrence is disliked and avoided. The learner is conscious that something has happened although he does not pay specific attention to it. This level is too primitive for most classroom learning. The learner senses only the gross phenomenon or some of its interactive components. He figuratively says, "I am aware of it. But I couldn't care less about it."[9]

A child who thinks that science is only for scientists is either unaware of the role of science in modern society or, if he is aware, does not care. Although the child may not be willing to credit views different from his own, at least he knows they exist. The child who is aware of the existence of atoms and molecules may not be able to explain the diffusion of ink in water in terms of molecular motion; or he may not care to do so. Awareness and cognition are closely related; ability to recall a principle implies awareness of the principle.

   1.2 *Willingness to receive* implies desire to come into contact with a stimulus although not necessarily to form a positive prejudgment. The child may be hostile yet tolerant enough to listen; he does not actively seek out the stimulus. He may be willing to participate in an experiment if asked, but he does not volunteer.

Tolerance of different points of view, cooperative attitudes in class discussion, participation in discussional give-and-take, and acceptance of new units of study in the classroom are examples of this behavior. The willing child does not peremptorily reject an activity; he looks forward to participation.

1.3 *Selected attention* involves skill in observing and perceiving configurations and relationships. Although in this subcategory emphasis is on attending to individual activities rather than to the total setting, the child may not necessarily wish to know more about the activity. Rather, he is observing at a higher analytical level. He may not know the meaning of the significant components of the activity; he may not be able to describe them or tell what can be done with them.

The child who systematically follows a teacher's demonstration, attending to each step in the process, whether the procedure is meaningful, is giving selected attention. The child who prefers biographies of scientists or books about space exploration is similarly giving selected attention.

2.0 *Responding* is concerned with positive action—the responder does something; he does not merely look on.

2.1 *Acquiescence in responding* is at a "higher" level in the affective domain than willingness to receive. Attending is likely to be meaningless unless the child is willing to make use of his observations. Teachers expect children to comply, willingly or unwillingly, and to follow prescribed rules. They tend to reject forced acquiescence as an important behavioral goal, even though it may occasionally be important ("Don't mix chemicals randomly; don't experiment at home or in the classroom near electric currents; don't handle apparatus roughly."). Students should know and accept the reasons for these rules. Whether behavior is intelligent, safety is vital! The child who needs constant reminders of safety rules shows his unwillingness to comply.

2.2 *Willingness to respond* indicates interest in the task. Effective cooperation among children can occur if each child wishes to work closely with his peers, but this willingness comes from a combination of factors—desire for social approval, teacher insistence, innate interest, self-reward. In the primary and intermediate grades children become deeply involved and look forward to experimentation with concrete materials, to field trips, and to science "doing."

Children who go to the library to borrow science books, who bring in pertinent newspaper clippings, who practice conservation, who are home experimenters, who participate freely in class discussions exemplify this behavior. Teachers often equate willingness with interest, but the two are not necessarily the same.

2.3 *Satisfaction in response* is a self-rewarding goal. A child who enjoys an experiment or a book about insects will want to know more about the topic and strengthen his competence. Traditional teaching modes often discourage or even inhibit children. Few children *enjoy* textbook science. Older children may respond negatively to science teaching because of their dislike of traditional instruction. Cognitive growth does not necessarily result from satisfaction in responding. Children may be interested in a topic without trying to learn much about it. For example, many students are intensely involved in the raging controversies about fluoridation and vivisection. However, deep interest and excessive emotion do not necessarily promote knowledge of the chemistry of fluoridation or the importance of vivisection for medical research.

Pertinent examples of satisfaction in response are plentiful. In addition to the previous examples we might also mention enjoyment in observing and identifying birds, in collecting rocks and minerals, and in building model airplanes and learning why they fly.

3.0 *Valuing* blends together the different aspects of affective cognitive behavior. To give value to some phenomenon, attribute, or mode of acting is to endow it with worth; even if an individual chooses not to respond to the phenomena, he respects it and the reasons for its existence. In his *Science and Human Values* J. Bronowski expresses scientific values in terms of accuracy, elegance, truth, and simplicity.[10]

3.1 *Acceptance of a value,* one of the lower levels in the valuing hierarchy, does not require firm commitment and is open to change. Individuals may occasionally accept the traditional values of science yet violate these standards of behavior despite the disapproval of the scientific community and the ease with which scientists can detect deviations. For example, Paul Kammerer, a noted biologist, once exhibited several artificially altered salamanders in an attempt to prove that acquired characteristics can be inherited. In 1925 Kammerer was rewarded with a professorship at the University of Moscow because Communist doctrine at that time leaned heavily on Lamarckian evolution. He committed suicide shortly thereafter when he realized that the scientific world knew that he had rejected the accepted norms of scientific behavior.

The child who says he would like to become a scientist represents one aspect of value acceptance. If, in addition, he reads widely, collects, experiments at home, and persistently seeks to help his teacher in preparing science activities, he is probably at a higher level of valuing than simple uncommitted acceptance. If he willingly listens to evidence and seeks further information before coming to an unshakable conclusion, he is moving to an even higher level of the hierarchy. The child who accepts the values of process techniques as a class procedure is also at this level, but only if he gains some satisfaction and challenge from these values.

3.2–3.3 *Preference for a value, commitment to a value,* impels the child to appropriate action. For example, the child who truly believes in conservation does *not* pick protected plants, deface a nature center, or carve his initials on a tree. He pursues his faith in conservation, preferring it to contradictory beliefs. He invests time and effort in its active realization and defends his belief against the opinion of others if necessary. He prizes clean air, pure food and water, unspoiled lakes, rivers, and oceans. He picks up refuse from sidewalks and streets. He volunteers to complete a project or to plan an experiment because he genuinely wants to learn its outcome. He rejects superstition and the intervention of supernatural causation, which are not based on reason and objective evidence. He is committed to the criteria of scientific evidence and validity. These kinds of behavior do not arise quickly and naturally in the classroom. The child's upbringing and social environment so conditions attitude to his world that teachers will settle for reasonable progress toward willing acceptance and commitment to scientific values.

4.0 *Organization* involves conceptualizing by analytical and synthetic techniques and acquiring a rational system for making choices. Science education, like all education that is more than training, seeks to build an organized, coherent system of beliefs and attitudes. Children can develop an acceptance and preference for certain values simply from other individuals. However, they have difficulty conceptualizing these values analytically and synthetically and acquiring a rational system for making choices. Because science does not provide a ready-made system, children may perhaps choose to avoid science altogether. Therefore teachers should try to give children some experience in evaluating the adequacy of their belief systems.

4.1 *Conceptualization of a value* involves comparison of a belief in terms of other beliefs so that the learner can consciously maintain it in a conceptual structure. To interrelate his values the learner must clarify his understanding, either intuitively or logically. He must be able to think about it and to assess its relevance.

The learner should understand and be able to express scientific ideas as directly or indirectly connected with the real world; for example, the atom, even though it is a theoretical model, is represented in the physical world by a particle that shows the kinds of behavior the model illustrates. He should be able to explain why the advancement of science depends as much on unbiased and accurate observation and experiment as on great imaginative flights of scientific theorizing.

4.2 *Organization of a value system* involves integration of one's beliefs into a harmonious structure. One suggested cause of mental illness is that some individuals have not attained this consistent, dynamically integrated value system. The dissonance they encounter in living is sufficient to impair normal mental health. Hence mental illness may occur if the individual cannot harmonize values without destructive internal conflict.

Examples of behavior in this subcategory includes weighing the cost and benefit to society of more vigorous antipollution measures, evaluating the benefits and evils of nuclear energy, or accepting cooperative work in small-class groups, which conflicts with individual action. In one of the highest levels of this subcategory, the learner may answer such questions as: "Why should every citizen know what science *is?* What are the aims of scientists? What good or bad changes has science caused in our lives?"

5.0 *Characterization by a value or value complex* is meaningful in science instruction only if the learner shows that his value system effectively controls his behavior. This category, which is one of the highest levels in the valuing hierarchy, is probably inappropriate for the elementary school child. Ten year olds have not consciously thought through a philosophy of life; such thinking is a lifetime task. The following analysis is intended to suggest directions of desirable growth; it is not behavior to be expected of school children, although children do grow significantly in this as in every other effective category.

5.1 *Generalized set* has been defined as "a basic orientation which enables the individual to reduce and order the complex world about him and to act consistently and effectively in it."[11] In general terms this subcategory is the individual's frame of reference for meeting affective situations. This behavior is exemplified by "the scientific attitude," which is an entire complex of skills, understanding, attitude, belief, and action. The person who judges situations by pertinent facts, issues, intentions, and results possesses one kind of generalized set. He is rationally consistent. The scientist who, at whatever anguish, admits to himself that he has overlooked a point which invalidates a pet hypothesis vividly illustrates a generalized set. It is unthinkable for him to ignore this error! Joseph Lister once said, "Next to the promulgation of truth, the best thing I can conceive that a man can do is the recantation of a public error."[12]

5.2 *Characterization* is regarded as the highest level of affective behavior because it embraces the greatest range of behavioral objectives — the individual's complete world view. Because it is so abstract and personal, this subcategory does not fall within the domain of elementary school evaluation. Nevertheless this excerpt from John W. Gardner's book *Excellence: Can We Be Equal and Excellent Too?* is pertinent:

> To win our deepest respect the individual must both find himself and lose himself. This is not so contradictory as it sounds. We respect the man who places himself at the service of values which transcend his own individuality — the values of his profession, his people, his heritage, and above all the religious and moral values which nourished the ideal of individual fulfillment in the first place. But this "gift of himself" only wins our admiration if the giver has achieved a mature individuality and if the act of giving does not involve an irreparable crippling of that individuality. We cannot admire faceless, mindless servants of The State, of The Cause, of The Organization who were never mature individuals and who have sacrificed all individuality to the Corporate Good.[13]

The psychomotor domain

The psychomotor domain in science is a region of darkness and doubt, an unexplored wilderness that offers little of promise in the teaching of science. The psychomotor domain is the realm of motor skills, physical development, and neuromuscular coordination. What have these noncognitive, nonaffective patterns of behavior to do with science learning? Should teachers immediately begin remedial action if an awkward child takes five times longer to connect a dry cell than another child or if, on a field trip, he never catches a frog or a butterfly? Some children *are* awkward; girls tend to be less skilled mechanically than boys for reasons that are not at all psychomotor. Many children are inferior draftsmen; they are sometimes unable to plot a curve on a graph because of a neuromuscular problem. These deficiencies are not problems of science teaching although the teacher should be aware that they exist and that they may be symptomatic of a generally low level of psychomotor function.

Coordination and speed in elementary science are not significant behavioral objectives. Delicate manipulation is unimportant because appropriate experiments for younger children are well within the physical capacities of school children. The notion that "practice makes perfect" may be true, but the duration of manipulative tasks in elementary science is too short for the effect of practice to show itself. The tasks are not worthy of extended practice.

Many scientists are indifferent experimenters, lacking the insights and skills that characterize experimental scientists. Indeed, in the field of high-energy physics theoretical and experimental physics are sharply separated. Physicists are not usually adept in each domain. Manipulative skill is undoubtedly advantageous for children, but its order of priority is surely low. The teacher should not take on this additional burden in teaching elementary science.

Notes and references

1. Bloom, B. S., ed., *Taxonomy of Educational Objectives, Handbook 1: The Cognitive Domain* (New York: David McKay, 1956).

2. Cronbach, L. J., "Course Improvement through Evaluation," *Teachers College Record,* 64 (1963): 682.

3. *Ibid.*

4. Classifications are taken from Bloom, *op. cit.,* pp. 201–7.

5. Bruner, J. S., *The Process of Education* (Cambridge, Mass.: Harvard University Press, 1960), p. 33.

6. Suchman, J. R., *The Elementary School Training Program in Scientific Inquiry* (Urbana: College of Education, University of Illinois, 1962), pp. 21–22.

7. Cited in Cohen, I. B., *Science, Servant of Man* (Boston: Little, Brown & Co., 1948), p. 61.

8. Classifications are taken from D. R. Krathwohl, B. S. Bloom, and B. P. Masia, *Taxonomy of Educational Objectives, Handbook 2: The Affective Domain* (New York: David McKay, 1964).

9. *Ibid.*

10. Bronowski, J., *Science and Human Values* (New York: Harper & Row, 1956).

11. Krathwohl, D. R., B. S. Bloom, and B. P. Masia, *op. cit.,* p. 166.

12. Cited in Cannon, W. B., *The Ways of an Investigator* (New York: W. W. Norton, 1945), p. 126.

13. Gardner, J. W., *Excellence: Can We Be Equal and Excellent Too?* (New York: Harper & Row, 1961), p. 137.

Index